The Natural History of Europe

The Natural History of Europe

The Natural History of Europe

By Harry Garms / Illustrated by Wilhelm Eigener

Edited by A. Melderis (Plants) and Joyce Pope (Animals)

With an Introduction by Gerald Durrell

PAUL HAMLYN

Executive Editor–Monte Jacobson

Published 1967 by The Hamlyn Publishing Group Ltd
Hamlyn House, The Centre, Feltham, Middlesex
Second impression 1968
Originally published as **Pflanzen und Tiere Europas**
© Copyright 1962 Georg Westermann Verlag, Brunswick
Translation by H. Korman © Copyright 1967 The Hamlyn Publishing Group Ltd
Printed in Czechoslovakia by Polygrafia, Prague
T 1911

Introduction

The Victorian era was the heyday of the amateur naturalist. People collected things with the assiduousness of pack rats—anything from beetles to sea-shells, from ferns to fossils. But then the amateur naturalist began to fall into some disrepute. He joined the realm of the comic joke, together with the nagging wife and the indestructible mother-in-law. To be a naturalist meant that you were either an absent-minded, bearded professor with egg stains down your waistcoat, or else an eccentric spinster. For a young man to be a naturalist was considered slightly effeminate—why should he watch birds when he could be playing rugger? But just recently there has been a resurgence of the amateur naturalist, due in part, I think, to television. The most astonishing people now lie for hours in damp ditches vying with each other for their first glimpse of a Spotted Flycatcher; jovial red-faced stockbrokers go into raptures over their collection of Lesser Coleoptera (they're called beetles in this book). This being so, it has always seemed curious to me that so few good handbooks on the European flora and fauna exist that are easily transportable and inexpensive.

Between the ages of 10 and 14, I was lucky enough to live in Greece, particularly on the island of Corfu, and here I became an assiduous amateur naturalist. I collected and studied everything that I could find. My collection of butterflies, moths, beetles and dragonflies was (although I say it myself) remarkably fine. But the one great difficulty for a young naturalist, I found, was the correct identification of the specimens. There were one or two handbooks dealing with specialized groups of creatures, but that was all. If you wanted information on some obscure species of crab or spider or dragonfly, you generally had to wade through massive transactions of some learned society or other until you chanced upon a contribution that would answer your questions. There was certainly nothing in those days approaching a handbook which could guide your eager but faltering footsteps through the amazing natural world around you. How I used to long for a book that would at least give me a clue as to what a particular plant or insect or reptile was, for once you knew roughly were it fitted in the scheme of things you could then—by dint of careful detective work—find out nearly everything you wanted to know about it. But, as I say, no such book existed and it has taken 25 years for this need to be realized.

Garms has undertaken here a Herculean task. He has tried to collect together the majority of plants and trees, mammals, birds, insects, fishes and crustaceans that you are likely to see in the British Isles or on the continent of Europe. That he has succeeded admirably is obvious to anyone who glances through the book. In such a massive undertaking as this there are bound to be certain gaps, but by and large you can, with the aid of this book, pinpoint the thing that you want to know about and then, with the aid of other works which it recommends, learn even more about it.

I think this guide will prove to be absolutely indispensable to anyone interested in natural history who travels in Britain or on the Continent. It is compact and concise and the illustrations make identification easy. To a naturalist on holiday in Europe it will, I am sure, become as essential a part of his equipment as the Guide Michelin.

Even if one did not require it as a scientific guide book, it is worth possessing for the sheer poetry that it contains. Who would mind an insect bite or two providing you were sure that they had been inflicted by the Spangle-winged Mosquito? Who, when swimming in the sea, would not be charmed to meet a fish called a Dentex (which sounds faintly like a new brand of toothpaste) or the Painted Comber (which must surely have some connection with mermaids). But it is among the plants that the botanists have really let themselves run wild. Who would not stop, even on an autobahn, to get more closely acquainted with a Nodding Bur-marigold or Curtis's Mouse-ear or the Ramping Fumitory or even the Hawkweed Treacle-mustard? Who would not love to watch some worthy farmer gathering his crop of Annual Moon Carrot? Whichever way you look at it, this book must be the most important piece of your luggage when you go on holiday. It is certainly going to be one of mine.

Gerald Durrell
Les Augres Manor
Jersey

How to Use this Book

This has been designed as a guide to all the wild plants and animals most likely to be seen in the British Isles and on the European mainland. The main text describes over 2100 plants and 1400 animals, under seven sections which represent the most typical habitats found within the area. These are: Woods and Forests; Heath, Moor and Tundra; Freshwater; Sea and Shore; Meadows and Pastureland; Field, Garden and Park; Mountains.

Each of these sections begins with an account of the general features of the habitat it covers, with information on terrain and climate, and on the main parts of Europe in which it occurs. Within each section, first plants and then animals are treated in a sequence which is uniform throughout the book (see Contents page). Each plant and animal is illustrated in colour and described in a series of concise notes. Where possible, similar species are grouped together for ease of comparison, often with an indication of typical surroundings, but it should be noted that not all the illustrations have been drawn to the same scale. Important distinguishing features are pointed out by short lines on each illustration and in some cases they are detailed.

The notes accompanying the illustrations also have a fixed sequence. For plants this is as follows: common name or names (the most frequently used names are given), scientific (Latin) name (brought up to date in accordance with the International Rules of Botanical Nomenclature); longevity, that is whether the plant is a woody perennial (tree or shrub), a perennial herb, biennial or annual; size, which unless otherwise stated is the height above ground; description of features important for identification, especially those which distinguish it from generally similar species, or which are not visible in the illustration; flowering time, where applicable, or in the case of ferns, fungi, etc., sporing time (1–12 = January to December); frequency of occurrence (common, rare, etc.), typical habitat and geographical distribution; family.

For animals the sequence is similar: common names and scientific name; size, which unless otherwise stated is total body length (+ tail length for mammals); flying period (winged insects) or spawning time (fishes); habitat and distribution; family. Additional information is usually given on behaviour, and in particular on migration in birds.

For various reasons it may be found that this scheme is not always adhered to throughout the book. In cases where two or more species depicted in one illustration share the same habitat, distribution, family, etc., this is given once only, after all the species have been described. Where this information is not given at all, it is to be understood that the species is common and widely distributed throughout Europe in the habitat under which it is included, and that its family name is the same as its common name or obvious from it. In the case of those species which are described in the centre of each page, information on habitat, distribution and family is given in a single introductory paragraph.

Generally, the sizes given are an average, and somewhat larger or smaller individuals of many species may well be observed. Similarly, there may be quite a wide variation in the appearance of individuals, for example in the colouring of flowers or of many animals, particularly the invertebrates.

All measurements in the book are given in metric units, and for readers not familiar with this system equivalents in feet and inches of the main units are supplied below. Also given below are explanations of all the abbreviations used in the text, including the two signs which indicate species native to Britain and those which are introduced and naturalized here. Many species, particularly animals, which are not marked in this way may occur in Britain (and in other parts not indicated in the text) as casuals or rare visitors. Another point which should be noted is that many of the plants and animals described also occur outside Europe, but information on this is not within the scope of this book.

The first section of the book deals with classification. As explained, the family to which each species belongs is given in the main text; using the tables in this section the reader can see how the species in question is related to the others in the book and to many non-European types. It is divided into two parts—on plants and animals—and each opens with a brief explanation of the principles of classification and of the terms used.

Wherever possible, descriptions throughout the book have been made in plain language understandable to the layman, and for those technical words which have had to be included, a clear definition will be found in the Glossary at the end of the text. Where necessary, simple illustrations have been supplied, e.g. the parts of a typical flower and the plumage of a bird. The book ends with a full Index of all the plants and animals in the book, listed under both their common and scientific names, and a Bibliography of selected books for further reading for readers who wish to pursue a subject in more detail.

When using this book in the countryside, certain important points should be noted. Many species, both of plants and of animals, are protected by law in Britain and on the Continent. For example, in Britain almost all birds and their eggs are covered. Before taking any species for a collection, even if it seems to be only a common type of grass or an insect, it is best to consult with the local authorities, especially in a strange country. Information may usually be obtained at police stations or town halls.

Finally, remember that it may still be possible to make new observations, even for the amateur naturalist. Local museums and societies will give help on identification to serious students, and would be more than pleased to verify a genuine discovery.

Abbreviations Used in the Book

♃	perennial	⚥	hermaphrodite
⊙	biennial	subsp.	subspecies
○	annual	1–12	January to December
*	native in Britain	mm	millimetre; 1 mm = 1/25 inch
†	introduced and naturalized in Britain	cm	centimetre (= 10 mm); 2.5 cm = 1 inch, 30 cm = 1 foot
♂	male	m	metre (= 100 cm);
♀	female		1 m = 39 inches

Contents

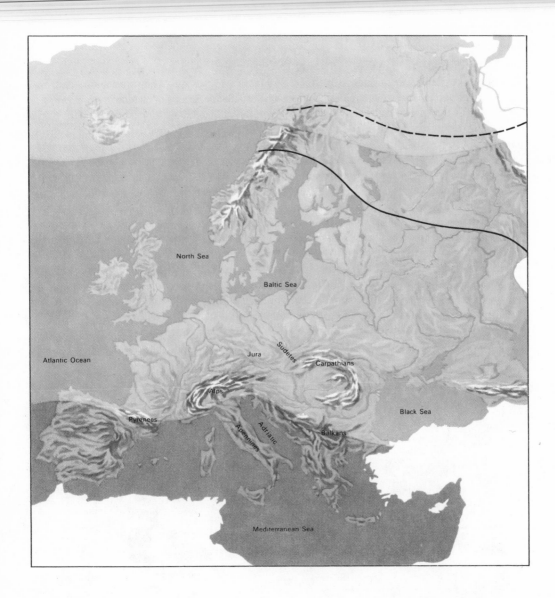

The Area

The plants and animals described in this book live in the British Isles and on the continent of Europe, which is shown as separated from Asia by a vertical line passing through the Ural Mountains (the right-hand border of the map), and is subdivided into the three belts shown – Arctic, Northern Forest, and Mediterranean.

The Arctic Belt lies north of the timber-line (which coincides with the 10° Centigrade July isotherm) and its vegetation is known as tundra, which occurs also above the timber-line on mountains. Tundra consists predominantly of very hardy, mostly 'cushion' herbs and dwarf shrubs; the short summer presents a carpet of brilliant green patterned with flowers of many colours (except in the far north and at the highest altitudes, where mostly only mosses and lichens are able to survive) and sees the return of innumerable birds and animals; during the long winter the vegetation is sparse and snow-covered and very little wild life is able to withstand the cold. The Northern Forest Belt encircles the world with the relics of what was once a continuous primeval forest of coniferous and deciduous trees; human activities have produced large areas of arable land and replanted woodland. The Mediterranean Belt in the south has mild wet winters and hot dry summers, and many of the plants exhibit adaptations such as thick succulent tissue or dense woolly hairs, which help to conserve water during the summer drought.

Of the two black lines on the maps, the upper, broken line represents the northern limit of the range of amphibians, the solid line that of the range of reptiles.

1

Classification of Plants

The **Plant Kingdom** contains in all about 360 000 known species, the descendants of forms which first appeared in Pre - Cambrian times, 7 600 million years ago. They are classified according to the possession of certain common characteristics. The basic unit of classification is the species, which is a group of individuals differing from each other but having various definite and permanent features in common and normally breeding with other individuals in the species and producing similar offspring. Species with some more general characteristics in common are grouped into a genus (plural genera); each species is given two Latin names, the first being the genus, the second the species (specific name). Latin is used as an international language in many sciences; a plant's common name may differ from place to place, but this scientific name is understood by botanists all over the world. Genera are grouped into families, orders, classes and finally divisions; between these are several minor groupings, e.g., subspecies and suborders.

The two main groups of plants are **Flowerless Plants (Cryptogams)** and **Flowering Plants (Phanerogams** or **Spermatophytes).** Cryptogams form three divisions: **Thallophytes,** in which one or more cells form a simple structure called a thallus, with no differentiation into root, stem and leaf; **Bryophytes,** with stem and leaves and a simple conducting system for transport within the plant; **Pteridophytes** (vascular cryptogams), differentiated into roots, stem and leaves, and with a well-developed conducting system of tubes (vascular bundles).

Green plants manufacture food in a process known as photosynthesis, from carbon dioxide

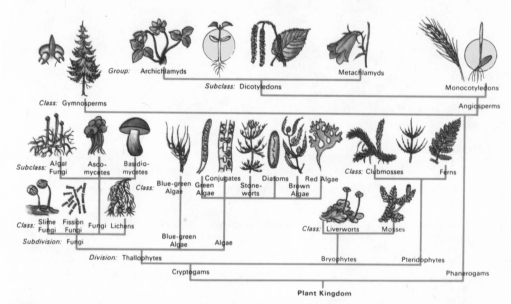

and the elements of water, using energy absorbed from sunlight by a pigment called chlorophyll. Plants which do not have chlorophyll have to take food which has been prepared by green plants, and are thus parasites or saprophytes. Of the **Thallophytes: Fungi** are parasites or saprophytes; **Algae** have chlorophyll and are self-supporting; **Lichens** are symbiotic organisms which comprise the thallus of a fungus consorting with cells of algae, the former performing the sexual reproduction of the partnership, the latter the photosynthesis.

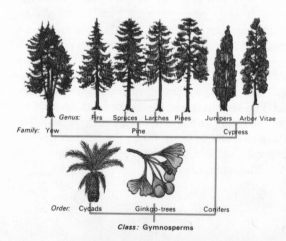

Phanerogams (Spermatophytes), which contain 250 000 of all the known species of plants, are divided into **Gymnosperms** and **Angiosperms.** Three major orders of gymnosperms are illustrated in this table: **Cycads** occur in tropical and subtropical regions; **Ginkgo-trees** are natives of China and Japan; **Conifers,** with very many species and by far the largest order in gymnosperms, have needle-shaped or scale-shaped leaves and fruits which are woody (cones) or berry-like. Most conifers are monoecious, but members of the Cypress Family are mostly dioecious. Individual species in the Pine Family are identified from their general appearance and their needles and cones.

2

Angiosperms are divided into two groups:
Dicotyledons and **Monocotyledons.** The
first are described on this and the next page,
the latter on page 5. The Dicotyledons have
an embryo with two seed-leaves (cotyledons).
The leaves are normally net-veined. The floral
parts are usually in fives or fours, rarely in
threes. The vascular bundles of the stem are
open, generally arranged in a ring around a
central pith, a spongy substance which is a
food-store for the plant. They are further
divided into **Archichlamyds** and **Metachlamyds.**

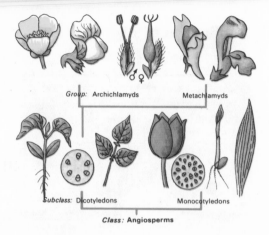

Group: Archichlamyds   Metachlamyds

Subclass: Dicotyledons   Monocotyledons

Class: Angiosperms

Thirteen orders of **Archichlamyds** are shown schematically in the centre and at the bottom
of the page. Nearly all have a double perianth, consisting of sepals and separate petals, but there
is great diversity in the structure of the flowers. The typical flower of the Archichlamyds is
regular, with 5 sepals and 5 petals. It is present in a large number of families, the largest of
which are: Buttercup Family (stamens and carpels numerous, free), Rose Family (stamens
usually numerous, carpels 1 to many, free or sometimes united [to each other and to the recep-

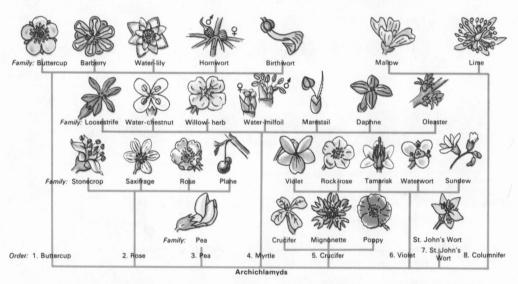

Family: Buttercup   Barberry   Water-lily   Hornwort   Birthwort   Mallow   Lime

Family: Loosestrife   Water-chestnut   Willow-herb   Water-milfoil   Marestail   Daphne   Oleaster

Family: Stonecrop   Saxifrage   Rose   Plane   Violet   Rock-rose   Tamarisk   Waterwort   Sundew

Family: Pea   Crucifer   Mignonette   Poppy   St. John's Wort

Order: 1. Buttercup   2. Rose   3. Pea   4. Myrtle   5. Crucifer   6. Violet   7. St. John's Wort   8. Columnifer

Archichlamyds

tacle]) and Carrot Family (flowers usually in umbel-like inflorescences, stamens 5, ovary
inferior). Stamens in some families are united in bundles: e.g. St John's Wort Family, Lime
Family; or in a tube: e.g. Mallow Family; or at the base: e.g. Flax Family, Cranesbill Family
and Wood-sorrel Family. Irregular flowers are characteristic of: Pea Family (corolla papilionate,
stamens 10, of which usually 9 are fused and 1 free), Balsam Family (sepals often coloured, the
lowest one spurred, lateral petals united) and Violet Family (the lower petal spurred).

A perianth of 4 parts occurs in: Crucifer Family (stamens usually 6 :2 short and 4 long),
Poppy Family (sepals 2, stamens usually numerous; in Fumitories, flowers irregular, the
upper petal spurred), Willow-herb Family
(ovary inferior) and Daphne Family (sepals
coloured, petals absent). In some families the
flowers are small and inconspicuous: e.g.
Water–milfoil Family (flowers tetramerous,
ovary inferior), Marestail Family (the perianth
a rim round the top of the ovary) and Oleaster
Family (sepals usually 2, petals absent).

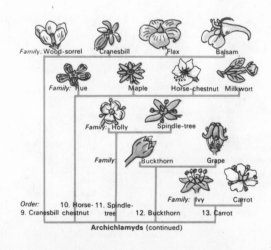

Family: Wood-sorrel   Cranesbill   Flax   Balsam

Family: Rue   Maple   Horse-chestnut   Milkwort

Family: Holly   Spindle-tree

Family: Buckthorn   Grape

Family: Ivy   Carrot

Order: 9. Cranesbill   10. Horse-chestnut   11. Spindle-tree   12. Buckthorn   13. Carrot

Archichlamyds (continued)

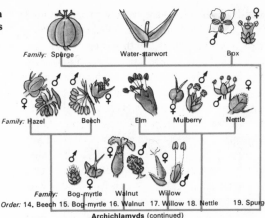

Family: Spurge   Water-starwort   Box

Family: Hazel   Beech   Elm   Mulberry   Nettle

Family: Bog-myrtle   Walnut   Willow

Order: 14. Beech 15. Bog-myrtle 16. Walnut 17. Willow 18. Nettle   19. Spurge

Archichlamyds (continued)

Nearly all the **Archichlamyd** orders (14–22, at the top and bottom of this page) have an inconspicuous perianth or naked flowers. In some families the flowers are arranged in catkins, e.g. in the Beech and Walnut Families (in both, the flowers are unisexual, monoecious), Willow Family (flowers dioecious) and Bog-myrtle Family (flowers monoecious and dioecious). In the Elm Family the flowers are hermaphrodite or unisexual, in the Mulberry and Nettle Families unisexual, either monoecious or dioecious, in the Water-starwort and Box Families unisexual, monoecious. In the Spurge Family, the flowers are grouped within a cup-shaped involucre.

In the **Metachlamyds,** the flower normally comprises 5 sepals and 5 petals, a single whorl of stamens and an ovary of 2 carpels. The sepals and petals are more or less completely fused, forming a calyx and corolla respectively. In the table in the centre of the page, 9 orders with 29 families of this group are shown. In the Heath Family the corolla is normally nearly globular or subcylindric, strongly contracted at the mouth; in the Bindweed, Gentian, Primrose and Bellflower Families usually either funnel-shaped or bell-shaped; in the Nightshade Family

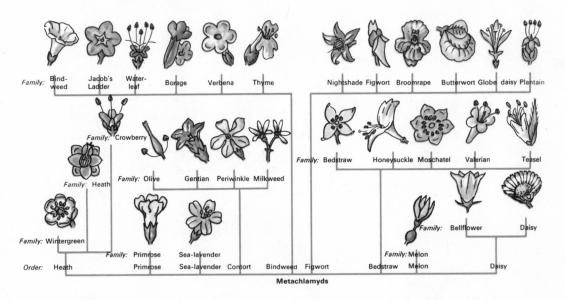

Family: Bindweed   Jacob's Ladder   Water-leaf   Borage   Verbena   Thyme   Nightshade Figwort Broomrape   Butterwort Globe daisy Plantain

Family: Crowberry

Family: Bedstraw   Honeysuckle Moschatel   Valerian   Teasel

Family: Heath   Family: Olive   Gentian Periwinkle Milkweed

Family: Wintergreen

Family: Bellflower   Daisy

Family: Primrose   Sea-lavender   Family: Melon

Order: Heath   Primrose   Sea-lavender Contort   Bindweed Figwort   Bedstraw Melon   Daisy

Metachlamyds

rotate; in the Thyme, Broomrape, Figwort and Butterwort Families usually 2-lipped. In some families, e.g. Globe-daisy, Teasel and Daisy Families, the flowers are aggregated into heads and surrounded by a calyx-like involucre of bracts. The heads of the Daisy Family could comprise either tubular or strap-shaped (ligulate) flowers or both types in the same head (in which case the ligulate flowers are situated on the margin of the head).

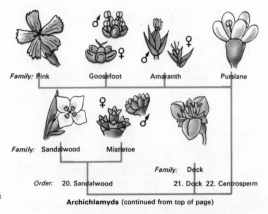

Family: Pink   Goosefoot   Amaranth   Purslane

Family: Sandalwood   Mistletoe

Family: Dock

Order: 20. Sandalwood   21. Dock 22. Centrosperm

Archichlamyds (continued from top of page)

The members of the Sandalwood Family are semiparasites on roots of various herbs; the Mistletoe is parasitic on branches of trees. The Dock Family is characterized by having sheathing stipules which embrace the stem. In the Goosefoot Family, the flowers are crowded in small globose inflorescences. The flowers of the Amaranth Family have 2 large bracteoles and a dry, often highly coloured perianth. In the Pink and Purslane Families, the perianth is usually differentiated into sepals and petals; in the former the sepals number 2, petals 4–6, in the latter sepals 5 and petals 5, sometimes none.

Classification of Animals

The **Animal Kingdom** includes about a million different types of creature so far discovered, described and named, and more are constantly being found. They are classified, in a similar way to plants, according to the possession of certain common characteristics. The groupings indicate the evolution of the Animal Kingdom from the earliest living forms to the highly specialized creatures of today. The main division is into the subkingdoms of **Single-celled Animals** and **Multicellular Animals.** Single-celled animals are microscopically small, and are not described in this book. The largest classification group is the phylum. Representatives of ten phyla of multicellular animals are described, and their relationship is explained in the table on this page, together with further divisions into subphyla. Each contains animals which have a basic similarity in their method of survival, and is of very ancient origin, representing a division of the original animal stock in remote geological time. Almost all of the major phyla are known from fossils of Cambrian Age, dating back about 600 million years, and each is divided into a number of classes, sometimes superficially very different from each other, but with a fundamental similarity of body plan, sometimes apparent only in the larval stages. The classes are split into orders, groups of considerable antiquity significantly different from every other order in the. class. The orders are broken down into families. These include animals which can usually be seen to be related, and they in turn are divided into genera, which are still more closely related. Each genus contains one or more species of animal. The species comprises the individuals,

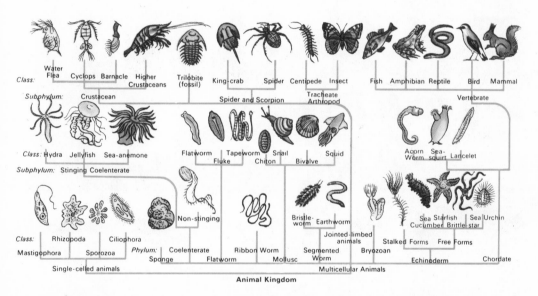

which differ in minor respects only, and are capable of continued interbreeding in nature. As with plants, each species has a two-part Latin name, showing genus and species, which is universally understood.

Generally a species lives in a continuous geographical area. If part of a species becomes separated by some kind of barrier, it may in time develop characteristics which make it recognizably different. This may be seen in Great Britain, where the animal populations, separate from the Continental forms since the end of the Ice Age, have developed in many cases into distinct forms or subspecies. These, however, are still capable of interbreeding fully with the mainland forms. Animals of closely related species may also be capable of interbreeding, but the offspring may be sterile or incapable of normal existence. Generally this does not occur in nature, as complex patterns of mating display behaviour have developed within each species, and these exclude all others.

Most of the animals described in this book belong to the phylum **Chordates;** this contains the **Vertebrates,** animals with a true backbone—**Fishes, Amphibians, Reptiles, Birds** and **Mammals,** the group of which Man is one member. All other types, including the lower Chordates, are **Invertebrates,** animals without a backbone.

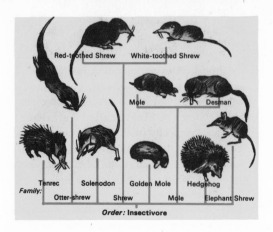

Red-toothed Shrew   White-toothed Shrew

Mole   Desman

Tenrec   Solenodon   Golden Mole   Hedgehog

Family: Otter-shrew   Shrew   Mole   Elephant Shrew

Order: Insectivore

Insectivores are the most primitive of the **Placental Mammals.** All present-day Placentals have probably developed from an ancestor similar to the least specialized of living insectivores, which have remained relatively unchanged for over 60 million years. The group is not found in Australia, but is otherwise world-wide. It is divided into eight families, three of which occur in Europe. Typically, insectivores are small animals, the world's smallest mammal being a species of shrew. They feed on any small creatures that they can subdue; many have a metabolic rate so high that they require huge amounts of food and may hunt day and night, with only short rests.

The 3500 species of **Mammals** are warm-blooded **Vertebrates,** of which the females give milk to their young. They are subdivided into three groups: the **Egg-laying Mammals,** which occur only in Australia and New Guinea; the **Marsupials,** the pouched mammals of Australia and the Americas; and the **Placentals,** which comprise the largest group of all. In these there is a connection, the placenta, between the mother and the foetus through which the latter is

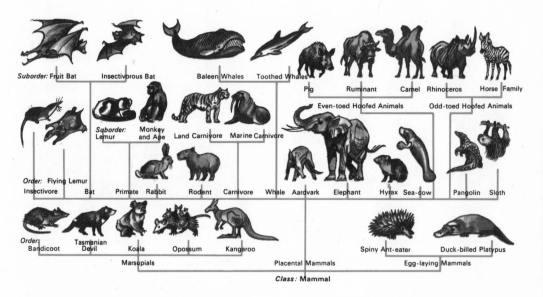

Suborder: Fruit Bat   Insectivorous Bat   Baleen Whales   Toothed Whales

Pig   Ruminant   Camel   Rhinoceros   Horse Family

Even-toed Hoofed Animals   Odd-toed Hoofed Animals

Suborder: Lemur   Monkey and Ape   Land Carnivore   Marine Carnivore

Order: Flying Lemur

Insectivore   Bat   Primate   Rabbit   Rodent   Carnivore   Whale   Aardvark   Elephant   Hyrax   Sea-cow   Pangolin   Sloth

Order: Bandicoot   Tasmanian Devil   Koala   Opossum   Kangaroo   Spiny Ant-eater   Duck-billed Platypus

Marsupials   Placental Mammals   Egg-laying Mammals

Class: Mammal

nourished while it develops inside the womb. The Placentals include sixteen orders, groups significantly different from each other in many respects and which the fossil record shows to have been separate since the early Tertiary Era, almost 60 million years ago. European mammals include representatives of nine of these orders.

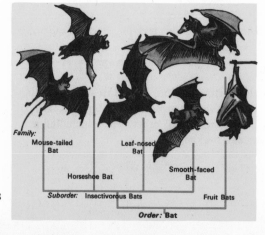

Family: Mouse-tailed Bat   Leaf-nosed Bat

Horseshoe Bat   Smooth-faced Bat

Suborder: Insectivorous Bats   Fruit Bats

Order: Bat

Bats are the only **mammals** with true flight. A wing membrane stretches between the fore and hind limbs, supported by the greatly elongated finger bones. The order, which is very large, is divided into two groups: the **Fruit-eating Bats,** which are all tropical, and the **Insectivorous Bats,** found also in temperate regions. European bats are nocturnal and virtually blind; they navigate by emitting high-pitched sounds, calculating the size and position of obstacles by the strength of the echo that bounces back to their large, acute ears, and by the time it takes to return. All European bats are harmless to man, and in some parts are protected animals.

Carnivores are mainly flesh-eaters. **Marine Carnivores** (Seals and Walruses) form one branch of this very large group, **Land Carnivores** the other. The teeth of the latter characteristically include large canines for tearing, and carnassial teeth in the back of the mouth for slicing meat; they do not normally grind their food, but swallow it in lumps. Their young are generally born blind and helpless and have a long period of parental care and education. They are usually considered to be intelligent. The young of marine carnivores are born singly in a highly developed state. Members of all of the families of land carnivores are present in Europe, except the Hyaena Family.

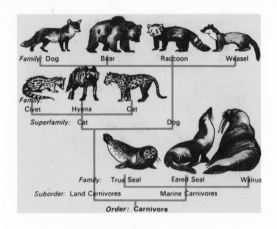

Rodents form over half of the world's species of mammals. **Rabbits** and **Hares,** although similar, are not closely related and geological evidence shows that they have developed separately since the beginning of the Tertiary Era. Rodents all have a pair of open-rooted gnawing teeth in the front of the mouth. These continue growing throughout the life of the animal, and because of their efficiency the group is able to make use of a very large number of foodstuffs, and they

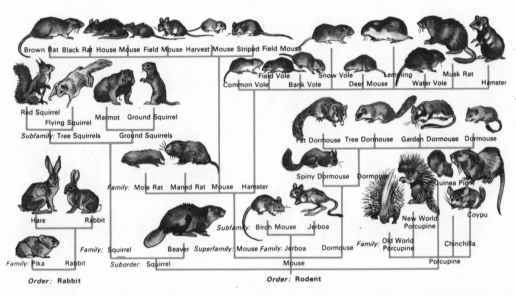

have colonized a large range of habitats all over the world. Rodent limbs have become specialized for many different tasks, including digging, climbing and gliding. Most rodents are small and defenceless animals, which are preyed on by many enemies. That they survive is due largely to their very high breeding rate. Most European rodents belong to the Mouse and Squirrel groups of the order.

Primates include **Man,** the **Apes, Monkeys** and **Lemurs.** Other than Man the order is entirely tropical and subtropical. There are four main kinds of Great Ape, and many species of Monkey, those of the Old World being very different from those of the New World. Lemurs are centred in Madagascar, the Tarsier and Tree Shrews, the most primitive members of the order, in SE Asia. Most primates are highly social animals. Many species are now becoming very rare, chiefly because of destruction of their habitat. The only native European species of primate, apart from Man, of course, is the Barbary Ape, which lives on Gibraltar.

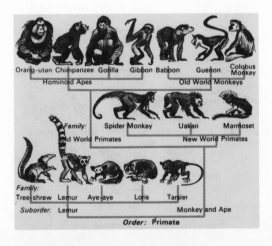

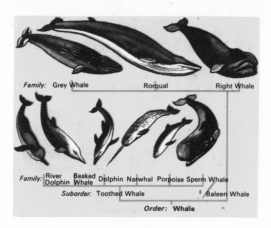

Family: Grey Whale   Rorqual   Right Whale

Family: River Dolphin   Beaked Whale   Dolphin   Narwhal   Porpoise   Sperm Whale

Suborder: Toothed Whale   Baleen Whale

Order: **Whale**

Whales are **mammals** completely adapted to an aquatic life. Although they have to come to the surface to breathe, they live, feed and breed in the water. The order is divided into two groups, the **Toothed Whales**, which generally have numerous small pointed teeth and feed on fishes or squids, and the **Baleen Whales**, which filter shrimp-like animals (plankton) from the sea through a series of triangular plates of horny material (baleen or whalebone), hanging from the roof of the mouth. Some of the smaller toothed whales, the Porpoises and Dolphins, are seen quite frequently in European waters. The larger species may occur there occasionally.

Hoofed animals do not form a natural unit, but consist of two orders, the **Odd-toed Hoofed Animals** or **Perissodactyls,** and the **Even-toed** or **Cloven-hoofed** ones or **Artiodactyls.** Both orders are herbivorous and many species within them are adapted for running. These animals all walk on the tips of a reduced number of toes, two in the Artiodactyls and usually three in the Perissodactyls, although in the Horse Family it has been reduced to one. **Pigs** and

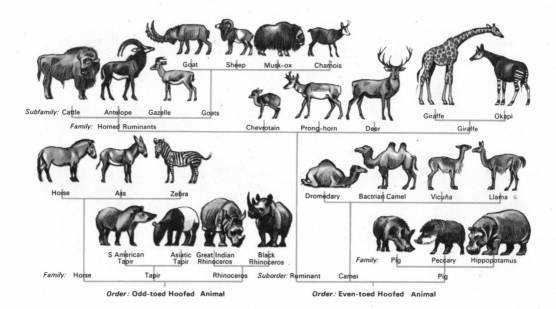

Goat   Sheep   Musk-ox   Chamois

Subfamily: Cattle   Antelope   Gazelle   Goats

Family: Horned Ruminants   Chevrotain   Prong-horn   Deer   Giraffe   Okapi   Giraffe

Horse   Ass   Zebra   Dromedary   Bactrian Camel   Vicuña   Llama

S American Tapir   Asiatic Tapir   Great Indian Rhinoceros   Black Rhinoceros   Family: Pig   Peccary   Hippopotamus

Family: Horse   Tapir   Rhinoceros   Suborder: Ruminant   Camel   Pig

Order: **Odd-toed Hoofed Animal**   Order: **Even-toed Hoofed Animal**

Ruminants are the main divisions of the Artiodactyls; **Horses, Tapirs** and **Rhinoceroses** of the Perissodactyls. The Ruminants form the largest and most successful of these groups, with more species than all the others together. In most cases the young are born singly in a very advanced state and can walk within minutes of birth.

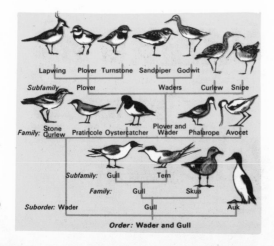

Lapwing   Plover   Turnstone   Sandpiper   Godwit

Subfamily: Plover   Waders   Curlew   Snipe

Family: Stone Curlew   Pratincole   Oystercatcher   Plover and Wader   Phalarope   Avocet

Subfamily: Gull   Tern

Family: Gull   Skua

Suborder: Wader   Gull   Auk

Order: **Wader and Gull**

Waders, Gulls and **Auks** are medium-sized, generally black and white or brown-coloured birds, which are found throughout the world, almost always near water. In most cases they feed exclusively on animal food. Generally the sexes are alike and both parents take part in caring for the eggs and young which, except in the Auks, are precocious. Waders are long-legged birds, usually found in estuaries and by freshwater. Gulls generally prefer the edge of the sea while the auks are exclusively marine. Waders and auks are long-distance migrants; gulls are not.

Geese, Ducks, Swans and the **Screamers** of S America form one order. They are all medium to large birds adapted to an aquatic life by their thick waterproof feathers and, except in the Screamers, their webbed feet. The bill is long and generally flattened, except, again, in the Screamers. The fish-eating ducks have a saw-edged bill. The order is world-wide, and the ducks in particular have spread into a large range of habitats. One peculiarity of the Ducks, Geese and Swans is that in moulting they loose all the flight feathers simultaneously. At this 'eclipse' period they are unable to fly.

Birds are warm-blooded **Vertebrates;** they form a class which includes about 8600 species. All are feathered, toothless and egg-laying, with specializations such as lightweight bones and air sacs in the body which are adaptations towards efficient flight. The front limbs are normally modified to form wings, although in some cases evolution has returned the birds to a flightless state, with only small, weak wings. In the table the orders listed include all those represented

in Europe and a few foreign groups such as Parrots and Penguins. Two recently extinct groups, the Moas and the Dodo, are also included. Fewer than 600 species of birds occur in Europe. The larger groups of these are shown on this page.

This table shows European Song Birds, representing 19 families of the **Perching Bird Order.** These range in size from the Goldcrest, which is only 9 cm long and weighs 5–6 grammes, to the Raven, which is over 60 cm long and weighs 1700 grammes. Most perching birds have distinctive form and colouring, but in some cases it is necessary to hear the song to be certain of identification in the field. Many of them are good songsters; this is related to the fact that they are mostly strongly territorial during the breeding season.

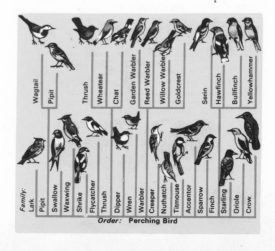

11

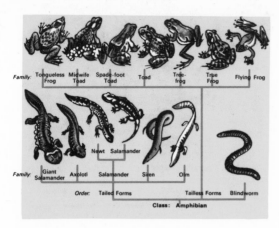

Amphibians are the most primitive of the land **Vertebrates.** They have to pass through a fish-like larval stage before they metamorphose to their adult form. There are in all about 1100 species. All are rather small, soft-skinned animals. Many breathe largely through their skin, which must, therefore, be kept moist. As a result they tend to be secretive animals, hiding in damp places. The **Tailed Forms** are lizard-like in appearance. **Frogs** and **Toads** are tailless and have very large hind legs which they use for jumping. The legless **Blindworm** represents a third small non-European group of the class.

Fishes form the largest class of the **Vertebrates.** They are all water-living, gill-breathing animals. They are classified into three subclasses. The **Lampreys** are survivals of the most primitive jawless fishes of ancient times. The 600 species of **Sharks** and **Rays** are all flesh-eaters which live mainly in tropical seas; they have cartilaginous skeletons and give birth to living young or lay a few large-yolked eggs. The remaining 20 000 species, **Bony Fishes,** possess a skeleton

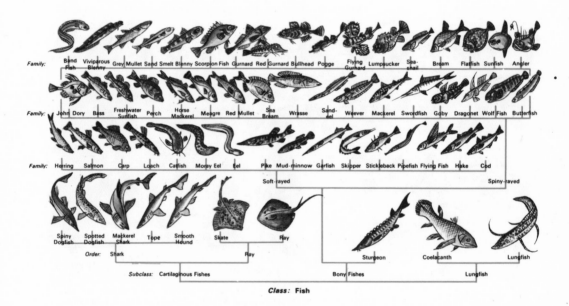

of true bone and generally have a covering of scales over the body. They usually produce a very large number of minute eggs. They are found in seas, rivers and lakes throughout the world. In the table only bony fish families with European representatives are shown, except in the case of the Lungfish, which has none.

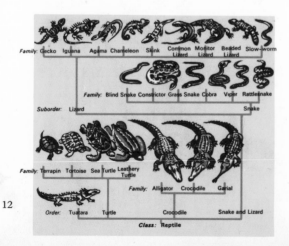

Reptiles, of which there are about 4300 species, are cold-blooded land **Vertebrates,** usually covered with horny scales. They nearly all reproduce by means of shelled eggs. In the past, reptiles of many kinds, some of gigantic size, lived in all parts of the world. Now most of these are extinct, and only four orders survive. These are the **Crocodiles,** which survive in tropical areas only; the **Tuataras** which survive only on a few islands off the coast of New Zealand; the **Turtles** and **Tortoises;** and the **Snakes** and **Lizards,** which are rather sparsely represented in Europe.

Echinoderms are all marine creatures. The name means 'hedgehog-skinned', for many members of the group bear spines or tubercles. They always have a system of water conducting vessels connected with tube feet, and there may be an internal skeleton of calcium carbonate. The phylum contains five classes, which bear little superficial resemblance to each other, but are all built on a similar wheel-shaped body plan, described as radial symmetry. These are the **Sea Lilies, Sea-cucumbers, Starfishes, Brittle Stars** and **Sea Urchins** – all of these classes are represented in European waters.

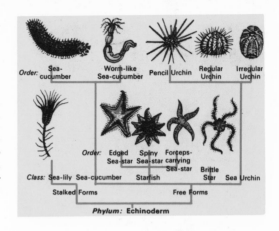

Molluscs are a highly successful group of soft-bodied, limbless animals, which usually carry a protective shell of lime salts. The apparently diverse creatures which make up this group include 1000 species of **Chitons,** in which the shell is made up of articulating plates; the **Bivalves,** 25 000 species with a hinged shell, most of which are burrowers or of sedentary habit; the **Snails** and **Slugs,** about 85 000 species, all except the latter generally with a single,

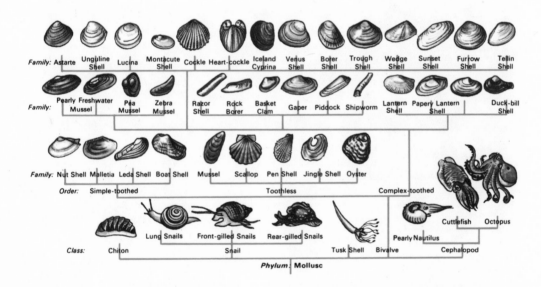

usually spiral shell; the **Tusk Shells,** a small group of burrowing animals with a single tusk-shaped shell; and the **Octopus** group or **Cephalopods,** containing about 600 species in all of which, except the Pearly Nautilus of the South Pacific Ocean, there is no visible shell. Of the snails and bivalves illustrated in the table, the families shown are all mentioned in the text.

The **Snails** and **Slugs** are the largest group of the **Molluscs.** They can generally be recognized by their method of movement, creeping on a large muscular foot, and by the spiral shell, which is lacking only in the slugs. This group has colonized a very wide range of habitats, and is found in the sea, in freshwater and on land. Snails may breathe by means of gills or lungs. They may feed on plant or animal food, and are themselves used for food by man in many parts of the world. Space has not allowed the inclusion in the text of the family name of each species described, but most of them may easily be traced in these tables.

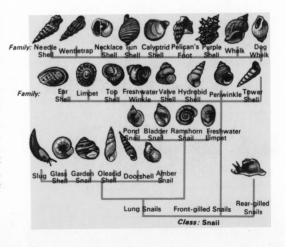

13

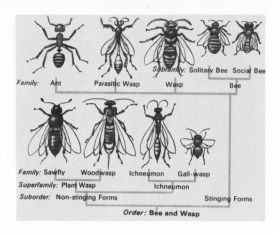

Family: Ant — Parasitic Wasp — Wasp
Subfamily: Solitary Bee — Social Bee
Family: Bee

Family: Sawfly — Woodwasp — Ichneumon — Gall-wasp
Superfamily: Plant Wasp — Ichneumon
Suborder: Non-stinging Forms — Stinging Forms
Order: Bee and Wasp

Bees, Ants and **Wasps** are **Insects** characterized in the adult by two pairs of membranous wings, joined by a series of tiny hooks. They have a complete metamorphosis from the worm-like grub to the flying adult. The group is well known to most people as it contains the only social insects of temperate regions. Other members of the group are the **Sawflies,** some species of which are agricultural and forest pests in their larval stages, and the parasitic forms, which because they control large numbers of pests, are useful to man. The social forms live in colonies, the members of which are all the offspring of a single female, often called the queen.

Arthropods, Invertebrates with a hard supporting external skeleton and jointed limbs, form the largest group of living animals; they include the **Insects,** over 750 000 species of which are already known. Closely related to them are the **Centipedes** and the **Millipedes.** All breathe by means of tracheae. In insects, the body segments are grouped into three main areas, the head, thorax and abdomen, in which the primary segmentation may still be seen. The thoracic segments usually carry three pairs of legs and two pairs of wings in the adults. Insects are the

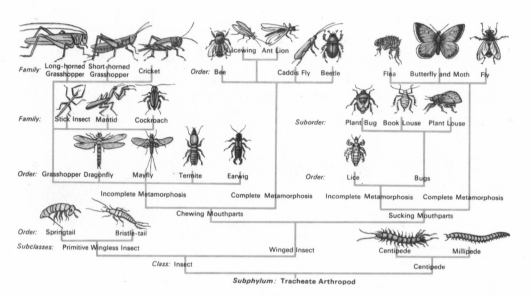

Family: Long-horned Grasshopper — Short-horned Grasshopper — Cricket
Order: Bee — Lacewing — Ant Lion — Caddis Fly — Beetle — Flea — Butterfly and Moth — Fly
Family: Stick Insect — Mantid — Cockroach
Suborder: Plant Bug — Book Louse — Plant Louse
Order: Grasshopper — Dragonfly — Mayfly — Termite — Earwig — Lice — Bugs
Incomplete Metamorphosis — Complete Metamorphosis — Incomplete Metamorphosis — Complete Metamorphosis
Chewing Mouthparts — Sucking Mouthparts
Order: Springtail — Bristle-tail
Subclasses: Primitive Wingless Insect — Winged Insect — Centipede — Millipede
Class: Insect — Centipede
Subphylum: Tracheate Arthropod

only flying invertebrates. The first insects to evolve were wingless, as are the most primitive living orders, e.g. Springtails and Silverfish. Some groups, e.g. Fleas and Lice, have become secondarily wingless in the course of evolution. According to whether they have a complete metamorphosis from grub to adult, e.g. butterflies, or not, e.g. grasshoppers, and on structures associated with feeding, insects are classified into many orders, the major ones shown here.

Family: Click Beetle — Spider Beetle — Oil Beetle — Leaf Beetle — Bark Beetle
Glow-worm — Black Beetle — Timber Beetle — Weevil
Family: Rove-beetle — Histerid Beetle — Cockchafer — Ladybird
Burying Beetle — Stag Beetle — Water Beetle — Hide Beetle
Family: Tiger Beetle — Ground Beetle — Carnivorous Water Beetle — Haliplid — Whirlygig
Ground-feeders — Water-feeders
Suborder: Adephaga — Polyphaga
Order: Beetle

Beetles are **Insects** whose fore wings have become horny covers to the membranous hind wings, which are folded in a complex fashion underneath them. Nearly half a million different kinds of beetles are known—more than any other single order of animals. They are to be found in a great variety of habitats, from deserts to freshwater. In feeding, their habits vary from general scavenging to specialized parasitism, although most have chewing mouthparts which are relatively unspecialized. All species of beetles undergo a complete metamorphosis, and have a pupal stage.

Flies are **Insects** with one pair of wings used for flying; the second pair are called halteres and are used as sense of balance organs. All flies have a complete metamorphosis. This large and very successful order includes the Crane Flies and Mosquitoes, which have long soft bodies and long legs. The suborder to which House Flies, Dung Flies and many parasitic forms belong is usually harder and shorter-bodied, with short legs and sparsely veined wings. Flies feed on a great range of foods, making them very common pests; some have piercing and sucking mouthparts, others lick their food.

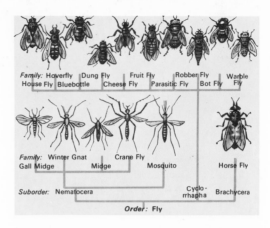

Butterflies and **Moths** are **Insects** which have four large scale-covered wings and a retractile proboscis. The larvae (caterpillars) usually have false legs on the abdomen, as well as the true legs on the thorax. Butterflies, most of which are brightly coloured, generally fly by day; moths, which have more sombre colours, more often fly by night. Both use their very good sense of smell to help find their mates and their food, which is the nectar of flowers. Also, butterflies have a knobby or club-shaped end to the antennae, while those of the moths, except for the small

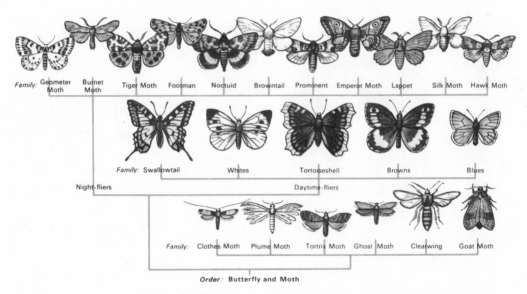

intermediate group of Burnet Moths, have pointed, often feathery antennae. The order, which is very large, is arbitrarily divided into the **Macrolepidoptera**, which contains almost entirely species of a large size, and the **Microlepidoptera**, which, in Europe at least, contains species which are almost all small. The families shown in the table are all illustrated in the book, in most cases with the caterpillars.

Spiders are related to various **Arthropods** which have neither antennae nor wings, and which breathe either through tracheal spiracles or lung books. The **King-crabs** which today survive mainly in tropical waters are the descendants of a once common section of the group. Other members of the class include the **Scorpions, False Scorpions, Harvestmen** and **Mites**. Of the many living families of spiders, only those representative of species described in the text are shown here. All true spiders and many of the other members of this group are able to manufacture silk.

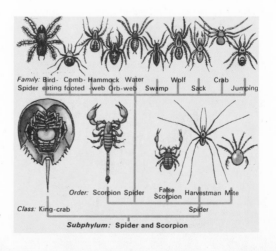

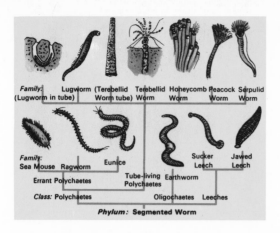

Family:
(Lugworm in tube) Lugworm (Terebellid Terebellid Honeycomb Peacock Serpulid
                   Worm tube) Worm   Worm   Worm   Worm

Family:
Sea Mouse Ragworm   Eunice   Sucker   Jawed
                                              Leech   Leech
      Errant Polychaetes   Tube-living   Earthworm
                                Polychaetes
Class: Polychaetes   Oligochaetes   Leeches

Phylum: Segmented Worm

Segmented Worms are all soft-bodied animals made up of similar segments joined one behind the other. There are about 6000 different species of this group, the majority of them sea-dwellers. Many of these are very beautiful creatures. Some protect themselves by building a tube or shelter in which they live. In freshwater, **Leeches** are important members of the group, while on land the **Earthworms** are the best known. Worms are the basic food for many other kinds of animals. Of the very large numbers of families which are known, only those represented in the text are shown here.

Crustaceans form a major division of the **Arthropods,** with about 25 000 known species. All have a hard external skeleton of chitin, often thickened by lime salts. Almost all are aquatic, mostly marine, the majority breathing through gills. Only the Wood Lice are true land-dwellers and these are generally found in humid places, although a few marine forms, such as some crabs,

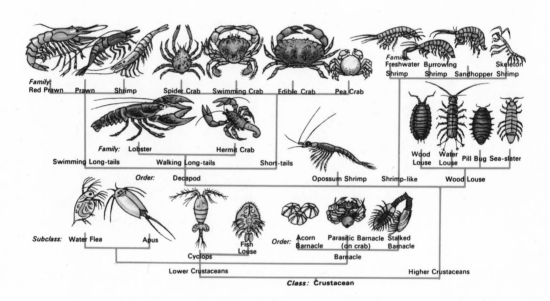

Family:
Freshwater Burrowing   Skeleton
Shrimp   Shrimp   Sandhopper   Shrimp

Family:
Red Prawn Prawn   Shrimp   Spider Crab Swimming Crab Edible Crab Pea Crab

Family: Lobster   Hermit Crab
Swimming Long-tails   Walking Long-tails   Short-tails

                                                          Wood   Water
                                                          Louse Louse   Pill Bug Sea-slater
Order: Decapod   Opossum Shrimp   Shrimp-like   Wood Louse

Subclass: Water Flea   Apus
                                  Fish   Order: Acorn   Parasitic Barnacle Stalked
                       Cyclops   Louse   Barnacle (on crab)   Barnacle
                                                           Barnacle
        Lower Crustaceans   Higher Crustaceans

Class: Crustacean

can remain out of the water for long periods. Many crustaceans are microscopically small; only a few larger members of the groups to which they belong are shown here. Barnacles, which in their adult stage look like molluscs, betray the fact that they are crustaceans in their larval forms. Many crustaceans are important links in the food-chains of the sea.

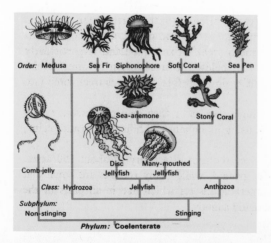

Order: Medusa   Sea Fir Siphonophore Soft Coral   Sea Pen

                      Sea-anemone   Stony Coral

                 Disc   Many-mouthed
                 Jellyfish Jellyfish
Comb-jelly
Class: Hydrozoa   Jellyfish   Anthozoa
Subphylum:
Non-stinging   Stinging
Phylum: Coelenterate

Coelenterates are radially symmetrical, mostly marine animals. They all consist basically of a simple column with an opening at one end, usually surrounded with tentacles, through which food is taken in and waste matter ejected. Many of the 9000 species look like flowers, but they are in fact carnivorous creatures, subduing their prey by poisonous stings. The majority are completely soft-bodied, but some, like the corals, make hard supports and shelters for themselves. In tropical waters these may form huge reefs, housing many millions of animals. The comb-jellies are free-living, non-stinging members of the group, sometimes placed in a separate phylum.

Woods and Forests

Various names may be given to an area covered with trees. Several terms are used for quite small groups, larger tracts are called woodland, and the name forest is applied to the most extensive areas. Natural primeval wooded areas are now rare, surviving in nature reserves and in a few inaccessible mountainous areas. Most of today's woodlands and forests are the result of tree-felling and replanting by man. Trees themselves are of two kinds: deciduous, which shed their leaves in autumn and are bare until spring, and evergreen, which are clothed in leaves throughout the year.

There are three main types of woodland and forest: coniferous (in the north and in mountain areas); broadleaved, of deciduous trees (in the temperate parts); and mixed, of both coniferous and deciduous trees (in the south and Mediterranean area). Mixed woodland is particularly rich in animal life, and plant communities flourish below the trees, often at three levels: 1. mosses, lichens, fungi, etc.; 2. herbs which usually flower before deciduous trees come into leaf; 3. berry-bearing shrubs.

All these wooded areas may have trees of a single species or they may comprise a mixed population, and they are to be found in most terrains, in mountains and hills, valleys and plains, marshes and swamps.

Few large animals live in woodlands; one red deer requires a territory of about 150 acres. Foxes, wild cats, stoats, etc., live mainly on the ground, while many rodents are equally at home on the ground or in the trees. The innumerable insects which live in all parts of the trees are fed on by many of the birds in the woodland canopy.

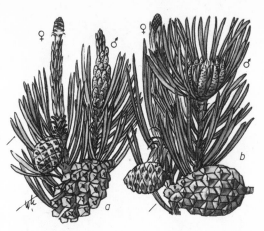

a *Scots Pine, *Pinus sylvestris:* tree up to 45 m; crown usually flat at maturity, needles in pairs, 3–8 cm long, blue-green, rigid, twisted; 5–6; on sandy soils in N and C Europe, extending southwards to S Spain, the Apennines and C Balkans, ascending to 2000 m in mountainous areas, in Britain native in the Highlands, cultivated elsewhere. **b †Austrian Pine,** *Pinus nigra:* tree up to 50 m; crown usually pyramidal, needles in pairs, 8–16 cm long, dark dull green, very rigid, nearly straight (in the same race: **†Corsican Pine,** subsp. *laricio*, frequently planted for forestry, leaves lighter and somewhat twisted); 5–6; occurs *in* C and S Europe.

Of the conifers shown in the table the European Larch, the Swiss Pine and the Mountain Pine occur in forests on C and S European mountains, ascending to 2400–2700 m. The Japanese Larch and the Weymouth Pine, a native of N America, are much cultivated in C Europe. The Yew is widely distributed in Europe from S Scandinavia southwards, often on limestone, sometimes forming pure woods, ascending to 1200 m on mountains; Yew Family. All the other species on this page belong to the Pine Family.

	†European Larch	†Japanese Larch	†Swiss Pine	†Weymouth Pine	†Mountain Pine	*Yew
Scientific Name	*Larix decidua*	*Larix kaempferi*	*Pinus cembra*	*Pinus strobus*	*Pinus mugo*	*Taxus baccata*
Longevity, Size	Tree up to 35 m	Tree up to 30 m	Tree up to 25 m	Tree up to 50 m	Shrub, 3.5 m	Tree up to 20 m
Distinguishing Features; Flowering Time	Young shoots green, needles with two greenish bands below, cone-scales loosely appressed; 3–5	Shoots blue-green, needles with two white bands below, cone-scales recurved at tip; 3–5	Needles in bundles of five, 5–8 cm long, **bright green, rigid,** seeds wingless; 6–7	Needles in bundles of five, 5–14 cm long, soft, slender, straight, seeds winged; 5	Branches decumbent and ascending, needles 3–8 cm long, in pairs, rigid, curved, seeds winged; 6	Needles solitary, 1–3 cm, flat, dark green, seed in red fleshy aril; green parts poisonous; 3–5

a †Norway Spruce, *Picea abies:* tree up to 40 m; needles 4-angled, 1–2 cm, acute, cones 10–15 cm long, pendulous, falling entire at maturity; 4–5; N Europe, southwards to the Pyrenees, S Alps and Bulgaria. **b †Silver Fir,** *Abies alba:* tree up to 50 m; needles nearly flat, 1.5–3 cm, notched at apex, cones 10 to 16 cm, erect, cone-scales finally falling from axis; 5–6; forming forests in the mountains of C and S Europe. **c †Douglas Fir,** *Pseudotsuga menziesii:* tree up to 40 m; needles 2–4 cm, with smell of oranges, cones 5–10 cm, pendulous, falling entire; 4–5; introduced from N America, planted for forestry.

a ***Traveller's Joy,** *Clematis vitalba:* a woody climber with stems up to 25 m; leaves pinnate, usually with five rather distant leaflets, sepals greenish white, downy, fruits with long plumose whitish styles; 6–9; abundant in hedgerows and damp thickets; Buttercup Family. b ***Gooseberry,** *Ribes uva-crispa:* spiny shrub up to 1 m; berries usually yellowish green, 1–2 cm wide; 3–5; widespread, commonly cultivated for its fruits. c ***Downy Red Currant,** *Ribes spicatum:* shrub up to 2 m; berries red, 6–10 mm wide, acid; 4–5; N Europe, south to N Germany and Poland; similar to widely grown ***Red Currant,** *Ribes rubrum.* All belong to the Gooseberry Family.

The Rowan or Mountain Ash is very widespread, ascending to 2400 m in the mountains. The Common Whitebeam occurs in open situations in NW and C Europe, the Wild Service Tree locally from England to Denmark, southwards to S Europe. The Dwarf Whitebeam occurs in woods in mountain areas of C Europe. The Service Tree grows scattered in woods of C Europe, the Mougeot's Whitebeam in the mountains of C Europe and the Apennines. All belong to the Rose Family

	*Common Whitebeam	***Wild Service Tree**	**Dwarf Whitebeam'**	***Rowan**	**†Service Tree**	**Mougeot's Whitebeam**
Scientific Name	*Sorbus aria*	*Sorbus torminalis*	*Sorbus chamaemespilus*	*Sorbus aucuparia*	*Sorbus domestica*	*Sorbus mougeotii*
Longevity, Size	Tree 6–12 m	Tree 12–20 m	Shrub 0.5–1 m	Tree 10–17 m	Tree up to 20 m	Tree up to 20 m
Distinguishing Features; Flowering Time	Leaves rigid, entire, fruit red, mealy, palatable after frost; 5–6	Leaves deeply lobed, fruit brown-yellow, pulpy and palatable when overripe; 5–6	Calyx-lobes downy inside, fruit oblong, red, edible; 6–7	Leaves pinnate, flowers mostly 3-styled, fruits coral-red, bitter; 5–6	Similar to the Rowan but flowers 5-styled, fruit pear-shaped, palatable when ripe; 5	Leaves ovate with 8–10 veins on both sides, fruit roundish, red; 5–6

a ***Black Currant,** *Ribes nigrum:* shrub, 1.3–1.7 m; leaves 3–5-lobed, strongly scented, berries black, aromatic; 4–5; widespread. b ***Mountain Currant,** *Ribes alpinum:* shrub up to 2.5 m; flowers dioecious, insipid; 4–5; cliffs and rocky woods, often on limestone; outside Britain in mountains from Scandinavia to S Europe. c **Rock Currant,** *Ribes petraeum:* shrub up to 2 m; differs from the Red Currants by having fringed lobes on the calyx, flowers reddish, bell-shaped, berries red, acid; 4–6; rare, on wet slopes of mountains in C Europe, the Pyrenees and Balkans. All are members of the Gooseberry Family.

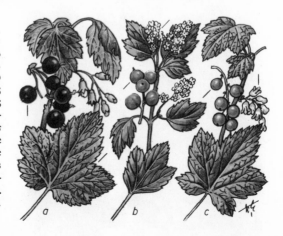

a Black-fruited Cotoneaster, *Cotoneaster peduncularis:* shrub up to 2 m; leaves hairy beneath, fruits blue-black; 5; rare, in open woodlands of N, E and EC Europe. **b *Midland Hawthorn,** *Crataegus oxyacanthoides:* thorny shrub or small tree 2–10 m; leaves ovate with shallow lobes, stalks glabrous, styles mostly 2; 5–6; from S Sweden and Finland southwards to E Poland. **c *Common Hawthorn,** *Crataegus monogyna:* similar to **b** but leaves deeply cut, stalks usually woolly, style usually one; 5–6; widespread throughout Europe. All are members of the Rose Family occurring in open situations, particularly in the mountains.

The Bramble or Blackberry (which is split into numerous microspecies) and the Wild Raspberry are widespread in open woodlands and hedgerows. The Wild Pear and the Crab Apple, ancestors of cultivated pears and apples, occur scattered in open woodlands. The Medlar is a native of SE Europe and SW Asia, grown for its fruits and naturalized in many places. The Stone Bramble is widespread from Iceland and Arctic Russia to the Pyrenees, the mountains of Italy and N Greece. All belong to the Rose Family.

	*Wild Pear	*Crab Apple	†Medlar	*Wild Raspberry	*Bramble	*Stone Bramble
Scientific Name	*Pyrus communis*	*Malus sylvestris*	*Mespilus germanica*	*Rubus idaeus*	*Rubus fruticosus*	*Rubus saxatilis*
Longevity, Size	Tree up to 20 m	Tree up to 10 m	Shrub up to 6 m	♃, 0.7–1.3 m	♃, up to 3 m	♃, 8–40 cm
Distinguishing Features; Flowering Time	Petals white, anthers red; 4–6	Petals with a reddish tinge, anthers yellow; 5–6	Plant thorny, flowers large, 5-styled, anthers red, fruit sub-globose; 5–6	Stems woody, prickly, petals narrow, wedge-shaped, fruit red, with numerous druplets; 5–6	Stems woody, prickly, petals ovate, fruit black, with numerous druplets; 6–8	Stems stoloniferous, usually unarmed, flowers in terminal cyme, fruit scarlet, druplets few; 5–6

a *Dewberry, *Rubus caesius:* ♃, up to 3 m; stems prickly, leaves of three leaflets, petals white or pinkish, notched at tip; 5–6. **b *Dog Rose,** *Rosa canina:* deciduous shrub up to 3 m; leaves pinnately compound, with 5–7 leaflets, flowers conspicuous, fruits (hips) scarlet; 5–7; an extremely variable species. **c *Blackthorn** or **Sloe,** *Prunus spinosa:* shrub, 1–4 m; with very thorny twigs, flowers white, drupes (sloes) blue-black, acid; 4–5. All these species are widely distributed members of the Rose Family, occurring in open woodlands and thickets.

a ***Wild Cherry** or **Gean,** *Prunus avium:* tree 5–25 m; flowers large, white, usually in stalkless umbels of 2–6; fruit bright or dark red, bitter-sweet; 4–5; from Scandinavia and SW Russia southwards. **b** ***Bird Cherry,** *Prunus padus:* 3–15 m; flowers in long, drooping racemes, fruits shiny black, bitter-sweet; 5–6; widespread. Both these species occur in water meadows and mixed woods. **c** ***Dwarf Cherry,** *Prunus fruticosa:* shrub, 0.5–2 m; flowers pure white, 1–3 in umbels, fruits red, sour; 4–5; rare, in E, SE and C Europe. All three of these species belong to the Rose Family.

The Sour Cherry is common on lowlands and in mountains, the Mahaleb or Rock Cherry occurs only in S and C Europe. Both belong to the Rose Family. The Common Laburnum is a native of the S Alps, the Bladder Senna of the Mediterranean region, naturalized elsewhere. Both are members of the Pea Family. The Box Tree occurs in S Europe, Albania, northwards to S Britain. The Holly Tree, an evergreen shrub or small tree, is distributed from Norway, Denmark and Britain southwards. The last two species each form a family.

	†Sour Cherry	Mahaleb Cherry	†Common Laburnum	†Bladder Senna	*Box Tree	*Holly Tree
Scientific Name	*Prunus cerasus*	*Prunus mahaleb*	*Laburnum anagyroides*	*Colutea arborescens*	*Buxus sempervirens*	*Ilex aquifolium*
Longevity, Size	Shrub to 10 m	Shrub, 1–7 m	Tree up to 7 m	Shrub, 1–4 m	Shrub, 3–5 m	Shrub, 3–15 m
Distinguishing Features; Flowering Time	Similar to Wild Cherry, but leaves dark, glossy, fruits red, rarely blackish, sour; 4–5	Flowers 4–5 in racemes, mature fruits black, bitter; 4–5	Leaflets 3, flowers golden yellow, papilionate; poisonous; 4–6	Leaves pinnate, with 7–13 leaflets, silky beneath, fruit (pod) membranous, inflated; 5–6	Flowers monoecious, leaves small, leathery, fruit a brown capsule; 4–5	Leaves thick, leathery, with undulate, spiny margin, fruit a drupe, coral red, unpalatable; 5–6

a ***Large-leaved Lime,** *Tilia platyphyllos:* tree up to 30 m; leaves broadly ovate, obliquely heart-shaped at the base, pubescent beneath and often also above, flowers usually in threes, fruits with 3–5 prominent ribs; 6. **b** ***Small-leaved Lime,** *Tilia cordata:* tree up to 25 m; leaves smaller, glabrous beneath except for tufts in the axils of veins, fruits ribless or barely ribbed; 6–7. Both are members of the Lime Family, found abundant or scattered in woods in most of Europe. **c** ***Ivy,** *Hedera helix:* woody evergreen climber, climbing by adventitious roots, flowers in umbels, berries blue-black; 9–10; common, from Norway and Britain southwards; Ivy Family.

a ***Spindle-tree,** *Euonymus europaeus:* tree or small shrub up to 6 m; branches green, 4–angled, fruit a 4–lobed capsule, deep pink, exposing the bright orange aril after opening; 5–6; widespread. b **Warty-barked Spindle-tree,** *Euonymus verrucosus:* shrub up to 2 m; branches with black cork warts; 5–6; EC and E Europe, extending to N Italy and Albania. Both are members of the Spindle-tree Family, occurring in woods and scrubs. c **†Bladder-nut,** *Staphylea pinnata:* shrub up to 5 m; flowers in branched racemes, fruit a green, bladder-shaped capsule; 5–6; a member of the Bladder-nut Family, native in C and S Europe, naturalized elsewhere.

The Sycamore is a native of the mountains of C and S Europe, introduced and now common in Britain. The Norway Maple occurs from S Scandinavia to Greece, N Italy and N Spain. The Common Maple is widespread from S Scandinavia to N Greece and Sicily. The French and Italian Maples are widely distributed in the Mediterranean region and occur also in C Europe. The American Maple, a native of N America, is naturalized in some places. All belong to the Maple Family.

	†Sycamore	†Norway Maple	*Common Maple	French Maple	Italian Maple	American Maple
Scientific Name	*Acer pseudo-platanus*	*Acer platanoides*	*Acer campestre*	*Acer monspes-sulanum*	*Acer opalus*	*Acer negundo*
Longevity, Size	Tree up to 30 m	Tree up to 25 m	Tree up to 20 m	Tree up to 10 m	Tree up to 12 m	Tree 15–20 m
Distinguishing Features; Flowering Time	Leaves with 5 irregularly serrate lobes, wings of the fruit spread at an acute angle; 5–6	Leaves with 5 lobes, each with a few large teeth, wings of fruit spreading at a wide angle; 4	Leaves with 5 blunt lobes, wings of fruit spreading horizontally; 5	Leaves with 3–5 entire lobes, wings of fruit spreading at an acute angle; 4	Leaves heart-shaped at base, wings of fruit form a right angle between them; 4	Dioecious, leaves pin-nate, wings of fruit spreading at an acute angle; 4

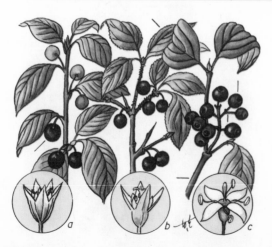

a ***Alder Buckthorn,** *Frangula alnus:* shrub or small tree up to 7 m; flowers pentamerous, mature berries black, unpalatable; 5–6. b ***Common Buckthorn,** *Rhamnus catharticus:* a rather thorny shrub or a small tree commonly 4–6 m; polygamous or dioecious, leaves entire, finely serrate, flowers greenish, inconspicuous, with their parts in fours; 5–6. Both belong to the Buckthorn Family and occur in most of Europe except the extreme north and south. c ***Dogwood,** *Cornus sanguinea:* shrub 1–3.5 m; twigs red, fruits black, on red stalks; 5–7; most of Europe except the extreme north; Cornel Family.

a †Grape Vine, *Vitis vinifera* subsp. *sylvestris:* a woody climber with palmately lobed leaves and tendrils which twine round a support, inflorescence a racemose panicle, flowers dioecious; 6–7; dry meadow woods in the Mediterranean region, C Europe and S Russia; Grape Family. **b †Cornelian-cherry,** *Cornus mas:* shrub 1–6 m; flowers yellow, appearing before the leaves; 2–4; C and S Europe, except Spain and Portugal; Cornel Family. **c *Silver Birch,** *Betula pendula:* monoecious, ♀ catkins upright, ♂ catkins pendent, twigs glabrous, with pale warts; 4–5; this tree, with its characteristic silvery bark, is a widespread member of the Birch Family.

The Hazel or Cob Nut is widespread in open woodlands and scrubs; the Hornbeam occurs often in oak or beech woods in most of Europe except the extreme north. Both belong to the Hazel Family. The Alder is widespread, the Grey Alder grows in NE and C Europe and on mountains of S Europe, the Green Alder on the mountains of C Europe and in the Balkans. The Alders belong to the Birch Family. The Beech, a member of the Beech Family, is native in W and C Europe, southwards to Greece, Sicily and C Spain.

	*Hazel	*Hornbeam	*Alder	†Grey Alder	Green Alder	*Beech
Scientific Name	*Corylus avellana*	*Carpinus betulus*	*Alnus glutinosa*	*Alnus incana*	*Alnus viridis*	*Fagus sylvatica*
Longevity, Size	Shrub 1–6 m	Tree up to 30 m	Tree up to 20 m	Tree up to 20 m	Shrub to 2.5 m	Tree up to 45 m
Distinguishing Features; Flowering Time	♀ catkins short, bud-like, fruit a nut, subtended by a lobed involucre; 2–4	Fruit greenish, ovoid, compressed, subtended by a 3-lobed or serrate involucre; 5–6	Buds stalked, wings of fruit narrower than the achene; 3–4	Buds stalked, stalks of catkins with thick down, **wings of fruit about as broad as achene**; 2–3	Buds stalkless, ♂ catkins stalkless, ♀ catkins on long stalks; 4–7	Leaves fringed when young, fruit 3-sided; 5

a *Common or **British Oak,** *Quercus robur:* tree up to 45 m; monoecious, leaves with short stalks, with small reflexed auricles at the base, fruit long-stalked; 4–6; widespread. **b *Durmast Oak,** *Quercus petraea:* tree up to 40 m; leaves with stalks 1 cm long or more, without reflexed auricles at the base, fruits almost stalkless; 4–6; usually on poorer soil than the Common Oak. **c Hairy Oak,** *Quercus pubescens:* tree up to 25 m; leaves with long stalks, densely downy beneath when young, twigs densely hairy; 4–5; W, C and S Europe. All these species belong to the Beech Family.

a *Goat Willow or **Palm**, *Salix caprea:* shrub or small tree 3–10 m; catkins appearing before the leaves, densely woolly before flowering, later ♂ catkins thick, golden yellow, ♀ catkins greenish, stipules half-heart-shaped; 3–4. **b** *White Willow, *Salix alba:* tree 10–25 m; young twigs yellow, silky, later olive, glabrous, leaves with white silky appressed hairs, ♀ flowers with one nectary; 4–5. **c** *Crack Willow, *Salix fragilis:* tree 10 to 25 m; ♂ flowers with two stamens, ♀ flowers usually with two nectaries, twigs fragile; 4–5. All are widespread members of the Willow Family growing in woods, scrub and on river-banks.

The Aspen and the poplars in the table are all members of the Willow Family. The Aspen is widely distributed in Europe, but only on mountains in the south. The Poplars occur in C, E and S Europe, often planted elsewhere and sometimes naturalized. The Smooth Elm and the Wych Elm are widespread, especially on lowlands. The European White Elm occurs in a very wide range of habitats, in C, E and SE Europe, extending to S Sweden. All belong to the Elm Family.

	*Aspen	*Black Poplar	†White Poplar	*Smooth Elm	*Wych Elm	European White Elm
Scientific Name	*Populus tremula*	*Populus nigra*	*Populus alba*	*Ulmus minor*	*Ulmus glabra*	*Ulmus laevis*
Longevity, Size	Tree up to 20 m	Tree up to 30 m	Tree up to 30 m	Tree up to 40 m	Tree up to 40 m	Tree up to 35 m
Distinguishing Features; Flowering Time	Leaves glabrous when mature, stalks strongly compressed laterally, stigmas purple; 3–4	Leaves glabrous when mature, stalks flattened laterally, stigmas greenish; 3–4	Leaves very variable, white or grey downy beneath, stigmas yellowish; 3–4	Leaves nearly stalkless, asymmetrical at the base, seed above middle of fruit; 3–4	Leaf-base nearly symmetrical, fruits on short stalks, seed central in the fruit; 3–4	Leaf-base strongly asymmetrical, fruits on long stalks, fringed; 3–4

a *Common Ash, *Fraxinus excelsior:* tree up to 40 m; leaves pinnate with 9–15 leaflets, flowers naked, ♂, ♀ or ☿; 4–5. **b** Manna Ash, *Fraxinus ornus:* tree up to 8 m; leaves pinnate, with 5–11, mostly with 7 leaflets, petals narrow, white; 5–6. **c** *Common Privet, *Ligustrum vulgare:* shrub up to 5 m; leaves entire, opposite or in whorls of three, flowers in terminal panicles; 4–5. All these species are members of the Olive Family. **a** and **c** are widespread, occurring in woods and scrubs, **b** is a native of S Europe and W Asia, introduced and naturalized in many other parts of the world.

a *Common Honeysuckle, *Lonicera peri-clymenum:* twining shrub reaching 6 m; leaves elliptic or ovate, flowers yellow, two-lipped; 5–6; from Scandinavia and Germany to the Mediterranean. **b †Perfoliate Honey-suckle,** *Lonicera caprifolium:* twining glaucous shrub up to 5 m; leaves below the inflorescence fused by the greater part of their bases; 5–6; C and S Europe. **c Blue-berried Honeysuckle,** *Lonicera coerulea:* shrub up to 2 m; flowers in pairs, yellowish white, fruits bluish black; 6–7; occurring in N and C Europe, especially in the mountainous areas. All belong to the Honeysuckle Family; they grow at the edges of woods and in scrub.

The Linnaea grows in N Europe, extending southwards to Germany, the Alps and the Carpathians; in Britain from Yorkshire to Sutherland. The Fly Honeysuckle and Common Elder are widespread. The Tartarian Honeysuckle is a native of W Asia, cultivated and naturalized in some places. The Scarlet-berried Elder is common in mountainous areas of N and C Europe but rare on lowlands. The Danewort occurs in S and C Europe, growing scattered in the Alps. All belong to the Honeysuckle Family.

	*Linnaea	*Fly Honeysuckle	Tartarian Honeysuckle	*Common Elder	†Scarlet-berried Elder	*Danewort
Scientific Name	*Linnaea borealis*	*Lonicera xylosteum*	*Lonicera tatarica*	*Sambucus nigra*	*Sambucus racemosa*	*Sambucus ebulus*
Longevity, Size	♃, up to 20 cm	Shrub, 1–3 m	Shrub, 1.5–3 m	Shrub, to 10 m	Shrub, to 4 m	♃, 60–120 cm
Distinguishing Features; Flowering Time	Stems prostrate, slender, glandular, hairy, flowers usually in pairs on long stalks; 5–6	Flowers in pairs, yellowish white, fruits red, globose; 4–5	Flowers red or white, stalks about as long as the flowers, berries red with a 'crown'; 5–6	Leaves with 5–7 leaflets, inflorescence flat-topped, fruits (drupes) black, rarely greenish; 6–7	Inflorescence panicle-like, flowers yellowish, fruits (drupes) red; 4–5	Stipules conspicuous, inflorescence flat-topped, flowers pink, fruits (drupes) black; 6–8

a *Guelder Rose, *Viburnum opulus:* shrub 2–4 m; leaves 3–5-lobed, outer flowers sterile and much larger than the inner, fruits (drupes) red; 5–7; widespread, in woods and scrub. **b *Wayfaring Tree,** *Viburnum lantana:* shrub 2–4 m; leaves entire, oval, ovate or obovate, densely downy beneath, flowers all alike, fruits (drupes) black; widespread in C and S Europe, occurring in woods and scrub. **c †Snowberry,** *Symphoricarpos rivularis:* shrub 1–2 m; leaves entire, oval or ovate, flowers in short spike-like racemes, berries white; a native of N America, commonly cultivated and naturalized in some places. All belong to the Honeysuckle Family.

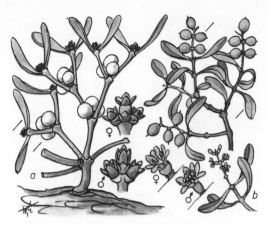

a *Mistletoe, *Viscum album:* evergreen shrub up to 50 cm; leaves in pairs, leathery, flowers usually dioecious, berries white, sticky; 4–5; parasitic on the branches of deciduous trees, spruces and pines, occurring in scattered localities in most of Europe. **b Yellow-berried Mistletoe,** *Loranthus europaeus:* deciduous shrub 30–120 cm; leaves oblong-ovate, flowers dioecious, in terminal racemes, berries yellow; 3–4; parasitic on branches of deciduous trees, mainly oaks; rare, found in SE and C Europe. Both are members of the Mistletoe Family.

The Common Baneberry or Herb Christopher occurs throughout most of Europe, but in the south is found only on mountains. The Bugbane occurs in E and C Europe, the Columbine in W, C and S Europe. The Upright Clematis is rather rare, growing in C, S and E Europe, northwards to C Russia and westwards to N Spain. The Woolly Crowfoot occurs mainly in woods of C and S Europe. The Wood Goldilocks is widespread. All are members of the Buttercup Family.

	*Common Baneberry	Bugbane	*Columbine	Upright Clematis	Woolly Crowfoot	*Wood Goldilocks
Scientific Name	*Actaea spicata*	*Cimicifuga europaea*	*Aquilegia vulgaris*	*Clematis recta*	*Ranunculus lanuginosus*	*Ranunculus auricomus*
Longevity, Size	♃, 20–60 cm	♃, 40–150 cm	♃, 30–90 cm	♃, 50–150 cm	♃, 25–80 cm	♃, 4–20 cm
Distinguishing Features: Flowering Time	Fetid, fruit a black, ovoid berry; 5–6	Fetid, follicles mostly 4, hairy; 7–8	Spur strongly hooked; 6–7	Not climbing, flowers in panicles, fruits with persistent long feathery styles; 6–7	Hairy, basal leaves 5-lobed, with irregularly toothed segments; 5–6	Basal leaves kidney-shaped, 3-5-lobed, with long stalks, stem leaves dissected; 4–6

a *Wood Anemone, *Anemone nemorosa:* ♃, 5-30 cm; rhizome creeping, radical leaves long-stalked, palmately divided into 3 toothed segments, stem-leaves 3, whorled, resembling radical leaves, flowers white, tinged with pink or purple beneath; 3–4. **b †Yellow Wood Anemone,** *Anemone ranunculoides:* ♃, 3–30 cm; flowers usually solitary or 2, yellow, flower- and leaf-stalks hairy; 3–4. **c †Noble Liverleaf,** *Hepatica nobilis:* 4–15 cm; leaves 3-lobed, heart-shaped at base, flowers bluish purple, flower- and leaf-stalks hairy; 3–4. All are widespread except in the north, and rare in the Mediterranean region. All are members of the Buttercup Family.

a **Great Stonecrop**, *Sedum maximum:* ♃,
20–80 cm; leaves flat and broad, succulent,
flowers yellowish green; 8. b ***Orpine** or
Livelong, *Sedum telephium:* ♃, 25–60 cm;
upper leaves with a truncate base, stalkless,
flowers purplish red to dark red; 7. Both are
members of the Stonecrop Family, occurring
in most of Europe (**b** often as an escape near
dwellings). c ***Asarabacca**, *Asarum europaeum:* ♃, 5–20 cm; leaves usually 2, flowers
solitary, brownish red, with short stalks;
poisonous; 4–5; from Finland, Belgium and
Germany to N and E Spain, C Italy; Birthwort Family.

The Wild Strawberry is common in woods, scrub and grassland throughout Europe. The other
strawberries depicted and the Fragrant Agrimony grow scattered in open woodlands and scrub
in various parts. The Cinquefoils occur in open woodlands, dry grassland and in mountainous
districts, the Seven-leaved in E and C Europe, eastwards to the Balkans, the Rock Cinquefoil
from S Scandinavia to C Spain, Sicily, Bulgaria and SW Russia, very rare in Britain, in Mont-
gomery and Radnor. All belong to the Rose Family.

	Seven-leaved Cinquefoil	*Rock Cinquefoil	*Barren Strawberry	*Wild Strawberry	†Hautbois Strawberry	*Fragrant Agrimony
Scientific Name	*Potentilla heptaphylla*	*Potentilla rupestris*	*Potentilla sterilis*	*Fragaria vesca*	*Fragaria moschata*	*Agrimonia odorata*
Longevity, Size	♃, 20 cm	♃, 15–70 cm	♃, 15 cm	♃, 4–25 cm	♃, 15–30 cm	♃, 40–100 cm
Distinguishing Features; Flowering Time	Leaflets at base narrowed, stalk-like, flowers yellow, 1 cm wide; 5–6	Lower leaves pinnate, petals white, roundish; 3–5	Leaflets crenate-toothed, with 4–6 teeth on each side; 3–5	Lateral leaflets stalkless or nearly so, petals white; 5–6	Plants often dioecious or polygamous, all leaflets with short stalks; 5–6	Leaves with numerous stalkless glands beneath, basal spines of fruit deflexed; 6–8

a ***Meadow Saxifrage**, *Saxifraga granulata:*
♃, 10–50 cm; stem glandular, sticky, with
bulbils at base; 5–6; widespread in N, C
and W Europe. b ***Alternate-leaved Gold-
en Saxifrage**, *Chrysosplenium alternifolium:*
♃, 2–20 cm; stem leaves alternate, basal leaves
heart-shaped at base; 4–5; absent from the
extreme north and west of Europe and most of
the Mediterranean region. c ***Opposite-
leaved Golden Saxifrage**, *Chrysosplenium
oppositifolium:* ♃, 5–20 cm; leaves opposite,
basal leaves truncate or wedge-shaped at base;
5–6; confined mainly to W Europe and parts
of C Europe. All are members of the Saxifrage
Family, growing in woods.

a **Lupinaster,** *Trifolium lupinaster:* ♃, up to 30 cm; leaves of 5 leaflets, flowers usually red; 6–7; in dry woods. b **Red Clover,** *Trifolium rubens:* ♃, 20–70 cm; flowers in cylindrical heads 3–7 cm long; 6–7; in woods in hilly districts. c **Oval-headed Clover,** *Trifolium alpestre:* ♃, 10–50 cm; flowers in roundish heads, stipules gradually acuminate; 6–8; usually in mountain forests. d **German Dorycnium,** *Dorycnium pentaphyllum* subsp. *germanicum:* ♃, 30–60 cm; leaves of 5 leaflets, the lowest pair simulating stipules, flowers white; 7–8; coniferous woods of C Europe and the Balkans. All four species belong to the Pea Family.

The Milk-vetch is common in scrub and open woodlands in most of Europe, northwards to C Scandinavia, rare in the south. The Pea Vetch and the Great Wood Vetch occur in woods of E and C Europe (except NW Germany), the Wood Vetch scattered in lowland or mountain forests, from N Norway to N Italy, the Cassubian Vetch in SE, C and southern N Europe. The Slender-leaved Vetch occurs in most of Europe except the north. All these plants belong to the Pea Family.

	*Milk-vetch	Pea Vetch	Great Wood Vetch	*Wood Vetch	†Cassubian Vetch	†Slender-leaved Vetch
Scientific Name	*Astragalus glycyphyllos*	*Vicia pisiformis*	*Vicia dumetorum*	*Vicia sylvatica*	*Vicia cassubica*	*Vicia tenuifolia*
Longevity, Size	♃, 40–100 cm	♃, 1–2 m	♃, up to 1.5 m	♃, 1–2 m	♃, 30–60 cm	♃, 50–60 cm
Distinguishing Features; Flowering Time	Leaves with 9–13 leaflets, flowers greenish yellow, in many-flowered racemes; 5–8	Flowers yellowish white, racemes one-sided, 10–30-flowered; 7–8	Flowers dirty purple, racemes 4–8-flowered; 5–8	Stipules semilunate, much incised, flowers whitish lilac; 6–8	Flower-stalks 1–2 mm long, leaflets 2–7 mm wide; 6–7	Flowers pale blue, racemes one-sided, loose; 6–7

a ***Narrow-leaved Everlasting Pea,** *Lathyrus sylvestris:* ♃, 1–2 m; racemes 1–3 flowered, leaflets 1 pair; 7–8. b **Pea Vetchling,** *Lathyrus pisiformis:* ♃, 40–100 cm; stipules very large; 6–7. c ***Black Pea,** *Lathyrus niger:* ♃, 40–80 cm; leaflets often mucronate, stem angled; 6–7. d ***Bitter Vetch,** *Lathyrus montanus:* ♃, 15–40 cm; stem winged, flowers bluish red, rarely white; 4–6. All are widespread members of the Pea Family, growing in woods and in scrub. **a, b** and **d** are distributed throughout most of Europe, **c** grows scattered in SE Europe and the U.S.S.R.

a **Rosebay Willow-herb* or **Fireweed**, *Chamaenerion angustifolium:* ♃, 50–150 cm; flowers in long, spike-like racemes, petals clawed; 7–8; common in clearings at altitudes of up to 2400 m. **b** **Broad-leaved Willow-herb*, *Epilobium montanum:* ♃, 15–150 cm; leaves irregularly toothed, petals 6–10 mm long; 7–9. **c** **Spear-leaved Willow-herb*, *Epilobium lanceolatum:* ♃, 30–60 cm; leaf-stalks 3–7 mm long; 6–8. **d** **Obscure Willow-herb*, *Epilobium obscurum:* ♃, 60 to 100 cm; leaves linear-lanceolate, stalkless; 6–9. All are members of the Willow-herb Family growing in woods and scrub in most parts of Europe.

The members of the Poppy Family shown below all grow scattered in woodlands and scrub; the White Climbing Fumitory in W Europe, eastwards to E Denmark; the Intermediate Fumewort in N and C Europe, southwards to S France, C Italy and the Ukraine; the Bulbous Fumewort or Hollow-wort and the Solid-rooted Fumewort or Bird-in-a-bush in most of Europe, except the extreme north; the Dwarf Fumewort in S and C Europe, S Scandinavia. The Pale-yellow Fumewort is a native of Italy and the W Balkans, naturalized in many parts.

	*White Climbing Fumitory	Intermediate Fumewort	†Bulbous Fumewort	†Solid-rooted Fumewort	Dwarf Fumewort	Pale-yellow Fumewort
Scientific Name	Corydalis claviculata	Corydalis intermedia	Corydalis bulbosa	Corydalis solida	Corydalis pumila	Corydalis ochroleuca
Longevity, Size	☉, 50–100 cm	♃, 7–15 cm	♃, 10–60 cm	♃, 7–25 cm	♃, 7–20 cm	♃, 10–40 cm
Distinguishing Features; Flowering Time	Climbing, leaves pinnate, the axis ending in a branched tendril, flowers cream; 6–9	Racemes 1–5-flowered, bracts ovate, entire, stem with an ovate scale at base; 3–5	Racemes 10–20-flowered, old tubers hollow, stem without scales at base; 4–5	Racemes many-flowered, uppermost bracts entire, lobed or laciniate; 4–5	Racemes 1–5-flowered, bracts digitate, wedge-shaped, incised; 3–4	Flowers pale yellow, leaf-stalks distinctly winged; 5–9

a **Common Enchanter's Nightshade*, *Circaea lutetiana:* ♃, 30–70 cm; leaves half-heart-shaped, petals 2, 2-lobed less than halfway; 7–8. **b** **Intermediate Enchanter's Nightshade*, *Circaea intermedia:* ♃, 15 to 25 cm; leaves heart-shaped at base, petals 2, as long as calyx; 7–8. **c** **Alpine Enchanter's Nightshade*, *Circaea alpina:* ♃, 8–25 cm; leaves heart-shaped at base, distinctly toothed, petals 2, shorter than calyx; 6–7. All are members of the Willow-herb Family occurring in most of Europe; **a** and **b** particularly in deciduous woods, **c** in mountain areas and in shady rocky situations (in Britain in the western and northern parts).

a *Garlic Mustard or Jack-by-the-hedge or Hedge-garlic, *Alliaria officinalis:* ⊙-♃, 12–110 cm; leaves kidney- to heart-shaped, smelling of garlic; 5–6. **b *Common Coral-wort,** *Cardamine bulbifera:* ♃, 25–60 cm; flowers pale red, upper leaves with brownish purple axillary bulbils; 5–6. **c Pale Coral-wort,** *Cardamine enneaphyllos:* ♃, 18–30 cm; flowers in spreading racemes; 5–7. **d †Common Moonwort,** *Lunaria rediviva:* ♃, 50 to 100 cm; flowers pale purple to violet, rarely white, pods small; 5–6. All belong to the Crucifer Family; shady woods in most of Europe, **c** only in mountain areas, from the Carpathians and E Alps to S Italy and Macedonia.

Sweet, Wood and Common Violets are widespread in Europe, except for the extreme north in damp habitats, usually in woodlands and scrub. The Broad-leaved Violet occurs mainly in woodlands in most of Europe, but is absent from much of the south and west and from the islands; the Upright Violet in damp situations in C and E Europe, southwards to N Italy and C France. The Hill Violet grows scattered in hilly districts, in open woodlands and scrub. All belong to the Violet Family.

	***Sweet Violet**	**Broad-leaved Violet**	***Wood Violet**	**Upright Violet**	***Common Violet**	**Hill Violet**
Scientific Name	*Viola odorata*	*Viola mirabilis*	*Viola reichenbachiana*	*Viola elatior*	*Viola riviniana*	*Viola collina*
Longevity, Size	♃, up to 20 cm	♃, 15–25 cm	♃, 8–25 cm	♃, 20–50 cm	♃, 3–30 cm	♃, up to 20 cm
Distinguishing Features; **Flowering** Time	With leaf-rosette and long rooting stolons, flowers deep violet or white, scented; 3–4	Stems and leaf-stalks with a line of hairs, flowers pale lilac, scented; 4–5	Appendages of sepals small, petals narrow, lilac, spur slender, deep violet; 4–5	Petals pale blue with a white spot at the base, stipules entire or coarse-toothed at base; 5–6	Appendages of sepals large, petals rather wide, overlapping, blue-violet, spur stout, pale; 4–5	Stipules with long fringes, flowers pale violet, scented; 3–4

a *Narrow-leaved Bitter-cress, *Cardamine impatiens:* ⊙, 15–60 cm; leaves with basal stipule-like auricles, clasping stem; 5–7; widespread, local in Britain. **b *Wood Bitter-cress,** *Cardamine flexuosa:* ⊙-♃, 10–50 cm; stem flexuous, stamens 6; 4–6; widespread. **c †Three-leaved Bitter-cress,** *Cardamine trifolia:* ♃, 20–30 cm; leaves of 3 leaflets; 4–6, C Europe, southwards to C Italy and C Yugoslavia. **d *Tower Mustard,** *Arabis glabra:* ⊙-⊙, 30–150 cm; stem leaves stalkless, clasping stem; 6–7; widespread except the extreme north and south, local in Britain. All are members of the Crucifer Family found mainly in shady woods.

a *Common Wood-sorrel, *Oxalis acetosella*: ♃, 5–15 cm; flowers white or pinkish, solitary, in the axils of leaves borne on a creeping rhizome. **b †Procumbent Yellow Wood-sorrel**, *Oxalis corniculata*: ⊙-♃, 5–30 cm; stems procumbent, rooting at nodes, leaves with stipules adnate to stalk; 6–8; a weed of tropical and warmer temperate regions. **c †Upright Yellow Wood-sorrel**, *Oxalis europaea*: 7–60 cm; stem solitary, upright, leaves without stipules; 6–8; a native of N America. All belong to the Wood-sorrel Family; **a** widespread in woods, **b** and **c** naturalized in many places, mainly in wasteland and gardens.

The Burning Bush (Rue Family) is found in dry open scrub or on rocks, in S and C Europe, eastwards to C Russia; the Mountain St John's Wort (St John's Wort Family) locally, in woods and scrub. The Bohemian Cranesbill is a native of E and SE Europe naturalized in N and C Europe. The Wood Cranesbill and the Herb Robert grow in damp lowland woods and scrub or on rocks in mountain scrub, on dry grassland, rocks and dunes. These four belong to the Cranesbill Family.

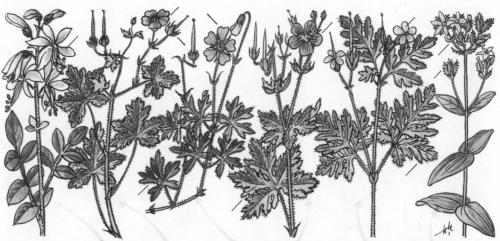

	Burning Bush	Bohemian Cranesbill	*Bloody Cranesbill	*Wood Cranesbill	*Herb Robert	*Mountain St John's Wort
Scientific Name	*Dictamnus albus*	*Geranium bohemicum*	*Geranium sanguineum*	*Geranium sylvaticum*	*Geranium robertianum*	*Hypericum montanum*
Longevity, Size	♃, 40–100 cm	⊙, 25–50 cm	♃, 15–40 cm	♃, 15–70 cm	⊙, 10–45 cm	♃, 25–70 cm
Distinguishing Features; Flowering Time	Lemon-scented, flowers purplish, with dark veins; 6–7	Petals bluish violet, sepals with a bristle 1–3 mm long at the tip, glandular; 7–9	Leaves deeply 5–7 lobed, flowers usually solitary on long stalks, bright purplish crimson; 5–9	Petals reddish violet, with a hairy claw, leaves 5–7-lobed; 6–7	Strong-smelling, leaves very deeply divided, with 3–5 2-pinnatisect segments; 7–9	Inflorescence dense, head-like, sepals acute, strongly glandular-toothed; 5–9

a *Hairy St John's Wort, *Hypericum hirsutum*: ♃, 40–130 cm; stem and leaves hairy; 6–8; woods and damp grassland in N and C Europe. **b *Slender St John's Wort**, *Hypericum pulchrum*: ♃, 15–80 cm; stem and leaves glabrous; 7–8; dry woods and grassland in W and C Europe, northwards to Norway. Both of St John's Wort Family. **c *Touch-me-not**, *Impatiens noli-tangere*: ⊙, 20–70 cm; flowers large, hanging, spur curved downwards; 7–8; damp woods, not in extreme north and south. **d †Small-flowered Balsam**, *Impatiens parviflora*: ⊙, 15–60 cm; flowers small, upright; 5–11; a native of Asia, naturalized in N and C Europe in woods and shady waste ground. Both of Balsam Family.

a Long-leaved Hare's-ear, *Bupleurum longifolium:* ♃, 30–150 cm; upper leaves strongly heart-shaped, clasping the stem, bracteoles roundish; 7–8. **b Bristly Chervil,** *Chaerophyllum hirsutum:* ♃, 10–150 cm; margins of petals fringed, often reddish, leaves 2- to 3-pinnate or dissected; 5–7. Both are found mainly in forests of hilly districts, mainly in C Europe. **c *Greater Burnet-saxifrage,** *Pimpinella major:* ♃, 25–120 cm; stem prominently angled, glabrous, leaves simply pinnate, those of radical leaves shortly stalked; 6–10; occurs in scrub and at the edges of woods. All belong to the Carrot Family.

The Wood Sanicle grows widespread, in patches, in deciduous forests; the Hacquetia in deciduous woods in the E Alps and W Carpathians; the Herb-frankincense or Broad-leaved Laserwort in hilly districts; the Masterwort in scrub and meadows of S and C Europe; the Sheathed Hemlock-parsley in woods and on bushy slopes in E and EC Europe, extending to the S Carpathians and N Norway. The Goutweed or Ground Elder is widespread in hedges and open woods, and as a weed on waste ground. All belong to the Carrot Family.

	†Goutweed	*Wood Sanicle	†Great Black Masterwort	Hacquetia	Herb-frankincense	Sheathed Hemlock-parsley
Scientific Name	*Aegopodium podagraria*	*Sanicula europaea*	*Astrantia major*	*Hacquetia epipactis*	*Laserpitium latifolium*	*Conioselinum vaginatum*
Longevity, Size	♃, 20–120 cm	♃, 15–50 cm	♃, 30–100 cm	♃, 10–25 cm	♃, 60–125 cm	♃, up to 150 m
Distinguishing Features; Flowering Time	Lower leaves in 3 segments, each divided into 3, bracts and bracteoles usually absent; 6–8	Leaves deeply palmate, 3–7-lobed, flowers in small subglobose partial umbels; 5–6	Leaves palmately lobed or cut, 3–7-lobed, flowers in a simple umbel; 6–8	Flowers in a simple head-like umbel, surrounded by 5–8 serrate bracts; 4–5	Leaves pinnate, with ovate segments which are heartshaped at the base, fruit 8-winged; 6–9	Leaves 2–3-pinnate, bracts absent, fruit 8-winged; 7–8

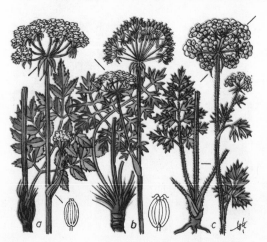

a Mountain Hartwort or **Sulphur Wort,** *Peucedanum cervaria:* ♃, 50–150 cm; stalks of primary and secondary divisions of leaves upright, upper leaves with inflated sheaths; 7–8. **b Mountain Parsley,** *Peucedanum oreoselinum:* ♃, 30–100 cm; petals white or reddish, stalks of primary and secondary divisions of leaves spreading or deflexed; 7–8. **c Prussian Laserwort,** *Laserpitium prutenicum:* ☉, 40–150 cm; flowers yellowish white; 7–8. All are members of the Carrot Family occurring in dry woods, **a** mainly in C Europe, **b** widespread but absent from the extreme north and south, **c** in C and E Europe and some parts of S Europe.

a †**Slender Spurge**, *Euphorbia dulcis:* ♃, 20–50 cm; leaves short-stalked, glands green, soon purple; 5–6; in S and C Europe. **b** *****Wood Spurge**, *Euphorbia amygdaloides:* ♃, up to 70 cm; partial bracts fused in pairs; 4–6; mainly in S and SC Europe. **c Warty Spurge**, *Euphorbia verrucosa:* ♃, 30—50 cm; flower-stalks densely crowded; 5–6; in the Mediterranean region and C Europe. **d** *****Dog's Mercury**, *Mercurialis perennis:* ♃, 15–40 cm; plant dioecious, stem terete, unbranched; 3–5; common. All belong to the Spurge Family and are found growing mainly in woods.

The Wood Pink is a rare plant of SW and WC Europe. The Berry Catchfly grows in scattered localities in woods of C and S Europe, the Deptford Pink occurs in C and S Europe, and the Three-nerved Sandwort and Wood Stitchwort are widespread, all being herbs of scrub and deciduous woods. The Green-flowered Catchfly is found in coniferous woods of SE and EC Europe. All belong to the Pink Family.

	*****Deptford Pink	Wood Pink	†Berry Catchfly	Green-flowered Catchfly	*****Three-nerved Sandwort	*****Wood Stitchwort
Scientific Name	*Dianthus armeria*	*Dianthus seguieri*	*Cucubalus baccifer*	*Silene chlorantha*	*Moehringia trinervia*	*Stellaria nemorum*
Longevity, Size	♃, 15–80 cm	♃, 15–45 cm	♃, up to 3 m	♃, 15–70 cm	○, 6–40 cm	♃, 15–60 cm
Distinguishing Features; Flowering Time	Flowers small, bright rose-red, with pale dots, involucral bracts and calyx hairy; 7–8	Flowers 1–3, pink, with a ring of dark red spots; 6–8	Climbing, flower usually solitary, petals with coronal scales, fruit a black berry; 7–9	Flowers greenish, petals narrow; deeply bifid; 7–8	Leaves ovate, flowers pentamerous, petals shorter than the calyx; 6–8	Lower leaves stalked, petals twice as long as the calyx, styles 3; 7–9

a *****Primrose**, *Primula vulgaris:* ♃, up to 15 cm; flower stalks 5–10 cm long, radical, with a solitary flower; 3–4; found in damp woods, hedgebanks and in open grassy places of W Europe, from C Norway to S Portugal, Italy and the Balkans. **b** *****Oxlip**, *Primula elatior:* ♃, 5–30 cm; flowers pale yellow, calyx narrow; 3–4; in woods, mainly on chalky boulder clay, from S Sweden to the N Alps and S Russia. **c** *****Cowslip**, *Primula veris:* ♃, 7–35 cm; flowers deep yellow, calyx inflated; 4–5; widespread in Europe, occurring at the edges of woods, in scrub and grassland, especially on calcareous soils. All belong to the Primrose Family.

a *Wood Pimpernel, *Lysimachia nemorum:* ♃, 10–30 cm; flowers solitary, axillary; 5–7; woods, hedgebanks, scrub, mainly in W and C Europe. **b *Chickweed Wintergreen,** *Trientalis europaea:* ♃, 7–25 cm; corolla with 5–9 lobes; 5-6; coniferous woods and grassland in N and C Europe. Both belong to the Primrose Family. **c *Lesser Periwinkle,** *Vinca minor:* procumbent shrub, 30–60 cm; flowers axillary, stalked; 4–5; widespread in woods, copses and hedgebanks; Periwinkle Family. **d Umbellate Wintergreen,** *Chimaphila umbellata:* small shrub, 7–15 cm; inflorescence almost umbellate; 7; dry woods and scrub in N and C Europe; Wintergreen Family.

The members of the Wintergreen Family shown below are widespread or local, found in woods on lowland or in mountainous districts. The One-flowered Wintergreen grows in damp mossy coniferous or deciduous woods, the Green-flowered Wintergreen in dry coniferous woods. The Serrated and the Intermediate Wintergreen occur in shady woods, damp rock-ledges, moors and heaths. The Common and the Round-leaved Wintergreen occupy similar habitats, but are found also in dune-slacks or on dunes.

	*One-flowered Wintergreen	*Serrated Wintergreen	*Common Wintergreen	*Intermediate Wintergreen	*Round-leaved Wintergreen	*Green-flowered Wintergreen
Scientific Name	*Moneses uniflora*	*Orthilia secunda*	*Pyrola minor*	*Pyrola media*	*Pyrola rotundifolia*	*Pyrola chlorantha*
Longevity, Size	♃, up to 7 cm	♃, up to 15 cm	♃, up to 20 cm	♃, up to 20 cm	♃, up to 25 cm	♃, 6–20 cm
Distinguishing Features; Flowering Time	Flowers solitary, large, white, rotate, wide open; 5	Raceme one-sided, leaves with small serrations; 6–7	Flowers reddish or white, style included, not thickened below the stigma; 6–7	Leaves ovate-orbicular, style almost straight, exserted; 6–7	Mostly with 2 bracts on the stem, style long, curved, raceme with 3–15 flowers; 7–10	Leaves orbicular, calyx ¼ to ⅓ length of the corolla, racemes with 3–7 flowers; 6–7

a *Yellow Birdsnest, *Monotropa hypopitys:* ♃, 8–30 cm; leaves scale-like, flowers in short racemes, drooping in flower; 6–8; widespread, a saprophyte, occurring in coniferous and deciduous woods; Birdsnest Family. **b Swallowwort,** *Vincetoxicum hirundinaria:* ♃, 30—120 cm; leaves short-stalked, opposite, corolla rotate; 5–9; widespread in woods and scrub, and on rock-ledges; Milkweed Family. **c †Common Lungwort,** *Pulmonaria officinalis:* ♃, 4–20 cm; leaves with white spots; 3–5; found in woods and scrub, and in meadows; Borage Family.

a Bark Lungwort, *Pulmonaria obscura:* ♃, up to 30 cm; leaves unspotted, with stalked glandular hairs beneath; 3–5. **b Tuberous Lungwort,** *Pulmonaria tuberosa:* ♃, 20 to 35 cm; leaves with stalked glandular hairs on the upper surface; 4–5. Both are members of the Borage Family and grow in open woodland. **c †Yellow Figwort,** *Scrophularia vernalis:* ♃, 15–60 cm; flowers in cymes in the axils of the upper leaves; 4–5; a native of C and S Europe; Figwort Family. **d Lesser Honeywort,** *Cerinthe minor:* ☉-♃, 15–75 cm; upper leaves clasping the stem; 5–7; in C and SE Europe; Borage Family.

The Hedge Woundwort, the Wood Betony and the Wild Basil are common in woods and hedges, sometimes occurring in grassland. The Pyramidal Bugle grows dispersed in open woodlands, moors and rock-crevices in N Europe and in mountainous districts of C and S Europe; the Glutinous Clary or Jupiter's Distaff only in woods and on rock-ledges in C and S Europe; the Common Calamint in open deciduous woods, bushy slopes and on dry banks in C and S Europe (rather local in Britain). All belong to the Thyme Family.

	*Pyramidal Bugle	Glutinous Clary	*Hedge Woundwort	*Wood Betony	*Wild Basil	*Common Calamint
Scientific Name	*Ajuga pyramidalis*	*Salvia glutinosa*	*Stachys sylvatica*	*Betonica officinalis*	*Clinopodium vulgare*	*Calamintha ascendens*
Longevity, Size	♃, 5–30 cm	♃, 70–120 cm	♃, 30–120 cm	♃, 20–120 cm	♃, 25–80 cm	♃, 25–80 cm
Distinguishing Features; Flowering Time	Corolla with a short upper lip and 3-lobed lower lip, bracts large, ovate, violet; 7–8	Plant glandular, sticky, leaves hastate, upper lip large; 6–9	Leaves heart-shaped, stalked, serrate, flowers dark purplish red; 6–9	Leaves coarsely crenate, flowers reddish purple, in a dense spike; 6–10	Leaves, stem and calyx woolly, flowers red or white, in whorls of 10–20; 7–10	Leaves up to 4 cm long, flowers stalked, in whorls of 6–10; 7–11

a *Foxglove, *Digitalis purpurea:* ☉-♃, 30 to 180 cm; flowers large, bell-shaped, with dark spots; 6–11; widespread. **b †Yellow Foxglove,** *Digitalis grandiflora:* ♃, 50–150 cm; leaves downy; 6–9; in deciduous woods, scrub and grasslands of C Europe. **c Blue-topped Cow-wheat,** *Melampyrum nemorosum:* ☉, 15–50 cm; bracts deeply toothed; 7–8; in deciduous woods, scrub and in grassland of N, E and C Europe. **d *Wood Cow-wheat,** *Melampyrum sylvaticum:* ☉, 7–30 cm; stem with hairs in two lines, leaves lanceolate; 6–9; in mountain woods of N, C and S Europe. All are members of the Figwort Family.

a *Crested Cow-wheat, *Melampyrum crista-tum:* ☉, 15–50 cm; bracts finely pectinate; 6–9; local, at edges of woods, mainly in N and C Europe. b *Wood Speedwell, *Vero-nica montana:* ♃, 10–50 cm; leaves long-stalked, capsule broader than long; 5–6; widespread in damp woods. Both belong to the Figwort Family. c *Toothwort, *Lathraea squamaria:* ♃, 5–35 cm; leaves scale-like, white or pale pink, inflorescence a one-sided raceme; 3–5; widespread, parasite on roots of woody plants. d *Ivy Broomrape, *Oro-banche hederae:* ♃, up to 60 cm; stem glan-dular-hairy; 5–7; local, S, C and W Europe, parasite on roots of Ivy. Both belong to the Broomrape Family.

The Wood Scabious is a member of the Teasel Family found in woods in hilly districts of C Europe. All the other plants below belong to the Bellflower Family. The Nettle-leaved Bellflower or Bats-in-the-belfry and the Peach-leaved Bellflower are common in woods and scrub. The others occur in scattered localities. The Gland-bellflower is a rare species of damp woods in SE and C Europe. The Spiked and the Black Rampion grow in deciduous woods and thickets, mainly in C Europe.

	Wood Scabious	*Peach-leaved Bellflower	Nettle-leaved Bellflower	Gland-bellflower	*Spiked Rampion	Black Rampion
Scientific Name	*Knautia sylvatica*	*Campanula persicifolia*	*Campanula trachelium*	*Adenophora liliifolia*	*Phyteuma spicatum*	*Phyteuma nigrum*
Longevity, Size	♃, 30–120 cm	♃, 10–90 cm	♃, 50–100 cm	♃, 30–100 cm	♃, 20–90 cm	♃, 30–100 cm
Distinguishing Features; Flowering Time	Leaves mostly entire, serrate, calyx with 8 bristles; 6–9	Stem mostly simple, few-flowered, corolla sky-blue, up to 4 cm long; 6–7	Stem sharply angled, with stiff hairs, corolla bluish violet, up to 4 cm long; 7–8	Leaves serrate, flowers droop-ing, bluish lilac, style very long; 7–9	Basal leaves heart-shaped, inflorescence cylindrical, flowers yellow-ish white or pale blue; 5–7	Basal leaves half-heart-shaped, inflorescence cylindrical, flowers dark violet; 5–7

a *Moschatel, *Adoxa moschatellina:* ♃, 3 to 5 cm; inflorescence head-like, with 5–7 flow-ers; 3–5; a widespread member of the Mos-chatel Family. b *Sweet Woodruff, *Galium odoratum:* ♃, 10–60 cm; leaves oblong-ovate, 6–8 in each whorl; 4–5; locally abundant in woods in N and C Europe and on mountains of S Europe. c Wood Bedstraw, *Galium sylvaticum:* ♃, 30–140 cm; flower-stalks thread-like; 7–9; in woods of S and C Europe. d Round-leaved Bedstraw, *Galium rotundi-folium:* ♃, 10–30 cm; leaves roundish and prickly hairy; 6–8; in coniferous woods in C Europe. b, c and d belong to the Bedstraw Family.

a *Golden-rod, *Solidago virgaurea*: 2+, 5–80 cm; heads 6–12 mm long, flowers in a panicle with straight erect branches or in a raceme, receptacle without scales; 7–10; widespread. **b *Wood Cudweed,** *Gnaphalium sylvaticum*: 2+, 8–80 cm; stem simple, leaves single-veined, heads in clusters of 2–8, in an elongate spike, bracts scarious; 7–10; widespread. **c Carpesium,** *Carpesium cernuum*: ☉-☉, 20–80 cm; leaves lanceolate, stalked, head solitary, drooping, outer bracts leaf-like; 7–9; in open woodlands of S and C Europe. All three are members of the Daisy Family.

Of the members of the Daisy Family illustrated below, the Lachenal's Hawkweed is common in woods and in scrub, and the Wood Burdock, the Woolly Thistle and the Spotted Cat's-ear are found in scattered localities in most of Europe. The Hare's-lettuce occurs in shady woods in mountainous districts of S and C Europe, the Aposeris in woods and scrub and in meadows in the Alps.

	Wood Burdock	*Woolly Thistle	Aposeris	*Spotted Cat's-ear	Hare's-lettuce	Lachenal's Hawkweed
Scientific Name	*Arctium nemorosum*	*Cirsium eriophorum*	*Aposeris foetida*	*Hypochoeris maculata*	*Prenanthes purpurea*	*Hieracium lachenalii*
Longevity, Size	2+, up to 2 m	☉, 60–150 cm	2+, 15–40 cm	2+, 20–60 cm	2+, 50–150 cm	2+, 40–120 cm
Distinguishing Features; Flowering Time	Leaves heart-shaped-ovate, heads 3–4 cm wide, in clusters; 7–9	Bracts very cottony, ending in a long narrow prickly point; 7–9	Resembling the Common Dandelion (page 190), sap stinking, milky, no pappus, heads solitary; 7–8	Hairs of pappus in single row, pinnate, bracts entire; 6–8	Leaves clasping the stem, heads violet, in a loose panicle; 7–8	Basal leaves forming a rosette; stem leaves 4–7, diminishing upwards, bracts acute; 6–7

a *Wood Groundsel, *Senecio sylvaticus*: ☉, 10–90 cm; plant not sticky, heads small, bracts 13, fruits stiffly hairy on ribs; 7–9; in open situations, locally common. **b** *Senecio nemorensis*: 2+, 40–200 cm; ray-florets 5–8, teeth of leaves straight; 7–8; in woods, clearings and along streams in scattered localities in various parts of Europe. **c *Hoary Ragwort,** *Senecio erucifolius*: 2+, 30–120 cm; ray-florets and bracts 13, leaves cottony beneath; widely distributed, at the margins of woods, in scrub, on shingle banks and grassy slopes. All three are members of the Daisy Family.

a St Bernard's Lily, *Anthericum liliago:* ♃, 30–80 cm; flowers white, inflorescence racemose, unbranched, style ascending; 5–6; in dry woods of C Europe and the Alps. **b Spiderwort,** *Anthericum ramosum:* ♃, 30 to 100 cm; flowers white, inflorescence branched, style straight; 6–7; in dry woods and grasslands of C Europe. **c *Bluebell,** *Endymion non-scriptus:* ♃, 20–50 cm; perianth-segments violet-blue or white, fused at the base; 3–5; in woods, hedgebanks, rarely in grassland, of C and W Europe. All belong to the Lily Family.

The members of the Lily Family shown below are early-flowering plants growing in deciduous woods and in scrub. The Wood Yellow-star-of-Bethlehem, the May Lily and the Solomon's Seals are common, the others are local. The Angular Solomon's Seal occurs in dry and open deciduous and coniferous woods and on stony, bushy slopes, the Common Solomon's Seal in shady deciduous woods. The Ramsons is a member of the Daffodil Family growing locally in deciduous damp woods in most of Europe.

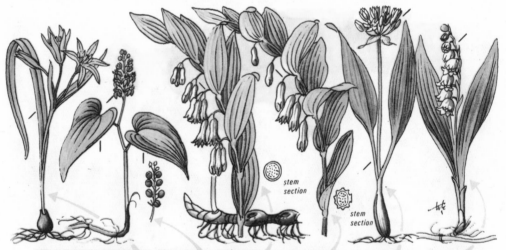

	Wood Yellow-star-of-Bethlehem	*May Lily	*Common Solomon's Seal	*Angular Solomon's Seal	*Ramsons	*Lily-of-the-valley
Scientific Name	*Gagea sylvatica*	*Maianthemum bifolium*	*Polygonatum multiflorum*	*Polygonatum odoratum*	*Allium ursinum*	*Convallaria majalis*
Longevity, Size	♃, 7–35 cm	♃, 10–25 cm	♃, 30–80 cm	♃, 10–50 cm	♃, 15–50 cm	♃, 15–25 cm
Distinguishing Features; Flowering Time	Radical leaf single, bulb 1; 4–5	Leaves 2, heart-shaped, flowers tetramerous, in a terminal raceme; 5–6	Stem cylindrical, flowers in groups of 2–5, filaments hairy; 5–6	Stem angled, flowers solitary or 2, filaments glabrous; 5–6	Leaves 2, radical, long-stalked, inflorescence umbellate, smell of garlic; 5	Flowers in one-sided raceme, berries red; poisonous; 5

a †Martagon or **Turk's Cap Lily,** *Lilium martagon:* ♃, 30–120 cm; perianth-segments recurved; 6–7; local, in deciduous woods. **b *Herb Paris,** *Paris quadrifolia:* ♃, 15 to 40 cm; fruit a black berry; 5–6; in damp woods. **c Slender Hyacinth,** *Muscari tenuiflorum:* ♃, 25–50 cm; flowers greenish white with blackish teeth; 5–6; in scrub and on sunny slopes in SE and W Europe. **d Streptopus,** *Streptopus amplexifolius:* ♃, 20–100 cm; stem densely leafy; in shady mountain woods, rare, in C Europe and the Alps. All are members of the Lily Family.

a *Hairy Woodrush, *Luzula pilosa:* 2↩, 15–30 cm; flowers single, in loose cyme, capsule acuminate; 3–6. **b** †White Woodrush, *Luzula luzuloides:* 2↩, 30–60 cm; flowers in clusters of 2–6, perianth whitish; 5–7. **c** *Greater Woodrush, *Luzula sylvatica:* 2↩, 30–80 cm; leaves 6–10 mm wide; 4–6. **d** *Field Woodrush, *Luzula campestris:* 2↩, up to 15 cm; leaves flat, usually 2–4 mm wide, flowers in 3–6 clusters, anthers 2–6 times as long as filaments. *Many-headed Woodrush, *Luzula multiflora:* (not illustrated) flowers in up to 10 clusters, anthers equal filaments; 4–6. All are common members of the Rush Family occurring mainly in woods and scrub.

The plants shown below are members of the Sedge Family, having spikes dissimilar in appearance (the terminal one or ones male, the lateral ones wholly or mainly female). The Pill-headed Sedge grows scattered in open woods, or on peaty soils and in mountainous districts up to 2000 m. All the other species are found in deciduous and mixed forests, the Pale, the Loose-flowered and the Hairy Sedges being local, the others widespread.

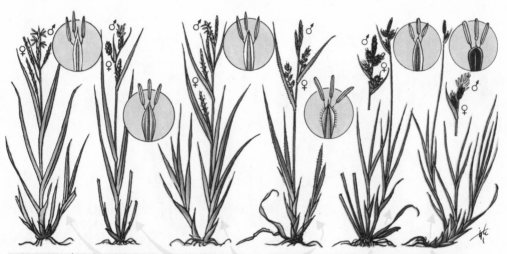

	*Wood Sedge	*Pale Sedge	*Loose-flowered Sedge	Hairy Sedge	*Pill-headed Sedge	*Mountain Sedge
Scientific Name	Carex sylvatica	Carex pallescens	Carex strigosa	Carex pilosa	Carex pilulifera	Carex montana
Longevity, Size	2↩, 40–60 cm	2↩, 7–50 cm	2↩, 35–80 cm	2↩, 20–50 cm	2↩, 6–45 cm	2↩, 7–30 cm
Distinguishing Features; Flowering Time	Spikes 3–4, distant, ♀ long-stalked, more or less nodding, ♂ spike usually 1; 5–6	♀ spikes 2–3, contiguous or lower distant, stalked, dense, stigmas 3, ♂ spike terminal; 4–7	♀ spikes 5–6, slender, up to 7 cm long, distant, more or less upright; 4–6	♀ spikes 2–4, stalked, loose-flowered, ♂ spikes 1–2, leaves hairy, up to 1 cm wide; 4–6	Inflorescence dense, ♀ spikes mostly 3, ♂ 3, globular; 4–5	Sheaths of leaves blood-red, ♀ spikes 1–2, stalkless, ovate-orbicular; 4–6

a *Grey Sedge, *Carex divulsa:* 2↩, 20–40 cm; upper spikes crowded, lower distant; 6–7; widespread. **b** *Remote Sedge, *Carex remota:* 2↩, 30–60 cm; plant densely tufted, bracts exceeding the inflorescence; 5–6; widespread. **c** Alpine Sedge, *Carex brizoides:* 2↩, 15–60 cm; spikes 6–8, at the base ♂, above ♀; 5–6; occurs in C Europe. All grow in woods and have spikes similar in appearance (with male and female flowers together). **d** Wood White Sedge, *Carex alba:* 2↩, 10–40 cm; bracts shining white, spikes dissimilar, ♀ spikes few-flowered; 5–6; in C Europe. All belong to the Sedge Family.

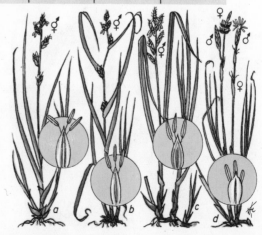

a *Wood Barley, *Hordelymus europaeus:* ♃, 40–120 cm; spikelets usually in threes at each node of the axis; 6–7; fairly widespread in some places, but generally uncommon. **b *Bearded Couch**, *Agropyron caninum:* ♃, 30–110 cm; lemma awned, awn 7–20 mm long; 6–7; widespread. **c *Wood False-brome**, *Brachypodium sylvaticum:* ♃, 30–90 cm; racemes spike-like, often nodding, awn longer than the lemma; 7–8. All have spikes. **d *Wood Millet**, *Milium effusum:* ♃, 45–180 cm; panicles very loose, nodding, with spreading or deflexed branches, spikelets 1–flowered; widespread in deciduous woods. All belong to the Grass Family.

The panicled grasses illustrated below are common and widespread, but might be absent in some districts. They occur in woods, wooded valleys, on rocky slopes, wood margins and streamsides; the Wavy Hair–grass usually in dry habitats, often abundantly, but also in moor and heathlands, the Creeping Soft–grass also in shrubby heath and in hedgerows, sometimes as a weed on sandy arable lands. All belong to the Grass Family.

	*Wavy Hair-grass	*Creeping Soft-grass	*Mountain Melick	*Wood Melick	*Wood Fescue	*Giant Fescue
Scientific Name	Deschampsia flexuosa	Holcus mollis	Melica nutans	Melica uniflora	Festuca altissima	Festuca gigantea
Longevity, Size	♃, 20–100 cm	♃, 20–100 cm	♃, 20–60 cm	♃, 20–60 cm	♃, 50–120 cm	♃, 45–150 cm
Distinguishing Features; Flowering Time	Leaves terete, bristle-like, branches of panicle hairlike, flexuous, spreading; 7–8	Culm hairy at nodes, spikelets 2-flowered, the upper with an awn 3.5–5 mm long; 6	Spikelets nodding, onesided, ligule very short; 5–6	Panicles very loose, branches usually upright, spikelets upright; 5–6	Panicle loose, 10–18 cm long, lemmas finely pointed, awnless, leaves without auricles; 6–7	Panicle up to 40 cm long, awn of lemma up to 20 mm long, often flexuous; 7–8

a *Twayblade, *Listera ovata:* ♃, 20–50 cm; lip bifid halfway; 5–7; widespread. **b *Man Orchid**, *Aceras anthropophorum:* ♃, 20 to 30 cm; flowers greenish yellow, often edged with reddish brown, lip with bifid central and 2 lateral lobes; 5–7; scrub, open woods, grassland. **c *Creeping Lady's Tresses**, *Goodyera repens:* ♃, 10–25 cm; flowers small, scented, lip like pouch with projecting tongue; 7–8; locally, in pine-woods, rarely in deciduous woods or on fixed sand-dunes. **d *Lady's Slipper** or **Common Slipper Orchid**, *Cypripedium calceolus:* ♃, 15–45 cm; lip large, inflated, slipper-shaped; 5–6; rare. All belong to the Orchid Family.

a *Bird's-nest Orchid, *Neottia nidus-avis:* ♃, 15–60 cm; rhizomes creeping, with mass of short, fleshy, blunt roots, stem with dense brownish scales; 5–7; widespread. b *Coral-root, *Corallorhiza trifida:* ♃, 7–30 cm; rhizome fleshy, much branched, coral-like, lip short, white with red dots; 5–8; widespread, but local. c Violet Limodor, *Limodorum abortivum:* ♃, 30–60 cm; stem violet, flowers in loose raceme of more than 4; 6–7; Mediterranean, S and W Europe. d *Ghost Orchid, *Epipogium aphyllum:* ♃, 5–20 cm; rhizomes coral-like, fleshy, flowers 1–7, yellowish or reddish, drooping, spurred; 7–8; very rare. All are saprophytes of the Orchid Family.

The Violet Helleborine, the Dark-red Helleborine and the Common Helleborine grow scattered in shady woods, the others are rare. The Lady Orchid occurs in deciduous woods, scrub, rarely in open grassland, in Europe from Denmark southwards, the Pale Orchid in open deciduous woods in SE and C Europe, and the Small-leaved Helleborine in shady woods in mountainous areas of S and C Europe. All belong to the Orchid Family.

	*Lady Orchid	Pale Orchid	*Violet Helleborine	Small-leaved Helleborine	*Dark-red Helleborine	*Common Helleborine
Scientific Name	*Orchis purpurea*	*Orchis pallens*	*Epipactis purpurata*	*Epipactis microphylla*	*Epipactis atrorubens*	*Epipactis helleborine*
Longevity, Size	♃, 30–75 cm	♃, 10–30 cm	♃, 15–50 cm	♃, 15–50 cm	♃, 15–75 cm	♃, 20–100 cm
Distinguishing Features; Flowering Time	Lip whitish, flushed with purple, dotted, segments toothed, helmet dark reddish purple; 5–6	Flowers yellow, lip slightly 3-lobed, spur nearly as long as ovary; 4	Leaves as long as the internodes, often violet beneath, flowers greenish; 7–9	Leaves small, flowers greenish white, tinged with red, raceme few-flowered; 6–8	Leaves stiff, reddish, flowers reddish brown, lower part of lip with 3 large swellings; 5–7	Leaves longer than the internodes, outer perianth segments greenish, inner ones purplish; 6–8

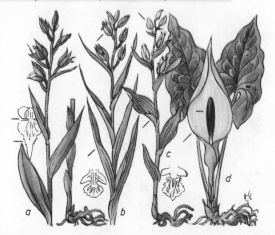

a *Red Helleborine, *Cephalanthera rubra:* ♃, 15–80 cm; lower part of the lip longer than broad; 6–7. b *Long-leaved Helleborine, *Cephalanthera longifolia:* ♃, 20–60 cm; leaves narrow, lanceolate, flowers white; 5. c *White Helleborine, *Cephalanthera damasonium:* ♃, 15–70 cm; leaves oblong-ovate, flowers yellowish; 5–6. All are members of the Orchid Family growing in woods and shady places. d *Cuckoo-pint or Lords-and-Ladies, *Arum maculatum:* 10–50 cm; spathe 15–25 cm, erect, yellowish green, spadix cylindrical, with a dull purple upper part; poisonous; 4–5; in woods and shady hedgebanks; Arum Family.

a Jerusalem Pine, *Pinus halepensis:* tree up to 20 m; bark smooth, silvery grey, becoming reddish brown and deeply fissured, crown rounded; 3–4. **b Stone Pine,** *Pinus pinea:* tree up to 30 m; bark greyish brown, flaking to leave reddish orange patches, crown parasol-shaped; 3–4. **c †Maritime Pine,** *Pinus pinaster:* up to 40 m; bark deeply fissured, reddish, crown conical, needles rigid and spiny; 2–4. All are widespread conifers of the Mediterranean region, especially of coastal areas. The Maritime Pine occurs in SW Europe, extending eastwards to S Italy. All belong to the Pine Family.

Of the plants illustrated below, the Spanish Nut belongs to the Iris Family, the Branched Asphodel or King's Rod and the Yellow Asphodel or King's Spear to the Lily Family, and the remainder to the Orchid Family. These species all occur mainly in woods in the Mediterranean region, especially in olive scrubs. The Spanish Nut grows also in sandy places, and the Bertoloni's Bee Orchid also in mountain woods.

	Spanish Nut	Branched Asphodel	Yellow Asphodel	Tongue Orchid	Bertoloni's Bee Orchid	Butterfly Orchid
Scientific Name	*Iris sisyrinchium*	*Asphodelus ramosus*	*Asphodeline lutea*	*Serapias lingua*	*Ophrys bertolonii*	*Orchis papilionacea*
Longevity, Size	♃, 10–30 cm	♃, 50–100 cm	♃, up to 30 cm	♃, 20–35 cm	♃, 10–35 cm	♃, 10–35 cm
Distinguishing Features; Flowering Time	Outer perianth-segments with a blue-dotted patch; 3–4	Flowers white, with a red midrib, in a large, branched raceme; 2–4	Flowers yellow, in a raceme, leaves narrow, grass-like; 2–4	Bracts large, red, flowers brownish red, without a spur; 3–4	Lip blackish violet with a pale spot, perianth-segments pale pink, spreading; 3–4	Bracts purplish red, with green veins, perianth-segments, dark purplish red; 1–4

a *Cork Oak, *Quercus suber:* tree up to 16 m; bark thick, corky, leaves evergreen, leathery; 4–5. **b †Evergreen Oak** or **Holm Oak,** *Quercus ilex:* tree up to 20 m; leaves evergreen, leathery, densely grey-downy beneath, dark green and glabrous on upper side. Both are members of the Beech Family, growing in woods in the Mediterranean region. **c European Hop-hornbeam,** *Ostrya carpinifolia:* tree, 9–18 m; infructescence similar to a hop cone, leaves similar to those of the Hornbeam (page 23); 4–5; a member of the Birch Family, distributed in S Europe, extending northwards to C Europe.

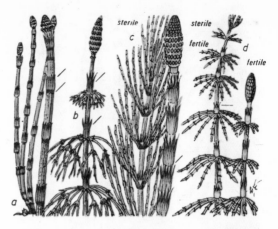

a *Rough Horsetail, *Equisetum hyemale:* 4, up to 1.25 m; fertile and sterile shoots similar, evergreen, not usually branched, sheath with two black cross bands; 7–8. **b *Wood Horsetail,** *Equisetum sylvaticum:* 4, 15–60 cm; sheath with 4–6 teeth; 5–6. **c *Giant Horsetail,** *Equisetum telmateia:* 4, 30–150 cm; fertile stem without branches, sheaths close together; 3–5. **d *Shady Horsetail,** *Equisetum pratense:* 4, 10–50 cm; sheaths with 12–20 white-margined teeth; 5–6. All are members of the Horsetail Family. They grow scattered throughout most of Europe, usually on stream-banks, **b** also in moorlands.

Of the members of the Polypody Family (now regarded as comprising several families) illustrated below, the Oak Fern, the Ostrich Fern and the Beech Fern occur mainly in damp woodlands, while Bracken is widespread in many different habitats. The Hard Fern grows in woods, heaths, moors and mountain grassland. The Hart's-tongue Fern is found in rocky woods and shady hedge-banks and is locally common throughout most of Europe, but rare in the Mediterranean region.

	*Hard Fern	*Ostrich Fern	*Bracken	*Hart's-tongue Fern	*Oak Fern	*Beech Fern
Scientific Name	*Blechnum spicant*	*Matteuccia struthiopteris*	*Pteridium aquilinum*	*Phyllitis scolopendrium*	*Gymnocarpium dryopteris*	*Thelypteris phegopteris*
Longevity, Size	4, 15–20 cm	4, 150 cm	4, 60–200 cm	4, 15–60 cm	4, 5–40 cm	4, 15–30 cm
Distinguishing Features; Sporing Time	Fronds 1-pinnate, sterile frond decumbent, fertile frond erect, with narrow pinnae; 7–9	Fronds 1-pinnate, fertile fronds with rolled-up pinnae, surrounded by sterile fronds; 6–7	Fronds 3-pinnate, sori contiguous, around margins of pinnae; 7–9	Frond simple, strap-shaped, heart-shaped at base; sori narrow and long; 7–9	Fronds 2-pinnate, with lowest pair of pinnae 3-angled, sori without indusium; 6–8	Fronds 1-pinnate, with colourless hairs, sori without indusium; 6–8

a *Lady-fern, *Athyrium filix-femina:* 30 to 100 cm; sori oval or crescent-shaped; 7–8. **b *Alpine Lady-fern,** *Athyrium distentifolium:* 4, 30–90 cm; sori orbicular, indusium usually absent; 7–8. **c *Male Fern,** *Dryopteris filix-mas:* 4 up to 1 m; stalks densely scaly; 7–9. **d *Mountain Fern,** *Thelypteris limbosperma:* 4, 30–80 cm; with two vascular strands in the stalk; 7–9. All are members of the Polypody Family. They are widespread in most of Europe, **a** and **c** in woodlands and also in hedgebanks, **b** and **d** in mountain districts, on screes and rocks and in alpine pastureland.

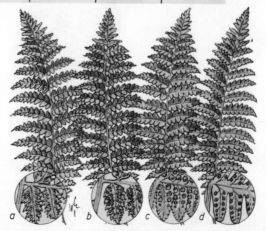

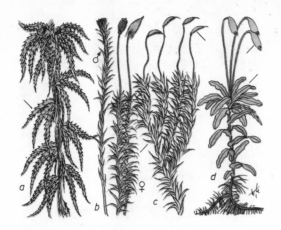

a *Spreading-leaved Bog Moss, *Sphagnum squarrosum:* ♃, 15 cm; branches slender, spreading, tapering, in groups of 2-5. **b *Common Hair-moss**, *Polytrichum commune:* ♃, 30 cm; capsule with a hairy, golden-fawn calyptra. **c *White Fork-moss**, *Leucobryum glaucum:* ♃, 5–10 cm; forming very compact, roundish, bluish green (whitish green when dry) cushions. **d *Palm-tree Moss**, *Mnium undulatum:* ♃, up to 15 cm; leaves large, often forming a rosette at the end of the stem. **b, c** and **d** are members of the Eubryales found growing together in shady woods.

Most of the Lichens illustrated below are found growing on the bark of trees, some particularly on coniferous trees as, for example, the Common Lichen, the Inflated Lichen, the Beard Lichen, the Channelled Lichen and the Wiry Lichen. The Iceland Lichen flourishes on the ground in open mountain woods or on mountain heaths.

	Beard Lichen	*Common Lichen	*Wiry Lichen	*Inflated Lichen	*Channelled Lichen	*Iceland Lichen
Scientific Name	*Usnea glauca*	*Xanthoria parietina*	*Alectoria fuscescens*	*Parmelia physodes*	*Ramalina calicaris*	*Cetraria islandica*
Longevity, Size	♃, 30–50 cm	♃, to 10 cm	♃, 30 cm	♃, 7 cm	♃, 10 cm	♃, 10 cm
Distinguishing Features	Thallus thread-like, apothecia disc-shaped	Thallus of yellow leaf-like lobes with orbicular apothecia	Thallus grey of finely branched filaments	Thallus greenish grey, deeply lobed	Thallus grey-green, strap-shaped, with orbicular apothecia	Thallus brown, forked, apothecia rare, orbicular, at edges of lobes

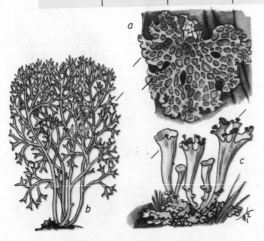

a *Tree Lungwort, *Lobaria pulmonaria:* ♃, lobes 10 cm or more in length, thallus leaf-like, strongly lobed, underside downy, upper side pitted in a net-like pattern; grows on rocks and old deciduous trees, in mountainous areas with high rainfall. **b *Reindeer Lichen**, *Cladonia impexa:* ♃, 10 cm; podetia branched, bush-shaped, in greyish green tufts. **c *Scarlet Cup-lichen**, *Cladonia coccifera:* ♃, 2.5 cm; podetia greyish green cups, on whose edge are red apothecia; common on acid humus in moors and woods. **Common Cup-lichen**, *Cladonia pyxidata:* (not illustrated) differs from **c** in having brown apothecia. All are Lichens.

a *Horse Mushroom, Psalliota arvensis:* cap up to 15 cm wide, whitish, becoming stained with yellow, gills pink, later brownish; 6–10. **b *Brown Wood** or **Red-fleshed Mushroom;** *Psalliota sylvatica:* cap up to 8 cm wide, brown, with dark brown scales, gills whitish, later flesh-coloured to violet-brown, blood-red when bruised; 7–11. **c *Wood Mushroom,** Psalliota sylvicola:* cap up to 12 cm wide, yellowish white, shining, almost smooth, becoming yellow-spotted when bruised. All are edible Gill Fungi occurring in woods.

Some more edible Gill Fungi are shown below. They are usually found in woods, the Shaggy Parasol in dry situation, the Saffron Milk Cap only in coniferous woods; the Changeable Agaric and the Honey Fungus grow in clumps on old tree-trunks, the former only on deciduous trees, particularly on the Beech (page 23), the latter also on roots.

	*Parasol Mushroom	*Shaggy Parasol	*The Blusher	*Changeable Agaric	*Saffron Milk Cap	*Honey Fungus
Scientific Name	Lepiota procera	Lepiota rhacodes	Amanita rubescens	Pholiota mutabilis	Lactarius deliciosus	Armillaria mellea
Width of Cap	10–30 cm	8–15 cm	8–15 cm	3–6 cm	4–10 cm	5–10 cm
Distinguishing Features; Sporing Time	Cap whitish with brown scales, stem brownish, skin breaking up into snake-like markings; 7–11	Cap brown with large scales, stem without stripe-like markings, with bulbous base; 7–10	Cap reddish brown or grey, sometimes pale with mealy warts, ring white, large, striate; 6–10	Cap cinnamon to leathery brown, stem with a ring and brown scales; 4–12	Cap brick-colour, with darker concentric markings, milk (sap) bright red-saffron; 6–11	Cap yellowish or pinkish, with dark scales, gills white, later brown, spores white; 7–12

a *Russula vesca: cap 6–10 cm wide, flesh-red, yellowish-spotted, gills white; 6–10. **b *Russula integra:** cap 6–10 cm wide, brown to purple-red, gills white, later pale yellow to dark yellow; 7–10. **Wood Blewits,** *Tricholoma nudum:* (not illustrated) cap 6–10 cm wide, reddish brown, gills pale violet, stem dark violet; 9–10. All three are edible members of the Gill Fungi. **c *Chanterelle,** Cantharellus cibarius:* cap up to 10 cm wide, trumpet-shaped, egg-yellow, 'gills' forked, shallow, blunt, flesh yellowish, with apricot smell; 6–11; an edible member of the Cantharell (Chanterelle) Family.

45

a ***Edible Boletus,*** *Boletus edulis:* cap 8 to 20 cm wide, cushion-shaped, brown, tubes white to yellowish green, stem brownish, with fine white net-like pattern at apex; 5–11. **b Sweet-chestnut Boletus,** *Boletus badius:* cap 5–12 cm, resembling the Edible Boletus but stem tubes becoming bluish green when bruised; 7–11. **c** ***Red-cracked Boletus,*** *Boletus chrysenteron:* cap up to 7 cm, becoming cushion-shaped, tubes olive-yellow to olive-green, stem dark red; 7–11. All are edible Pore Fungi, widespread in deciduous and coniferous woods.

Several other species of Boletus are shown below. All are edible. The Yellow-cracked Boletus occurs both in coniferous and deciduous woods, the Elegant Boletus, common in some places, prefers coniferous woods, usually growing under the Larch (page 18); the Brown-yellow and the Granulated Boletus are found in coniferous woods, the Rough-stem and the Orange-cap Boletus almost always under Birches (pages 23, 69), the Orange-cap also being found in coniferous woods, heaths and pastures.

	*Yellow-cracked Boletus	*Rough-stem Boletus	*Orange-cap Boletus	*Brown-yellow Boletus	*Elegant Boletus	*Granulated Boletus
Scientific Name	*Boletus subtomentosus*	*Boletus scaber*	*Boletus versipellis*	*Boletus luteus*	*Boletus elegans*	*Boletus granulatus*
Width of Cap	5–10 cm	5–10 cm	7–20 cm	4–10 cm	5–12 cm	7–20 cm
Distinguishing Features; Sporing Time	Cap olive-green to velvet olive-brown, tubes lemon-yellow; 7–10	Stem long and slender, with grey scales; 6–10	Cap orange-red, stem with brown or grey fibrous scales; 6–10	Cap brownish, sticky, tubes yellow, stem with ring; 6–10	Cap golden yellow, tubes yellow to olive-brown, ring yellow; 7–10	Cap sticky in damp weather, reddish yellow, stem pale yellow; 6–10

a ***Surgeon's Agaric,*** *Fomes fomentarius:* base 15—30 cm wide; dull green, concentrically furrowed; grows on trunks of trees; Telephora Family (Bracket Fungi). **b *Wood Hedgehog,*** *Hydnum repandum:* cap 6—12 cm wide, yellow with a tinge of red, spines yellowish; 7—11. **c *Imbricated Hydnum,*** *Hydnum imbricatum:* cap 5—20 cm wide, greyish brown, spines greyish white; 8—11. **b** and **c** are edible; both belong to the Hydnum Family. **d *Horn of Plenty,*** *Craterellus cornucopioides:* cap up to 12 cm, funnel-shaped; 6—10; belongs to the Cantharell (Chanterelle) Family.

a Crusted Fairy Club, *Clavaria flava:* fruit-body 10–12 cm long, branches firm, yellow, later yellowish brown at tips; 7–10; palatable when young. **b *Coral Fungus,** *Clavaria botrytis:* fruit-body 3–6 cm long, thick, fleshy, irregularly branched, white with reddish tips; 7–11; palatable when young. **c *Sparassis** or **Cauliflower Fungus,** *Sparassis crispa:* fruit-body up to 40 cm wide, fleshy, much-branched, with flattened crisped branches, whitish or pale yellow tinged with red; 8–10; edible. All belong to the Club Fungi (Fairy Club Family).

The Puffballs and the Bovista are Earth Balls, the Morels and the Common Helvel are Cup Fungi. The Puffballs occur in coniferous or deciduous woods and in pastures. The Pear-shaped Puffball grows in clumps on old stumps. The Edible Morel grows in clearings in woods, the Conical Morel in grassy places under trees and in woods, and Common Helvel amongst grass, usually in woods. All are edible, the Puffballs and Bovista when young, the Edible Morel when boiled.

	*Warted Puffball	***Pear-shaped Puffball**	***Dark Bovista**	***Edible Morel**	***Conical Morel**	***Common Helvel**
Scientific Name	*Lycoperdon perlatum*	*Lycoperdon pyriforme*	*Bovista nigrescens*	*Morchella esculenta*	*Morchella conica*	*Helvella crispa*
Width of Cap	3–5 cm	4–6 cm	3–5 cm	3–7 cm	Up to 5 cm	2–5 cm
Distinguishing Features; Sporing Time	Fruit-body cone-shaped with elongate, cylindrical stem-like base, with spines; 6–11	Fruit-body pear-shaped, yellow-brown, with minute pointed spines and granules; 7–8	Fruit-body globose, white, almost smooth, finally dark brown; 6–8	Cap usually globose, with firm branched ribs, forming deep, wide, irregular pits; 4–6	Cap conical, with elongated pits; very tasty; 3–6	Cap with 3 undulate lobes, stem deeply grooved, pitted, with longitudinal ribs; 7–11

a *Death Cap, *Amanita phalloides:* cap 7 to 12 cm wide, greenish; 7–10; deadly poisonous. **b *False Death Cap,** *Amanita citrina:* cap 7–12 cm wide, yellowish green or whitish yellow; 7–10; harmless, but taste disagreeable; easily confused with the Death Cap. **c *Avenging Angel,** *Amanita virosa:* cap 5–10 cm wide, white, sticky, conical; 6–11; deadly poisonous. **d *Fools' Mushroom,** *Amanita verna:* cap up to 8 cm, white, convex, finally flat; 4–11; deadly poisonous. All these species belong to the Gill Fungi. They are uncommon, but may be found growing scattered in woodlands.

a *Fly Agaric, *Amanita muscaria:* cap 8 to 20 cm wide, scarlet or yellowish red, covered with thick white or yellowish fragments of volva; 7–11; poisonous. b *Panther Cap, *Amanita pantherina:* cap 5–10 cm wide, brown, with white fragments of volva, deeply grooved at the margin; 7–11; very poisonous. Both are found mainly in coniferous woods and contain two nerve-paralysing poisons, atropine and muscarine. c *Woolly Milk Cap, *Lactarius torminosus:* cap up to 12 cm wide, pale flesh-coloured, zoned, downy and shaggy; 7–11; grows in mixed woods and on heaths; unpalatable. All belong to the Gill Fungi.

The Red-staining Inocybe and the Sickener belong to the Gill Fungi, the others to the Pore Fungi. The Inocybe is rare, the Sickener common in coniferous woods, being replaced in beech woods by the Maire's Russula, *Russula mairei* (not illustrated), in which the cuticle of the cap half peels, showing white flesh. The Red-stalked Bitter Boletus and the Bitter Boletus occur mainly in coniferous woods, the Lurid Boletus and the rare Satan's Boletus in deciduous woods.

	*Red-staining Inocybe	*The Sickener	*Bitter Boletus	*Red-stalked Bitter Boletus	*Lurid Boletus	*Satan's Boletus
Scientific Name	*Inocybe patouillardii*	*Russula emetica*	*Boletus felleus*	*Boletus calopus*	*Boletus luridus*	*Boletus satanas*
Width of Cap	4–8 cm	5–9 cm	7–12 cm	6–15 cm	6–14 cm	6–18 cm
Distinguishing Features; Sporing Time	Cap conical-bell-shaped, split at the margin, very poisonous; 5–6	Cap pale red, shiny, cuticle peels to show reddish flesh, gills shining white; poisonous; 7–10	Tubes pink to reddish, stem reticulated with brownish veins; bitter, unpalatable; 7–10	Tubes lemon-yellow, stem dark red at base, with white veins; bitter, unpalatable; 6–11	Tubes and, usually, stem orange-red, with blood-red veins; poisonous; 6–10	Tubes blood-red, stem brick-red, lighter above, veins blood-red; very poisonous; 7–9

a *Sulphur Tuft, *Hypholoma fasciculare:* cap 3—5 cm wide, yellow, often darker on top, gills yellowish green; 4–11; on tree-stumps; poisonous; Gill Fungi. b *Stinkhorn, *Phallus impudicus:* cap 2–3 cm wide, white or olive-green, very fetid; 6–10; woods, thickets, gardens; unpalatable. c *Earth Ball, *Scleroderma aurantium:* fruit-body 4–8 cm wide, base short, stem-like, wall leathery, breaking up irregularly; 7–11; open places near trees; poisonous. b and c are Earth Balls. d *Spring Helvel, *Gyromitra esculenta:* cap up to 12 cm wide, tawny, then coffee-brown, irregularly undulated; 9–11; in coniferous woods; Helvel Family.

a ***Common Shrew,** *Sorex araneus:* up to 8.5 cm + 4.5 cm, weight 10 grammes; yellowish brown stripe between the colouring of the upper and lower sides, tail less than $^2/_3$ head and body length. **b *Pygmy Shrew,** *Sorex minutus:* up to 6 cm + 4.5 cm, weight about 4 grammes; upper-side colouring extends well underneath, tail $^2/_3$ body length, thicker than on **a,** snout more pointed. Both live in woods, but also on grasslands and in marshes throughout Europe. **c *Barbastelle,** *Barbastella barbastellus:* 4.4–5.8 cm + 4.1–5.4 cm, wingspan 26 cm; wide ears, touching at the centre; lives in wooded, hilly country.

The bats shown in the table below belong to the Smooth-faced Bat Family. The muzzle carries no nose-leaf, and the ear has an extra flap or tragus. All the species shown here live in wooded areas, but are also found in open country. Bechstein's Bat is the rarest British species, the Noctule is the largest and Geoffroy's Bat does not occur here. They are otherwise all widespread throughout Europe.

	*Noctule	***Leisler's Bat**	***Whiskered Bat**	**Geoffroy's Bat**	***Natterer's Bat**	***Bechstein's Bat**
Scientific Name	*Nyctalus noctula*	*Nyctalus leisleri*	*Myotis mystacinus*	*Myotis emarginatus*	*Myotis nattereri*	*Myotis bechsteini*
Size	8 cm + 5 cm	6.3cm+4.4cm	5 cm + 4 cm	4.5cm+4.3cm	5 cm + 4.3 cm	5.3cm+4.4cm
Distinguishing Features	Wingspan up to 38 cm, tragus short, broadening towards the top	Wingspan up to 32 cm, similar to the previous species, but smaller	Wingspan up to 24.5 cm, tragus tapers from the bottom, lips bearded	Body of reddish colour, edge of ears notched	Wingspan 28 cm, membrane between legs fringed with stiff hairs, tragus spear-shaped	Wingspan 25 cm, ear very long, tragus narrow, bending outwards and upwards

a ***Greater Horseshoe Bat,** *Rhinolophus ferrumequinum:* up to 6.9 cm + 4.3 cm, wingspan up to 38 cm; nose-leaf rounded, swollen, body rather light coloured. **b *Lesser Horseshoe Bat,** *Rhinolophus hipposideros:* up to 4.1 cm + 3 cm, wingspan up to 25 cm; nose-leaf tapers from the bottom, darker than the previous species. Both belong to the Horseshoe Bat Family, the members of which have complicated flaps of skin on the muzzle, but no tragus to the ear. They like wooded country, hibernate in caves, and are found in Europe south of Scandinavia across to Asia. Both these bats hunt insects throughout the night.

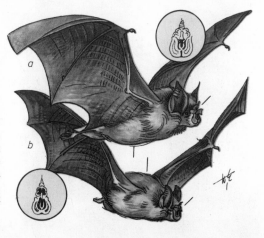

a *Bank Vole, *Clethrionomys glareolus:* 11 cm + 6 cm; upper side red-brown, flanks grey, tail comparatively long; mainly diurnal, lives in hedgerows and fields, feeding on a very varied diet; a member of the Mouse Family, native to most of Europe except the far north, the Mediterranean and Ireland (a number of forms are found on islands round Britain).
b Northern Birch Mouse, *Sicista betulina:* 7 cm + 10.6 cm; tail very long, sharply defined black stripe on back; belongs to the Birch Mouse Subfamily and occurs from Scandinavia and N Europe south into Hungary, east into Asia. Birch Mice live in holes in the ground in woods and on moors.

Members of the Dormouse Family are small, nocturnal rodents living in wooded and overgrown areas. Only the Dormouse and the Edible or Fat Dormouse are found in Great Britain, where the Dormouse, for unknown reasons, is now becoming very rare. The Edible Dormouse was introduced during the last century and has now established itself in the Tring area of Hertfordshire. The Garden or Oak Dormouse lives in S and E Europe. Dormice hibernate throughout the winter in holes, buildings or nests.

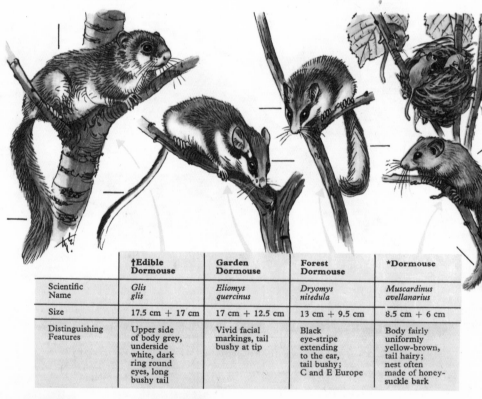

	†Edible Dormouse	Garden Dormouse	Forest Dormouse	*Dormouse
Scientific Name	*Glis glis*	*Eliomys quercinus*	*Dryomys nitedula*	*Muscardinus avellanarius*
Size	17.5 cm + 17 cm	17 cm + 12.5 cm	13 cm + 9.5 cm	8.5 cm + 6 cm
Distinguishing Features	Upper side of body grey, underside white, dark ring round eyes, long bushy tail	Vivid facial markings, tail bushy at tip	Black eye-stripe extending to the ear, tail bushy; C and E Europe	Body fairly uniformly yellow-brown, tail hairy; nest often made of honeysuckle bark

***Red Squirrel,** *Sciurus vulgaris:* 28 cm + 24 cm; tail long, densely haired, back red-brown (occasionally black, particularly on those living in mountains), underside white, ears tufted in winter; the British subspecies has a paler coloration, especially the tail, which becomes almost white in winter. This is a member of the Squirrel Family found throughout almost the whole of Europe, although in Britain it is rarer than formerly. It lives in woods, especially of conifers, parks and gardens, and builds a spherical nest of twigs lined with grass, moss and hair as a summer home. Squirrels are diurnal animals which do not hibernate.

a Common Wolf, *Canis lupus:* 110–140 cm + 30–40 cm; large, fur grey, similar to the Alsatian dog. **b *Fox**, *Vulpes vulpes:* about 65 cm + 40 cm; red-brown above, white below, back of ears dark, white tail; tip a dark form is **c Brant-fox**, blackish above, dark below. These are carnivores belonging to the Dog Family; they inhabit mainly wooded country, the Fox over the whole of Europe and the Wolf normally in remote and mountainous regions, although in times of hardship family parties may join together as packs and invade inhabited areas. The Wolf became extinct in the British Isles in the 18th century.

Illustrated in the centre of the page are carnivores of the Weasel Family. The Sable is extinct in Europe, where formerly it lived principally in coniferous forests. The other species shown are native to large parts of Europe, although in Britain the Pine Marten and Polecat are rare and the Beech or Stone Marten does not occur. In Europe the Beech Marten and the Polecat may sometimes be found in cultivated areas, but generally they live in wild country.

	*Badger	***European Polecat**	***Pine Marten**	**Beech Marten**	**Sable**
Scientific Name	*Meles meles*	*Mustela putorius*	*Martes martes*	*Martes foina*	*Martes zibellina*
Size	81.5 cm + 10 cm	41 cm + 18 cm	53 cm + 28 cm	48 cm + 26 cm	46 cm + 18 cm
Distinguishing Features	Stocky build, grizzled colour, black and white head markings, long snout	♀ smaller (35 + 14 cm), coat uniformly dark brown, mask-like facial markings	♀ smaller (45 + 26 cm), red-brown, cream to orange throat-patch, legs short, feet large	Throat marking mostly white, with lower edge divided and often extending to the shoulder	Throat marking ochre, not sharply defined

*European Wild Cat, *Felis sylvestris:* 60 cm + 31.5 cm; tail thick, ringed, with black tip, body pale or yellowish grey to black-grey, with black stripes; a carnivore of the Cat Family, it inhabits the larger woodlands and other areas with good cover, especially in mountainous regions, surviving in parts of the Scottish Highlands but extinct elsewhere in Britain. Wild Cats live in hollow trees or other secure dens, and hunt rabbits and rodents, mainly at night. Domestic cats are not descended from the Wild Cat (said to be untamable) but are related closely enough to interbreed successfully, and may themselves return to the wild.

a Mongolian Wild Horse, *Equus caballus:* shoulder height 115–130 cm; coat mouse-grey, mane short, erect, black, no forelock, dark stripe along the back, zebra-stripes on forelegs; very common in Europe in pre-historic times, finally died out in S Russia in 1851, but back-breeding from primitive types of wild horse has produced a type much like the wild ancestor. **b Dülmen 'Wild Horse',** *Equus caballus:* coat varied, long mane and forelock; a feral wild horse in Westphalia comparable to the 'wild' ponies of Britain. Horses are odd-toed hoofed animals, not closely related to cattle and deer, which have cloven hoofs.

The Roe Deer, the Red Deer and the Fallow Deer are antler-bearing Artiodactyls. All inhabit deciduous and mixed forests and are widespread on the plains and in mountains, where they live in herds and may be valuable game animals (although in the breeding season and in winter they can damage young trees). Deer are principally dusk and nocturnal animals; they only graze in the day-time in places where they are undisturbed. All British deer tend to be smaller than their European counterparts. The Fallow Deer was probably introduced by the Romans.

	†Fallow Deer	*Roe Deer	*Red Deer
Scientific Name	*Dama dama*	*Capreolus capreolus*	*Cervus elaphus*
Size	♂ 160 cm + 19 cm	135 cm + 2 cm	250 cm + 15 cm
Distinguishing Features	♀ smaller, many colour variants but usually brown coat with white spots, ♂ (buck) with palmate antlers, ♀ (doe) without antlers	Summer reddish brown, winter greyish brown, young (kid)white-spotted, head roundish, ♂ (buck) has branched antlers, each branch with up to 4 tines, ♀ (doe) without antlers	Summer reddish brown, winter greyish brown, long head, ♂ (stag) with branched antlers, each branch with 10 tines in full-grown animal, ♀ (hind) without antlers

a European Elk, *Alces alces:* 290 cm + 5 cm; the male has palmate antlers with many tines, the female is without antlers, muzzle extended over lower jaw, ♂ with long back and neck manes, ♀ with short back mane; lives in rough marshland and moors in N and E Europe, but does not occur in Britain. **b †Sika** or **Japanese Deer,** *Cervus nippon:* 120 cm + 5 cm; summer coat reddish brown with white spots, black stripe on back, in winter of almost uniform colour, ♂ with branched antlers; introduced into Europe from Japan, in Britain may be seen in many parks and in some scattered areas living successfully in the wild.

a †Chinese Water Deer, *Hydropotes inermis:* 90 cm + 6 cm; ♂ without antlers, but with upper canine teeth which project downwards. **b †Reeves' Muntjac,** *Muntiacus reevesi:* 100 cm + 15 cm; antlers on long hairy pedicles, simply forked, ♀ without antlers; introduced into England and France from India, has become naturalized in some parts. **c White-tailed** or **Virginian Deer,** *Odocoileus virginianus:* 180 cm + 30 cm; summer coat reddish brown, winter coat grey, antlers many-tined, bending upwards and forwards, ♀ without antlers; introduced from America, this animal has become naturalized in Finland.

The Wild Aurochs, once widespread, became extinct in 1627, but an animal resembling it has been bred back from domestic cattle and may be seen in some zoos; also, there are in England semi-wild White Cattle, like the Chillingham Herd, which are generally similar to it. European Bison are kept in a few areas, and the Indian or Domestic Water Buffalo lives in a semi-wild state in SE Europe. The Moufflon, from Sardinia and Corsica, has been widely introduced into Europe.

	European Bison	Aurochs	*English White Cattle	Indian Buffalo	Moufflon
Scientific Name	*Bison bonasus*	*Bos primigenius*	*Bos taurus*	*Bubalus bubalis*	*Ovis musimon*
Size (or Weight)	290 cm + 60 cm	♂ 280 cm + 80 cm	♂ 500 kg, ♀ 375 kg	625 kg	130 cm + 6 cm
Distinguishing Features	Short horns, broad, triangular head and front part of body covered with long woolly hair	♂ blackish brown, ♀ much smaller, reddish brown, horns light with black tips	Coat white, ears brown or black, horns similar to those of Aurochs	Coat uniformly greyish black, horns project sideways	♂ with curling horns, in winter coat has white patch ('saddle') on the back, ♀ small horns

Wild Boar, *Sus scrofa:* 155 cm + 20 cm; coat dark to light grey with long bristles, tusks or canines of upper jaw twisted upwards and considerably elongated, particularly in ♂, long head with cartilaginous snout, young brownish yellow with dark stripes along the sides. The Wild Boar is a solitary animal occupying a large territory, which may contain a number of lairs. It is found in many parts of Europe in deciduous and mixed forests, marshland, and cultivated areas with sufficient cover; it is hunted in many places by sportsmen. Pigs are non-ruminant Artiodactyls; the wild form has been extinct in England since the early 17th century.

53

a Mediterranean Horseshoe Bat, *Rhinolophus euryale:* 5.8 cm + 3 cm; centre part of
nose-leaf carries pointed projection. **b Mehe-
ly's Horseshoe Bat,** *Rhinolophus mehelyi:*
6.4 cm + 2.9 cm; centre part of nose-leaf
with bluntly wedge-shaped projection. Both
belong to the Horseshoe Bat Family. **c Long-
fingered Bat,** *Myotis capaccinii:* 5.3 cm +
3.8 cm; ears short, with four cross-wrinkles,
spur of hind limb very long; a member of the
Smooth-faced Bat Family. All are cave-dwel-
lers native to the Mediterranean region, Me-
hely's Bat more in the west.

The Grey Squirrel was introduced into England from America and has become well established
there, being a serious pest in some areas; the Flying Squirrel lives in the north of the U.S.S.R.
and in Finland. Both are rodents belonging to the Squirrel Family. The Southern Birch Mouse
is a member of the Birch Mouse Subfamily and lives in the grass- and tree-steppes of the
southern U.S.S.R. and west to Czechoslovakia. All the other rodents in the table are northern
forest-dwellers of the Mouse Family.

	†Grey Squirrel	Flying Squirrel	Wood Lemming	Large-toothed Red-backed Vole	Northern Red-backed Vole	Southern Birch Mouse
Scientific Name	*Sciurus carolinensis*	*Pteromys volans*	*Myopus schisticolor*	*Clethrionomys rufocanus*	*Clethrionomys rutilus*	*Sicista subtilis*
Size	26 cm + 21.5 cm	17 cm + 13 cm	9.5 cm + 1.9 cm	13 cm + 4 cm	11 cm + 3.5 cm	6.8 cm + 8.2 cm
Distinguishing Features	Upper side grey, ears never tufted, tail bushy	Membrane between front and hind legs (a sitting, b gliding)	Dark grey, lighter in winter, back reddish brown, tail short	Back dark reddish brown, otherwise grey, particularly on the flanks	Back reddish brown, belly brownish yellow, tail rather short	Black back-stripe with light side-stripes, tail very long

a Raccoon-like Dog, *Nyctereutes procyonoi-
des:* 60 cm + 16 cm; facial markings like a
raccoon; belonging to the Dog Family, originates in E Asia but extends across the
U.S.S.R. to Finland and Sweden. **b Lynx,**
Lynx lynx: body 80–130 cm, tail 11–25 cm;
tufts of hair on ears; inhabits the U.S.S.R. and
Scandinavia. **c Spanish Lynx,** *Lynx pardel-
lus:* 110 cm + 13 cm; body distinctly spotted;
lives on the Iberian Peninsula and in the
Balkans. Both lynxes are rare members of the
Cat Family living in large forests and isolated
wild areas. Considerable efforts are now being
made to preserve the Spanish Lynx from
extinction.

a Black Stork, *Ciconia nigra:* 97 cm; back shining black, under parts white; migrant; a member of the Stork Family native east of the Elbe and in C Spain, where it lives in marshy countryside surrounded by coniferous and mixed forests. **b Short-toed Eagle,** *Circaëtus gallicus:* 63–65 cm; under-wings and breast almost all pure white, eyes large, yellow, talons bluish white; belongs to the Birds-of-Prey Family. The Short-toed Eagle nests in trees in isolated forests on marshy plains and in mountain gorges in E and S Europe, occasionally being seen elsewhere.

Most of the Birds of Prey illustrated below are widespread throughout Europe. The Honey-buzzard and the Lesser Spotted Eagle are mainly E and S European species. Birds of Prey are becoming very rare in many areas, partly at least because of the increased use of chemical insecticides which accumulate in their bodies, being taken in very small amounts from the many animals on which they prey.

	Lesser Spotted Eagle	Black Kite	*Red Kite	*Honey-buzzard	*Goshawk	*Sparrow-hawk
Scientific Name	*Aquila pomarina*	*Milvus migrans*	*Milvus milvus*	*Pernis apivorus*	*Accipiter gentilis*	*Accipiter nisus*
Size	61–66 cm	55–56 cm	60–61 cm	51–58 cm	48–61 cm	28–38 cm
Distinguishing Features	Legs fully feathered, plumage uniformly earth-coloured; migrant	Plumage dusky reddish brown, tail only slightly forked; migrant	Plumage reddish, tail deeply forked; partial migrant	Tail long, under tail-coverts with three broad cross-stripes; migrant	Under parts barred, tail much longer than wings; resident	♂ with grey back and red-brown barring on breast, ♀ with brown back and barring

a *Peregrine Falcon, Falco peregrinus:* 38–48 cm; adult with dark 'moustaches' on white cheeks, juvenile with light brown, streaked under parts; a partial migrant native to the whole of Europe, nests at the edge of forests and on cliffs. **b Red-footed Falcon,** *Falco vespertinus:* 30 cm; ♂ slate-black with red feet, ♀ with reddish yellow crown and belly; a gregarious migrant, native to SE Europe. Falcons have pointed wings and fly fast, killing their prey in the air. **c Booted Eagle,** *Hieraëtus pennatus:* 43–45 cm; legs feathered, tail of almost uniform colour; a migrant native to Spain and SE Europe, nests in trees.

Eagle-owl, *Bubo bubo:* 66–71 cm; plumage yellowish brown, upper parts with dark brown spots, breast broadly streaked, whitish throat marking; eyes large, orange-red; long, prominent, feathered ear-tufts; resident. The Eagle-owl hunts at dawn and dusk in rocky mountain forests and on the open steppe; its prey is mainly small mammals. It nests on the ground in hollows under bushes or rocks, occasionally also in trees in old birds-of-prey nests or in hollow trees. The Eagle-owl is not found in far northern Europe or Great Britain or in large areas of France and Germany. Elsewhere it is becoming rarer.

All the birds shown below are Waders. The beautifully camouflaged Woodcock rests by day and feeds at dusk. It nests in forests, mostly at the foot of trees, and is native from C Europe to Great Britain. The Green Sandpiper, the Wood Sandpiper, the Spotted Redshank and the Greenshank nest on the ground in clearings in forests in the far north; the Greenshank nests occasionally in Scotland. All except the Wood Sandpiper, which is a rare passage migrant, are often seen as sea-shore birds in Britain.

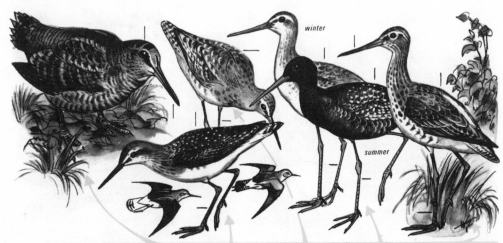

	*Woodcock	*Green Sandpiper	Wood Sandpiper	*Spotted Redshank	*Greenshank
Scientific Name	*Scolopax rusticola*	*Tringa ochropus*	*Tringa glareola*	*Tringa erythropus*	*Tringa nebularia*
Size	28 cm	23 cm	20.5 cm	30.5 cm	30.5 cm
Distinguishing Features	Long bill, crown and under parts with narrow diagonal stripes; partial migrant	Back black speckled with large spots, rump white, legs greenish; migrant	Lighter than Green Sandpiper, legs greenish yellow; migrant	Summer plumage soot-black with white spots, winter plumage ash-grey; migrant	Legs green, back and rump white, wings uniformly dark; migrant

a *****Tawny Owl,** *Strix aluco:* 40 cm; basic colour brown or grey, head large, round, no ear-tufts; resident. **b** *****Long-eared Owl,** *Asio otus:* 38 cm; plumage brown, barred, eyes red, large ear-tufts; partial migrant. Both are native throughout almost all of Europe. They live in old woods, parks and large gardens, the Long-eared Owl preferring coniferous woods. The Tawny Owl usually nests in hollow trees, but both use the old nests of large birds and occasionally nest on the ground. Tawny Owls are often found in large cities, where they feed on mice and sparrows; in the countryside their hoot and 'ke-wick' hunting call are familiar night sounds.

Golden Oriole, *Oriolus oriolus:* 24 cm; ♂ body bright yellow, wings and tail black with yellow markings, ♀ greenish with darker wings, difficult to locate in foliage; rapid undulating flight; migrant, belongs to the Oriole Family. The nest hangs free between horizontally forked branches high up in trees in parklands, orchards and meadow forests, more rarely in coniferous forests. Golden Orioles are native throughout most of Europe with the exception of the north. They occur in small numbers as summer visitors in SE England, where they occasionally nest.

The Collared Dove comes from SE Europe but has recently increased its range as far west as Great Britain. The others are native throughout Europe except the far north. The Stock Dove, the Wood Pigeon or Ring Dove, and the Turtle Dove live in woods and park-like countryside, the Feral Pigeon, Wood Pigeon and Collared Dove also in towns and villages. Feral Pigeons and Collared Doves nest in and on buildings, all the other species in trees. All belong to the Pigeon Family.

	*Feral Pigeon	*Wood Pigeon	*Stock Dove	*Collared Dove	*Turtle Dove
Scientific Name	*Columba livia domestica*	*Columba palumbus*	*Columba oenas*	*Streptopelia decaocto*	*Streptopelia turtur*
Size	33 cm	36 cm	33 cm	28 cm	28 cm
Distinguishing Features	Domestic form gone wild, plumage very variable, at times similar to Rock Dove; resident	White patch on side of neck, black tail-bands; partial migrant	Glittering green patch on side of neck, two black, interrupted wing-bands; partial migrant	Black nape-band, wide tail end edged with white; resident	Tail narrow with a white edge, black and white striped patch on side of neck; migrant

*Jay, *Garrulus glandarius:* 34 cm; body reddish brown, rump white, wing-coverts conspicuously banded with blue, black and white, crest of barred feathers which can be raised; partial migrant, belongs to the Crow Family. Native throughout Europe except in the extreme north, Jays live in deciduous and coniferous forests and mostly nest in dense foliage. They sometimes congregate in small, noisy communities. Jays are among the most alert birds; their warning screech on the approach of an enemy is a danger signal to many animals. They themselves prey on many smaller birds, taking their eggs and young, but also eat a very wide range of foods.

a *Great Spotted Woodpecker, *Dendrocopus major:* 25 cm; white patch on each side below black nape-band, ♂ with red spot on the nape, ♀ top of head quite black without any red, young with entirely red crown; resident. **b Syrian Woodpecker,** *Dendrocopus syriacus:* 25 cm; similar to the above but without cheekband; resident. Both inhabit deciduous and coniferous forests and parklands, the Great Spotted Woodpecker almost throughout Europe; the Syrian Woodpecker lives mainly in Greece and Rumania but is extending its range. Like many other Woodpeckers, these species drum with their beaks on dead trees as a call in springtime.

The birds shown below belong to the Woodpecker Family. They have climbing feet, with two toes at the front and two at the back, and stiff tails which support them on tree-trunks. All are native throughout most of Europe wherever there are suitable forests. Black Woodpeckers prefer old coniferous or beech forests in mountainous areas. All the others inhabit deciduous forests and parklands or, more rarely, coniferous forests. Woodpeckers nest in holes which they bore in trees with their beaks.

	Black Woodpecker	*Lesser Spotted Woodpecker	Middle Spotted Woodpecker	Grey-headed Woodpecker	*Green Woodpecker
Scientific Name	*Dryocopus martius*	*Dendrocopus minor*	*Dendrocopus medius*	*Picus canus*	*Picus viridis*
Size	46 cm	14.5 cm	22 cm	25 cm	32 cm
Distinguishing Features	Plumage black, ♂ with red crown markings, ♀ only red at the nape; resident	White cross-stripes on back, ♂ crown red, ♀ colour whitish yellow; resident, usually found in high trees	Crown red, no black cheekband, back black; resident	Green, back grey, ♂ with forehead to centre of head red, ♀ without red; resident	Green, crown to nape red, black chin-stripe with, on ♂, a red centre; resident, often seen on the ground, feeding

a White-backed Woodpecker, *Dendrocopus leucotus:* 25 cm; rump white; resident. **b Three-toed Woodpecker,** *Picoides tridactylus:* 22 cm; back white, flanks barred, ♂ with yellow, ♀ with dark crown; resident. Both are species native to mountainous areas of the north and east of Europe. **c *Wryneck,** *Jynx torquilla:* 16.5 cm; plumage bark-coloured, shot with grey, brown and reddish yellow; migrant. The Wryneck is still found occasionally in SE England but is becoming very rare there; it nests in holes in trees. It is related to the woodpeckers, and clings to tree-trunks in a similar way, although more often seen feeding on the ground.

a *Nuthatch,** *Sitta europaea:* 14 cm; upper parts greyish blue, under parts a pale apricot colour; resident; can walk head-first down tree-trunks. **b** *Tree Creeper,** *Certhia familiaris:* 12.5 cm; hind toe elongated, bill slender; resident in E and N Europe, including Great Britain; Creeper Family. **c Short-toed Tree Creeper,** *Certhia brachydactyla:* 12.5 cm; short hind toe, bill longer than that of the Tree Creeper; resident in S and W Europe, where **b** does not occur. **b** and **c** nest in holes in trees or in other nooks and crannies; they are fast-moving as they search for insects on the bark, but always descend tree-trunks backwards.

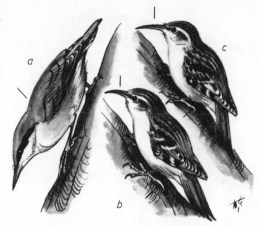

The members of the Tit Family shown below are very lively and extremely agile small insectivorous birds. All are native almost throughout Europe, breeding in holes in trees or walls. Great and Blue Tits prefer mixed forests, Crested and Coal Tits coniferous forests; the Crested Tit occurs also in old forests in E Scotland. The Long-tailed, Great and Blue Tits are also found in gardens and shrubberies, where they may become very tame.

	*Blue Tit	*Great Tit	*Crested Tit	*Coal Tit	*Long-tailed Tit
Scientific Name	*Parus caeruleus*	*Parus major*	*Parus cristatus*	*Parus ater*	*Aegithalos caudatus*
Size	11.5 cm	14 cm	11.5 cm	11 cm	14 cm
Distinguishing Features	Cap, wings and tail cobalt blue, under parts yellow, black eye-band; resident	Head and neck black, cheeks white, black belly-stripe, narrower on ♀; resident	Crest large, speckled black and white, black bib and neck-ring; resident	Head black with white patch on nape and white cheeks; resident	a Northern form: head white; b Southern form: broader, darker eye-band; resident

a Greenish Warbler, *Phylloscopus trochiloides:* 11 cm; white wing-bar, legs dark; occurs in NE Europe. **b Bonelli's Warbler,** *Phylloscopus bonelli:* 11.5 cm; yellow rump; found in most of France and S Europe. Both nest on the ground in deciduous and coniferous forests, **b** lives in very varied habitats, and may occur at altitudes over 3 000 m. **c Arctic** or **Eversmann's Warbler,** *Phylloscopus borealis:* 12 cm; long eye-stripe, light yellowish legs; nests in northern forests, usually near to water. All are migrants belonging to the Warbler Family; they feed on small insects.

a *Willow Warbler, *Phylloscopus trochilus:*
11 cm; upper parts olive-brown, under parts
pale yellow, legs light brown, very similar to
the Chiffchaff (page 253), but can be distinguished by leg colour and song. **b *Wood
Warbler,** *Phylloscopus sibilatrix:* 13 cm;
throat yellow, belly white; nests in forest
undergrowth. Both are native throughout
much of N Europe. **c Yellow-browed
Warbler,** *Phylloscopus inornatus:* 10 cm;
wings with two white bars; inhabits coniferous and mixed forests in Asia and passes
over E Europe during migration. All three
are migrant species belonging to the Warbler
Family.

The Redwing is a common winter visitor to Britain from N and E Europe and the Fieldfare
from E and C Europe. All the remainder are native throughout almost the whole of Europe. All
nest in trees and bushes in woods and open countryside and, with the exception of the Redwing
and Mistle-thrush, occasionally on buildings. All belong to the Thrush Family.

	*Blackbird	*Fieldfare	*Mistle-thrush	*Song-thrush	*Redwing
Scientific Name	*Turdus merula*	*Turdus pilaris*	*Turdus viscivorus*	*Turdus ericetorum*	*Turdus musicus*
Size	25.5 cm	25.5 cm	27 cm	23 cm	21 cm
Distinguishing Features	♂ plumage black, beak yellow, ♀ plumage brown; resident	Head and rump blue-grey, back brown; winter migrant to Britain	Upper parts greyish brown, tail darker, under parts thickly spotted; partial migrant	Back uniformly brown, breast and flanks covered with small spots; resident	Flanks rust-red, breast striped, upper eye-band cream-coloured; winter migrant to Britain

a *Nightingale, *Luscinia megarhynchos:*
16.5 cm; back and tail chestnut-brown, under
parts whitish brown, eyes large; migrant, in
Britain found in woods as far north as C England, and as far west as Devon. Nightingales
are normally very shy birds, but in the breeding season their song advertises their presence;
they are among the few species that sing at
night, although they may also be heard during
the day. **b Thrush-nightingale,** *Luscinia
luscinia:* 16.5 cm; breast mottled, otherwise
very similar to the Nightingale; migrant to
E Europe. Both belong to the Thrush
Family and nest near the ground in dense
thickets of blackberry and other bushes.

a *Crossbill, *Loxia curvirostra:* 16.5 cm; upper and lower mandibles cross one another, wings and tail dark, (♂ dull red, ♀ olive-green); resident, lives in flocks in coniferous forests in E Anglia and Scotland, and much of Europe. Crossbills betray their presence in woods by the characteristically shredded pine-cones which they leave on the ground. **b Parrot Crossbill**, *Loxia pityopsittacus:* 17 cm; bill much thicker than on the Crossbill. **c Two-barred Crossbill**, *Loxia leucoptera:* 15 cm; wings with two white bands, bill smaller; visits W Europe from time to time on migration from the north. Crossbills belong to the Finch Family.

Of the song-birds shown below, the Flycatchers nest in crannies or holes in trees or walls, the Warblers in bushes, and the Tree Pipit on or just above the ground. Only the Tree Pipit is native throughout N and C Europe; the others are from E and S Europe, although the Pied Flycatcher is a summer visitor to C England and Wales, and the Olivaceous Warbler is a rare visitor from S Spain and the Balkans.

	*Tree Pipit	Barred Warbler	Olivaceous Warbler	*Pied Flycatcher	White-collared Flycatcher	Red-breasted Flycatcher
Scientific Name	*Anthus trivialis*	*Sylvia nisoria*	*Hippolaïs pallida*	*Muscicapa hypoleuca*	*Muscicapa albicollis*	*Muscicapa parva*
Size	15 cm	15 cm	13 cm	13 cm	13 cm	11.5 cm
Distinguishing Features	Similar to the Meadow Pipit (page 202) but with reddish legs, spur small; migrant, a few birds resident	Breast barred, eyes sparkling yellow; migrant	Upper parts light earth-coloured, wings and tail darker; migrant	♂ black upper parts, white under parts, white forehead, ♀ olive-brown upper parts; migrant	White neck-band, rump and forehead; migrant	White tail-bars, ♂ orange-red throat, ♀ white throat; migrant

a *Chaffinch, *Fringilla coelebs:* 15 cm; wings with two white bands, ♂ crown bluish green, breast and cheeks reddish; partial migrant, a common bird which nests in trees and bushes and is often found in gardens and near houses; once thought to be the commonest British bird, its numbers have fallen in recent years. **b Pine Grosbeak**, *Pinicola enucleator:* 20 cm; pinkish red, wings with white bands. **c Rustic Bunting**, *Emberiza rustica:* 15 cm; crown and cheeks of ♂ black, of ♀ brown, pure white throat patch; migrant. **b** and **c** live in coniferous and mixed forests in the north and visit Britain as vagrants. All three species belong to the Finch Family.

a Spectacled Warbler, *Sylvia conspicillata:* 13 cm; similar to the Whitethroat (page 202) but with darker cheeks, white eye-ring; migrant, common among glassworts and scrub near the coast. **b Sardinian Warbler,** *Sylvia melanocephala:* 13 cm; head-cap extends to below the eye, throat white, eye-ring conspicuously red; resident. **c Subalpine Warbler,** *Sylvia cantillans:* 12 cm; white chin-stripe, breast and throat rust-red; migrant. All belong to the Warbler Family and nest in the thick undergrowth of evergreen woods and dwarf shrub in the Mediterranean region, but may occur as vagrants further north.

The Great Spotted Cuckoo lives in Spain and Portugal, and the Scops-owl nests in tree holes in S Europe. All the other birds shown below live in the far north, the Ural Owl also in E Europe. All the owls nest in holes in trees or in the old eyries of birds of prey. The Siberian Jay, a member of the Crow Family, usually builds its nest in pine trees. The Great Spotted Cuckoo is a parasite on members of the Crow Family, especially on Magpies.

	Great Spottted Cuckoo	Hawk-owl	Great Grey or Lapland Owl	Ural Owl	Scops-owl	Siberian Jay
Scientific Name	*Clamator glandarius*	*Surnia ulula*	*Strix nebulosa*	*Strix uralensis*	*Otus scops*	*Perisoreus infaustus*
Size	40 cm	36–40 cm	69 cm	61 cm	19 cm	30.5 cm
Distinguishing Features	Grey crest, tail long, edged with white; migrant	Under parts barred, eye-discs bordered with black; partial migrant	Eye-discs with concentric lines, eyes yellow; resident	Eye-discs with delicate, radial stripes, eyes dark; resident	Very small, with ear-tufts; partial migrant	Rump and out-side tail feathers reddish brown; resident in Scandinavia

a Orphean Warbler, *Sylvia hortensis:* 15 cm; much like ♂ of Blackcap (page 254), white in outer tail feathers, eyes straw-coloured, head-cap extends below the eyes; migrant, a member of the Warbler Family, nesting low in trees in the Mediterranean region. **b Siberian Tit,** *Parus cinctus:* 13 cm; crown and nape brown; resident, breeding in holes in birch forests in the far north of Europe. **c Sombre Tit,** *Parus lugubris:* 14 cm; crown, nape and throat brownish black, beak powerful; resident in Balkan forests; much like Great Tit in behaviour, but does not join mixed flocks after breeding.

a ***Silver-washed Fritillary,*** *Argynnis paphia:* wingspan 6 cm; 7–8; three rows of black spots on the edges of the wings; lays eggs on violets, nettles, raspberries and blackberries.
b ***Purple Emperor,*** *Apatura iris:* 6.5 cm; 6–8; fore and hind wings have a broad, white band, hind wings a dark, red-edged eye, purple sheen on ♂; eggs on sallow and poplar; usually flies high, especially over oak woods. Both species belong to the Tortoiseshell Family.
c Grayling, *Eumenis semele:* 5.5 cm; 6–9; upper side dark brown with yellowish bands, fore wings with two eye-spots, hind wings with one; eggs on grasses; belongs to the Browns Family and is found in open country and deciduous forests.

Satyrus hermione and *Pararge achine* belong to the Browns Family, the remainder to the Tortoiseshell Family. All are native throughout most of Europe. *Satyrus hermione* is confined to the south and east, where its caterpillars live on grasses. The Poplar Admiral lays its eggs on aspens and Lombardy poplars, the Dark Green Fritillary on dog violets, *Araschnia levana* on nettles, and *Pararge achine* on various grasses.

	Poplar Admiral	*Dark Green Fritillary				
Scientific Name	*Limenitis populi*	*Mesoacidalia charlotta*	*Satyrus hermione*	*Araschnia levana* form *prorsa*	*Araschnia levana*	*Pararge achine*
Size; Flying	♂ 6 cm; 6–7	5.5 cm; 6–8	6.5 cm; 7–8	3.5 cm; 7–9	♂ 2.7 cm; 4–5	4.5 cm; 6–7
Distinguishing Features	♀ larger (7.5 cm), with white bands and rust-red moon-like spots on hind wings, ♂ often without bands	Reddish yellow with black spots above, hind wing greenish with iridescent spots beneath	Broad yellow-ish white wing-bands with two small eye-spots	Upper side black with light cross-bands and narrow reddish brown lines	♀ larger (3.5 cm), upper side reddish yellow with blackish spots, white spots at wing tips	Upper side brownish, wings each with a row of dark, yellow-bordered spots

a ***Purple Hairstreak,*** *Quercusia quercus:* 3.5 cm; 6–8; upper surface dark violet-blue; eggs laid on oaks. **b** ***Brown Hairstreak,*** *Thecla betulae:* ♂ 3.3 cm, ♀ slightly larger; 7–8; ♂ with a black spot, ♀ also a reddish yellow spot, on the fore wing; eggs on sloes.
c ***Silver-studded Blue,*** *Lycaena argus:* 2.8 cm; 6–7; ♂ bluish, ♀ dark brown; eggs on melilots and mountain clover. **d** ***Large Blue,*** *Lycaena arion:* ♂ 2.3 cm, ♀ 2.7 cm; 3–5; upper surface of wings blue, under surface speckled brown; eggs on wild thyme; the caterpillars produce honey-dew and are very attractive to ants, always being found in association with them. All are members of the Blues Family.

a ***Pine Beauty,** *Panolis flammea:* 3.3 cm; 3–5; fore wings reddish brown with multi-coloured camouflaging cross-bands; Noctuid Moth Family. b ***Pine Hawk Moth,** *Hyloicus pinastri:* 8.5 cm; 4–8; fore wings greyish brown, with dark wedge-shaped spots; a member of the Hawk Moth Family; rare in Great Britain. c ***Green Tortrix,** *Tortrix viridana:* 2 cm; 6–7; fore wings light green, hind wings grey; caterpillars make cigar-shaped rolls out of oak leaves; Tortrix Family. All three lay their eggs on pines or oaks. The caterpillars of the Pine Beauty and Green Tortrix are woodland pests and may entirely defoliate large areas of trees.

Some common moths are described below. Most of them are very difficult to see, even when they are present in some numbers, because of the camouflaging effect of the colours of their wings. They rest during the day and are active at night. Some of these moths are orchard pests; the caterpillars which hatch from the large batches of eggs which they lay can completely defoliate the trees.

	*Black Arches		***Lackey**	***Gipsy**	***Pale Tussock**	***Buff-tip**
Scientific Name	*Lymantria monacha*	*Dendrolimus pini*	*Malacosoma neustria*	*Lymantria dispar*	*Dasychira pudibunda*	*Phalera bucephala*
Size; Flying	5 cm; 7–8	♂ 7 cm; 7–8	♂ 4 cm; 7–8	♂ 4 cm; 8–9	♀ 5 cm; 7–9	6 cm; 5–6
Distinguishing Features	Fore wings white with dark zigzag bands, back of abdomen with rose-red bands	♀ larger; snow-white moon-shaped spot on fore wings	♀ larger; fore wings with two reddish or yellowish cross-bands	♂ brownish, ♀ larger, (6.8 cm) whitish, fore wings of both with black cross-bands	♀ fore wings whitish grey, with darker cross-bands, ♂ darker	Large yellow spot on tips of fore wings, resembles a broken dead twig when at rest

a **Processionary-caterpillar Moth,** *Thaumatopoea processionea:* ♂ up to 2.9 cm; ♀ up to 3.2 cm; 8–9; fore wings with dark cross-lines; caterpillars gregarious, travel in single file; Notodontid Moth Family. b **Bordered White,** *Bupalus piniaria:* 2 cm; 5–6; ♂ yellowish white, edges of wings sepia, ♀ rusty yellow. c **Peppered Moth,** *Biston betularis:* 5.5 cm; 5–6; wings chalk-white, black-spotted. b and c belong to the Geometer Moth Family, and are common on oaks, pines and birches. The Peppered Moth is often completely black in the neighbourhood of large towns, and so camouflaged on foliage made sooty by air pollution.

a *Stag Beetle,** *Lucanus cervus:* 2–7.5 cm; ♂ with 'antlers' up to 2.6 cm long, used in fighting for mates. In spite of their ferocious appearance they are quite harmless, the larvae feeding only on rotten wood and the adult, which is short-lived, probably not feeding at all. **b** *Dorcus Beetle,** *Dorcus parallelopipedus:* 1.2–2.2 cm; 5–6; body dull black, thorax very wide, ♂ with elongated mandibles; adults feed on exuding tree sap. **c** *Platycerus caraboides:* 1.1–1.3 cm; 4–5; upper side green or blue, elytra finely dotted; eats the buds of oaks and other trees. **d** *Dor Beetle,** *Geotrupes stercorosus:* 1.1–1.7 sm; 6–9; upper side bluish black; lives on dung.

The Cockchafer and its relatives are more or less common throughout Europe. The May Bug or Common Cockchafer and the June Bug or Midsummer Chafer feed on tree foliage, the Walker, which is a rare migrant to Britain, on pine needles; the larvae live in the ground as grubs for several years and feed on roots. The Bronze Anomala is found on bushes and cereal crops. The larvae of the Rose Chafer and Rhinoceros Beetle develop in rotten tree-stumps. May and June Bugs are attracted to lights at night.

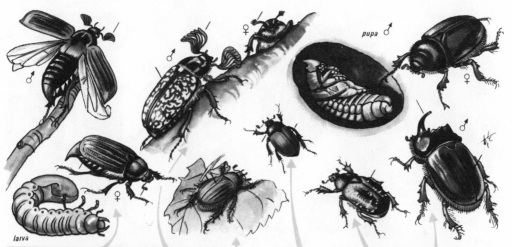

	*May Bug	*Walker	*June Bug	*Bronze Anomala	*Rose Chafer	European Rhinoceros Beetle
Scientific Name	Melolontha melolontha	Polyphylla fullo	Amphimallon solstitialis	Anomala dubia	Cetonia aurata	Oryctes nasicornis
Size; Flying	2.5 cm; 5–6	3.5 cm; 6–7	1.7 cm; 6–7	1.5 cm; 6–7	2.2 cm; 5–6	3.7 cm; 6–7
Distinguishing Features	Abdomen with black and white jagged bands, ♂ with large, ♀ small, club on antennae	Pronotum and elytra with white marbled veins, ♂ with large, ♀ small, club on antennae	Similar to the May Bug but smaller, head reddish yellow, elytra pale yellow	Head and pronotum green, elytra yellow or green	Beetle shining golden-green, elytra with white spots	Body shining chestnut-brown, ♂ with horn 10 mm long

a *Cerambyx cerdo:* 3–5 cm; 6–7; antennae very long, pronotum with one spine on each side. **b** *Lamia textor:* 2.6–3.2 cm; 5–6; body broad, first segment of antennae very thick. **c** *Large Poplar Longhorn,** *Saperda carcharias:* 2.4–3 cm; 6–7; upper side covered with thick yellow-brown downy hairs, spotted black. **d** *House Longhorn,** *Hylotrupes bajulus:* 0.9–2 cm; 5–7; brown or black, wings with two whitish haired bands; larvae make oval holes, often in house timbers. All are members of the Longhorn Beetle Family, the larvae of which burrow in wood and may be serious pests of forest trees, or in the case of the House Longhorn in cut timber.

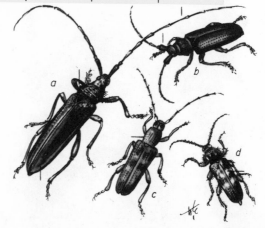

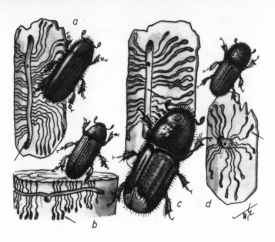

a Pine-shoot Beetle, *Blastophaga piniperda:* 3.8–4.4 mm; 3–4; larva lives in pines, main bore-hole slightly crooked. **b** *Blastophaga minor:* 3.5–4 mm; 4–5; also in pines, main bore-hole horizontal, larva-runs vertical, short. **c** *Ips typographicus:* 6 mm; 4–5 and 7–8; in pines, main bore-hole almost straight. **d** *Cryphalus piceae:* 1.5–2 mm; 3–4 and 6; lives on firs, main bore-hole small, room-like, eating pattern star-shaped. All belong to the Bark Beetle Family, which lay their eggs under bark inside niches in a main bore-hole. The larvae do not bore deeply into the wood, but make a series of tunnels which may often be seen when the bark is stripped off a tree or log.

Small members of the Weevil Family are described below. This group includes the True Weevils (with angled antennae) and their relatives, the Leaf Rollers. All are native throughout Europe and lay their eggs in skilfully constructed leaf-rolls or in bore-holes in fruit. The Birch Leaf Roller Weevil forms bags with birch leaves, *Attelabus nitens* with oak leaves, and the Nut Apoderus with hazel leaves; *Byctiscus betulae* rolls vine leaves. Nut Weevils lay eggs in hazel nuts, Pine Weevils on roots.

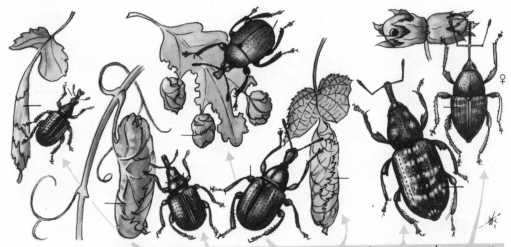

	*Birch Leaf Roller Weevil			*Nut Apoderus	*Pine Weevil	*Nut Weevil
Scientific Name	*Deporaus betulae*	*Byctiscus betulae*	*Attelabus nitens*	*Apoderus coryli*	*Hylobius abietis*	*Curculio nucum*
Size: Flying	4.4 mm; 5–7	6 mm; 4–5	6 mm; 5–6	6–8 mm; 4–5	9–13 mm; 4–9	6–7 mm; 5–6
Distinguishing Features	Body shining black; head small, ♀ constructs rolls out of birch leaves	Body green or blue, ♂ with spine on each side of pronotum; ♀ makes cigar-shaped roll	Elytra red; ♀ makes rolls with oak leaves	Head black, thorax, elytra and upper leg joints red; ♀ rolls hazel leaves	Chestnut-brown or black, matt, elytra with rust-yellow cross spots	Body ovate, brown, elytra spotted; ♀ bores into hazel nuts

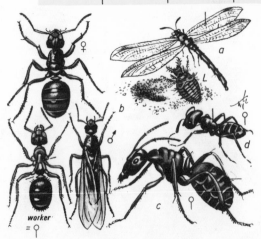

a Ant Lion, *Myrmeleon formicarius:* 2–3 cm, wingspan 6.5 cm; 7–8; four similar net-veined wings; larva (L) lies hidden in a pit which it digs in the sand, feeding on ants which fall in and cannot climb out; belongs to the Lacewing Order. **b** *Wood Ant, Formica rufa:* 5–11 mm; 6–9; thorax and scale red, abdomen black; builds large hills, especially in coniferous woods. **c** *Camponotus herculeanus:* 8 to 14 mm; 6; reddish brown, abdomen black. **d** *Lasius fuliginosus:* ♀ up to 5 mm; 7–8; shining black, nests in tree-stumps. **b, c** and **d** are all common species belonging to the Ant Family.

a *Oak-apple Gall-wasp, Diplolepis quercus-folii:* up to 4 mm; 5–6; gall spherical, up to 2 cm in diameter, adult wasp with long wings. **b *Rose Gall-wasp,** Diplolepis rosae:* up to 5 mm; abdomen red and black, gall (bedeguar) with woolly, curly fibres, up to 5 cm in diameter, called 'robin's pincushion'. Both belong to the Gall-wasp Family. **c *Mikiola fagi:*** up to 3 mm; 6–7; gall ovate, pointed, smooth, found on beech leaves; belongs to the Gall-gnat Family. **d Eastern Spruce Gall-aphid,** *Sacciphantes abietis:* aphid very small, yellowish green, gall cone-like, gall scales with spikes; belongs to the Gall-aphid Family and is found in spruce woods.

The Birch Sawfly is a leaf-eating relative of bees and wasps; its grub feeds on birch trees. *Xeris spectrum* and the Great Wood-wasp bore holes in coniferous trees and lay their eggs in them; their larvae feed on the wood. The Great Black Ichneumon can bore over 2 cm through wood with its ovipositor to reach the larvae of wood-wasps, on which it lays its eggs. *Therion circumflexum* attaches its eggs to caterpillars. The Sand Wasp female paralyses caterpillars and drags them into a prepared hole as food for its young.

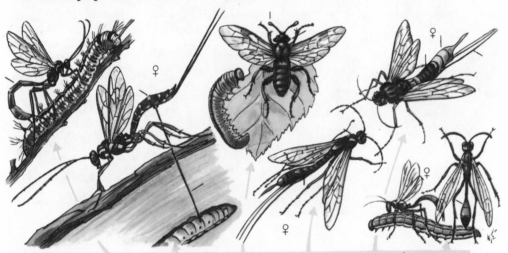

		*Great Black Ichneumon	*Birch Sawfly		*Great Wood-wasp	*Sand Wasp
Scientific Name	*Therion circumflexum	Rhyssa persuasoria	Cimbex femorata	*Xeris spectrum	Sirex gigas	Ammophila sabulosa
Size; Flying	3.5 cm; 5–8	4 cm; 5–8	2.5 cm; 5–6	4 cm; 4	4.5 cm; 7–8	2 cm; 6–9
Distinguishing Features	Abdomen curved like a sickle, ♀ with short ovipositor	Body black, abdomen with light spots, ovipositor of ♀ up to 6 cm long	Antennae knobbed, head widens behind the eyes	Body slender, black, first segment of thorax with two yellow lengthwise stripes	♂ abdomen reddish yellow, ♀ reddish yellow and black, with long ovipositor	Abdomen club-shaped, half red, half blue

a *Garden Cross Spider, Araneus diadematus:* ♂ 4–8 mm, ♀ 10–15 mm; yellowish brown, white cross on abdomen; an Orb-web Spider. **b *Crab Spider,** Misumena vatia:* ♂ 3–4 mm, ♀ 9–11 mm; 1st and 2nd pairs of legs very long; active in early summer, when it hides in flowers and changes colour to match the background, catching honey bees and other insects which come to feed. **c *Wolf Spider,** Pardosa prativaga:* ♂ and ♀ 4–6 mm; body covered with dark brown hairs with pattern of black and white; has good eyesight and hunts actively, not making a web. **d *Tarentula aculeata:*** ♂ and ♀ 8–12 mm; light lengthwise stripes. All are found in woods from Sweden to C Europe.

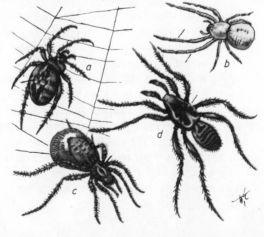

Heath, Moor and Tundra

These habitats are open, exposed, usually without trees, but characterized by dwarf shrubs, mosses and lichens. Heaths and moors are typical of the Northern Forest Belt, and Tundra of the Arctic. Heaths are similar to moors but are drier, and are of several types, e.g. Bell-heather Heath, Broom Heath, Crowberry Heath, Ling Heath; moors, with their wetter conditions, also have Bog Mosses, Bog Myrtle, Cottongrasses, Cranberries, Ledum, Marsh Andromeda, etc., and usually occur, in upland areas, as Heather Moor or Moss Moor. Tundra has 'cushion' herbs with dwarf shrubs, and in the short summer awakes from snow-covered sleep to the sounds of animals and birds among its profusion of flowers. Other areas included in this group of habitats are sandy tracts, sunny hillocks, and steppe-like places which, because of their variety of dwarf shrubs, superficially resemble bushy heaths. Typical steppes (as in Spain, Hungary, Rumania, Serbia, and southern Russia) occur on various dust-forming soils, the humus-rich 'black earth' in Russia and sand in Serbia, and have two resting periods during the year, one in the summer drought and one during the winter; their vegetation is characterized by annual and perennial herbs, and many of the dwarf shrubs have small leathery leaves.

A characteristic of the tundra area is the huge number of small insects which live there during the brief summer months. These are eaten by many of the migrant birds which during the long summer days hunt for food for their young. Many reptiles survive in the heath and moor areas, where there is little human activity to disturb them.

a *Juniper, *Juniperus communis:* shrub or small tree, evergreen, up to 10 m; procumbent to columnar, needles with a spiny point, fruits berry-like; 4–6; widespread; Cypress Family.
b *Sweet Gale or **Bog Myrtle**, *Myrica gale:* shrub up to 1.5 m; leaves lanceolate, serrate near the tip, dotted with resinous glands, fragrant, male catkin 7–15 mm, female 5–10 mm; 4–5; widely distributed, in bogs, on wet heaths and in fens; Bog Myrtle Family.
c Hare's-foot Greenweed, *Chamaespartium sagitalle:* shrub, 12–25 cm; stem broadly winged; 5–7; dry meadows, heaths, thickets and open woods of S and C Europe; Pea Family.

The members of the Pea Family shown below are shrubs occurring on heaths, moors, dry and poor grassland and pastures, and sometimes in open woodlands. The German Greenweed grows mostly in C and E Europe, the Petty Whin or Needle Furze in W Europe, northwards to S Sweden, and the Hairy Greenweed in W, C and northern S Europe. The other species are more widespread.

	German Greenweed	*Petty Whin	*Dyer's Greenweed	*Hairy Greenweed	*Gorse Furze	*Broom
Scientific Name	*Genista germanica*	*Genista anglica*	*Genista tinctoria*	*Genista pilosa*	*Ulex europaeus*	*Sarothamnus scoparius*
Size	30–60 cm	30–60 cm	30–70 cm	10–40 cm	Up to 150 cm	60–200 cm
Distinguishing Features; Flowering Time	Stem spiny, hairy, leaves hairy, flowers golden yellow, in terminal racemes; 5–6	Stem spiny, glabrous, leaves glabrous, flowers golden yellow, in short racemes; 5–6	Stem spineless, glabrous, leaves fringed on margins, flower glabrous, in terminal racemes; 6–7	Stem spineless, leaves densely hairy, flowers silky-hairy, 1–3 together in axils of leaves; 4–6	Stem densely spiny, flowers 1–3 together on short shoots, calyx with spreading hairs; 5–6	Twigs spineless, green, rod-like, 5-angled, flowers solitary, large, yellow; 5–6

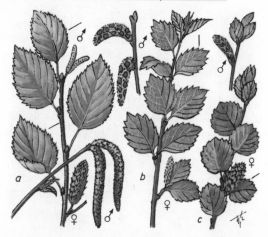

a *Common Birch, *Betula pubescens:* tree up to 20 m; young twigs hairy, leaves ovate, usually hairy at least on the veins beneath or in their axils; 4–5; widespread. **b Shrubby Birch**, *Betula humilis:* shrub, 50–150 cm; leaves blunt, longer than wide, up to 3.5 cm long, short-stalked, irregularly serrate; 4–5; N and C Europe. **c *Dwarf Birch**, *Betula nana:* shrub, 30–60 cm; leaves small, circular, broader than long; 4–5; in mountain moors in N and C Europe, and in tundra of the Arctic Zone. All are members of the Birch Family.

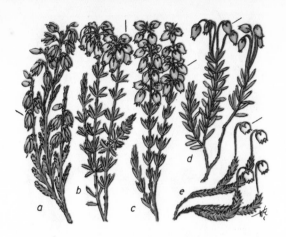

a *Heather or **Ling,** *Calluna vulgaris:* up to 60 cm; inflorescence terminal, raceme-like; 6–9; common. **b *Bog Heather** or **Cross-leaved Heath,** *Erica tetralix:* 10–60 cm; flowers in umbel-like clusters; 7–9; bogs and moors of W and C Europe, northwards to S Scandinavia. **c*Bell Heather,** *Erica cinerea:* 10–60 cm; inflorescence raceme-like; 6–7; dry heaths and moors of W Europe. **d *Blue Heather,** *Phyllodoce coerulea:* 10–20 cm; flowers in terminal clusters; 6–7. **e Moss Heather,** *Cassiope hypnoides:* up to 10 cm; flowers long-stalked; 6–7. **d** and **e** occur on rocky moorland of C Europe and in Arctic tundra. All are evergreen shrubs of the Heath Family.

The dwarf shrubs in the table belong to the Heath Family. All are evergreen, with the exception of the Common Bilberry or Whortleberry and the Bog Bilberry. The Marsh Andromeda occurs in N and C Europe, C Russia, mainly in mountains in the southern part of its distributional area. The Chamaedaphne usually grows on high moorlands of N Europe. All the other species are common on heaths and in lowland and mountain moors.

	*Cranberry	*Cowberry	*Common Bilberry	*Bog Bilberry	*Marsh Andromeda	Chamae-daphne
Scientific Name	*Vaccinium oxycoccus*	*Vaccinium vitis-idaea*	*Vaccinium myrtillus*	*Vaccinium uliginosum*	*Andromeda polifolia*	*Chamaedaphne calyculata*
Size	Up to 10 cm	10–30 cm	Up to 40 cm	25–35 cm	10–40 cm	Up to 100 cm
Distinguishing Features; Flowering Time	Flowers 1–4, with reflexed lobes, berries globe- or pear-shaped, red or brown-spotted, edible; 5–8	Leaves gland-dotted beneath, flowers in short terminal racemes, berries red, edible; 5–8	Twigs angled, flowers solitary, 5-lobed, berries black, glaucous, globose, sweet, edible; 5–6	Stem terete, flowers 1–4 in each axil, berries black, sweet, edible in small quantities; 5–6	Flowers pinkish red, long-stalked, nodding, in terminal umbellate clusters; 4–6	Leaves with rust-brown glands, whitish green beneath, flowers bell-shaped, white; 5–7

a *Bearberry, *Arctostaphylos uva-ursi:* evergreen shrub up to 30 cm; flowers 5-toothed; 5–9; widespread. **b *Marsh Tea** or **Wild Rosemary,** *Ledum palustre:* evergreen shrub, 50–100 cm; flowers in terminal racemes, leaves rusty downy beneath, with enrolled margins; 5–7; in bogs and woods of N Europe. **c Lapland Rose-bay,** *Rhododendron lapponicum:* shrub, 50–100 cm; flowers large, leaves ovate; in tundra of Scandinavia and Finland. All belong to the Heath Family. **d *Crowberry,** *Empetrum nigrum:* evergreen shrub, 15–60 cm; leaves needle-shaped, with a white keel; widespread on heaths; Crowberry Family.

a *Pasque Flower, *Pulsatilla vulgaris:* ♃, 3–50 cm; basal leaves bi- or tripinnate; 4–5; N and C Europe. **b Heath Anemone,** *Pulsatilla patens:* ♃, 5–50 cm; basal leaves palmate, usually ternate with leaflets also divided into 3 parts; 4–5; heaths and coniferous woods of E and EC Europe, northwards to Sweden. **c †Shaggy Anemone,** *Pulsatilla vernalis:* ♃, 3–30 cm; brown-hairy, outer perianth-segments often flushed violet; 4–5; on heaths in C Europe. **d Snowdrop Wind-flower,** *Anemone sylvestris:* ♃, 15–45 cm; perianth-segments silky-hairy beneath; 4–5; sunny slopes and open woods in N and C Europe. All belong to the Buttercup Family.

The Meadow Anemone is widespread but local on heaths and sunny slopes; Buttercup Family. The Hairy Stonecrop grows on peat-moors in N, W and C Europe; Stonecrop Family. All the other plants shown below belong to the Rose Family. The Cloudberry occurs in bogs and moors in N Europe, extending to S Germany and C Russia, the cinquefoils on heaths and in dry situations, mainly in C Europe.

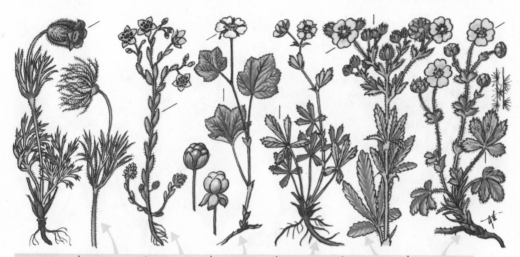

	Meadow Anemone	Hairy Stonecrop	*Cloudberry	Hill Cinquefoil	†Sulphur Cinquefoil	Sand Cinquefoil
Scientific Name	*Pulsatilla pratensis*	*Sedum villosum*	*Rubus chamaemorus*	*Potentilla collina*	*Potentilla recta*	*Potentilla arenaria*
Longevity, Size	♃, 5–50 cm	☉–♃, 5–20 cm	♃, 10–25 cm	♃, 10–30 cm	♃, 30–70 cm	♃, 15 cm
Distinguishing Features; Flowering Time	Flowers nodding, perianth-segments recurved at tip; 4–6	Usually glandular-hairy, sticky, leaves semi-terete, flat on upper surface; 7–8	Leaves heart-shaped to kidney-shaped, flowers solitary, terminal; 5–6	Stem often decumbent, leaves palmate with 5 leaflets, densely white-downy beneath; 5–8	Leaves palmate with 5–7 leaflets, inflorescence a many-flowered cyme, flowers 2–2.5 cm wide; 6–7	Leaves palmate mostly with 5 leaflets, petals 5–10 mm long; 4–5

a White Cinquefoil, *Potentilla alba:* ♃, up to 15 cm; leaflets with 1–4 teeth on each side towards the tip; 5–6; grassy slopes and open woods of E Europe and in mountain areas of C Europe. **b†Greyish Cinquefoil,** *Potentilla canescens:* ♃, up to 40 cm; leaves grey-downy beneath, stem long-hairy; 6–7; in dry habitats in E Europe and in mountains of C Europe. **c Green Strawberry,** *Fragaria viridis:* ♃, 4–35 cm; lateral leaflets stalkless, the terminal one with a short stalk; 5–6; widespread. **d †Agrimony,** *Aremonia agrimonoides:* ♃, 5–40 cm; flowers with 6–10-lobed involucre; 5–6; SE Europe, westwards to Italy and Austria. All belong to the Rose Family.

a **Yellow-flowered Broom**, *Cytisus nigricans*: shrub, 50–120 cm; flowers in upright racemes, leaves composed of 3 leaflets; 6–7; in S, SE and C Europe. b **Trailing Broom**, *Cytisus supinus*: shrub, 60–120 cm; flowers in twos to sixes, in terminal head-like inflorescences; 6–9; in most of Europe. c **Twin Broom**, *Cytisus ratisbonensis*: shrub, 15–60 cm; flowers in twos or threes in the axils of leaves; 5–6; C Europe. d **Spring Vetchling**, *Lathyrus vernus*: ⳇ, 10–40 cm; leaves with 2 or 3 pairs of ovate leaflets; 4–5; in most of Europe. All are members of the Pea Family, found on sunny hills and in hedges.

The Spring Vetch is widespread in grassy places, the Bitter Vetch grows scattered throughout Europe, in rocky and woody places, the Horse-shoe Vetch on dry pastures and cliffs in S and W Europe. All three belong to the Pea Family. The Hill Willow-herb (Willow-herb Family) is found in various parts of Europe, mainly on rocks and slopes; the Hoary Rock-rose and the Common Rock-rose, which both belong to the Rock-rose Family, are widespread, the former on rocky limestone pastures, the latter on basic grassland and in scrub.

	*Spring Vetch	*Bitter Vetch	*Horse-shoe Vetch	Hill Willow-herb	*Hoary Rock-rose	*Common Rock-rose
Scientific Name	*Vicia lathyroides*	*Vicia orobus*	*Hippocrepis comosa*	*Epilobium collinum*	*Helianthemum canum*	*Helianthemum chamaecistus*
Longevity, Size	ⳇ, 2–16 cm	ⳇ, 15–60 cm	ⳇ, 10–40 cm	ⳇ, 10–40 cm	ⳇ, 5–20 cm	ⳇ, 8–30 cm
Distinguishing Features; Flowering Time	Leaves pinnate, in pairs, rarely with a tendril, flowers solitary, small, lilac, 5–8 mm; 4–6	Leaves pinnate, without a tendril, flowers white, purpletinged with standard violet-veined; 5–6	Flowers 5–12 in umbel-like inflorescences, stalk curved, pod segments horse-shoe-shaped; 5–7	Leaves toothed, flowers 4–6 mm long, capsule with appressed glandless hairs; 6–9	Stem woody, leaves opposite, grey or white-downy beneath, stipules absent; 5–9	Stem woody, leaves opposite, stipules lanceolate, flowers yellow; 5–9

a ***White Rock-rose**, *Helianthemum apenninum*: shrubby ⳇ, up to 50 cm; leaves greydowny, with stipules; 5–7; S, C and W Europe. b ***Spotted Rock-rose**, *Tuberaria guttata*: ☉, 5–40 cm; basal leaves forming rosette; 5–8; Mediterranean, C Europe and Atlantic coast of Europe. c **Heath-rose**, *Fumana procumbens*: ⳇ, 10–20 cm; leaves needle-shaped; 6–8; sunny hillocks in Mediterranean and C Europe. All belong to the Rock-rose Family. d ***Teesdale Violet**, *Viola rupestris*: ⳇ, 4–6 cm; stipules deeply toothed; 4–5; on rocks, open mossy turf and open coniferous woods in N Europe and mountains of C Europe; in Britain, in upper Teesdale; Violet Family.

a *Common Sundew, Drosera rotundifolia:* ♃, 5–25 cm; leaves circular, long-stalked; 6–9. **b *Long-leaved Sundew,** Drosera intermedia:* ♃, 3–10 cm; leaves obovate, more or less erect, gradually tapering at the base into a long stalk; 6–8. **c *Great Sundew,** Drosera anglica:* ♃, 5–30 cm; leaves linear-oblong to narrowly obovate, gradually tapering at the base into a long stalk; 7–8. The leaves in these species form a rosette and are densely glandular and fringed with long glandular hairs. The sundews are insectivorous plants of the Sundew Family, growing on moorland.

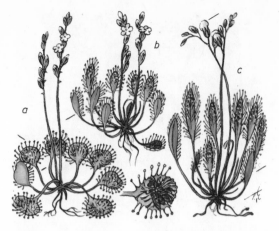

The Marsh St John's Wort (St John's Wort Family) occurs in bogs and wet places on acid soils, in Italy, W and C Europe. The Vervain Mallow (Mallow Family) grows in meadows, hedgerows and at the edges of woods in S and C Europe. The Long-stalked Cranesbill (Cranesbill Family) is widespread in dry grassland and in scrub. The Sticky Flax (Flax Family) grows in meadows and open scrub in mountain areas of S and C Europe. Both Milkworts (Milkwort Family) are widely distributed on heaths and in grassy places.

	*Marsh St John's Wort	†Vervain Mallow	*Long-stalked Cranesbill	Sticky Flax	*Thyme-leaved Milkwort	*Common Milkwort
Scientific Name	*Hypericum elodes*	*Malva alcea*	*Geranium columbinum*	*Linum viscosum*	*Polygala serpyllifolia*	*Polygala vulgaris*
Longevity, Size	♃, 6–8 cm	♃, 30–100 cm	☉, 15–45 cm	♃, 20–60 cm	♃, 10–20 cm	♃, 8–25 cm
Distinguishing Features; Flowering Time	Leaves and stem densely hairy, sepals with fine, red or purplish glandular teeth; 6–9	Stem with star-like hairs, leaves 3–7-lobed, flowers rose-red, in clusters; 6–9	Leaves deeply divided, flowers purplish pink, with very long and thin stalks; 5–9	Stem and leaves woolly, petals pink, with dark veins; 5–7	Lower leaves opposite, racemes with 3–8 flowers, sepals longer than capsule; 5–9	Leaves alternate, inner sepals longer and wider than the capsule; 5–8

a *Striated Catchfly, Silene conica:* ☉, 5–20 cm; inflorescence 1- to few-flowered, petals bifid with coronal scales at the base; 5–7. **b *Red German Catchfly,** Viscaria vulgaris:* ♃, 20–70 cm; stem very sticky beneath each node; 5–8. **c †Wall Gypsophila or Chalkwort,** *Gypsophila muralis:* ☉, 4 to 18 cm; flowers pink, with dark veins; 6–10. **d †Spring Spurrey,** *Spergula morisonii:* ☉, 5–50 cm; leaves not furrowed beneath, petals ovate; 4–7. These species grow scattered throughout Europe; all belong to the Pink Family.

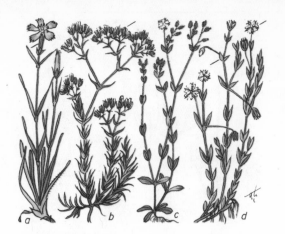

a *Cheddar Pink, *Dianthus gratianopolitanus:*
♃, 5–25 cm; flowers usually solitary, calyx-
tube 16–20 mm long; 5–7; W and C Europe,
rare in Britain (N Somerset). b *Perennial
Knawel, *Scleranthus perennis:* ♃, 3–35 cm;
sepals blunt, incurved over the ripe fruit;
5–8; widespread. c *Bearded Mouse-ear
Chickweed, *Cerastium brachypetalum:* ⊙-⊙,
8–25 cm; fruit-stalks about twice as long as
calyx; 5–6; in various parts of Europe (in Britain: Bedfordshire). d Thick-leaved Stitchwort, *Stellaria crassifolia:* ♃, 5–20 cm;
bracts herbaceous, petals 2–3 mm long; 5–8;
marshy meadows and bogs in the Arctic and
mountain areas of C Europe. All belong to the
Pink Family.

The Dwarf Cornel, a rare member of the Cornel Family, occurs on moors on mountains in
Arctic Europe, extending southwards to N Germany. The Bog Pimpernel (Primrose Family)
grows in damp peaty and grassy places and bogs of Atlantic, C and S Europe. The Slender
Cicendia, the Yellow-wort and the Bladder-shaped Gentian belong to the Gentian Family and
grow on moors, the latter mainly in the Alps. The Wild Thyme is a widespread member of the
Thyme Family.

	*Dwarf Cornel	*Bog Pimpernel	*Slender Cicendia	*Yellow-wort	Bladder-shaped Gentian	*Wild Thyme
Scientific Name	*Chamaepericly-menum suecicum*	*Anagallis tenella*	*Cicendia filiformis*	*Blackstonia perfoliata*	*Gentiana utriculosa*	*Thymus serpyllum*
Longevity, Size	♃, 10–15 cm	⊙, 5–15 cm	⊙, 1–12 cm	⊙, 5–50 cm	⊙ 7–30 cm	♃, 7–25 cm
Distinguishing Features; Flowering Time	Flowers red-brown, with 4 white involucral bracts; berries red; 5	Stem prostrate, leaves with short stalks, flowers pink, with thread-like stalks; 7–8	Stem simple or branched, leaves small, flowers golden yellow, long-stalked, tetra-merous; 7–10	Leaves ovate-triangular, opposite, fused at the base, flowers hexa-merous to octa-merous; 6–8	Calyx with broadly winged margins, cor-olla pentamer-ous, dark blue, style deeply split; 6–8	Stem hairy all round, leaves small, firm, involute at the margin, calyx 2-lipped; 4–9

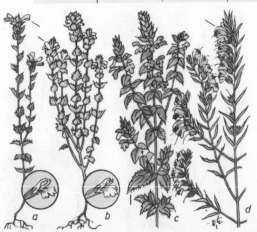

a *Slender Eyebright, *Euphrasia micrantha:*
⊙, 3–20 cm; stem with few branches; 6–9.
b *Small-flowered Eyebright, *Euphrasia
curta:* ⊙, 3–20 cm; upper lip densely hairy on
the outside; 6–10. Both grow on heaths and
dry grasslands in N and C Europe. c *Red
Bartsia, *Odontites verna:* ⊙, 7–50 cm; leaves
remotely toothed; 5–11; widespread. d Yellow Bartsia, *Odontites lutea:* ⊙, 15–50 cm;
flowers yellow; 5–11; in grassy places and
in scrub in S and C Europe. All these plants
are members of the Figwort Family.

a Marsh Cow-wheat, *Melampyrum paludosum:* ⊙, 10–30 cm; bracts not toothed; 7–8; mountain areas of C Europe; Figwort Family.
b *Squinancy Wort, *Asperula cynanchica:* ♃, 5–40 cm; cymes few-flowered, stem four-angled, glabrous; 6–9; calcareous grassy places and sand dunes in C and SE Europe.
c *Three-lobed Woodruff, *Asperula tinctoria:* ♃, 15–50 cm; flowers in forked cymes, corolla three-lobed; 6–7; rocky slopes and grassy places on calcareous soils of SE and C Europe. **d *Fen Bedstraw,** *Galium uliginosum:* ♃, 5–40 cm; stem four-angled, leaves 5–8 in a whorl; 5–9; on moors and in fens, widespread. **b, c** and **d** belong to the Bedstraw Family.

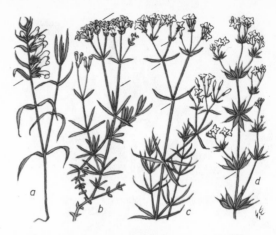

The King Charles Sceptre, the Red-rattle and the louseworts belong to the Figwort Family. The King Charles Sceptre grows dispersed in N and C Europe, the Many-leaved Lousewort in the Swabian Jura and in the N and S Alps, the others are common on moors and peatfields. The butterworts belong to the Butterwort Family; they are found on mountains up to 2300 m but also grow on low ground.

	King Charles Sceptre	Many-leaved Lousewort	*Red-rattle	*Lousewort	*Common Butterwort	*Alpine Butterwort
Scientific Name	*Pedicularis sceptrum-carolinum*	*Pedicularis foliosa*	*Pedicularis palustris*	*Pedicularis sylvatica*	*Pinguicula vulgaris*	*Pinguicula alpina*
Longevity, Size	♃, 25–100 cm	⊙–♃,15–50cm	♃, 6–80 cm	♃, 2–20 cm	♃, 5–18 cm	♃, 5–15 cm
Distinguishing Features; Flowering Time	Leaves pinnatisect, flowers up to 3.2 cm long, yellow, lower lip edged with red; 7–8	Flowers pale yellow, upper lip densely woolly, raceme with leaves; 6–8	Flowers solitary, in leaf-axils, light red, rarely white, calyx-teeth leaf-like; 5–7	Branches decumbent, flowers pale red, rarely white, calyx 5-toothed; 5–6	Leaves radical, sticky, flowers violet, spur 4–7 mm long; 5–8	Flowers white, with yellow spot at the throat, spur 2–3 mm long; 5–6

a Violet Butterwort, *Pinguicula leptoceras:* ♃, 5–18 mm; lower calyx lobe divided to base; 5–7; wet grassy places in the Alps, Pyrenees and mountains of SE Europe; Butterwort Family. **b Throat-wort,** *Campanula cervicaria:* ⊙-♃, 30–100 cm; plant bristly; 6–7; mainly in C and SE Europe. **c Siberian Bellflower,** *Campanula sibirica:* ⊙, 15–80 cm; leaves elongate–spathulate, forming a rosette; 6–8; C, S and SE Europe. **d *Clustered Bellflower,** *Campanula glomerata:* ♃, 15–90 cm; leaves heart-shaped at the base; 6–9; widespread. **b, c** and **d** are all members of the Bellflower Family.

75

a Hoary Scabious, *Scabiosa canescens:* ♃, 5–60 cm; basal leaves entire, marginal flowers symmetrical; 7–9; SE and C Europe. **b Yellow Scabious,** *Scabiosa ochroleuca:* ☉-♃, 30–130 cm; basal leaves deeply crenate, flowers yellowish white; 6–10; E and C Europe. **c *Small Scabious,** *Scabiosa columbaria:* ♃, 15–70 cm; leaves more or less hairy, flowers mostly bluish red; 6–10; widespread. All are members of the Teasel Family. **d Sand Jurinea,** *Jurinea cyanoides:* ♃, 25–75 cm; stem white-downy, leaves pinnatisect; 7–9; in sandy places, rich in chalk, in C Europe and in the steppe, on 'black earth' in SE Europe; Daisy Family.

The plants illustrated below belong to the Daisy Family. The Greater Goatsbeard has disc-florets, the others ligulate florets. All are widespread on heaths, dry hillocks, slopes and in open woods. The Italian Starwort, the Hairy Inula and the Greater Goatsbeard are absent in northern parts of Europe.

	Italian Starwort	*Cat's-foot	Yellow Everlasting	Hairy Inula	Wood Chrysanthemum	Greater Goatsbeard
Scientific Name	*Aster amellus*	*Antennaria dioica*	*Helichrysum arenarium*	*Inula hirta*	*Chrysanthemum corymbosum*	*Tragopogon dubius*
Longevity, Size	♃, 3–50 cm	♃, 2–25 cm	♃, 10–40 cm	♃, 30–75 cm	♃, 60–120 cm	☉, 30–90 cm
Distinguishing Features; Flowering Time	Leaves obovate, heads in cymes, ray-florets ligulate, blue-violet, in 1 row; 7–10	Leaves white-downy beneath, hermaphrodite heads with white, ♀ with pink outer bracts; 5–7	Plant white-woolly, outer bracts straw-yellow, dry, heads in umbellate racemes; 7–10	Stem and leaves bristly, heads solitary, rarely up to 3, golden yellow; 6–10	Leaves 1–3 times pinnate, ray-florets linear, white, 1–20 mm long; 6–8	Stem hollow, thickening in the upper part, outer bracts 10–12, longer than florets; 5–6

a Brook Ragwort, *Senecio rivularis:* ♃, 20–60 cm; basal leaves heart-shaped, lower stem leaves with broadly winged stalks; 4–8; in moist grassy places in C Europe. **b Brook Thistle,** *Cirsium salisburgense:* ♃, 30–150 cm; stem white-downy, leafy in the lower part, heads 2–4, terminal; 6–7; widespread, in moist meadows, bogs and on moors, but absent in the southern parts of Europe. **c †Small-eared Hawkweed,** *Hieracium lactucella:* ♃, 2 to 25 cm; basal leaves spathulate, glaucous, shining, heads 2–5; 5–8; widespread. All are members of the Daisy Family.

a Common False-asphodel, *Tofieldia caly-culata:* ♃, 5–50 cm; inflorescence spike-like, dense, styles free; 6–9; widespread in alpine peat meadows or on calcareous soils. **b *Bog-asphodel,** *Narthecium ossifragum:* ♃, 10 to 40 cm; inflorescence racemose, flowers long-stalked, style 1; 6–8; in bogs and on wet heaths and moors, becoming rarer or absent in southern parts of Europe. Both belong to the Lily Family. **c †Pale-blue Iris,** *Iris spuria:* ♃, 30–60 cm; stem terete, pithy, leaves 5–12 mm wide; 5; wet meadows and moors of C Europe and S Russia; Iris Family.

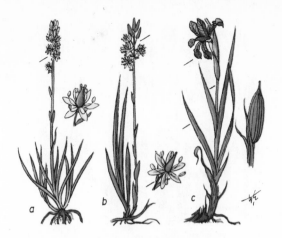

The White Sedge is widespread in bogs, fens and marshes throughout Europe, except the south. The others grow scattered on moors and peat meadows; the Many-stemmed Spike-rush in S and W Europe, northwards to S Scandinavia; the Rust-red Bogrush in C Europe, northwards to Scandinavia, in Britain very local (in mid-Perth); the Black Bogrush in mountain areas up to 1500 m, in S and C Europe northwards to Denmark and S Norway. All belong to the Sedge Family.

	*Many-stemmed Spike-rush	*Black Bogrush	*Rust-red Bogrush	*White Beak-sedge	*Brown Beak-sedge	*White Sedge
Scientific Name	*Eleocharis multicaulis*	*Schoenus nigricans*	*Schoenus ferrugineus*	*Rhynchospora alba*	*Rhynchospora fusca*	*Carex curta*
Longevity, Size	♃, 15–50 cm	♃, 15–50 cm	♃, 15–30 cm	♃, 10–50 cm	♃, 10–30 cm	♃, 10–45 cm
Distinguishing Features; Flowering Time	Plant densely tufted, spikelet solitary, up to 13 mm long, stigmas 3; 5–7	Stem leafless, spikelets 5–10 in each head, lowest bracts 2–5 times as long as inflorescence; 5–7	Spikelets 2–3 in each head, lowest bract shorter than or just longer than inflorescence; 5–7	Stem leafy, spikelets whitish, in cyme, perianth of 9–13 bristles; 7–9	Stem leafy, spikelets yellowish brown, perianth of 5–6 bristles; 6–7	Leaves 2–3 mm wide, pale green, spikes 5–10 mm long, 3–8 in inflorescence, ♂ below; 5–8

a *Hare's-tail Cottongrass, *Eriophorum vaginatum:* ♃, 10–50 cm; stem terete below, three-angled above, spike solitary, erect; 3. **b *Common Cottongrass,** *Eriophorum angustifolium:* ♃, 20–60 cm; heads 3–7, stalks smooth; 4–5. **c *Broad-leaved Cottongrass,** *Eriophorum latifolium:* ♃, 15–70 cm; heads 2–12, stalks rough; 4–6. **d *Slender Cottongrass,** *Eriophorum gracile:* ♃, 10 to 60 cm; spikes 3–5, erect, stalks rough. All are members of the Sedge Family growing in wet bogs and damp peaty places.

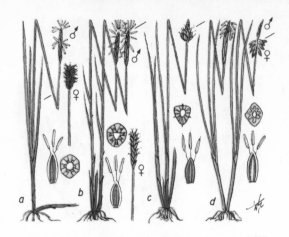

a *****Dioecious Sedge,** *Carex dioica:* ♃, 5–30 cm; plant usually dioecious, stem smooth, spike unisexual or nearly so; 4–5.
b *****Davall's Sedge,** *Carex davalliana:* ♃, 5–35 cm; plants densely tufted, stem rough, spike loose, dioecious; 4–5; C Europe.
c *****Round-headed Sedge,** *Carex capitata:* ♃, 15–20 cm; plants densely tufted, stigmas 2, infructescence up to 8 mm long; 5–6; widespread, mainly in N Europe (in Britain: South Uist, Outer Hebrides). **d** *****Flea Sedge,** *Carex pulicaris:* ♃, 5–25 cm; loosely tufted, inflorescence 1–2 cm long, ♂ above, ♀ below, stigmas 2; 5. All are uncommon members of the Sedge Family; peat meadows and on moors.

All the plants illustrated below are sedges with several spikes of similar appearance on the same plant. They occur in scattered localities or are rare or very rare on moors and in peaty places. The Peat Sedge grows in Scandinavia, N Russia and in some places in C Europe; the Rye-grass Sedge in Finland and Scandinavia, E Prussia and Russia; the Delicate Sedge in northern parts of Europe. The Slender Sedge is found in N and C Europe, up to 1300 m in mountainous districts.

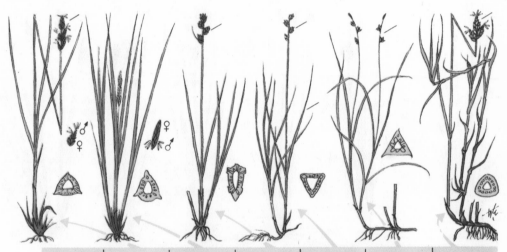

	*****Strange Sedge**	*****Slender Sedge**	**Peat Sedge**	**Rye-grass Sedge**	**Delicate Sedge**	*****Cord-rooted Sedge**
Scientific Name	*Carex appropinquata*	*Carex elongata*	*Carex heleonastes*	*Carex loliacea*	*Carex disperma*	*Carex chordorrhiza*
Longevity, Size	♃, 30–60 cm	♃, 30–50 cm	♃, 10–30 cm	♃, up to 30 cm	♃, up to 20 cm	♃, 5–25 cm
Distinguishing Features; Flowering Time	Leaves 2–3 mm wide, spikes distinctly stalked, ♂ above, ♀ below, leaf-sheaths black; 5–6	Plant rough, spikes 8–12 in loose inflorescence, ♂ above, ♀ below, fruit with entire beak; 5–6	Upper stem very rough, sharply 3-angled, spikes globose, fruits ovate, grey-brown; 5–6	Leaves glaucous, very narrow, spikes 3–5-flowered, ♂ below, fruits without beak; 5	Spikes 2–4, very delicate, distant, 1–3-flowered; 5–6	Rhizome giving off lateral sterile shoots, head-like inflorescence, leaf-sheaths red-brown; 5–6

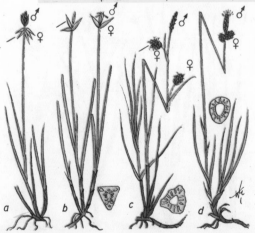

a *****Small-bristle Sedge,** *Carex microglochin:* ♃, 7–15 cm; spike 1 cm long, fruits deflexed when ripe, narrowly conical, with 'awns'; 5.
b *****Few-flowered Sedge,** *Carex pauciflora:* ♃, 5–16 cm; ♂ flowers 1–2 above, ♀ 2–6 below; 6–7. Both are plants with solitary spikes.
c *****Mud Sedge,** *Carex limosa:* ♃, 15–45 cm; ♂ spike 1, ♀ spikes 1–2, nodding; 5. **d** *****Heath Sedge,** *Carex ericetorum:* ♃, 5–25 cm; ♂ glumes with a rounded transparent tip, finely fringed, fruits hairy; 4–5. All belong to the Sedge Family.

a *Thread Rush, *Juncus filiformis:* ♃, 5 to 50 cm; inflorescence 5–7-flowered, usually placed halfway or lower down the visible stem; 6–9. **b *Heath Rush,** *Juncus squarrosus:* ♃, 15–50 cm; leaves radical, numerous, wiry, grooved, reflexed, inflorescence loose, erect, the stems ending in clusters of 2–3 flowers; 6–7. **c Sand Rush,** *Juncus tenageia:* ☉, 5 to 25 cm; inflorescence with sickle-like branches; 6–8; in S and C Europe. **d Moor Rush,** *Juncus stygius:* ♃, 10–30 cm; stem with 2–3 leaves, inflorescence usually 2–3-flowered; 7–9; in N and C Europe. These species belong to the Rush Family, and grow on heaths and moorlands.

The orchids illustrated below are rare species occurring on moorlands and in peat bogs, mostly in N and C Europe. The Lesser Twayblade grows not only on peaty moors, but also in damp mountain woods. All belong to the Orchid Family.

	*Bog Orchid	Marsh Orchid	*Crimson Marsh Orchid	*Lesser Twayblade	*Fen Orchid	One-leaved Malaxis
Scientific Name	*Hammarbya paludosa*	*Orchis palustris*	*Dactylorhiza incarnata*	*Listera cordata*	*Liparis loeselii*	*Malaxis monophyllos*
Longevity, Size	♃, 5–15 cm	♃, 20–60 cm	♃, 20–50 cm	♃, 4–20 cm	♃, 7–20 cm	♃, 7–45 cm
Distinguishing Features; Flowering Time	Flowers in many-flowered raceme, lip acute, erect, with its base clasping the column; 7–8	Stem hollow, leaves up to 1 cm wide, flowers purple, rarely pink to whitish, spur straight; 6–7	Stem tubular, leaf-blades broadest at base, usually unspotted, lip obscurely 3-lobed; 5–7	Leaves 2, thin, raceme few-flowered, lip reddish, with 2 lateral lobes; 5–8	Leaves 2, greasy-looking and shining, flowers 3–10 in loose raceme, lip entire; 6–8	Leaf single, sometimes 2, inflorescence many-flowered, flowers yellow, lip points upwards; 6–7

a *Sharp-flowered Rush, *Juncus acutiflorus:* ♃, 30–100 cm; perianth-segments acute, tapering to awn-like points, leathery brown; 7–9. **b *Blunt-flowered Rush,** *Juncus subnodulosus:* ♃, 40–120 cm; perianth-segments blunt, with wide scarious margins; 7–9. **c *Head-like Rush,** *Juncus capitatus:* ☉, 8–20 cm; inflorescence head-like, outer perianth-segments with fine recurved points; 6–9. All belong to the Rush Family and grow in scattered localities throughout Europe. **d *Purple Moor-grass,** *Molinia coerulea:* ♃, 30–150 cm; culm 1-noded, ligule a dense fringe of short hairs; 8–9; Grass Family; common in damp peaty moorland, heaths and in fens.

a *Forked Spleenwort, *Asplenium septentrionale*: ⚁, 8–15 cm; leaf comprising 2–5 linear pinnae and with the stalk longer than the blade; 7–8. b *Black Spleenwort, *Asplenium adiantum-nigrum*: ⚁, 15–40 cm; fronds leathery, triangular-ovate; 6–8. Both occur on rocky banks, in rock-crevices and walls, and belong to the Polypody Family, which is now regarded as comprising several families. c †Branched Moonwort, *Botrychium matricarifolium*: ⚁, up to 20 cm; sporophyll branched in the upper half of the leaf; 6–7; a rare species of the Adder's Tongue Family found on heaths and in open woodlands.

Clubmosses occur on moors, heaths, in woods or on poor grassland throughout Europe. The Fir Clubmoss and the Alpine Clubmoss are found in the mountainous districts of C Europe and in N Europe. The remainder are found scattered, or occasionally together, throughout the whole of Europe; only the Stag's-horn Clubmoss is commoner, particularly on heaths and in coniferous forests.

	*Marsh Clubmoss	*Fir Clubmoss	*Flattened Clubmoss	*Interrupted Clubmoss	*Stag's-horn Clubmoss	*Alpine Clubmoss
Scientific Name	*Lycopodium inundatum*	*Lycopodium selago*	*Lycopodium complanatum*	*Lycopodium annotinum*	*Lycopodium clavatum*	*Lycopodium alpinum*
Longevity, Size	⚁, 4–8 cm	⚁, 5–15 cm	⚁, up to 40 cm	⚁, up to 30 cm	⚁, up to 20 cm	⚁, up to 15 cm
Distinguishing Features; Sporing Time	Stems creeping 2–10 cm long, cones solitary, longer than 15 mm, leaves soft; 8–9	Stems upright, no cones, sporangia in leaf-axils, leaves narrow, rigid; 7–10	Stems creeping underground, cones 2–6, long-stalked, leaves 4-ranked, branches flat; 8–9	Stems creeping, over 1 m long, cones 1, stalkless, over 15 mm, leaves with spiny tips; 8–9	Stems creeping on the ground, up to 1 m long, cones 2–3, long-stalked, leaves spirally arranged; 7–8	Stems creeping on the ground, up to 60 cm long, leaves in 4 rows, cones 1–2, 10–15 mm long; 8–9

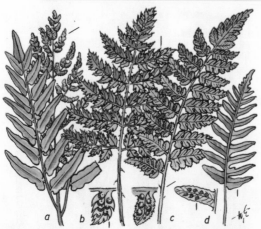

a *Royal Fern, *Osmunda regalis*: ⚁, 50 to 150 cm; spores produced on upper pinnae of inner fronds; 6–7; infrequent, in wet places; Royal Fern Family. b *Greater Bucklerfern, *Dryopteris dilatata*: ⚁, 15–100 cm; indusium fringed with stalked glands, segments with mucronate teeth; 7–9; widespread in woods, hedgebanks and rock-crevices. c *Crested Buckler-fern, *Dryopteris cristata*: ⚁, 30–50 cm; leaf-stalk half as long as blade; rather rare, on wet heaths, reed-beds and marshes. d *Common Polypody, *Polypodium vulgare*: ⚁, 9–30 cm; frond pinnate; 8–9; common on banks, walls, rocks and tree-trunks. All belong to the Polypody Family.

a Spiny Greenweed, *Genista aspathaloides:* shrub, 30–90 cm; branches twiggy, spiny, leaves small, deciduous, calyx with silky hairs; 6–8. **b Stinking Wood,** *Anagyris foetida:* shrub or small tree, 1–3 m; densely hairy, stinking, leaves of three leaflets, flowers yellow, often with a black spot; 12–3. **c Hairy Broom,** *Cytisus triflorus:* shrub, 2–4 m; flowers usually in threes to fives; 5–6. These species, which are members of the Pea Family, usually grow on dry hillocks in the Mediterranean region. The Stinking Wood is found also in hedgerows and in scrub (Maquis).

Dwarf shrubs are common in the Mediterranean region on poor soils on sunny hillocks and stony slopes. Many are spiny, e.g. Thorny Spurge, others sticky-hairy (Montpellier Rock-rose), or hairy (Rosemary and Tanner's Sumach). The leaves in nearly all are small and often leathery, e.g. Tree-like Spurge and French Lavender. The Montpellier Rock-rose belongs to the Rock-rose Family, the Thorny and Tree-like Spurges to the Spurge Family, the Rosemary and the French Lavender to the Thyme Family, the Tanner's Sumach to the Sumach Family.

	Montpellier Rock-rose	Thorny Spurge	Tree-like Spurge	Rosemary	French Lavender	Tanner's Sumach
Scientific Name	*Cistus monspeliensis*	*Euphorbia spinosa*	*Euphorbia dendroides*	*Rosmarinus officinalis*	*Lavandula stoechas*	*Rhus coriaria*
Longevity, Size	Shrub up 2 m	Shrub, 20 cm	Shrub, 1–2 m	Shrub, 50 cm	Shrub, 30 cm	Shrub, 1–3 m
Distinguishing Features; Flowering Time	Leaves sticky-hairy on both surfaces; 3–4	Branches of previous year spiny, cymes few-flowered; 12–3	Leaves glaucous, bracts yellow; 3–4	Leaves scented, linear, covered with white downy hairs; 3–10	Inflorescence with violet bracts, flowers small; 3–6	Plant densely white-hairy, fruits with red hairs; 5–7

a Prickly False-ivy, *Smilax aspera:* a shrubby, climbing, dioecious plant; leaves leathery with spiny teeth, berries red; 4; in stony places and on cliffs and walls; Lily Family. **b Dyer's** or **Scarlet Oak,** *Quercus coccifera:* evergreen shrub up to 2 m; leaves small, rigid, leathery, spiny-toothed, grey-downy beneath, ♂ flowers in catkins, ♀ flowers solitary; 4–5; Beech Family. **c Dwarf Palm,** *Chamaerops humilis:* woody evergreen, dioecious ♃, 3–4 m; leaves palmate with up to 15 segments, stem covered with fibrous remains of the leaves; 5–7; in stony places; Palm Family. All are Mediterranean plants.

a **Laxmann's Shrew**, *Sorex caecutiens:*
6.7 cm + 4.4 cm; a lot of white on belly and
throat; lives in the tundra and northern forests,
also in Poland. b **Pyrenean Desman**, *Galemys
pyrenaicus:* 13.5 cm + 15.5 cm, mobile snout
2 cm long; lives in well oxygenated rivers in
N and W Spain and Portugal. c **Shreiber's**
or **Long-winged Bat**, *Miniopterus schreibersi:*
6 cm + 6 cm; ears short, as if cut off; lives
in groups, often in large colonies, in open
countryside throughout S Europe. Schrei-
ber's Bats hibernate in caves or cellars. Laxmann's Shrew belongs to the Shrew Family,
the Pyrenean Desman to the Mole Family.

There are two forms of Arctic Fox: the White Fox is brown in summer and white in winter,
the Blue Fox brownish grey turning to bluish grey. Like the Glutton or Wolverine, which
belongs to the Weasel Family, and the Reindeer, they live in the northern tundra; the Reindeer
has been introduced into Scotland. The Saiga lives on the steppes of S Russia; at one time
nearly extinct, through careful conservation it is now common again. The Jackal lives in the
Balkans.

	Asiatic Jackal	Arctic Fox	Glutton	Saiga	Reindeer	Musk-ox
Scientific Name	*Canis aureus*	*Alopex lagopus*	*Gulo gulo*	*Saiga tatarica*	*Rangifer tarandus*	*Ovibos moschatus*
Size	105 cm + 24 cm	65 cm + 33 cm	82 cm + 15 cm	135 cm + 9 cm	215 cm + 15 cm	245 cm + 10 cm
Distinguishing Features	Similar to the Wolf (page 51) but smaller and redder, tail tip blunt	Ears small, tail single-coloured, no white tip (cf. Fox page 51)	Short-legged, thickset body dark brown, whitish front-let, yellowish flank and back markings	Arched, 'Roman' nose, ♂ with lyre-shaped horns, ♀ mostly without horns	♂ and ♀ with branched antlers, winter coat much paler than summer coat	Horns bent downwards; extinct in Europe, but reintroduced into Norway from America

a **European Souslik**, *Citellus citellus:* 22 cm
+ 7.5 cm; similar to a small Marmot (page
295), body without spots or only slightly spotted. **b Spotted Souslik**, *Citellus suslicus:*
26 cm + 4 cm; back white-spotted. Both are
found in steppe-like country in the east of the
U.S.S.R. **c Bobak Marmot**, *Marmota bobak:*
57.5 cm + 14.5 cm; similar to a marmot, but
tail shorter and almost single-coloured; native
to the southern U.S.S.R. and the Balkans.
All are rodents related to the Squirrels; they
hibernate through the winter in deep burrows,
and are active for a comparatively brief period
during each year.

Crane, *Grus grus:* 115 cm; plumage slate-grey, crown red, face and throat black, with white stripe curving from behind the eye; migrant, Crane Family; native in the whole of NE Europe where it nests on the ground on moorland tracts, in reed-beds or open marshy forests. The crane is normally very shy, but its mating dance is among the most spectacular bird displays. Migrating cranes fly in a V or line formation with neck and feet stretched out. They winter on the Mediterranean and further south, principally on riverbanks. During winter they avoid wooded country. They once bred in Great Britain, but now only appear there as rare visitors.

The Pheasant occurs through most of W and C Europe, the Black Grouse or Black Cock mainly to the east and north and in Scotland, N England and Devon, the Hazel Hen in C and E Europe. The legs of the Pheasant are unfeathered, those of the Black Grouse and Hazel Hen are feathered. The plumage of Pheasants is very variable because many forms are reared, but most have a white neck-ring. They nest on moors, in fields, and in mixed forests. Confusing hybrids occur between several species of game-bird.

	†Pheasant	*Black Grouse	Hazel Hen
Scientific Name	*Phasianus colchicus*	*Lyrurus tetrix*	*Tetrastes bonasia*
Size	♂ 89 cm, ♀ 64 cm	♂ 53 cm, ♀ 41 cm	♂ and ♀ 36 cm
Distinguishing Features	Very long pointed tail, ♂ very colourful, head and neck dark green, eye-patches scarlet, ♀ brown; resident	♂ tail lyre-shaped, plumage bluish black, white wing-bands, ♀ tail forked, plumage brown; resident	Tail fan-shaped, with a black band, ♂ black throat, head with small crest, ♀ whitish throat; resident

Pallid Harrier, *Circus macrourus:* 48 cm; the male is considerably whiter than the similar male of the Hen Harrier (which, however, has a large white rump-patch – page 201), breast, head and under parts white, rump grey, female larger than the male, brown, hardly distinguishable from the female of the Hen Harrier; partial migrant; a Bird of Prey. The Pallid Harrier nests in the U.S.S.R. on the ground on steppes, moors and fields, and winters in S Italy, the Balkans and the southern part of the Soviet Union, occurring also as a vagrant in other parts of Europe, including Great Britain.

male

female

*Marsh Harrier, *Circus aeruginosus*: 48–56 cm; flies with few wing-beats and long wavering glides; plumage variable; ♂ plumage more or less chestnut-brown, with large, bluish grey wing-coverts and tail, ♀ dark brown, crown, throat and shoulders light-coloured; partial migrant; a Bird of Prey. It occurs widely on marshes where there are many reed-beds; its display flight is spectacular, and involves the ♂ looping the loop; nest large, often entirely surrounded by water. Marsh Harriers are native throughout Europe with the exception of the north, and occur in SE England. They hunt low over the reed-beds and drop on their prey.

The snipe and curlews shown below nest on the ground between clumps of grass and heather in marshes and on moors. They are native throughout Great Britain and much of Europe. The others breed in N and NE Europe and winter further south. During its display flight the Snipe makes a peculiar drumming noise with its outer tail feathers; outside the breeding seasons, all of these birds are often found with huge flocks of other waders on sea-coasts and estuaries.

	*Snipe	Great Snipe	Jack Snipe	*Whimbrel	*Curlew
Scientific Name	*Capella gallinago*	*Capella media*	*Lymnocryptes minimus*	*Numenius phaeopus*	*Numenius arquata*
Size	27 cm	28 cm	19 cm	41 cm	53–58 cm
Distinguishing Features	Long, straight bill; zigzag flight; partial migrant	Similar to the Snipe, but with a lot of white on sides of tail; migrant	Bill relatively short, dark centre stripe on crown; migrant	Long decurved bill, crown clearly striped; migrant	Plumage closely striped, very long decurved bill; partial migrant

*Short-eared Owl, *Asio flammeus*: 38 cm; plumage yellowish brown, breast striped, ear-tufts very small, under parts with clear stripes; partial migrant, inhabits the whole of C and N Europe and Italy with the exception of the Alps. It is the only owl which normally hunts by day and may be recognized on the wing by its buoyant soaring flight; it also flies at dusk. The display flight includes wing-clapping by the male. It nests on the ground between clumps of heather and reeds on moors, marshy countryside, damp meadows and sand-dunes. Short-eared owls often congregate in areas where there are plagues of field voles.

a *Nightjar, *Caprimulgus europaeus:* 27 cm; head large, flattened, bill very small, very wide mouth, upper parts bark-coloured, under parts barred; difficult to see, but can be heard at night making a noise like a distant 2–stroke engine; migrant to almost the whole of Europe except the far north. **b Red-necked Nightjar**, *Caprimulgus ruficollis:* 32 cm; white throat-spot, rust-yellow neck-band; makes a noise like tapping on wood; migrant, nests in Spain and Portugal. Both inhabit woods and bushy moors where they lay their camouflaged eggs on the ground. During the day nightjars rest, usually lengthwise on branches or on the ground.

With the exception of the Ring Ouzel, which belongs to the Thrush Family, all the birds shown below are Waders. They nest on moors and heaths. The Stone Curlew or Thick Knee is found in SE England and in Europe south of Great Britain, the Ring Ouzel on high moorland in Great Britain, Scandinavia and S Europe. All the others nest in the far north and in E Europe and winter further south. The Golden Plover breeds in northern Great Britain, most of Scandinavia and parts of E Europe.

summer

winter

	*Temminck's Stint	Broad-billed Sandpiper	*Golden Plover	*Stone Curlew	*Ring Ouzel
Scientific Name	*Calidris temminckii*	*Limicola falcinellus*	*Charadrius apricarius*	*Burhinus oedicnemus*	*Turdus torquatus*
Size	14 cm	16.5 cm	28 cm	40 cm	24 cm
Distinguishing Features	Like the Little Stint (page 148), but greyer, legs yellowish or greenish; migrant	Doubled eye-stripe, upper parts dark with creamy white stripes; migrant	Upper parts golden brown, under parts light in winter, in summer black and white; partial migrant	White wing-bands, bill yellow and black, eyes large, yellow; partial migrant	♂ with white crescent on breast, plumage black, ♀ browner; partial migrant

a *Twite, *Carduelis flavirostris:* 13 cm; throat yellowish brown, ♂ rump reddish, ♀ rump yellowish brown with black stripes; keeps up constant twittering calls in flight; migrant; nests communally on moors in Norway and northern Great Britain, flocks of them move further south in winter. **b *Marsh Tit**, *Parus palustris:* 11.5 cm; shining black cap, small bib (cf. Willow Tit, page 116); resident throughout C Europe and England and Wales, nesting in holes in rotten trees, usually those growing by water. There is a northern form of the Marsh Tit which is generally paler in colour.

a–c **Willow Grouse**, *Lagopus lagopus:* 41 cm;
in summer (**a** and **b**) reddish brown with
white wings, in winter (**c**) white with black
tail and without facial markings; may be
confused with Ptarmigan (page 297); resident.
d *****Red Grouse**, *Lagopus scoticus:* 38 cm;
plumage reddish brown, wings and tail dark,
♂ larger and darker than ♀; resident. Both
are northern members of the Grouse Family
which nest on the ground on moors and
heaths; they are well camouflaged and will sit
still until danger is very close, when they fly
up steeply and noisily, startling the predator.
d is native to England and Scotland and has
been introduced into parts of Europe as a
game-bird.

The Black Vulture and the Bearded Vulture or Lammergeyer nest in trees or on rocks in plains
and remote mountain ranges in Spain, the Balkans and on many Mediterranean islands;
Bonelli's Eagle breeds in S Europe on steep cliff faces, the Long-legged Buzzard on the ground
in remote areas in Greece. All are rare vagrants further north, the vultures chiefly in the Alps.
All are Birds of Prey.

	Black Vulture	Bearded Vulture	Bonelli's Eagle	Long-legged Buzzard
Scientific Name	*Aegypius monachus*	*Gypaëtus barbatus*	*Hieraëtus fasciatus*	*Buteo rufinus*
Size	99–107 cm	102–114 cm	60–74 cm	61–66 cm
Distinguishing Features	Plumage uniformly dark brown, tail slightly wedge-shaped, black neck-ruff; resident	Tail long, wedge-shaped, head cream-coloured, black 'goat's beard'; resident	Upper parts dark brown, under parts silky white or cream-coloured, wing tips almost black; resident	Similar to the Buzzard (page 250), but tail light cinnamon colour, unbanded; resident

a **Sabine's Gull**, *Xema sabini:* 33 cm; a
northern gull; tail deeply forked, black-edged
in young, triangular white pattern on wings
very distinctive in flight, head in breeding
plumage slate-grey; builds no nest, partial
migrant. **b Arctic Redpoll**, *Carduelis horne-
manni:* 13 cm; crown carmine, under parts
light-coloured, rump white, unstriped, faintly
reddish on old ♂; migrant. **c Red-throated
Pipit**, *Anthus cervinus:* 15 cm; in breeding
plumage throat rust-red, rump conspicuously
striped; migrant. **b** and **c** nest on the ground
of northernmost Scandinavia, the Arctic Redpoll also in undergrowth.

a Barbary Partridge, *Alectoris barbara:* 33 cm; neck-band chestnut-brown speckled with white, cheeks, throat and upper breast greyish blue, flanks with conspicuous black and white bands, feet red; (very similar to the Red-legged Partridge, page 257); lives in flocks which are noisy at dawn and at dusk, resident in Sardinia and Gibraltar. **b Cretz-schmar's Bunting,** *Emberiza caesia:* 16 cm; throat cinnamon-brown, head and breast-band bluish grey, ♀ without yellow (cf. Ortolan Bunting, page 255); migrant, found from Greece to Dalmatia, occasionally seen as a vagrant elsewhere in Europe. Both nest on the ground on hilly slopes in semi-deserts.

The Birds of Prey illustrated below inhabit dry, open plains, the Imperial Eagle also living in marshes. Two nest on the ground, the Tawny Eagle in Rumania, the Lanner Falcon in Italy and the W Balkans. The others nest in trees, the Imperial Eagle in Spain and the E Balkans, the Saker Falcon in the southern U.S.S.R. and the E Balkans, the Spotted Eagle in E Europe.

	Saker Falcon	Lanner Falcon	Imperial Eagle	Tawny Eagle	Spotted Eagle
Scientific Name	*Falco cherrug*	*Falco biarmicus*	*Aquila heliaca*	*Aquila rapax*	*Aquila clanga*
Size	46 cm	43 cm	79–84 cm	66–79 cm	66–74 cm
Distinguishing Features	Head whitish, back and wings reddish brown; migrant	Crown sandy yellow, back brown, narrow moustache; resident	Plumage blackish brown, crown and nape light yellowish; partial migrant	Almost uniformly dark brown, tail with inconspicuous grey bands; partial migrant	Tail-coverts white, occasionally V-shaped; migrant

a Rose-coloured Starling or **Rosy Pastor,** *Sturnus roseus:* 22 cm; body pale reddish, head, neck, tail and wings black, distinct head-crest; partial migrant, SE Europe, nests in holes under stones and in walls; gregarious, even during the breeding season, and often associates with starlings. **b Calandra Lark,** *Melanocorypha calandra:* 19 cm; bill powerful, large black patch on each side of neck; predominantly resident, S Europe, breeds on the ground on stony plains and steppes; nests in Spain, S Italy and the Balkans. It has a song much like that of the Skylark (page 251), but flies in circles high above the ground while singing.

*Slow-worm, *Anguis fragilis*: 40–50 cm; back bluish grey to dark greyish brown with a fine black line down the centre, belly dark, back and belly with small, smooth, uniform scales; a legless lizard of the Slow-worm Family, distinguished from snakes by its lizard head and its slow, almost stiff, movements. Slow-worms are native throughout C and W Europe where they live in patches of grass and heather in woods, in undergrowth and on the edges of meadows. As with other lizards, the tail is very brittle and may be shed as a means of defence, but will grow again, usually appearing darker than the rest of the body during regeneration.

Lizards, like other cold-blooded animals, are found most abundantly in warm areas. There are, however, three species—the Slow-worm, the Sand Lizard and the Common Lizard—which are widespread in the cooler areas of Europe, including Great Britain. The Wall Lizard and the Green Lizard occur mainly in the south, where many subspecies of both are to be found, although the Wall Lizard extends as far north as Holland and the Green Lizard into the Rhine Valley.

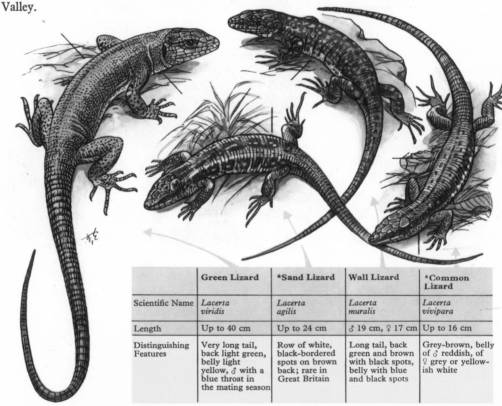

	Green Lizard	***Sand Lizard**	**Wall Lizard**	***Common Lizard**
Scientific Name	*Lacerta viridis*	*Lacerta agilis*	*Lacerta muralis*	*Lacerta vivipara*
Length	Up to 40 cm	Up to 24 cm	♂ 19 cm, ♀ 17 cm	Up to 16 cm
Distinguishing Features	Very long tail, back light green, belly light yellow, ♂ with a blue throat in the mating season	Row of white, black-bordered spots on brown back; rare in Great Britain	Long tail, back green and brown with black spots, belly with blue and black spots	Grey-brown, belly of ♂ reddish, of ♀ grey or yellowish white

European Pond Tortoise, *Emys orbicularis*: total length up to 36 cm with tail; moderately convex shape, not completely rigid, as there is a cartilaginous connection between the upper and lower halves of the shell. All the limbs have webbed toes, and the colouring is dark with radiating lines and spots of yellow, and more yellow spots on the head. In young animals the tail is nearly as long as the carapace, in adult males about 2/3 as long, in females about 1/2. The tortoise is found in muddy ponds and ditches from SC Europe to W Asia, a few living as far north as Germany. It hibernates in mud in winter and catches various small creatures for food.

a Grass or **Ringed Snake**, *Natrix natrix*: ♀ up to 1.5 m, ♂ less than 1 m; grey, with incomplete collar of yellow, edged with black behind head, belly paler, almost white, with series of small dark patches down sides; found throughout C and S Europe. **b *Barred Grass Snake**, *Natrix natrix helvetica*: up to 2 m; similar to Grass Snake, but yellow collar may be paler and with more dark markings on sides; occurs in Great Britain (except Ireland), W Europe and the W and S Alps. Both are non-poisonous, egg-laying snakes; the eyes have round pupils. Both belong to the Grass Snake Family; they are usually found near water and can swim well.

Of the snakes shown below, only the Smooth Snake occurs in S England, where it is rare. The others are all found in the warmer parts of Europe, although they may extend into the Rhine Valley and are mostly absent from S Italy. The Dice Snake or Tessellated Snake is always found near water. Smooth and Aesculapian snakes feed on small animals which they hold constrictor-like in their coils. All vipers are poisonous.

	Dice Snake	*Smooth Snake	Aesculapian Snake	Asp Viper	Field Adder
Scientific Name	*Natrix tesselata*	*Coronella austriaca*	*Elaphe longissima*	*Vipera aspis*	*Vipera ursinii*
Length	Up to 1.5 m	Up to 75 cm	Up to 2 m	♂ up to 75 cm	40–50 cm
Distinguishing Features	Back and belly darkly checkered, often with a V-shaped patch on the neck	Dark lengthwise stripes on the sides of head and neck, ♂ brown, ♀ grey	Back shining brown, darker at tail end, belly uniformly yellowish white	Snout upturned at a sharp angle, pupils vertical; venomous; ♀ smaller	Dark zigzag band on light back-stripe, pupils vertical; venomous

*Viper or **Adder**, *Vipera berus*: ♀ up to 84 cm; ♂ up to about 60 cm, but mostly not over 50 cm; stout, stumpy appearance, dark zigzag band on the back, body colouring very variable—grey, brown or almost black; viviparous; venomous. This species belongs to the Viper or Adder Family, which are all snakes with vertical, slit pupils and erectile poison fangs. Adders are widespread throughout C and N Europe. They are found in very varied habitats but prefer dry heaths and moors with plenty of undergrowth. Although venomous, adders are shy animals which avoid human beings whenever possible; human deaths from bites are very rare indeed.

Freshwater

Included under this heading are plants and animals living in or around freshwater, which may be the running water of rivers, streams or brooks, the still water of lakes, pools and ponds, or the watery habitats provided by springs, damp rocks and temporary inundation such as from melting snow. Ponds are small areas of water, pools are larger; both are usually not more than two or three metres in depth. Commercial fishponds are often man-made and can be drained. Lakes are large areas of water sometimes covering many square kilometres, and usually shelve down from shallow margins to considerable depth and darkness at their centres. Water plants may grow entirely submerged, or they may have most of their leaves floating on the surface, or the whole plant may be freely floating. Marsh plants grow rooted in marshy ground, with their upper parts either partly submerged or completely in the air. Water animals are adapted to life in or around water; the fishes which occur in Europe spend their whole lives in water; amphibians and many insects are dependent on living in water for part of their life-cycle; many other creatures live near water, obtaining food by swimming and diving; some have webbed feet, and some marsh birds walk in shallow water on long stilt-like legs.

Many water mammals are hunted by man for their fine furs; three species have been introduced into Europe from the Americas and have subsequently escaped and returned to the wild. These are the Muskrat and Mink from North America and the Coypu from South America. As always happens with introduced species, they have tended to damage the areas where thay have run wild, frequently destroying the native plants and animals. This is because they have no natural enemies to keep down their numbers.

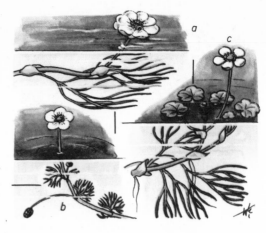

a *River Crowfoot, *Ranunculus fluitans:* ♃, 1–6 m; submerged leaves trifid at base, then with few very long, firm segments which are forked twice or three times, floating leaves rare; 6–8. **b *Rigid-leaved Crowfoot,** *Ranunculus circinatus:* ♃, 1 m; submerged leaves circular in outline, divided into numerous short, rigid segments; 6–8. **c *Water Crowfoot,** *Ranunculus aquatilis:* ♃, 1.5 m; floating leaves kidney-shaped in outline, more or less deeply lobed or cut, submerged leaves finely dissected, falling together like a brush when out of water; 5–8. All are members of the Buttercup Family, widespread and locally common in still and slow-flowing water.

Of the members of the Buttercup Family illustrated in the middle of this page, the Marsh-marigold or King-cup and the Lesser Spearwort are widespread, the others are locally common in damp places, brooks, ditches and marshes.

	*Ivy-leaved Crowfoot	*Great Spearwort	*Lesser Spearwort	*Celery-leaved Crowfoot	*Marsh-marigold	*Common Meadow-rue
Scientific Name	*Ranunculus hederaceus*	*Ranunculus lingua*	*Ranunculus flammula*	*Ranunculus sceleratus*	*Caltha palustris*	*Thalictrum flavum*
Longevity, Size	♃, 1 m	♃, up to 150 cm	♃, 20–50 cm	◯, 20–60 cm	♃, 20–40 cm	50–120 cm
Distinguishing Features; Flowering Time	Leaves shallowly 3–5-lobed, submerged, dissected leaves absent; 5–9	Leaves lanceo-late, pointed, flowers golden yellow, 2–5 cm wide; 6–7	Basal leaves stalked, ellipt-ical, stem leaves narrowly lanceolate, half-clasping, flow-ers small; 6–9	Flowers small, sepals reflexed, fruits numerous, in an oblong head; poison-ous; 6–11	Basal leaves large, kidney-shaped, glossy, flowers glossy, yellow, 10–25 mm wide; 3–5	Leaves 2- or 3-pinnate, flowers frag-rant, in clusters, in a panicle, petals whitish; 6–8

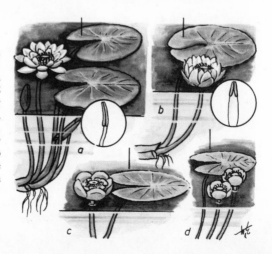

a *White Waterlily, *Nymphaea alba:* ♃, up to 3 m; leaves with a deep and wide basal cleft; 6–9; widespread. **b Pure-white Waterlily,** *Nymphaea candida:* ♃, up to 3 m; leaves with a deep and narrow basal cleft; 7–9; N and C Europe. **c *Yellow Waterlily,** *Nuphar lutea:* ♃, up to 3 m; leaf-blade 10–30 cm long, flowers 4–6 cm wide; 4–9; widespread. **d *Least Yellow Waterlily,** *Nuphar pumila:* ♃; leaf-blade up to 17 cm long, flowers 1.5 to 4 cm wide; 7–8; a local plant of lakes. All are members of the Waterlily Family, growing in still and slow-flowing water.

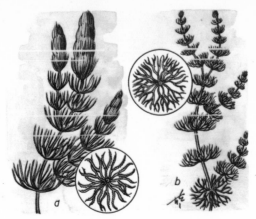

a *Common Hornwort, *Ceratophyllum demersum:* ♃, up to 2 m; leaves dark green, rigid, forked once or twice, closely but irregularly toothed, fruit with 2 spines at base when ripe, slightly shorter than or equalling the persistent style; 6–9. b *Spineless Hornwort, *Ceratophyllum submersum:* ♃, up to 1 m; leaves light green, softer, forked three or four times, with up to 13 hair-like segments, not toothed, fruit spineless, longer than the persistent style; 6–9. Both belong to the Hornwort Family and are submerged aquatic plants found in still and slow-flowing water. The flowers of hornworts are unisexual.

The Marsh Cinquefoil and the Meadowsweet are widespread in damp situations; the Trailing Tormentil and the Norwegian Cinquefoil are local plants, occurring particularly on moors. All four belong to the Rose Family. The Marsh Birdsfoot-trefoil and the Marsh Pea, which are members of the Pea Family, are widespread or local. Both are found in marshy habitats, the Marsh Birdsfoot-trefoil particularly in damp, grassy places.

	*Marsh Cinquefoil	*Trailing Tormentil	†Norwegian Cinquefoil	*Meadowsweet	*Marsh Birdsfoot-trefoil	*Marsh Pea
Scientific Name	Potentilla palustris	Potentilla anglica	Potentilla norvegica	Filipendula ulmaria	Lotus uliginosus	Lathyrus palustris
Longevity, Size	♃, up to 60 cm	♃, 15–80 cm	♃, 20–50 cm	♃, 60–150 cm	♃, 15–60 cm	♃, 60–120 cm
Distinguishing Features; Flowering Time	Leaves pinnate, with 5–7 leaflets, sepals purplish, much longer than the epicalyx segments; 6–7	Stem decumbent, flowers tetramerous and pentamerous mixed; 5–9	Leaves mostly ternate, leaflets green on both sides, calyx becoming larger later; 6–9	Radical leaves pinnate, flowers cream-white, numerous, in a dense cymose panicle; 6–8	Stem hollow, heads 5–12-flowered, on slender stalks; 6–7	Stem winged, stipules lanceolate, raceme few-flowered, flowers pale purplish blue; 6–8

a *Great Hairy Willow-herb, *Epilobium hirsutum:* ♃, 80–150 cm; petals 12–20 mm, deep purplish rose, upper leaves half-clasping the stem; 7–8. b *Hoary Willow-herb, *Epilobium parviflorum:* ♃, 15–60 cm; petals 6–9 mm, pale purplish rose, leaves stalkless; 7–9. c *Marsh Willow-herb, *Epilobium palustre:* ♃, 10–100 cm; leaves usually entire; 7–9. d *Pale Willow-herb, *Epilobium roseum:* ♃, 15–60 cm; flowers white at first, becoming pale pink, leaves short-stalked; 7–9. All belong to the Willow-herb Family, and are widespread, occurring on stream-banks and in marshes, fens and ditches.

a *****Whorled Water-milfoil,** *Myriophyllum verticillatum:* ♃, 50–300 cm; leaves usually 5 in a whorl, much exceeding the internodes, bracts comb-like or toothed; 6–9; widespread. **b** *****Spiked Water-milfoil,** *Myriophyllum spicatum:* ♃, 50–250 cm; leaves usually 4 in a whorl, inflorescence many-flowered; 6–9; widespread. **c** *****Alternate-flowered Water-milfoil,** *Myriophyllum alterniflorum:* ♃, 20 to 120 cm; leaves 3–4 in a whorl, inflorescence few-flowered; 5–8; northwards to S Scandinavia and Finland. All belong to the Water-milfoil Family. **d** *****Marestail,** *Hippuris vulgaris:* ♃, 15–75 cm; leaves 6–12 in a whorl; 5–8; Marestail Family. All grow in still or slow-flowing water.

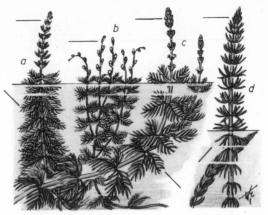

The Water Purslane, the Purple Loosestrife and the Grass Poly belong to the Loosestrife Family and are found on the banks of ditches, lakes and ponds. The Water-chestnut or Jesuits' Nut (Water-chestnut Family) grows in still water in most of Europe. The Marsh Ludwigia occurs locally in shallow pools in fens. The Small-flowered Evening-primrose, a native of N America, has established itself on river-banks and on sea-coasts in many parts of Europe. The last two species belong to the Willow-herb Family.

	Water-chestnut	*Water Purslane	*Purple Loosestrife	*Grass Poly	*Marsh Ludwigia	†Small-flowered Evening-primrose
Scientific Name	*Trapa natans*	*Peplis portula*	*Lythrum salicaria*	*Lythrum hyssopifolia*	*Ludwigia palustris*	*Oenothera parviflora*
Longevity, Size	⊙, up to 100 cm	⊙, 4–30 cm	♃, 60–120 cm	⊙, 5–25 cm	⊙–♃, 5–30 cm	⊙, up to 80 cm
Distinguishing Features; Flowering Time	Leaves rhombic, toothed, forming terminal floating rosette, leaf-stalks bladder-like; 6–9	Leaves opposite, flowers solitary in the axils of the leaves; 6–9	Flowers reddish lilac, arranged in whorls in the axils of bracts, stamens 12; 6–9	Flowers bluish purple-red, solitary in the axils of leaves, stamens 4–6; 6–9	Prostrate, leaves ovate to elliptical, flowers solitary, in leaf-axils, petals absent; 5–5	Leaves lanceolate, pointed, leaf-rosette 5–10 cm high, petals about 12 mm; 6–9

a Whorled Waterwort, *Elatine alsinastrum:* ♃, 3–50 cm; submerged leaves 8–16 in each whorl, aerial leaves 3 in each whorl, flowers greenish; 6–9; in most of Europe. **b** *****Eight-stamened Waterwort,** *Elatine hydropiper:* ⊙, 2–15 cm; flowers stalkless or nearly so, tetramerous, stamens 8; 6–9. **c** Three-stamened Waterwort, *Elatine triandra:* ⊙, 2–15 cm; decumbent, petals 3, stamens 3; 6–9. *****Six-stamened Waterwort,** *Elatine hexandra:* (not illustrated) ⊙, 2–10 cm; decumbent, flowers trimerous, stalked, stamens 6; 7–9. All belong to the Waterwort Family and occur locally in most of Europe in ponds and small lakes, also on wet mud.

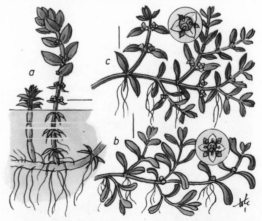

a Aldrovanda, *Aldrovanda vesiculosa:* 2,, 3 cm; stem submerged, with leaves specially adapted for trapping insects, roots absent; 7–8; occurs in S and C Europe; Sundew Family. **b *Marsh Mallow**, *Althaea officinalis:* 2,, 60–150 cm; stem and leaves velvety, flowers pale pink, clustered in axils of leaves; 7–9; upper margins of marshes and ditch sides and banks near the sea; Mallow Family. **c German Tamarisk**, *Myricaria germanica:* a shrub up to 200 cm; leaves small, scale-like, flowers pale pink; 6–8; grows locally on gravelly river-banks; Tamarisk Family.

Illustrated below are members of the Crucifer Family which are common and widespread in most of Europe on the banks of rivers and lakes and in damp places. The Common Watercress and the Great Yellow-cress occur mainly in running water. The One-rowed Watercress, *Nasturtium microphyllum*, (not illustrated) differs from the Common Watercress in having longer fruits and seeds more or less in one row; its leaves and stems turn purple-brown in autumn. The Awlwort is a local plant of lakes and pools, sometimes growing submerged.

	*Common Watercress	*Marsh Yellow-cress	*Awlwort	*Creeping Yellow-cress	*Great Yellow-cress	*Large Bitter-cress
Scientific Name	*Nasturtium officinale*	*Rorippa islandica*	*Subularia aquatica*	*Rorippa sylvestris*	*Rorippa amphibia*	*Cardamine amara*
Longevity, Size	2,, 10–60 cm	☉, to 60 cm	☉, 2–8 cm	2,, 10–60 cm	2,, 45–100 cm	2,, 10–60 cm
Distinguishing Features; Flowering Time	Flowers in terminal clusters, anthers yellow, seeds 2-rowed, leaves with peppery taste; 6–8	Leaves deeply lyrate-pinnatifid, fruits oblong, curved, about same length as stalks; 6–9	Leaves subulate, entire, terete, in a basal rosette, flowers small, white, in loose racemes; 6–7	Petals yellow, twice as long as the sepals, fruits 9–18 mm long, linear, as long as their stalks; 6–9	Petals bright yellow, fruits 3–6 mm long, ovoid, much shorter than stalks; 5–8	Petals white, anthers violet; 4–6

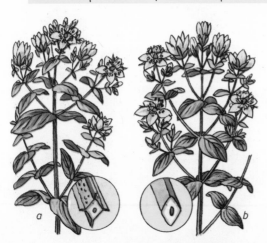

a *Square-stemmed St John's Wort, *Hypericum tetrapterum:* 2,, 20–70 cm; stem four-angled, angles winged, leaves densely and finely dotted, ovate, obtuse, stalkless or half-clasping; 7–9. **b *Imperforate St John's Wort**, *Hypericum maculatum:* 2,, 25–60 cm; stem four-angled, not winged, leaves sparsely dotted or without dots, elliptic, abruptly narrowed at base, stalkless; 7–8. Both are members of the St John's Wort Family, and are widespread in damp places, woods, swamps, moors and meadows.

a Marsh Cranesbill, *Geranium palustre:* ♃, 15–90 cm; stem bristly, without glandular hairs, flowers darkly veined; 6–9; occurs in most of Europe; Cranesbill Family. **b *Flaxseed,** *Radiola linoides:* ⊙, 1.5–10 cm; flowers tetramerous, numerous, in dichotomous cymes, sepals 2–3-toothed; 7–8; widespread; Flax Family. **c Flat-leaved Eryngo,** *Eryngium planum:* ♃, 25–70 cm; plant tinged with blue, basal leaves stalked, with heart-shaped base, heads ovate; 6–8; usually in damp places, in C and SE Europe; Carrot Family.

The Mudweed and the very poisonous Cowbane or Water-hemlock are widespread in still water (lakes, ponds and ditches), in canals, fens, marshes, and by brooks and springs; the Pennywort or White-rot, the Water-parsnip and the Lesser Water-parsnip in fens, bogs, marshes and other wet places in most of Europe; the Water Dropwort in marshy places and shallow water throughout Europe. All belong to the Carrot Family. The Pennywort is sometimes treated as a separate family—the Pennywort Family.

	*Mudweed	*Pennywort	*Cowbane	*Water-parsnip	*Lesser Water-parsnip	*Water Dropwort
Scientific Name	*Apium inundatum*	*Hydrocotyle vulgaris*	*Cicuta virosa*	*Sium latifolium*	*Berula erecta*	*Oenanthe fistulosa*
Longevity, Size	♃, 3–60 cm	♃, 15 cm	♃, 1 m	♃, 1.5 m	♃, 80 cm	♃, 30 cm
Distinguishing Features; Flowering Time	Stem often submerged or floating, umbels with 2–3 rays, bracts absent; 6–8	Leaves disc-like, shallowly lobed, stem creeping, flowers in small head-like umbels; 6–8	Leaves 2–3-pinnate, segments serrate, root-stock tuberous, with transverse cavities; 6–8	Leaves simply pinnate, with 3–6 pairs of segments; 7–9	Leaves simply pinnate, with 7–10 pairs of segments; 7–8	Stems swollen, hollow, rooting at lower nodes, leaf-stalks long, hollow; 6–8

a *Fine-leaved Water Dropwort, *Oenanthe aquatica:* ⊙-♃, up to 200 cm; aerial leaves 3-pinnate, with deeply lobed segments, submerged leaves with hair-like segments; 6–8. **b Cenolophium,** *Cenolophium fischeri:* ♃, up to 150 cm; leaves 2–5-pinnate, bracts absent, bracteoles numerous; 6–8. **c †Common Angelica,** *Angelica archangelica:* ♃, 30 to 200 cm; leaf-stalks round, hollow, flowers greenish white or green; 7–8. All are members of the Carrot Family and occur in most of Europe in still and running water, sometimes also in damp meadows.

a *Upright Spurge, *Euphorbia stricta:* ⊙, 20–30 cm; upper stem leaves stalkless, heart-shaped at base, umbel mostly 3-rayed; 6–7. **b Marsh Spurge,** *Euphorbia palustris:* ♃, up to 150 cm; stem thick, hollow, leaves stalkless, elongate-lanceolate, nearly entire, umbel many-rayed; 5–6; in most of Europe. Both belong to the Spurge Family. **c** *Common Blinks,** *Montia fontana:* ⊙-♃, 3–10 cm; stem often erect, forked; 4–5. **d** *River Blinks,** *Montia fontana* subsp. *variabilis:* ♃, 8-30 cm; stem prostrate, tufted; 6–8. Both are widespread members of the Purslane Family and occur by stream-sides, springs, in wet places among rocks and in moist pastures.

The Hop is a common plant on banks of rivers, in damp thickets and in meadow forests; it belongs to the Hemp Family. The Water Dock and the Great Water Dock are widespread in wet places and shallow water; the Sharp Dock and the Red-veined Dock are common in damp grassy places, woods and waste ground, the Golden Dock on bare muddy ground beside lakes and sea, and at the margins of reservoirs. All belong to the Dock Family.

	*Hop	*Golden Dock	*Sharp Dock	*Red-veined Dock	*Water Dock	*Great Water Dock
Scientific Name	*Humulus lupulus*	*Rumex maritimus*	*Rumex conglomeratus*	*Rumex sanguineus*	*Rumex aquaticus*	*Rumex hydrolapathum*
Longevity, Size	♃, up to 7 m	⊙-♃, 7–60 cm	♃, 60 cm	♃, 60–100 cm	♃, 80–200 cm	♃ up to 250 cm
Distinguishing Features; Flowering Time	Climbing, leaves deeply 3–5-lobed, infructescence cone-like, flowers dioecious; 5	Fruits golden yellow, leaves linear, inflorescence dense; 7–9	Stem usually flexuous, whorls of flowers distant, flower-spikes leafy nearly to the top; 7–9	Stems usually straight, branches with lowest whorls of flowers subtended by leaves; 7–8	Basal leaves heart-shaped-ovate, up to 50 cm long, with somewhat undulate margins; 7–8	Basal leaves lanceolate to ovate, usually wedge-shaped at base, up to 100 cm long; 7–8

a *Autumnal Water-starwort, *Callitriche hermaphroditica:* ♃, 2–50 cm; all leaves submerged, linear, fruit 2 mm, with broadly winged lobes; 6–9. **b** *Common Water-starwort,** *Callitriche stagnalis:* ♃, 25–100 cm; all leaves ovate, fruit 1.5 mm, with winged lobes; 5–8. **c** *Narrow-leaved Water-starwort,** *Callitriche intermedia:* ♃, up to 80 cm; all leaves linear, deeply notched at tip, fruit about 1 mm, with acutely keeled lobes; 4–9. **d** *Marsh Water-starwort,** *Callitriche platycarpa:* ♃, 30 cm; rosette-leaves obovate, submerged leaves linear, fruit 1 mm, with acutely keeled lobes; 4–9. All are widespread members of the Water-starwort Family.

a *Amphibious Bistort, *Polygonum amphibium:* 2, 20–100 cm; stamens 5, exserted, leaves, in terrestrial forms, oblong-lanceolate, rounded at base, in aquatic forms, floating, long-stalked, usually heart-shaped at base; 6–9. **b** *Tasteless Water-pepper, *Polygonum mite:* ⊙, 15–80 cm; stamens usually 6, margins and veins of leaves coarsely bristly, ochrea with bristles 3–5 mm long; 7–10. **c** *Least Water-pepper, *Polygonum minus:* ⊙, 10–60 cm; stamens usually 5, ochrea with long, unequal bristles; 7–10. All are widespread members of the Dock Family; **a** growing on banks and in still or slow-flowing water, **b** and **c** in ditches, beside ponds and lakes and in wet marshy habitats.

The Water-violet, the Tufted Loosestrife and the Yellow Loosestrife belong to the Primrose Family and are widespread in still and slow-flowing waters, by ponds and lakes and in marshes. The Bogbean or Marsh-trefoil is common in damp places in most of Europe. The Fringed Waterlily is a local plant, occurring in ponds and slow rivers. Both belong to the Bogbean Family. The Hop-like Dodder is a parasitic plant of the Bindweed Family, growing along river valleys in W, C and SE Europe.

	*Water-violet	*Tufted Loosestrife	*Yellow Loosestrife	*Bogbean	*Fringed Waterlily	Hop-like Dodder
Scientific Name	Hottonia palustris	Naumburgia thyrsiflora	Lysimachia vulgaris	Menyanthes trifoliata	Nymphoides peltata	Cuscuta lupuliformis
Longevity, Size	2, up to 60 cm	2, 30–60 cm	2, 60–150 cm	2, 15–30 cm	2, up to 100 cm	⊙, climbing
Distinguishing Features; Flowering Time	Leaves 1–2-pinnate, comb-like, flowers lilac with a yellow throat, 3–8 in a whorl; 5–7	Leaves opposite, rarely in whorls, flowers in dense bracteate racemes; 5–7	Leaves mostly in whorls of 3–4, dotted with black glands, flowers in terminal panicles; 6–8	Leaves with long stalks, of 3 leaflets, corolla pink outside, paler within, 5-lobed; 5–7	Leaves simple, circular, deeply heart-shaped at the base, with long stalks, floating; 7–9	Flowers solitary or in twos or threes, stigma two-lobed; 7–9

a *Water Chickweed, *Myosoton aquaticum:* ⊙-2, 8–80 cm; stem fragile, often trailing, styles 5; 6–9. **b** *Strapwort, *Corrigiola littoralis:* ⊙-⊙⊙, 3–30 cm; flowers small, in crowded terminal and axillary inflorescences, sepals green or red in centre, with broad white margins; 5–7. **c** *Coral Necklace, *Illecebrum verticillatum:* ⊙, 2–30 cm; flowers white, in clusters, bracteoles scarious, silvery, petals thread-like; 6–10. **d** *Common Pearlwort, *Sagina apetala:* ⊙, 1–15 cm; leaves tapering into an awn, petals minute. All belong to the Pink Family and grow in damp places, **a** and **d** in most of Europe except the north, **b** from SW Europe to Denmark, **c** in W and C Europe.

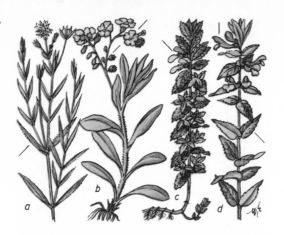

a *Marsh Stitchwort**, *Stellaria palustris:* ♃, 4–45 cm; bracts with broad membranous unfringed margins; 5–7; Pink Family. **b** *Water Forgetmenot**, *Myosotis palustris:* ♃, 15 to 45 cm; calyx with appressed hairs, with triangular teeth not more than $1/3$ length of calyx; 5–9; Borage Family. **c** *Water Germander**, *Teucrium scordium:* ♃, 10–70 cm; garlic smell, flowers purple, in whorls of 4, all bracts longer than flowers; 7–8. **d** *Skullcap**, *Scutellaria galericulata:* ♃, 15–70 cm; leaves with 4 to 8 shallow teeth, heart-shaped at base; 6–9. **c** and **d** belong to the Thyme Family. All are widespread on the banks of rivers and ditches, and in fens and water meadows.

The plants illustrated below are common and widespread by lakes and ponds, in ditches and in marshy places, the Marsh Woundwort also in damp fields and the Water Mint also in wet woods. The Water Mint occurs throughout Europe. The Penny-royal grows in the Mediterranean region, S and C Europe. The Apple-scented Mint and the Horse Mint occur in the same area, also extending to Denmark and Sweden. All belong to the Thyme Family.

	*Marsh Woundwort	*Gipsy-wort	*Water Mint	*Apple-scented Mint	*Horse Mint	*Penny-royal
Scientific Name	Stachys palustris	Lycopus europaeus	Mentha aquatica	Mentha rotundifolia	Mentha longifolia	Mentha pulegium
Longevity, Size	♃, 40–100 cm	♃, 30–100 cm	♃, 15–90 cm	♃, 60–90 cm	♃, 60–90 cm	♃, 10–30 cm
Distinguishing Features; Flowering Time	Leaves oblong-lanceolate, crenate, serrate, short-stalked, corolla twice as long as calyx; 6–8	Leaves pinnately shallowly lobed, flowers white with purple dots on lower lip, stamens 2; 7–9	Flowers in rounded axillary and terminal heads, stalks hairy, stamens exserted; 7–10	Stem with dense white hairs, leaves oblong, ovate or nearly circular, rugose; 7–9	Leaves lanceolate, green, hairy above, grey and downy beneath, scarcely rugose; 7–9	Leaves oblong or oval, flowers rounded, clustered in leaf-axils, throat of calyx hairy; 7–10

a †Spear-leaved Skullcap**, *Scutellaria hastifolia:* ♃, 15–50 cm; leaves hastate at base, otherwise entire, flowers blue-violet, 20 to 22 mm long; 6–8; widespread; Thyme Family. **b** *Bittersweet** or **Woody Nightshade**, *Solanum dulcamara:* ♃ (woody), 30–200 cm; leaves ovate, entire or with 1–4 deep lobes, upper leaves often in 3; 6–8; widespread; Nightshade Family. **c** †Moth Mullein**, *Verbascum blattaria:* ☉, 50–130 cm; flowers solitary in the axil of each bract, arranged in elongate racemes; 6–8; most of Europe except the north. **d** **Hedge-hyssop**, *Gratiola officinalis:* ♃, 15–40 cm; only 2 of 4 stamens with anthers; 6–8; NE and C Europe. **c** and **d** belong to the Figwort Family.

a *Common Figwort, *Scrophularia nodosa:*
♃, 40–80 cm; stem 4-angled, not winged,
leaves coarsely and unequally serrate; 6–9.
b *Water Betony, *Scrophularia auriculata:*
♃, 60–150 cm; leaves with 1 or 2 small
segments at base, which is usually half-
heart-shaped, flowers red-brown; 6–8.
c *Green-winged Figwort, *Scrophularia
umbrosa:* ♃, 60–150 cm; stem broadly
winged, leaves tapering at the base, flowers olive-brown, 6–8 mm long; 6–8; rare.
All are members of the Figwort Family, occurring on the edges of ponds, streams, on
banks and in damp and wet woods; **a** and **c**
in most of Europe, **b** in S and W Europe.

The Mudwort is a widespread local plant, growing in wet mud at the edges of pools, rivers and
ditches. The Lindernia occurs in damp sandy and muddy habitats in C Europe. The speedwells
and the Brooklime are widespread in Europe, including Britain, growing in streams, ponds,
ditches, marshes and wet meadows. The Water Speedwell, *Veronica anagallis-aquatica,* (not
illustrated) differs from the Pink Water Speedwell in having pale blue flowers with stalks
ascending after flowering. All belong to the Figwort Family.

	*Mudwort	Lindernia	†Long-leaved Speedwell	*Brooklime	*Pink Water Speedwell	*Marsh Speedwell
Scientific Name	*Limosella aquatica*	*Lindernia procumbens*	*Veronica longifolia*	*Veronica beccabunga*	*Veronica catenata*	*Veronica scutellata*
Longevity, Size	☉, 1–8 cm	☉, 3–10 cm	♃, 40–120 cm	♃, 20–60 cm	♃, 60 cm	♃, 10–50 cm
Dist'nguishing Features; Flowering Time	Leaves radical, spathulate, long-stalked, flowers white or lavender, may be purple-tinged; 6–10	Leaves stalk-less, entire, flowers stalked, solitary, white or pinkish; 8–9	Leaves sharply and doubly serrate, upper ones often in whorls of **3** to 4; 6–8	Stem terete, leaves short-stalked, shal-lowly crenate-serrate; 5–8	Stem slightly 4-angled, flow-ers pink with dark lines, flower-stalks spread after flowering; 5–9	Leaves linear-lanceolate, flowers white or blue with purple lines, in alternate racemes; 6–9

a *Common Bladderwort, *Utricularia
vulgaris:* ♃, 15–45 cm; stems with green
floating leaves bearing numerous bladders;
6–8. **b *Lesser Bladderwort,** *Utricularia
minor:* ♃, 5–20 cm; stems of 2 kinds: green,
bearing green leaves with a few bladders, and
colourless ones with bladders on much reduced leaves, corolla 6–8 mm long; 6–9.
c Brem's Bladderwort, *Utricularia bremii:*
♃, 10–20 cm; corolla 10 mm long; 6–9.
d *Intermediate Bladderwort, *Utricularia
intermedia:* ♃, 3–20 cm; similar to **b**, leaf-
segments toothed, with bristles on the teeth,
flowers larger; 6–9. All are widespread members of the Butterwort Family, occurring in
still waters.

a *Shore-weed, *Littorella uniflora:* ♃, 2 to 10 cm; ♂ flowers solitary, on short scapes, ♀ solitary or few, at base of ♂ scape; 6–9; lakes and ponds, C and N Europe; Plantain Family. b *Marsh Bedstraw, *Galium palustre:* ♃, 5–100 cm; leaves 1-veined, 4–6 in a whorl, anthers red; 5–9; marshes and wet places. c *Goosegrass or Cleavers, *Galium aparine:* ○, 30–150 cm; climbing, fruits with white hooked bristles; 6–9; hedges and waste ground. b and c are widespread; Bedstraw Family. d *Water Lobelia, *Lobelia dortmanna:* ♃, 20–60 cm; leaves in radical rosette, flowers pale lilac, in loose raceme; 7–8; lakes and ponds, W and N Europe; Bellflower Family.

The Common Valerian or All-heal is a widespread plant of the Valerian Family, found in marshy places. The other plants shown below belong to the Daisy Family. They all grow on banks, in ditches and in damp places. The Nodding Bur-marigold, the Three-partite Bur-marigold and the Small Fleabane are common or local in most of Europe, the Rayed Bur-marigold in N and W Europe. The Swamp Bur-marigold is a native of N America, introduced and naturalized in Europe.

	*Common Valerian	*Nodding Bur-marigold	Swamp Bur-marigold	Rayed Bur-marigold	*Three-partite Bur-marigold	*Small Fleabane
Scientific Name	*Valeriana officinalis*	*Bidens cernua*	*Bidens connata*	*Bidens radiata*	*Bidens tripartita*	*Pulicaria vulgaris*
Longevity, Size	♃, 20–150 cm	○, 8–100 cm	○, 15–100 cm	○, 10–100 cm	○, 15–60 cm	○, 7–50 cm
Distinguishing Features; Flowering Time	Leaves imparipinnate, with 5–11 leaflets, flowers pale pink; 5–9	Leaves simple, stalkless, coarsely serrate, heads drooping, usually with ray-florets; 7–9	Leaves simple, coarsely serrate, heads erect, usually without ray-florets; 8–10	Leaves mostly pinnatisect, 3–7 partite to pinnate, toothed, the teeth curved; 8–10	Leaves similar to those of the Rayed Bur-marigold, but teeth almost straight; 7–10	Leaves lanceolate, sinuate, hairy, heads dull yellow, up to 11 mm broad; 7–10

a *Common Fleabane, *Pulicaria dysenterica:* ♃, 20–60 cm; leaves half-clasping stem, pappus two-rowed; 6–9. b *Hemp Agrimony, *Eupatorium cannabinum:* ♃, 30 to 150 cm; leaves palmate, heads in dense terminal corymbs; 7–9. c †Willow-leaved Aster, *Aster salignus:* ♃, up to 200 cm; lower leaves serrate, involucral bracts of equal length; 8–9. d White-flowered Aster, *Aster tradescantii:* ♃, 50–200 cm; ray-florets usually white, outer involucral bracts shorter than the inner ones; 8–9. All belong to the Daisy Family; a and b are widespread in most of Europe, in marshy places; c and d are natives of N America, naturalized in many parts.

a *Coltsfoot,* *Tussilago farfara:* ♃, 5–20 cm; flower heads solitary, terminal, appear before the leaves; 3–4. **b** *Common Butter-bur,* *Petasites hybridus:* ♃, up to 100 cm; leaves very large, up to 100 cm long and 60 cm wide, heart-shaped to circular, flowers reddish; 3–5. **c** **Felted Butterbur,** *Petasites spurius:* ♃, 15–30 cm, in fruit up to 80 cm; leaves pale yellow; 3–4. All belong to the Daisy Family; **a** and **b** are widespread in most of Europe, on banks of streams and in wet meadows and copses, **c** grows only on the shores of the Baltic and its tributaries.

The Marsh Thistle is widespread in marshes, moist grassland, hedgerows and woods. The Broad-leaved Ragwort grows by stream-sides and in fen-woods in most parts. The Spreading Ragwort is a local plant of wet woods in C Europe. The Marsh Ragwort is common in marshes, wet meadows and ditches in W, C and southern N Europe. The Great Fen Ragwort is found in wet places in C and southern N Europe (extinct in Britain). The Cabbage Thistle is common in marshes and damp woods in C and N Europe. All belong to the Daisy Family.

	†Broad-leaved Ragwort	†Spreading Ragwort	*Marsh Ragwort	*Great Fen Ragwort	†Cabbage Thistle	*Marsh Thistle
Scientific Name	*Senecio fluviatilis*	*Senecio erraticus*	*Senecio aquaticus*	*Senecio paludosus*	*Cirsium oleraceum*	*Cirsium palustre*
Longevity, Size	♃, up to 200 cm	☉, 30–120 cm	☉, 20–60 cm	♃, 80–120 cm	♃, 50–120 cm	☉, 30–120 cm
Distinguishing Features; Flowering Time	Branches of corymb steeply ascending, teeth of leaves curved, ray-florets 7–8; 7–10	Branches of corymb spreading, leaves with large end-lobes; 7–10	Lateral lobes of leaves directed forwards; 6–10	Leaves sharply serrate, teeth curved, heads 3–4 cm wide, in a usually simple corymb; 6–8	Upper leaves usually un-lobed, heads large, clustered, yellowish white; 6–9	Stem spiny, uppermost leaves white-downy; 8–10

a *Marsh Dandelion,* *Taraxacum palustre:* ♃, 5–15 cm; leaves 3–10 mm wide, mostly entire, scape hollow, heads solitary, 1.2–2 cm long; 4–6. **b** *Marsh Sow-thistle,* *Sonchus palustris:* ♃, 90–300 cm; stem leaves with pointed auricles, heads in a dense corymbose panicle, branches and stalks and involucres of the heads densely covered with blackish glandular hairs; 7–9. **c** *Marsh Hawks-beard,* *Crepis paludosa:* ♃, 30–80 cm; stem tubular, stem leaves clasping the stem, with auricles, pappus yellow-white; 5–8. All belong to the Daisy Family and are widespread throughout Europe, occurring by streams, in wet copses, damp meadows and fens.

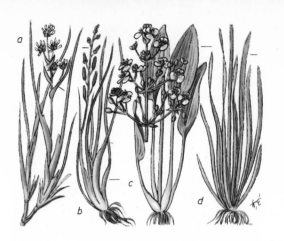

a *Rannoch-rush, *Scheuchzeria palustris:* ♃, 10–30 cm; stem leafy, bracts large, flowers in loose racemes; 5–7; Rannoch-rush Family. **b *Marsh Arrow-grass,** *Triglochin palustris:* ♃, 10–50 cm; leaves basal, flowers in racemes, without bracts; 6–9; Arrow-grass Family. **c *Common Water-plantain,** *Alisma plantago-aquatica:* ♃, 20–100 cm; leaves long-stalked, ovate, rounded or half-heart-shaped at base (in water forms, submerged leaves linear), style straight; 7–9. **d *Grass-leaved Water-plantain,** *Alisma gramineum:* ♃, 5–7 cm; leaves usually linear, style spirally coiled; 6–8. **c** and **d** belong to the Water-plantain Family and are widespread.

All the plants illustrated below grow in ponds, lakes and marshes, some also in flowing water. The Lesser Water-plantain and the Arrow-head are widespread throughout Europe; the Floating Water-plantain is a local plant of W, southern N and SE Europe; the Caldesia of S and C Europe. The Flowering-rush (Flowering-rush Family) and the Water-soldier (Frogbit Family) are common in most of Europe.

	*Floating Water-plantain	Caldesia	*Lesser Water-plantain	*Arrow-head	*Flowering-rush	*Water-soldier
Scientific Name	*Luronium natans*	*Caldesia parnassifolia*	*Baldellia ranunculoides*	*Sagittaria sagittifolia*	*Butomus umbellatus*	*Stratiotes aloides*
Longevity, Size	♃, up to 50 cm	♃, 10–40 cm	♃, 3–25 cm	♃, 30–100 cm	♃, 50–120 cm	♃, 15–50 cm
Distinguishing Features; Flowering Time	Submerged leaves linear, floating leaves long-stalked, ovate or elliptic; 6–9	Leaves long-stalked, heart-shaped-ovate, 5–11, veined; 7–9	Leaves in a basal rosette, flowers long-stalked, few, usually in an umbel; 6–8	Aerial leaves arrow-shaped, submerged linear, flowers monoecious, 3–5 in a whorl, white; 5–7	Leaves in a basal rosette, inflorescence umbel-like, many-flowered; 6–7	Leaves in a rosette, rigid, spiny-serrate, flowers white, dioecious; 5–7

a *Frogbit, *Hydrocharis morsus-ranae:* ♃, up to 40 cm; flowers unisexual, ♂ with stalks 1–6 cm long, ♀ smaller, stalkless; 5–9; widespread. **b Hydrilla,** *Hydrilla lithuanica:* ♃, 100–300 cm; leaves mostly 5 in a whorl, ♂ and ♀ flowers with long stalks; 7–8; rare, in C Europe. **c †Canadian Waterweed,** *Elodea canadensis:* ♃, up to 300 cm; leaves mostly 3 in a whorl, flowers long-stalked; 5–10; a native of N America, naturalized in Europe. **d Dense-leaved Pondweed,** *Egeria densa:* ♃, up to 300 cm; leaves mostly 4 in a whorl; 7–9; a native of S America, naturalized in Europe. All belong to the Frogbit Family.

a *Opposite-leaved Pondweed, *Groen-landia densa:* ♃, up to 100 cm; leaves opposite, spike usually of only 4 flowers; 6–7; widespread. **b** *Fen Pondweed, *Potamogeton coloratus:* ♃, 30–120 cm; stem terete, floating leaves mostly reddish, long-stalked; 6–9; Atlantic Europe. **c** *Loddon Pondweed, *Potamogeton nodosus:* ♃, about 100 cm; leaves long, transparent, conspicuously net-veined, long-stalked; 6–9; most of Europe. **d** *Grass-wrack Pondweed, *Potamogeton compressus:* ♃, up to 200 cm; stem strongly flattened, leaves with 5 main and many faint intermediate longitudinal veins; 6–8. C and N Europe. All belong to the Pondweed Family; locally, in still and slow-flowing water.

All the pondweeds illustrated below are widespread throughout Europe, growing in ditches, ponds, lakes, streams and canals, sometimes also in mountainous areas, occasionally at altitudes up to 2400 m or more. All belong to the Pondweed Family.

	*Slender-leaved Pondweed	*Broad-leaved Pondweed	*Curled Pondweed	*Perfoliate Pondweed	*Small Pondweed	*Fennel-leaved Pondweed
Scientific Name	*Potamogeton filiformis*	*Potamogeton natans*	*Potamogeton crispus*	*Potamogeton perfoliatus*	*Potamogeton pusillus*	*Potamogeton pectinatus*
Longevity, Size	♃, 5–30 cm	♃, 50–175 cm	♃, 30–120 cm	♃, 50–300 cm	♃, 30–60 cm	♃, 20–300 cm
Distinguishing Features; Flowering Time	Leaves hair-like, pointed, with a tubular sheath at the base; 6–8	Floating leaves ellipt-ical, leathery, stalks longer than the blades; 5–8	Leaves linear, about 10 mm wide, strongly undulate at margin when mature, stem 4-angled; 5–9	Submerged leaves stalk-less, clasping at the wide heart-shaped base, 6 cm long; 7–8	Submerged leaves up to 15 mm wide, spike 5–7 mm long, its stalk hair-like; 5–7	Stem very slender, leaf-sheaths 5 cm long, spike 4–6 cm long; 6–8

a *Bog Pondweed, *Potamogeton polygoni-folius:* ♃, 20–100 cm long; leaf-stalks flattened above, not jointed below the blade; 6–7. **b** *Shining Pondweed, *Potamogeton lucens:* ♃, 300 cm and more; leaves shining, upper ones cuspidate. **c** *Various-leaved Pondweed, *Potamogeton gramineus:* ♃, up to 100 cm; submerged leaves linear-lanceolate, stalkless, floating leaves ovate-lanceolate, stalked; 6–8. **d** *Hair-like Pondweed, *Potamogeton trichoides:* ♃, 50–100 cm; submerged leaves narrowly linear, longitudinal veins 3, midrib thick, lateral ones faint, spikes 4–8-flowered; 5–7. All are members of the Pondweed Family; widespread in most of Europe, in lakes, ponds and streams.

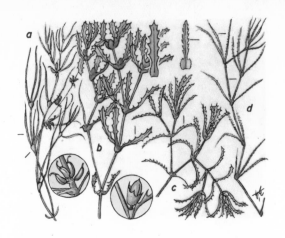

a **Horned-pondweed,* *Zannichellia palustris:* ♃, 25–90 cm; monoecious, leaves hair-like, 1–10 cm long, flowers in axils of leaves; 5–9; widespread, streams, ditches, pools; Horned-pondweed Family. **b** **Holly-leaved Naiad,* *Najas marina:* ☉, 20 cm; dioecious, stem with occasional teeth near the top, leaves strongly spinous-toothed; 6–7; widespread, brackish water. **c Lesser Naiad,** *Najas minor:* ☉, 5–25 cm; monoecious, leaf-blade constricted at junction with sheath; 6–9; C and S Europe. **d** **Slender Naiad,* *Najas flexilis:* ♃, 5–30 cm; monoecious, stem flexuous, leaves minutely toothed; 7–8; local, N and C Europe. **b, c** and **d** are local members of the Naiad Family.

All the plants shown below have stem-like, bristle-like leaves and small inconspicuous flowers with six perianth-segments. Most of the species are common and widespread throughout Europe, growing on banks, in ditches, damp meadows and wet places; the Common Rush and the Hard Rush are found on mountains up to 1800 m. The Bulbous Rush is a common plant of moors and pools. All belong to the Rush Family.

	*Soft Rush	*Common Rush	*Bulbous Rush	*Toad Rush	*Hard Rush	*Jointed Rush
Scientific Name	*Juncus effusus*	*Juncus subuliflorus*	*Juncus bulbosus*	*Juncus bufonius*	*Juncus inflexus*	*Juncus articulatus*
Longevity, Size	♃, 30–150 cm	♃, 25–100 cm	♃, 1–15 cm	☉, 3–25 cm	♃, 30–70 cm	♃, 8–60 cm
Distinguishing Features; Flowering Time	Stem scarcely ridged, pith continuous, inflorescence loose; 7–8	Stem with about 40 strong ridges, pith continuous, inflorescence usually dense, head-like; 5–7	Stem leafy, leaves slender, slightly swollen at base, inflorescence simple or branched; 7–8	Leaves deeply channelled, flowers solitary, perianth-segments green, transparent margin; 6–10	Stem glaucous, with 12–16 prominent ridges, pith interrupted, inflorescence loose; 6–8	Leaves with transverse walls, heads 5 mm long, outer perianth-segments acute; 6–9

a **Yellow Flag,* *Iris pseudacorus:* ♃, 50 to 150 cm; outer perianth-segments not bearded; 5–6; widespread, marshes and wet woods; Iris Family. **b** **Galingale,* *Cyperus longus:* ♃, 50–120 cm; branches of the compound umbel of unequal length, glumes reddish brown; 5–10; local, Mediterranean region, C Europe (rare) and England. **c** **Brown Cyperus,* *Cyperus fuscus:* ☉, 5–25 cm; stem sharply 3-angled, stigmas 3; 7–9; C, S and southern N Europe. **d Yellowish Cyperus,** *Cyperus flavescens:* ☉, 5–16 cm; stem bluntly 3-angled, stigmas 2; 7–10; S and C Europe. All belong to the Sedge Family and occur in marshy and damp places beside ponds and in ditches.

a *Prickly Cladium, *Cladium mariscus:* ♃, 80–200 cm; leaves up to 2 cm wide, sharply serrate, inflorescence much-branched, each branch with head of 3–10 spikelets; 6–7; widespread, but local. **b *Wood Club-rush**, *Scirpus sylvaticus:* ♃, 20–100 cm; inflorescence loose, spikelets solitary or in small dense clusters at ends of branches; 6–7; widespread. **c Rooting Club-rush**, *Scirpus radicans:* ♃, 30–120 cm; spikelets mostly solitary, otherwise similar to **b**; 6–7; N, C and E Europe. **d *Bristle Club-rush**, *Scirpus setaceus:* ○, 2–16 cm; spikelets 2–3 mm long, 1–3 together, bract distinctly longer than inflorescence; 7–10; most of Europe. All belong to Sedge Family; banks, marshes, **b** also wet woods.

The Bulrush or Great Club-rush is common throughout Europe in rivers, lakes and ponds. The Floating Club-rush grows in most of Europe in ditches and ponds. All the other species illustrated below are local or rare plants of banks, ponds and marshes; the Pointed Club-rush and the Three-angled Club-rush mainly in S and C Europe, the Clustered Club-rush in most of Europe; the Sharp Club-rush in SW Europe extending to England and N Germany.

	*Floating Club-rush	*Bulrush	Pointed Club-rush	*Three-angled Club-rush	*Clustered Club-rush	*Sharp Club-rush
Scientific Name	*Scirpus fluitans*	*Scirpus lacustris*	*Scirpus mucronatus*	*Scirpus triquetrus*	*Scirpus holoschoenus*	*Scirpus americanus*
Longevity, Size	♃, 15–30 cm	♃, 100–300 cm	♃, 30–150 cm	♃, 50–100 cm	♃, 30–100 cm	♃, 30–60 cm
Distinguishing Features; Flowering Time	Stems flat, branched, leafy, spike solitary, up to 5 mm long, long-stalked, stigmas 2; 7–10	Stem up to 1.5 cm thick, terete, glumes fringed, notched, with short awn, stigmas usually 3; 6–7	Stem 3-angled, inflorescence head-like, of 4–10 spikelets, bracts spreading finally, stigmas 3; 8–10	Stem 3-angled, mostly leafless, glumes with obtuse lateral lobes, stigmas 2; 6–7	Stem terete, striate, spikelets in globose long-stalked heads, stigmas 3; 7–8	Stem sharply 3-angled, with 2 leaves, spikelets stalkless, 3–5 in each head; 7–8

a *Slender Spike-rush, *Eleocharis acicularis:* ♃, 2–10 cm; stem 4-angled, spikelets 3–9 mm long, stigmas 3; 6–10. **b *Common Spike-rush**, *Eleocharis palustris:* ♃, 8–60 cm; stem terete, spikelet up to 20 mm, stigmas 2; 5–8. **c Ovoid Spike-rush**, *Eleocharis soloniensis:* ♃, 5–35 cm; stem terete, spikelets 3–5 mm, stigmas 2; 6–8. **d *Few-flowered Spike-rush**, *Eleocharis pauciflora:* ♃, 5 to 25 cm; stem terete, stout, spikelets 3–7-flowered, stigmas 3; 5–6. All are members of the Sedge Family; wet sandy and muddy places at margins of lakes and pools, damp peaty places on moors and fens, and marshes and ditches; **a, b** and **d** in most of Europe, **c** in S and C Europe.

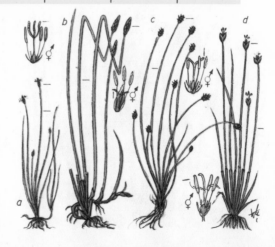

a Cyperus Sedge, *Carex cyperoides*: ☉-♃, 1–15 cm; spikes head-like, not white, bracts much exceeding inflorescence, stigmas 2; 6–10; local, S and C Europe. **b *Greater Fox Sedge**, *Carex vulpina*: ♃, 30–60 cm; stem 3-angled, side faces slightly concave, spikelets 4–8 in each spike; 5–6. **c *Lesser Fox Sedge**, *Carex diandra*: ♃, 20–60 cm; leaves flat, 1–2 mm wide, grey-green, inflorescence 1–4 cm, of several stalkless spikes, stigmas 2; 5–6. **d *Panicled Sedge**, *Carex paniculata*: ♃, 40–100 cm; leaves 4–6 mm wide, spikes distinctly stalked, stigmas 2; 5–6. All belong to the Sedge Family; reed-beds, river-banks and damp places; **b**, **c** and **d** in most of Europe.

The grasses shown below grow on muddy or grassy banks, by ponds, marshes, lakes and rivers and are common everywhere, except the Marsh Hair-grass which is rare, being found only in NW Germany, and the Swamp Meadow-grass, which is local plant, occurring by rivers, ponds and in wet meadows. The Floating Sweet-grass may also be called the Manna-grass. All belong to the Grass Family.

	Marsh Hair-grass	*Common Reed	*Swamp Meadow-grass	*Floating Sweet-grass	*Reed Sweet-grass	*Plicate Sweet-grass
Scientific Name	*Deschampsia wibeliana*	*Phragmites communis*	*Poa palustris*	*Glyceria fluitans*	*Glyceria maxima*	*Glyceria plicata*
Longevity, Size	♃, 30–120 cm	♃, 1–4 m	♃, 30–120 cm	♃, 40–120 cm	♃ 90–250 cm	♃, 30–75 cm
Distinguishing Features; Flowering Time	Loosely tufted, leaves scabrous above, awn whitish, slightly geniculate; 5	Panicles 20–40 cm long, loose, florets with a tuft of silky hairs at the base; 7–9	Loosely tufted, ligule 2–3 mm, oblong, lemma obscurely veined, usually with golden or brown tips; 6–7	Panicles becoming contracted, paleas 2-toothed, shortly projecting, anthers violet; 5–9	Plant reed-like, leaves 7–20 mm wide, panicle large, with many spikelets, lemmas blunt; 7–8	Panicles rather broad, loose, paleas usually shorter than the lemmas, anthers yellow; 6–8

a *Tawny Sedge, *Carex hostiana*: ♃, 30 to 60 cm; glumes dark brown with broad transparent margins, fruit ovoid, many ribbed; 5–6. **b *Bladder Sedge**, *Carex vesicaria*: ♃, 30–90 cm; leaves longer than inflorescence, ligule 5–8 mm long, fruits 4–5 mm long, ovoid, inflated, yellowish green, shining; 5–6. **c *Great Pond Sedge**, *Carex riparia*: ♃, 80–120 cm; ♂ spikes 5–6, lower ♀ spike long-stalked, nodding, fruit about 8 mm long; 5–6. **d *Lesser Pond Sedge**, *Carex acutiformis*: ♃, 40–120 cm; ♂ spikes 2–3, thick, contiguous, fruit about 4 mm long; 5–6. All are members of the Sedge Family widespread throughout Europe, on river-banks and in wet places.

a *Water Whorl-grass, *Catabrosa aquatica*:
♃, 10–60 cm; culm geniculate at base, panicle
loose, spikelets small, 1–3-flowered; 5–10.
b *Cut-grass, *Leersia oryzoides*: ♃, 30 to
120 cm; culm hairy at nodes, leaf-blades
spiny on margins; 8–9. **c** *Reed Canary-
grass, *Phalaris arundinacea*: ♃, 50–200 cm;
panicle long, lobed, sterile lemmas narrow,
short-hairy, fertile lemma firm, with appressed hairs, becoming smooth and shining
below; 6–7. **d** *Holy-grass, *Hierochloë odorata*: ♃, 20–50 cm; spikelets 3-flowered, lower
two florets ♂, uppermost bisexual; 4–6. All
are members of the Grass Family; river-banks,
ditches and wet places in most of Europe; **a**,
b and **d** local or rare, **c** common.

The Sweet Flag and the Bog Arum or Calla are widespread members of the Arum Family,
growing in ponds, ditches and on banks of rivers or lakes. The Bur-reeds are widespread in
most of Europe, growing in shallow water in rivers, ditches and lakes; the Small Bur-reed
is more common in the north, the Floating Bur-reed in mountainous areas up to 2300 m.
All belong to the Bur-reed Family.

	*Sweet Flag	†Bog Arum	*Small Bur-reed	*Floating Bur-reed	*Unbranched Bur-reed	*Branched Bur-reed
Scientific Name	*Acorus calamus*	*Calla palustris*	*Sparganium minimum*	*Sparganium angustifolium*	*Sparganium emersum*	*Sparganium erectum*
Longevity, Size	♃, 60–125 cm	♃, 10–40 cm	♃, 15–30 cm	♃, 10–100 cm	♃, 15–60 cm	♃, 60–160 cm
Distinguishing Features; Flowering Time	Leaves sword-shaped, frag-rant, scape flattened, spa-dix cylindrical, with numerous flowers; 7–8	Leaves rigid, spadix with hermaphrodite flowers below, ♂ above, in white spathe; 6–8	Leaves 2–6 mm wide, never keeled, ♂ head usually 1, ♀ heads 2–3; 6–7	Leaves usually semi-cylindric-al, not keeled, up to 8 mm wide, floating, ♂ heads 3–6, ♀ heads 2–3; 7–9	Stem unbran-ched, leaves 3-angled, floating leaves keeled, ♂ heads 3–8, distant, ♀ heads 2–5; 6–11	Stem branch-ed, branches with numerous ♂ and ♀ heads, leaves erect; 6–8

a *Great Duckweed, *Lemna polyrhiza*: ♃,
5 mm; thalli floating, each thallus with several
roots; 5–6. **b** *Ivy Duckweed, *Lemna trisulca*:
10 mm; thalli submerged, tapering at the base
into a stalk when mature; 6. **c** *Common
Duckweed, *Lemna minor*: ♃, 1.5–4 mm;
thalli floating, flat, each with a single root;
4–6. **d** *Gibbous Duckweed, *Lemna gibba*:
♃, 2–3 mm; thalli floating, strongly swollen
beneath, each thallus with a single root; 6–7;
rare. **e** *Rootless Duckweed, *Wolffia ar-
rhiza*: ♃, 1–1.5 mm; thalli ovoid to ellipsoid,
rootless; rare. All belong to the Duckweed
Family and grow in still water in most of
Europe.

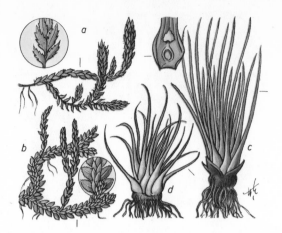

a ***Lesser Clubmoss**, *Selaginella selaginoides:* ♃, 2–5 cm; leaves spirally arranged; 7–8; in most of Europe. b **Swiss Clubmoss**, *Selaginella helvetica:* ♃, up to 20 cm; leaves in 4 rows, in pairs of differing size; 6–8; C and SE Europe. Both are members of the Selaginella Family found in damp grassy or mossy places, mainly on mountains. c ***Common Quillwort**, *Isoëtes lacustris:* ♃, up to 15 cm; leaves stiff, sporangia embedded in leaf-base below ligule; 7–9. d **Delicate Quillwort**, *Isoëtes setacea:* ♃, up to 10 cm; leaves flexible, megaspores with spines; 7–9. Both are members of the Quillwort Family found on lake beds in most of Europe.

All the plants illustrated below grow in reed-beds in still and slow-flowing water. The Lesser Reedmace and the Great Reedmace are local or widespread in most of Europe. Shuttleworth's Reedmace and the Least Reedmace are rare plants of S, E and SE Europe. The Slender Reedmace is a very rare species of SW Europe. All belong to the Reedmace Family. The Different-leaved Bur-reed occurs in C and N Europe; it belongs to the Bur-reed Family.

	Different-leaved Bur-reed	*Lesser Reedmace	Shuttleworth's Reedmace	*Great Reedmace	Least Reedmace	Slender Reedmace
Scientific Name	*Sparganium diversifolium*	*Typha angustifolia*	*Typha shuttleworthii*	*Typha latifolia*	*Typha minima*	*Typha gracilis*
Longevity, Size	♃, up to 60 cm	♃, 100–300 cm	♃, 50–100 cm	♃, 150–250 cm	♃, 30–75 cm	♃, up to 75 cm
Distinguishing Features; Flowering Time	Stems un-branched, leaves up to 5 mm wide, with a blunt tip, floating; 6–7	♂ and ♀ parts of spadix about equal in length, distant, usually 3–5 cm apart; 6–8	Leaves 5–10 mm wide, ♂ part of spadix shorter than ♀ part, contiguous; 7–8	Leaves 10–20 mm wide, ♂ and ♀ parts of spadix equal in length, usually contigous; 6–8	Stem leafy only at base, hermaphrodite part of spadix ovate, usually close to ♂ part; 5–6	Stem leafy, ♂ and ♀ parts of spadix slender, 5–25 mm apart; 5–9

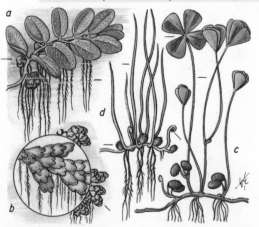

a **Salvinia** or **Water-fern**, *Salvinia natans:* ♃, up to 20 cm; leaves in whorls of three, one of which is finely split; 6–8; mainly C and SE Europe. b **†Azolla**, *Azolla caroliniana:* ♃, up to 1.2 cm; leaves imbricate, lobed; 6–7; a native of America, naturalized in many places. Both are floating members of the Water-fern Family. c **Marsilea**, *Marsilea quadrifolia:* ♃, 10–50 cm; leaves long-stalked, similar to Clover; 8–10; most of Europe. d ***Pillwort**, *Pilularia globulifera:* ♃, 3 to 10 cm; leaves subulate, sporangia of pea-size; 7–9; mainly W Europe. Both are members of the Marsilea Family found at the margins of still waters and on marshy ground.

a *Willow Moss, *Fontinalis antipyretica:* 2, 40 cm long; densely leafy, floating; grows entirely submerged. b *Floating Crystal-wort, *Riccia fluitans:* 2, up to 5 cm; thallus narrow or heart-shaped, forked; grows on or just below the surface of the water. c *Riccio-carpus, *Ricciocarpus natans:* up to 2 cm; thallus broadly-lobed, forked, somewhat fleshy, floating. d *Common Liverwort, *Marchantia polymorpha:* 2, 8 cm; dioecious, ♂ plants with antheridia, ♀ with archegonia; occurs on damp ground. a belongs to the True Mosses, b, c and d to the Liverworts.

The Water, Marsh and Field Horsetails are widespread throughout Europe, in damp places, the latter also on fields and meadows. The Boston Horsetail is found chiefly on the sandy banks of large rivers in S and C Europe, northwards to England, the Netherlands and Latvia. The Variegated Horsetail occurs mainly in north temperate zones of Europe and the Arctic, and in damp places in the Alps. All belong to the Horsetail Family. The Marsh Fern is widespread in marshes and fens and on moors; it belongs to the Polypody Family.

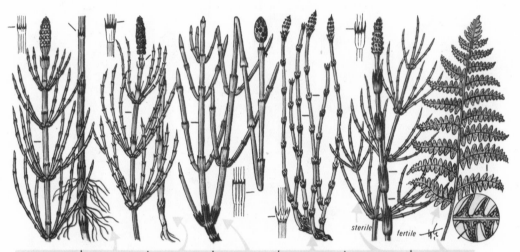

	*Water Horsetail	*Marsh Horsetail	*Boston Horsetail	*Variegated Horsetail	*Field Horsetail	*Marsh Fern
Scientific Name	*Equisetum fluviatile*	*Equisetum palustre*	*Equisetum ramosissimum*	*Equisetum variegatum*	*Equisetum arvense*	*Thelypteris palustris*
Longevity, Size	2, 30–120 cm	2, 15–50 cm	2, up to 80 cm	2, 20–50 cm	2, up to 50 cm	2, 30–80 cm
Distinguishing Features; Sporing Time	Sheaths with 10–30 teeth, black, at least at tip, not ribless, margins not scarious, stems grooved; 5–6	Sheaths with 4–12 teeth with wide whitish scarious margins, stems slightly scabrous; 7–8	Sheaths up to 22 mm long, stems with 6–16 convex ribs; 7–8	Sheaths bell-shaped, stems thin (3 mm in diameter) with 4–12 ribs; 6–8	Sheaths of fertile stems distant, with 6–16 teeth; 3–4	Fertile pinnae triangular, margins rolled back; 7–9

a Monk's Pepper Tree or Tree of Chastity, *Vitex agnus-castus:* shrub, 2–4 m; leaves white-downy beneath, flowers bluish violet, pink or white; 7–9; Verbena Family. b Rose Bay or Oleander, *Nerium oleander:* shrub up to 5 m; leaves leathery, flowers large, pink or white, sap milk-like, poisonous; 6–9; Periwinkle Family. c Spanish Reed, *Arundo donax:* 2, 2–4 m; similar to the Common Reed (page 106), but much stouter, culm up to 2 cm thick, panicle up to 70 cm long; 9–12; Grass Family. All are widespread at the edges of ponds and in the beds of streams in the Mediterranean region.

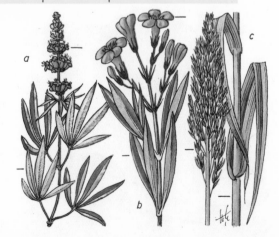

a **Pond Bat**, *Myotis dasycneme:* 6 cm + 5 cm, wingspan 20–28 cm; large ears. b ***Water** or **Daubenton's Bat**, *Myotis daubentonii:* 5 cm + 4 cm; small ears. Both are members of the Smooth-faced Bat Family which is native throughout much of Europe except the south; they prey on water insects. c ***Water Shrew**, *Neomys fodiens:* 9 cm + 7 cm; hind feet webbed, tail with keel of hair on underside; found almost through Europe, usually near water. d **Russian Desman**, *Desmana moschata:* 25 cm + 17 cm; no external ears, long snout; found in the region of the Lower Volga and the Don. c and d feed on insects, crustaceans, snails and other small animals.

The European Mink, the Mink and the Otter are members of the Weasel Family normally found by water. The European Mink has probably become extinct through much of the continent; the closely related Mink, introduced from N America, has escaped from fur farms and gone wild in some places, including parts of Great Britain. Raccoons, also introduced from N America, are found wild in a few localities in Holland and Germany, and a few European Beavers survive in remote areas in the northern part of Europe.

	Raccoon	†Mink	European Mink	*Otter	European Beaver
Scientific Name	*Procyon lotor*	*Mustela vison*	*Mustela lutreola*	*Lutra lutra*	*Castor fiber*
Size	70 cm + 26 cm	50 cm + 16 cm	40 cm + 14 cm	83 cm + 55 cm	90 cm + 31 cm
Distinguishing Features	Pointed muzzle, wide face with a black mask, tail ringed; Raccoon and Panda Family	Coat uniformly dark brown, woolly-haired, soft, chin white, many different-coloured varieties	Coat similar to the Mink but mostly with white upper lip, coat not so soft and woolly	Body elongated, legs short, feet webbed, broad muzzle	Coat brown, tail broad, flat, scaly, ears small, legs short; rodent of Beaver Family

a **Muskrat** or **Musquash**, *Ondatra zibethica:* 26–40 cm + 19–27.5 cm; body plump, tail flattened laterally; introduced from N America, it was once present in Britain but was exterminated because of the damage its burrows made in river-banks. b †**Coypu**, *Myocastor coypus:* 42–60 cm + 30–45 cm; round, sparsely haired tail, hind feet webbed; a fur-bearing relative of the porcupine introduced from S America, now spreading in Europe; attempts are being made to exterminate it in Britain. c ***Water-vole**, *Arvicola amphibius:* 16–22 cm + 9.8–14.4 cm; tail rather long, coat dark brown; lives near water in W Europe. a and c belong to the Mouse Family.

a *Goosander, *Mergus merganser:* 66 cm; large crest, ♂ head and neck dark, ♀ head and neck brown, throat white; partial migrant. b *Merganser, *Mergus serrator:* 58.5 cm; conspicuous crest, ♂ with white neck-band, ♀ head light brown, white throat-spot indistinct; partial migrant, usually found on the sea outside the breeding season. c *Smew, *Mergus albellus:* 40.5 cm; ♂ plumage white with black markings, ♀ smaller, greyer, with red cap; migrant. a and c winter on lakes, reservoirs, etc., and nest in tree holes, b among heather in the vicinity of water, in the far north, a and b also in Scotland. All are saw-bill ducks which feed on fish.

Grebes are diving birds with lobed feet, which nest in reed-beds on ponds and lakes. The Great Crested Grebe and the Dabchick or Little Grebe are common throughout Great Britain, and the Black-necked Grebe also occurs there; the Red-necked Grebe lives in E Europe; Slavonian or Horned Grebes around the C and N Baltic, in N Scotland and on the coast of Iceland. All are partial migrants. Grebes can swim long distances under water and when being watched may disappear, then surface some distance away.

	Red-necked Grebe	*Black-necked Grebe	*Dabchick	*Great Crested Grebe	*Slavonian Grebe
Scientific Name	*Podiceps griseigena*	*Podiceps caspicus*	*Podiceps ruficollis*	*Podiceps cristatus*	*Podiceps auritus*
Size	43 cm	30 cm	27 cm	48 cm	33 cm
Distinguishing Features	Summer: chin white, neck rust-red. Winter: neck grey; bill yellowish	Summer: neck black, yellow ear-tufts. Winter: neck grey; bill tilts upwards	Body dark, throat and cheeks chestnut-brown, light spot on bill	Neck white, ruff reddish, conspicuous black ear-tufts, no ruff in winter	Neck rust-red, head-tuft yellow, plumage black and white in winter

a *Common Pochard, *Aythya ferina:* 45 cm; ♂ plumage grey, head brown, breast dark, ♀ with blue band on bill. b *Ferruginous Duck, *Aythya nyroca:* 40.5 cm; ♂ head, neck and breast chestnut-brown, under tail-coverts white, ♀ paler. c *Tufted Duck, *Aythya fuligula:* 42.5 cm, ♂ with crest, head, neck, breast and back black, ♀ browner; increasing in numbers in Britain, the commonest diving duck in many ornamental waters. These are all diving ducks which nest in the reed-beds of inland lakes, chiefly in N Europe. All are partial migrants. Diving ducks normally swim away from the shore at night and remain in safety on the water until daylight.

111

a *Goldeneye, *Bucephala clangula*: 45.5 cm; ♂ with a white spot in front of the eyes, ♀ with brown head and white neck-band; breeds in holes; migrant. b Red-crested Pochard, *Netta rufina*: 56 cm; ♂ bill red, head light brown, ♀ cheeks white, crown dark; partial migrant. Both are diving ducks found on inland and coastal waters, a mainly in NE Europe, b also occurring there, but found in the extreme south. c White-headed Duck, *Oxyura leucocephala*: 45.5 cm; ♂ head white, bill blue, ♀ with cheek-stripe; a partial migrant, it is the only European stiff-tailed duck; lives on inland and brackish waters near the Mediterranean coast.

Water-birds of the Geese and Swans Subfamily are illustrated below. The Grey Lag Goose nests socially in E Europe, and on the coasts of Scandinavia, Scotland and Iceland in marshes and on moors. Bean Geese, Whooper Swans and Bewick's Swans are winter visitors from the tundra. Wild Mute Swans nest on remote lakes; in many places they have been domesticated but have subsequently returned to the wild.

juvenile

adult

cygnet

	*Grey Lag Goose	*Bean Goose	*Whooper Swan	*Bewick's Swan	*Mute Swan
Scientific Name	*Anser anser*	*Anser arvensis*	*Cygnus cygnus*	*Cygnus bewickii*	*Cygnus olor*
Size	76–89 cm	71–89 cm	151 cm	122 cm	151 cm
Distinguishing Features	Bill orange, without black, head light-coloured, legs flesh-coloured; partial migrant	Bill yellow, black at base and tip, head dark, legs orange; migrant	Much yellow at base of bill, coming to a point towards the front; neck held straight; migrant	Little yellow at base of bill, rounded towards the front; neck held straight; migrant	Bill orange red, with black knob which is smaller on ♀, neck S-shaped; partial migrant

a *Shoveller, *Spatula clypeata*: 51 cm; ♂ wing-coverts light blue, flanks dark brown, ♀ brown with blue shoulders; sifts its minute food from mud and water with its spoon-shaped bill; partial migrant. b *Mallard, *Anas platyrhynchos*: 58 cm; ♂ head green, white neck-ring, tail feathers turned up at tip, ♀ brown; the commonest wild duck in many areas, a partial migrant. Both are surface-feeders native to Britain and most of Europe. In winter they are found along the sea-coasts; they nest in damp meadows and marshes, the Mallard at times in holes and occasionally in trees. At night, surface-feeding ducks come ashore to roost.

a **Dalmatian Pelican**, *Pelecanus crispus:*
140–178 cm; hand-like dark brown pinions,
bill with throat pouch, legs lead-grey; breeds
in colonies in Greece. b **Pelican**, *Pelecanus
onocrotalus:* 140–178 cm; hand-like pinions
blackish, legs flesh-coloured; breeds in Bulgaria and Rumania. Both are partial migrants
belonging to the Pelican Family, and are rare
vagrants in C and W Europe. c **Flamingo**,
Phoenicopterus ruber: 127 cm; wings scarlet
and black; resident, a member of the Flamingo
Family, nests in colonies on mudbanks in
SW Europe, especially in the Camargue region
of France, where they have become a tourist
attraction.

Mandarin Ducks, introduced from E Asia as an ornamental species, are now widely established
in Europe. The other species shown are surface-feeders. All breed in Britain, the Garganey and
Teal also throughout Europe, the remainder mainly in the north and east. They nest on moors,
marshes and damp meadows, the Pintail at times on sand-dunes, the Teal sometimes away from
water in forests, where the Mandarin also nests in the trees. Diving ducks patter across water
before taking off, surface-feeders rise clear with a spring.

	*Gadwell	*Wigeon	*Pintail	*Garganey	*Teal	†Mandarin Duck
Scientific Name	Anas strepera	Anas penelope	Anas acuta	Anas querquedula	Anas crecca	Aix galericulata
Size	51 cm	46 cm	56 cm	38 cm	36 cm	43 cm
Distinguishing Features	♂ body grey, hind end black, speculum white, ♀ grey-ish brown, bill yellowish; par-tial migrant	♂ crown-stripe cream-colour-ed, bill short, ♀ brownish, shoulders lighter; par-tial migrant	♂ with pointed tail, bill grey, whiter neck-stripe, ♀ brown, tail pointed; par-tial migrant	♂ with white stripe over eyes, throat and sides of neck brown, ♀ brown; migrant	♂ with bluish white wing-stripes, ♀ dark brown, speculum green; par-tial migrant	♂ with an orange 'sail' on each wing, ♀ chin white; resident

a ***Bittern**, *Botaurus stellaris:* 76 cm; plumage brownish yellow, streaked and barred,
providing very effective camouflage, legs long,
green; now rare in Britain, surviving mainly
in the Fens, partial migrant. b **Little Bittern**,
Ixobrychus minutus: 36 cm; ♂ back black,
large, cream-coloured flight feathers, ♀ brownish, back dark brown; migrant. Both nest in
reed-beds on inland waters. c ***Heron**, *Ardea
cinerea:* 91 cm; plumage grey, long, black
crest; partial migrant, nests in heronries in
trees. All are members of the Heron and Bittern Family; they feed on fish and other water
animals, for which they stand in wait in the
shallows.

juvenile
a
adult
b
c

a Squacco Heron, *Ardeola ralloides:* 45.5 cm; body thickset, back brownish yellow, bill and legs greenish, young darker; migrant. **b Cattle Egret** or **Buff-backed Heron,** *Ardeola ibis:* 51 cm; bill and legs red, plumage with conspicuous yellowish brown feathers; migrant to S Spain and Portugal. **c Great White Heron,** *Egretta alba:* 89 cm; plumage white, legs and feet dark; partial migrant; Balkans and southern U.S.S.R. All are members of the Heron and Bittern Family which live in S Europe and nest on the ground in heronries, almost always near water. **b,** usually seen feeding on insects disturbed by herds of cattle, is now increasing its range throughout the world.

With the exception of the Demoiselle Crane, a member of the Crane Family, all the birds illustrated below are long-legged wading birds belonging to the Heron and Ibis Families. All are native to S Europe, the Ibises and Demoiselle Crane chiefly to Rumania; all like the proximity of water where they nest in reed-beds, on bushes, occasionally even in trees, the Demoiselle Crane always on dry ground.

	Little Egret	Purple Heron	Night Heron	Spoonbill	Glossy Ibis	Demoiselle Crane
Scientific Name	Egretta garzetta	Ardea purpurea	Nycticorax nycticorax	Platalea leucorodia	Plegadis falcinellus	Anthyopoides virgo
Size	56 cm	79 cm	61 cm	86 cm	56 cm	97 cm
Distinguishing Features	Plumage white, bill and legs black, feet yellow; partial migrant	Crown and crest black, neck rust-red with black stripes; migrant	Black head-cap and back, forehead white, legs yellowish; migrant	Plumage white, bill long, spoon-shaped, black, bill of young red; migrant	Bill decurved, plumage uniformly brown, glossy; migrant	Tuft of feathers behind eyes, chin, neck and breast black; partial migrant

*Osprey, *Pandion haliaëtus:* 51–58 cm; upper parts blackish, under parts snow-white, head white with black crest, talons bluish, outer toe opposable; migrant; Birds-of-Prey Family. Usually nests in trees in E Europe, Scandinavia and the Mediterranean region, and has recently returned to breed in Scotland after having been extinct there since about 1900. The osprey feeds on fish, mainly pike; it hovers over the water, drops suddenly and seizes the fish in its talons. When returning to land to eat its catch, the osprey shifts its hold and carries the fish head-first to reduce wind-resistance.

a *Coot, *Fulica atra:* 41 cm; white forehead, which gives it a bald appearance from a distance, legs green, toes with broad lobes; partial migrant. b *Moorhen, *Gallinula chloropus:* 33 cm; red bill and forehead, white stripe on flanks and white under tail-coverts, legs green with red 'garter', no webbing on toes; partial migrant. Both are water-birds of the Rail Family which swim with a jerking movement of the head. Both are noisy birds, and the coot is very aggressive. They nest by the water in reeds, moorhens at times also in trees in the old nests of large birds, throughout Europe except in the far north. Moorhens produce several broods in a season.

Long-legged birds of the Rail Family are described below. The Crested Coot and the Purple Gallinule live in S Spain, the latter also in Sardinia. Baillon's or Lesser Spotted Crakes are found in Spain, France, N Italy and the N Balkans. The Water Rail and the Spotted Crake are native to most of Europe, including Britain; the Little Crake is an E European species. All inhabit inland waters where they nest in reeds or other vegetation.

	Crested Coot	Purple Gallinule	*Water Rail	*Spotted Crake	Little Crake	Lesser Spotted Crake
Scientific Name	*Fulica cristata*	*Porphyrio porphyrio*	*Rallus aquaticus*	*Porzana porzana*	*Porzana parva*	*Porzana pusilla*
Size	40.5 cm	48 cm	28 cm	23 cm	19 cm	17.8 cm
Distinguishing Features	Similar to the Coot, but with red knobs on forehead; resident	Plumage dark blue, bill red, very large, legs red; resident	Bill longer than head, flanks with black and white bands; partial migrant	Plumage spotted, clearly banded on the flanks, legs green; partial migrant	Flanks unbanded, legs green, ♂ breast grey, ♀ brownish yellow; migrant	Legs brownish flesh-coloured, flanks with clear black and white bands; migrant

a Pratincole, *Glareola pratincola:* 23 cm; forked tail, light throat-spot, rust-red underwing linings show in flight; lives in the Balkans, Sicily, S France and S Spain. b Blackwinged Pratincole, *Glareola nordmanni:* 25.5 cm; similar to the Pratincole, but with black under-wings; lives in Rumania. a and b have both been recorded as vagrants in Britain. Both nest colonially in marshes. c Spur-winged Plover, *Haplopterus spinosus:* 26.5 cm; plumage black and white, with spur on wings; a N African and Asiatic species, nests from time to time in Greece. All three are migrants.

a *Common Sandpiper, Tringa hypoleucos:* 20 cm; back brown, dark patches at sides of breast, folded wings outlined in white at front; bobs tail when standing. **b *Little Ringed Plover,** Charadrius dubius:* 15 cm; white line over black forehead. Both nest in shingle on lake or river banks almost throughout Europe, including the British Isles. **c Marsh Sandpiper,** *Tringa stagnalis:* 23 cm; like a small Greenshank (page 56), but with white forehead. **d Terek Sandpiper,** *Xenus cinereus:* 23 cm; bill long and thin with a slight upward curve. Both nest on the waterside, **c** in the southern, **d** in the northern U.S.S.R. All are migrant Waders.

The Sand-martin, a member of the Swallow Family, nests in colonies on cliffs. Of the members of the Tit Family shown below the Bearded Tit nests low down among reeds, the Penduline Tit in a bag-shaped nest of moss, the Willow Tit in rotten tree-trunks and the Azure Tit in trees and bushes in the U.S.S.R., elsewhere as a vagrant. The White-spotted Bluethroat, which belongs to the Thrush Family, nests close to the ground in undergrowth. Sand-martins occur throughout Europe, the others more in N and E Europe.

	*Sand-martin	*Bearded Tit	Penduline Tit	*Willow Tit	Azure Tit	White-spotted Bluethroat
Scientific Name	*Riparia riparia*	*Panurus biarmicus*	*Remiz pendulinus*	*Parus atricapillus*	*Parus cyanus*	*Luscinia cyanecula*
Size	12 cm	16.5 cm	11 cm	11.5 cm	13.5 cm	14 cm
Distinguishing Features	Tail slightly forked, plumage earthy brown, under parts white, brown breast-band; migrant	Tail long, ♂ with black streak under chin, ♀ without streak; partial migrant, occurs in E Anglia	Back brown, head and nape light grey, ♂ with reddish brown sides to breast; partial migrant	Crown soot-black, throat-bib large, northern race lighter than southern; resident	Wings blue with a lot of white, cap snow-white, dark blue eye-stripe; partial migrant	♂ throat blue with white or red spot, ♀ U-shaped neck-spot; migrant

a Black-winged Stilt, *Himantopus himantopus:* 38 cm; legs very long, red; partial migrant, often wades in deep water, nests in colonies on mud, in Spain, S France and the Balkans. **b Grey Phalarope,** *Phalaropus fulicarius:* 20 cm; under parts rust-brown, cheeks white, ♂ paler, winter plumage white; migrant, nests by pools in the tundra. Phalaropes sit very high on the water when swimming. They are very trusting and will approach to within a few feet of humans. **c Pintailed Sand-grouse,** *Pterocles alchata:* 32 cm; ♂ with brown breast-band, ♀ with three breast-bands; resident, nesting on the ground in Spain, Portugal and the south of France. **a** and **b** occur occasionally in Britain.

*Kingfisher, *Alcedo atthis:* 16.5 cm; upper parts a magnificent blue, cheeks and under parts chestnut-brown, throat white, white spot on neck, tail and feet red, feet very small; a partial migrant, the only European species of the Kingfisher Family. It is found throughout Europe, except in the north, and nests near to all kinds of water in holes in banks which it excavates, and in which it lays about seven white eggs. Kingfishers usually spy out small fishes or insects from a branch overhanging the water and make sudden, lightning-swift dives to catch them; sometimes they hover over the water searching for food.

Dippers belong to the Dipper Family, the Warblers to the Warbler Family, and Reed Buntings to the Finch Family. All nest close to water in reed-beds, Reed Buntings also on the ground. Savi's Warbler is not found in the north. The Dipper is found by swift hill streams only, sometimes nesting in holes behind waterfalls; they can walk under water by spreading and angling their wings so that the pressure of water holds them down. Savi's Warbler and the Great Reed-warbler do not occur in Britain.

	*Dipper	**Savi's Warbler**	**Great Reed-warbler**	***Reed-warbler**	***Sedge-warbler**	***Reed Bunting**
Scientific Name	*Cinclus cinclus*	*Locustella luscinoides*	*Acrocephalus arundinaceus*	*Acrocephalus scirpaceus*	*Acrocephalus schoenobaenus*	*Emberiza schoeniclus*
Size	18 cm	14 cm	19 cm	13 cm	13 cm	15 cm
Distinguishing Features	Plumage dark brown, throat and breast snow-white, tail short; resident	Similar to the Reed-warbler, but tail often finely banded; migrant	Light eye-stripe, bill long, powerful; hanging nest on reed stems; loud song; migrant	Upper parts uniformly brown, under parts brownish white, eye-stripe indistinct; migrant	Eye-stripe cream-coloured, back striped, rump reddish brown; migrant	♂ head and throat black, white neck-band, ♀ with stripes under chin; partial migrant

a Yellow-breasted Bunting, *Emberiza aureola:* 14 cm; ♂ face black, ♀ head and sides striped; migrant, Finch Family; a rare winter visitor to Britain from the far north of Europe. **b Cetti's Warbler,** *Cettia cetti:* 14 cm; upper parts dark reddish brown, tail rounded; difficult to see in waterside undergrowth but has characteristic song; resident. **c Moustached Warbler,** *Lusciniola melanopogon:* 13 cm; crown almost black; nests usually in a bush overhanging water, partial migrant. **d Melodious Warbler,** *Hippolaïs polyglotta:* 13 cm; similar to Icterine Warbler (page 202), but browner; migrant. **b, c** and **d** are S European members of the Warbler Family which live in reed-beds.

a †Edible Frog, *Rana esculenta*: ♂ 7.5 cm, ♀ up to 12 cm; 5–6; back green, often with a pale line down the middle, underside pale, thighs yellow with dark blotches, vocal sacs whitish, hind foot webbing extends to the tips of the toes, metatarsal tubercle (M) large; lives in lowland waters from S Sweden to Italy and Rumania, and has been introduced into S England. **b †Marsh Frog**, *Rana esculenta ridibunda*: up to 17 cm; 4–5; back olive-green or brown, thighs pale grey and olive-brown, vocal sacs grey, webbing similar to **a**, but metatarsal tubercle (M¹) small; noisy in the breeding season; found from the Urals to Holland and introduced into SE England.

The European Tree-frog lives by water until it has spawned, then migrates to trees and bushes. Most toads lay strings of eggs; in the Midwife Toad, found from Spain to the Black Forest and introduced into England, the male carries the eggs. The Spade-foot Toad is a burrowing species. Common Toads are frequent in gardens, Green Toads are widespread, even in brackish water or dry places, and Spade-foot and Natterjack Toads are found in sandy and stony places, the latter also on dunes near the sea.

	European Tree-frog	*Common Toad	Green Toad	*Natterjack Toad	Spade-foot Toad	†Midwife Toad
Scientific Name	*Hyla arborea*	*Bufo bufo*	*Bufo viridis*	*Bufo calamita*	*Pelobates fuscus*	*Alytes obstetricans*
Size; Spawning	5 cm; 4–5	20 cm; 3–4	9 cm; 4–6	6–8 cm; 4–6	♂ 6.5 cm; 3–5	4.5–5.5 cm; 5
Distinguishing Features	Back leaf-green, pupils horizontal, adhesive discs on tips of fingers	Skin leathery brown, warty, iris gold to copper-red, pupil horizontal	Back with large green spots, iris greenish, pupil horizontal	Back with light-coloured lengthwise stripe, pupils horizontal, almost no webbing; walks	♀ larger (8 cm), back with long patches, pupils vertical, webbing large, horny 'spade' under foot	Upper parts bluish grey with warts, pupils vertical

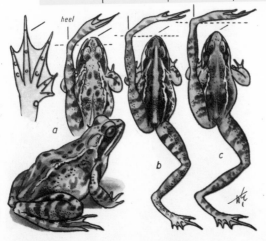

a *Common Frog, *Rana temporaria*: up to 10 cm; 3; colour very variable, webbing does not extend to the tips of the toes, snout blunt; swims using hind legs only; common throughout Europe except in the south, never found far from water as its skin, through which it breathes, must be kept moist. **b Moor Frog**, *Rana arvalis*: up to 8 cm; 3; similar to the Common Frog, but webbing hardly formed, snout pointed; found only in lowlands on marshy meadows. **c Agile Frog**, *Rana dalmatina*: ♂ 6 cm, ♀ up to 9 cm; 3; leg length without foot longer than body length; lives in deciduous forests in S Europe. All are True Frogs.

a Fire-bellied Toad, *Bombina bombina:* 4.5 cm; 5–9; belly bluish green with red patches and white spots, ♂ with two internal vocal sacs; lives on plains in E Europe. **b Yellow-bellied Toad,** *Bombina variegata:* up to 5 cm; 5–9; belly lemon-coloured with bluish grey patches; ♂ without vocal sacs; W Europe. Both toads always live in water. When alarmed, they assume a defence posture, arching the back and raising and twisting the forelegs outwards to show the bright warning colours on their bellies. **c Spotted Mud Frog** or **Parsley Frog,** *Pelodytes punctatus:* up to 4.5 cm; 4–9; pupils vertical, webbing very short; N Italy, France and Spain.

Newts are amphibians with long, laterally compressed tails. The Crested or Great Warty Newt, the Common or Smooth Newt and the Palmate Newt are native to Britain. The Palmate Newt is found only in C and W Europe, the others are common in ponds and lakes throughout the Continent. Alpine Newts live in hilly country, Smooth Newts in flat country, Carpathian Newts in the Carpathians, Tatra and Black Mountains, Marbled Newts in S France and the Iberian Peninsula. All feed on small water animals.

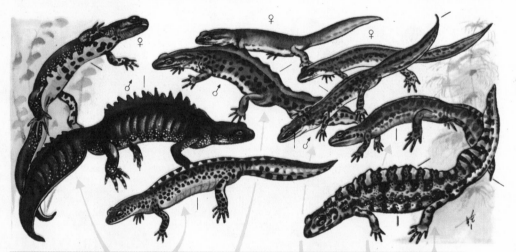

	*Crested Newt	Alpine Newt	*Common Newt	*Palmate Newt	Carpathian Newt	Marbled Newt
Scientific Name	*Triturus cristatus*	*Triturus alpestris*	*Triturus vulgaris*	*Triturus helveticus*	*Triturus montandoni*	*Triturus marmoratus*
Size; Spawning	18 cm; 3–5	10 cm; 5–6	11 cm; 3–5	9 cm; 3–7	♂ 7 cm; 4–5	16 cm; 2–5
Distinguishing Features	♂ with toothed crest on back and tail, back dark, ♀ with lighter line down back	Belly shining orange-red, sides covered with black spots	Head with 7 lengthwise stripes, back light olive-brown, ♂ with an undulate crest	♂ with thread-like tail end, two stripes along body, dark eye-stripe	Belly orange-red, tail with sharp edge at top and bottom and thread-like end; ♀ 10 cm	Body green with black marbling extending on to belly, back crest with cross bands

a Fire Salamander, *Salamandra salamandra:* 15–20 cm; 4–5 and up to 8; large yellow patches or stripes (striped form) on black skin; in damp copses in hilly country. **b Alpine Salamander,** *Salamandra atra:* 14–16 cm; skin shining black; gives birth on land to two fully-developed offspring; found in the Alps, often away from water. Both are land salamanders with poison-glands in the skin; their colouring warns off predators. **c Olm** or **Proteus,** *Proteus anguinus:* up to 25 cm; pinkish or yellowish white, red gills; lives in cave streams in Yugoslavia; it is blind, a typical feature of many cave-dwelling animals, which are often colourless.

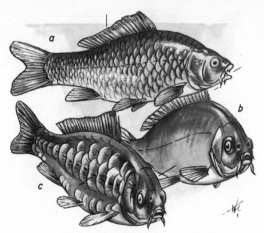

a †Common Carp, *Cyprinus carpio:* up to 1 m; 5–6; mouth terminal, upper lip with four barbels, dorsal fin long, with 3–4 hard and 17–22 soft rays, scales large and regularly arranged; originally a native of running and still water in Asia but now established throughout Europe, except in the north. There are two cultivated forms of the Common Carp: **b †Leather Carp,** almost devoid of scales; **c †Mirror Carp,** with a few very large scales. All are kept in carp ponds where, since they will use a wide variety of foods, they form a cheap and easily produced food for man.

The Crucian Carp, which is found throughout almost all of Europe in still, shallow water, has been introduced into E England. The Gibelio, which is the wild form of the goldfish, occurs in similar habitats on the Continent. Chub, Tench and Dace are found also in running water throughout most of Europe and in Great Britain. The Barbel is a bottom-dweler of swiftly flowing waters.

goldfish

	†Crucian Carp	Gibelio	*Tench	*Barbel	*Chub	*Dace
Scientific Name	*Carassius carassius*	*Carassius auratus gibelio*	*Tinca tinca*	*Barbus barbus*	*Squalius cephalus*	*Leuciscus leuciscus*
Size; Spawning	50 cm; 5–6	50 cm; 5–6	20 cm; 5–8	Up to 1 m; 5–7	20 cm; 4–6	27 cm; 3–5
Distinguishing Features	Dorsal fin high, anal fin short with 5–6 soft rays, no barbels, belly yellow	Like the Crucian Carp but scales larger, 27–31 scales along lateral line, no tail spot	Dorsal fin short, under fins rounded, two barbels, very slimy	Four barbels at the edge of the upper lip, dorsal fin shortly indented, 8–9 soft rays	Body elongate, almost cylindrical, base of scales black, lateral line with 44–46 scales	Body slender, caudal fin clearly forked, mouth inferior

a †Bitterling, *Rhodeus amarus:* up to 9 cm; 3–5; lateral line short, over 5–6 scales; ♀ lays its eggs, about 40 altogether, with a long ovipositor in the gills of the Swan Mussel or the Painter's Mussel (page 126), ♂ defends the mussel as its territory to prevent other Bitterling from spawning in it. **b *White or Silver Bream,** *Blicca björkna:* up to 30.5 cm; 5–6; similar to the Common Bream (facing page), body high, strongly compressed, eyes large. Both belong to the Carp Family and are found in still or slow-flowing waters from E Europe to France; the White Bream is found in E England, and the Bitterling has been introduced there.

a *Minnow, *Phoxinus phoxinus*: up to 13 cm;
5–7; back with about 15 transverse lines, mouth
terminal, lateral line usually incomplete.
b **Swamp Minnow**, *Phoxinus percnurus*:
up to 14 cm; 4–6; body plumper than the
Minnow, back high, sides thickly spotted;
found in E Europe and the U.S.S.R. c *Gudg-
eon, *Gobio gobio*: 15 cm; 5–6; mouth with
two short barbels, body almost cylindrical.
d *Gobio uranoscopus*: up to 15 cm; 5–6;
mouth inferior, upper jaw with two long
barbels; lives in the Danube area and the
Dniester. All are members of the Carp Family
which, apart from d, live in ponds and lakes
almost throughout Europe.

All the fish illustrated below belong to the Carp Family. The Common Bream and the Roach
are native throughout much of Britain and a large part of Europe. *Vimba vimba* is found in
S Scandinavia and, with the Zope, in rivers (chiefly the lower reaches) from the Elbe eastwards
to the Urals. The Pearlfish lives in some lakes and rivers north of the Bavarian Alps and the
Zobel occurs in the Danube basin. All carp are plant-feeders.

		Zope	*Common Bream	Zobel	Pearlfish	*Roach
Scientific Name	*Vimba vimba*	*Abramis ballerus*	*Abramis brama*	*Abramis sapa*	*Leuciscus meidingeri*	*Rutilus rutilus*
Size; Spawning	30 cm; 5–7	20–35 cm; 4–5	30–50 cm; 5–7	20–30 cm; 4–5	40–70 cm; 4–5	15–30 cm; 4–5
Distinguishing Features	Anal fin with 3 hard and 17–22 soft rays, mouth inferior, snout pointed, protruding	Lower rays of caudal fin very long, anal fin with 3 hard and 36–43 soft rays	Diameter of eye smaller than length of snout, anal fin with 3 hard and 23–28 soft rays	Eyes large, snout arched, anal fin with 3 hard and 38–45 soft rays	Body torpedo-shaped, almost cylindrical, mouth small; ♂ with 'pearls' during spawning time	Eyes with red ring, scales net-like, lateral line over 40–43 scales

a *Leuciscus virgo*: 20–40 cm; 4–5; mouth
inferior, 46–49 scales on lateral line. b **Ide**,
Idus idus: 30–75 cm; 4–7; mouth terminal,
54–59 scales on lateral line. c *Rudd, *Scard-
inius erythrophthalmus*: 20–30 cm; 4–6; top of
fins red, mouth opening narrow, very oblique. d **Moderlieschen**, *Leucaspius delineatus*:
6–10 cm; 4–5; mouth tilted upwards, lateral
line short. All four are small members of the
Carp Family found almost throughout Europe, although only the Rudd is native to Great
Britain, where it is common. The Rudd often
breeds with its near relatives the Dace and
the Roach, and fish showing mixed characteristics may sometimes be found.

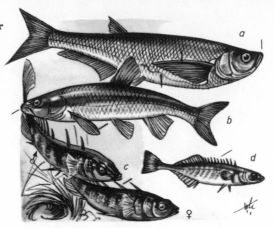

a Ziege, *Pelecus cultratus:* 25—40 cm; 5—7; similar to Sea Herring (page 152), but lateral line undulating, pectoral fins very long. **b Strömer,** *Telestes agassizii:* up to 24 cm; 3—5; pectoral fins with 1 hard and 13—14 soft rays, mouth opening almost horizontal. Both belong to the Carp Family. **a** occurs from the Baltic to the Caspian Sea and in associated rivers, **b** in S Europe. **c *Three-spined Stickleback,** *Gasterosteus aculeatus:* up to 10 cm; 5—6; three spines on back (shown in breeding colours, during the rest of the year usually silvery grey). **d *Ten-spined Stickleback,** *Pygosteus pungitius:* 5 cm; 5—6; 9—11 spines on back. Both belong to the Stickleback Family.

With the exception of the Shad all the fish shown below belong to the Carp Family. The Mairenke lives in brackish and slow-flowing water in the Danube area, the Bleak and the Nase generally north of the Alps, the Asp in E Europe. The Schneider likes swift-flowing, clear water, and the Shad, a member of the Herring Family, lives in the sea but comes to river estuaries for spawning. All these species are commercially valueless.

	Bleak	Mairenke	Schneider	Asp	Nase	*Twaite Shad
Scientific Name	Alburnus alburnus	Alburnus mento	Alburnus bipunctatus	Aspius aspius	Chondrostoma nasus	Alosa finta
Size; Spawning	10-15 cm; 4-6	15-25 cm; 5-6	9-15 cm; 5-6	40-70 cm; 4-6	25-40 cm; 3-5	30-40 cm; 5-6
Distinguishing Features	Mouth superior, anal fin with 3 hard and 17 soft rays; swims in shoals near the surface	Lower jaw thickened, protruding anal fin with 14-16 soft rays	Dark side-stripe, lateral line bent downwards slightly, fringed with black	Lower jaw thickened, projecting, dorsal fin with 3 hard and 8 soft rays	Snout protruding, edges of lips horny, dorsal fin with 3 hard and 9 soft rays	4-8 black spots in a row along each side, edge of belly serrated

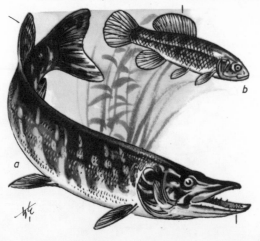

a *Pike, *Esox lucius:* average size 40–100 cm, but much larger fish recorded; 2–5; body elongated, snout protruding like a duck's bill, mouth slit to below the eyes, with numerous pointed teeth, dorsal fin far back on body; a powerful predator which will attack almost any prey, including water birds and mammals; found in still and slow-flowing water throughout Europe with the exception of Spain; Pike Family. **b Mud Minnow,** *Umbra krameri:* 9 cm; 2–5; dorsal fin long, situated well back; a member of the Mud Minnow Family, found in Austria and further east; the Pike's closest relative in Europe.

a Zingel, *Aspro zingel:* 15–20 cm; 3–5; front dorsal fin with 13–15 hard rays, back dorsal fin with 1 hard and 18–20 soft rays. **b Streber,** *Aspro streber:* 12–16 cm; 3–4; 1st dorsal fin with 8–9 spines, 2nd dorsal fin with 1 hard and 12–13 soft rays, long thin tail, body cylindrical. **c Schrätzer,** *Acerina schraetser:* up to 20 cm; 4–5; three to four dark, interrupted lines along the side, dorsal fin with 17–19 hard and 12–13 soft rays. All are elongated, spindle-shaped members of the Perch Family found in the Danube and its tributaries. The slightly flattened heads of these species indicate that they live on river-bottoms.

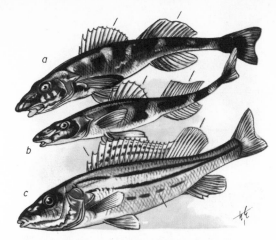

The Perch is widely distributed throughout the N Hemisphere, the Pikeperch and the Pope or Ruff are native to C and N Europe, including parts of the Baltic. The Pope occurs in E England and the Pikeperch has recently been introduced there. The tasty Common Sunfish, the Small-mouthed and the Large-mouthed Black Bass were introduced into Europe from America and have become well established in ponds and lakes. All are members of the Perch Family with pelvic fins set far forward.

	*Pope	*Perch	†Pikeperch	Small-mouthed Black Bass	†Large-mouthed Black Bass	Common Sunfish
Scientific Name	*Acerina cernua*	*Perca fluviatilis*	*Lucioperca lucioperca*	*Grystes nigricans*	*Micropterus salmoides*	*Eupomotis gibbosus*
Size; Spawning	25 cm; 3–5	30 cm; 3–6	40–50 cm; 4–6	45 cm; 4–6	35 cm; 3–7	10–15 cm; 5–6
Distinguishing Features	Body with dark spots, dorsal fin with 13–16 hard and 11–15 soft rays	Dark transverse band, both dorsal fins flexible, 1st spiny with black patches at rear	Dorsal fins with dark spots, 1st dorsal fin with 14, 2nd with 1 hard ray	Scales small, mouth small, extending to under the eyes	Scales large, mouth very large, extending to behind the eyes	Body very high, laterally compressed, mouth small, edged with small hooked teeth

a *Bullhead or **Miller's Thumb,** *Cottus gobio:* up to 18 cm; 2–5; fins large, flexible, scales along lateral line only, midway down body. **b Alpine Bullhead,** *Cottus poecilopus:* up to 13 cm; 2–5; lateral line along the upper third of the body, longest ray of ventral fin extends to the anus. Both belong to the Bullhead Family. **c *Burbot,** *Lota lota:* up to 60 cm; 11–3; lower jaw with barbel; belongs to the Cod Family and is good to eat. All are found in water with a stony bed, living on the bottom; they are predaceous on the eggs and fry of other fishes and may cause damage in trout-streams.

a †**Wels,** *Silurus glanis:* generally up to 150 cm but may grow up to over 3 m and weigh 300 kg; 5–6; head wide and flattened, mouth very wide, with two long sensory barbels on the upper jaw and four short barbels on the lower; lives in lakes and the larger rivers of C and E Europe and has been introduced into Britain in a few places. b †**Horned Pout,** *Ameiurus nebulosus:* up to 45 cm, 2 kg; 3–5; four barbels above and four below the mouth opening, adipose fin present, lateral line clearly marked; first introduced into Europe (including Britain) as a pond fish from America in 1885. Both belong to the Catfish Family.

The Spined Loach, the European Weatherfish or Pond Loach and the Loach live in brackish or running water throughout most of Europe, the latter being a prized edible fish; all belong to the Loach Family. The Eel, the sole representative of the Eel Family, is widely found in water with a muddy bottom. The Lampern or River Lamprey and the Brook or Planer's Lamprey (Lamprey Subclass) have no commercial significance, although they may in places damage more valuable fishes on which they are parasitic.

	Spined Loach	European Weatherfish	*Loach	*Common Eel	*Lampern	*Brook Lamprey
Scientific Name	Cobitis taenia	Misgurnus fossilis	Nemacheilus barbatulus	Anguilla anguilla	Lampetra fluviatilis	Lampetra planeri
Size; Spawning	10 cm; 4–6	30 cm; 4–6	15 cm; 4–5	♂ 50, ♀ 150 cm	13–50 cm; 4–5	12–30 cm; 3–6
Distinguishing Features	Upper jaw with 6 short barbels, row of 10–20 large spots under lateral line	Upper jaw with 6 long barbels, lower with 4 short ones, wide, brown band along side	Upper jaw with 4 shorter and 2 longer barbels, end of caudal fin straight	Dorsal, caudal and anal fins run together; mouth opening large; migratory; breeds in Sargasso Sea	Body eel-shaped, with 7 gill openings on each side, no pelvic or pectoral fins	Similar to the Lampern, but dorsal fins not separated, body of pencil thickness

a ***Sturgeon,** *Acipenser sturio:* up to 5.5 m; 4–7; four smooth, unfringed barbels, five rows of bony scutes along sides; occurs in the Atlantic and spawns in rivers flowing into it; rarely caught in British waters. b **Sterlet,** *Acipenser ruthenus:* up to 1 m; 5–6; snout long, four fringed barbels, 60–70 bony scutes along sides. c **Caspian Sturgeon,** *Acipenser stellatus:* up to 2 m; 5–6; snout very long, barbels unfringed. b and c inhabit the Black and Caspian Seas and the rivers flowing into them. All belong to the Sturgeon Family. Sturgeon have become rare in many of their old haunts through over-fishing and pollution of spawning grounds.

a *Great Pond Snail**, *Lymnaea stagnalis*: 5–6 cm high; first 4 of the 6–8 whorls very small; a general scavenger, but sometimes feeds on live animals up to the size of newts.
b *Ear Pond Snail**, *Lymnaea auriculata*: 2.5–3 cm high; body whorl very large, spire carried at right angles to foot, aperture ear-shaped. **c** *Lymnaea peregra*: up to 2.5 cm high; body whorl very large, spire (as in other pond snails except **b**) carried over foot.
d *Marsh Snail**, *Lymnaea palustris*: up to 3.5 cm high, 1.5 cm wide; aperture small, longish, whorls regular. All are members of the Pond Snail Family, which are widely found in still water.

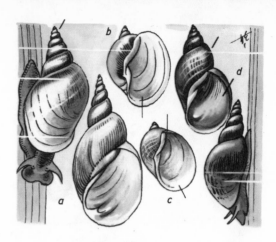

All the illustrations below are of lung-breathing snails of the Ramshorn Family, which without exception live in freshwater, chiefly in ponds and lakes with abundant plant life. All are widespread throughout Europe, many preferring hard water. Ramshorns have an hermaphrodite reproductive system. The flat, cake-shaped spawn contains 5–30 eggs.

	*Great Ramshorn	*Ramshorn	*Keeled Ramshorn	*Whirlpool Ramshorn	*Twisted Ramshorn	*Nautilus Ramshorn
Scientific Name	*Planorbis corneus*	*Planorbis planorbis*	*Planorbis carinatus*	*Planorbis vortex*	*Planorbis contortus*	*Planorbis crista*
Height; Width	12 mm; 30 mm	4 mm; 20 mm	2–3; 17 mm	1.5 mm; 10 mm	2 mm; 5–6 mm	1 mm; 3 mm
Distinguishing Features	Shell rounded, olive to brown, depressed like a funnel towards the centre	5–6 whorls, top deeply, bottom shallowly arched, keel near underside	Shell arched, similarly on both sides, keel on centre of last whorl	Shell very flat, lower edge of body whorl sharply keeled	7–8 whorls, tightly coiled, top flat, underside funnel-shaped	Shell with membranous ribs, top almost flat, underside forming wide funnel

a *Common River Snail**, *Viviparus viviparus*: 2.5–4 cm, ♀ larger than ♂ because eggs are retained until hatching; whorls arched, eyes on short stalks outside base of tentacles; herbivorous. **b** *Bythinia tentaculatus*: 1 cm; whorls flat. Both belong to the Freshwater Winkle Family. **c** *Common Valve Snail**, *Valvata piscinàlis*: 5 mm; whorls as high as the aperture. **d** *Flat Valve Snail**, *Valvata cristata*: 1–2 mm; disc-shaped. **c** and **d** have eyes inside bases of tentacles; both are found more commonly in running water. **e** *Paladilhia helvetica*: 2.5 mm; tower-shaped; occurs in the Jura.

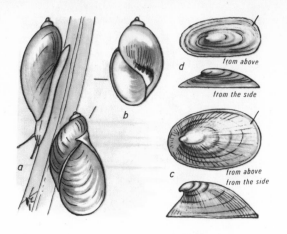

from above
from the side

from above
from the side

a *Large Amber Snail,** *Succinea putris:* up to 2.2 cm high, 1.2 cm wide; shell very thin, convex, amber-coloured; Amber Snail Family; lives near water and on damp meadows. **b** *Bladder Snail,** *Physa fontinalis:* up to 10 mm high, 6–8 mm wide; shell thin, highly polished, sinistral, three whorls very small, body whorl very large; Bladder Snail Family; very active, lives in running water with abundant plant life. **c** *River Limpet,** *Ancylus fluviatilis:* up to 4 mm high; shell cup-shaped; feeds on water-plants, especially on Willow Moss (page 109). **d Lake Limpet,** *Axiolotus lacustris:* 2 mm high; shell shield-shaped. **c** and **d** belong to the Freshwater Limpet Family.

All the molluscs illustrated below belong to the Freshwater Mussel Family. *Anodonta complanata* and the Swan Mussel live in still or slow-flowing water with a muddy bottom, the Painter's Mussel, *Unio crassus* and the Pearl Oyster or Pearl Mussel in quickly flowing water. The Swollen River Mussel prefers still water in backwaters and lakes. In some areas there is a minor industry gathering pearls from these mussels.

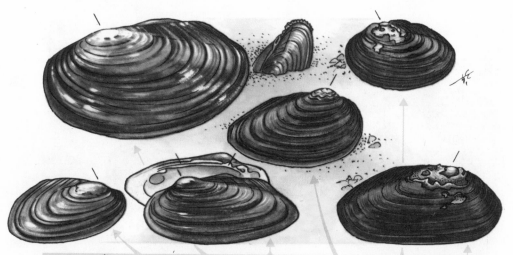

	*Swan Mussel	*Painter's Mussel	*Swollen River Mussel		*Pearl Oyster
Scientific Name	*Anodonta complanata	Anodonta cygnea	Unio pictorum	Unio tumidus	Unio crassus	Margaritifera margaritifera
Size	Up to 8 cm	Up to 20 cm	7–10 cm	6.5–9 cm	Up to 6 cm	Up to 12 cm
Distinguishing Features	Shell very flat, elliptic-ally ovate, thin-walled, edge of hinge without teeth	Shell broadly ovate, convex, greatest height under umbo, edge of hinge without teeth	Shell long, narrow, tongue-shaped, umbo inflated, hinge with teeth and fluting	Umbo with hooks, shell wedge-shaped, greenish brown	Shell ovate, thick-walled, umbo consid-erably inflated	Shell ovate to kidney-shaped, thick-walled, umbo not prominent

a *River Pea Mussel,** *Pisidium amnicum:* 11 mm long, 8.5 mm high; umbo situated right at the back. **b** *Lake Mussel,** *Sphaerium lacustre:* up to 8 mm long, 5.5 mm high; umbo elongated; widespread but not common in Britain. **c** *Sphaerium solidum:* 15 mm long, 11 mm high; shell convex, thin. All belong to the Pea Mussel Family; **a** has only one siphon, **b** and **c** have two. **d** *Zebra Mussel,** *Dreissena polymorpha:* 3–4 cm long, up to 1.8 cm high; shell triangular, thin, umbo pointed; similar to the Common Marine Mussel (page 165), but shell brown; one of the few freshwater molluscs to produce plank-tonic larvae; Zebra Mussel Family; lakes and rivers.

a ***Great Water Beetle** or **Diving Beetle**, *Dytiscus marginalis:* 30–35 mm; pronotum and elytra yellow-edged, underside yellow, hind legs fringed with long hairs for swimming, with two claws. **b** *Cybister lateralimarginalis:* 30–35 mm; hind feet with one claw, tibia of hind leg very short. **c** *Dytiscus latissimus:* 36–44 mm; elytra very broad. **d** **Graphoderus cinereus:* 15 mm; in Britain occurs only in East Anglia. All are Carnivorous Water Beetles feeding on many types of prey; found in pools and ponds, they may also cause considerable damage in fish hatcheries. They trap air for breathing under their wing-cases, coming to the surface tail-first to do so.

The Two-spotted Agabus and *Colymbetes fuscus* are Carnivorous Water Beetles—insects with long, flattened, long-haired hind legs. The Whirligig Beetle swims over the water in circles. The Great Silver Water Beetle and *Hydrochara caraboides* are plump, slow insects which put their heads above water to trap air for breathing under their wing-cases. The last three species mentioned are scavenging beetles of various families.

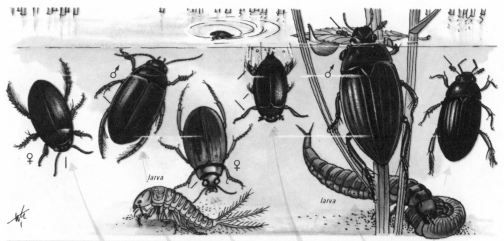

	*Two-spotted Agabus			***Whirligig Beetle**	***Great Silver Water Beetle**	
Scientific Name	*Agabus bipustulatus*	**Colymbetes fuscus*	**Hygrobia hermanni*	*Gyrinus natator*	*Hydrous piceus*	**Hydrochara caraboides*
Size	12 mm	15 mm	12 mm	5–7 mm	38 mm	14–18 mm
Distinguishing Features	Body black, head often with two red spots, antennae red	Similar to the Great Water Beetle, but smaller, edges rust-red, upper side brown	Brownish red, elytra with black lengthwise stripes	2 long prehensile legs, 4 short swimming legs, 2 pairs of eyes see above and below water	Large, pitch-black, antennae short, club-shaped	Similar to the Great Silver Water Beetle, but smaller

a ***Grooved Acilius**, *Acilius sulcatus:* 16 to 18 mm; pronotum with two black bands, ♀ elytra with 3–4 lengthwise ribs with thick hairs between them, front tarsi sucker-like, larva similar to that of the Great Water Beetle, but the thorax has a long first segment which gives it the appearance of a long neck; often found in still water. **b** **Platambus maculatus:* 8 mm; elytra striped with varying shades of yellow. **c** **Hyphydrus ovatus:* 4.5–5 mm; body very convex above and below. **d** **Hydroporus palustris:* 3.5–4 mm; upper side black with yellow patches. All belong to the Carnivorous Water Beetle Family; they attack a wide range of freshwater animals.

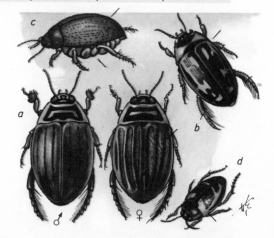

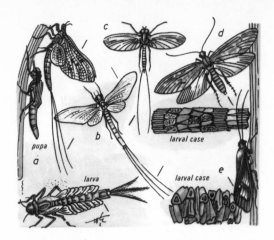

a *Mayfly or **Greendrake**, *Ephemera vulgata:* 1.7 cm; 5–7; wings transparent, shining, 3 tail bristles. b *Ephoron virgo:* 1.6 cm; 7–9; wings whitish, 3 tail bristles. c *Baëtis pumilus:* 6 mm; 6–8; hind wings very small, 2 tail bristles. All are Mayflies. They spend most of their lives in the larval stage in water; after emergence the adults mate and die within a few hours. d *Phryganea grandis:* 5 cm; 4–6; wings hairy. e *Limnephilus rhombicus:* 2 cm; 5–8; wings roof-like, with few hairs. d and e are both common Caddis Flies, found on still or slow-flowing water; the larvae build protective tubes which vary in material and form according to species.

The Dronefly belongs to the Hoverfly Family, *Lispa dentaculata* to the House Fly Family and the Blackfly to the Blackfly Family; the other species illustrated below are Mosquitoes. All are more or less tied to still or slow-flowing water, since they lay their eggs in water and the larvae develop there. Blackflies, Common Gnats and female Mosquitoes suck the blood of other animals.

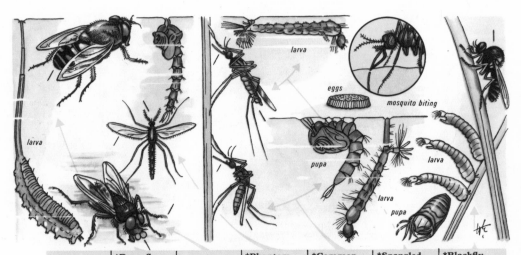

	*Dronefly		*Phantom	*Common Gnat	*Spangled-winged Mosquito	*Blackfly
Scientific Name	*Eristalis tenax*	*Lispa dentaculata*	*Corethra plumicornis*	*Culex pipiens*	*Anopheles maculipennis*	*Simulium reptans*
Size; Flying	12 mm; 6–9	6.5 mm; 6–8	6 mm; 5	♂ 5 mm; 5–9	6 mm; 4–8	2 mm; 7–9
Distinguishing Features	Body plump, covered with hair; bee-mimic; larva's rat-tail is a telescopic breathing tube	Mouth feelers spoon-shaped, resembles House Fly (page 264); runs on the surface	Wings hairy, unspotted, proboscis not adapted for piercing as in other mosquitoes	♀ 6 mm; sits parallel to support, ♀ sucks blood with long piercing proboscis	Sits obliquely to support, otherwise similar to the Common Gnat, wings spotted	Body of ♂ velvet black, of ♀ brownish black, wings very long, humpbacked appearance

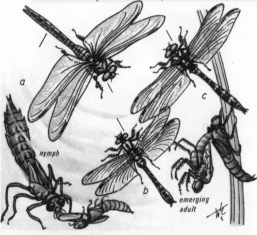

a *Emperor Dragonfly,** *Anax imperator:* 7–8 cm; 6–9; largest British dragonfly; eyes large, green. b ***Club-tail Dragonfly,** *Gomphus vulgatissimus:* length up to 5.5 cm; 5–7; eyes far apart. c *Cordulegaster bidentatus:* 7–8.5 cm; 6–7; eyes touch each other. All are swift-flying insect hunters of the Hawker Dragonfly Family found by brooks and rivers, a also by still water. Their prey may include large insects such as butterflies; the prey is carried in the basket formed by the dragonfly's hairy legs. Dragonflies cannot fold their wings; at rest they are held at right angles to the body; in flight, the pairs of wings are used independently, and make a rustling sound.

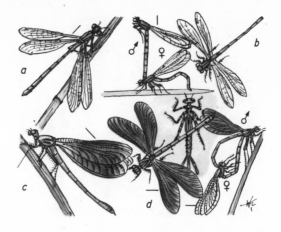

a *Lestes viridis:* up to 4.5 cm; 7–10; wings light, uniform colour, with distinct stalks. b ***Common Coenagrion,** *Coenagrion puella:* 3.5 cm; 5–9; ♂ body sky-blue with black joints and U-shaped mark on 2nd segments, ♀ back black, sides apple-green. c ***Banded Agrion,** *Agrion splendens:* 4–5 cm; 5–8; metallic colouring, ♂ blue, ♀ green, ♂ wings with broad blue band, ♀ wings greenish, without band. d ***Demoiselle Agrion,** *Calopteryx virgo:* 4–5 cm; 5–9; ♂ wings dark blue, ♀ wings dull greyish green. All are Damselflies, which are capable of folding the wings over the back when at rest. They may be found hawking for food by the banks of still and slow-flowing water.

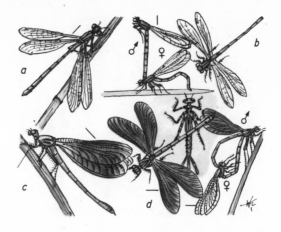

The species of *Aeschna* and *Cordulia* illustrated below are Hawker Dragonflies; the others are Darter Dragonflies. All are swift fliers which have a well defined beat over the pools and ponds where they hunt insects. They spread their wings out horizontally when at rest. They may sometimes be seen well away from water, occasionally in large numbers on migration.

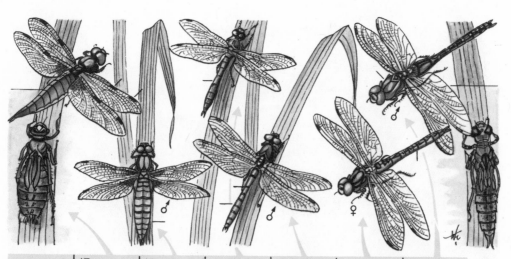

	*Four-spotted Libellula	*Broad-bodied Libellula	*Downy Emerald	*Brilliant Emerald		*Southern Aeschna
Scientific Name	*Libellula quadrimaculata*	*Libellula depressa*	*Cordulia aënea*	*Somatochlora metallica*	*Aeschna viridis*	*Aeschna cyanea*
Size; Flying	4–7.5 cm; 5–8	5 cm; 5–8	5.5 cm; 5–7	5.5 cm; 6–8	7 cm; 7–9	7 cm; 7–9
Distinguishing Features	Base of wings brownish yellow, each with a centre and end spot; a migratory species	♂ abdomen wide, flattened, bluish; ♀ abdomen yellowish brown	Body golden green, without any yellow spot, abdomen rather short	Body with brilliant metallic sheen, abdomen constricted at 3rd segment	Forehead with black stripe, ♀ body basically green, ♂ blue	Forehead with dark spot, top of thorax dark brown with two oval spots, colour variable with age

a ***Water Scorpion,** *Nepa cinerea:* 26 mm; body grey, flattened, rear end of abdomen with breathing tube; does not sting, but can bite. Found among plants at edge of water, locally in S England. b ***Water Stick Insect,** *Ranatra linearis:* 35 mm; body reddish, long breathing tube. Both belong to the Water Scorpion Family; they feed on small insects and other creatures, which they capture and hold with modified grooved forelimbs. c **Saucer Bug,** *Hyocoris cimicoides:* 35 mm; body compressed, hind legs with swimming hairs. d *Aphelocheirus aestivalis:* 8.5–10 mm; body compressed. c and d give their names to two families of swimming bugs.

a *Lestes viridis:* up to 4.5 cm; 7–10; wings light, uniform colour, with distinct stalks. b ***Common Coenagrion,** *Coenagrion puella:* 3.5 cm; 5–9; ♂ body sky-blue with black joints and U-shaped mark on 2nd segments, ♀ back black, sides apple-green. c ***Banded Agrion,** *Agrion splendens:* 4–5 cm; 5–8; metallic colouring, ♂ blue, ♀ green, ♂ wings with broad blue band, ♀ wings greenish, without band. d ***Demoiselle Agrion,** *Calopteryx virgo:* 4–5 cm; 5–9; ♂ wings dark blue, ♀ wings dull greyish green. All are Damselflies, which are capable of folding the wings over the back when at rest. They may be found hawking for food by the banks of still and slow-flowing water.

a *Water Spider, *Agyroneta aquatica:* ♀ 15 mm, ♂ 8 mm; abdomen with fine hairs which hold an air-bubble, which gives a silvery appearance under water; this is trapped under a small web to make a diving-bell to live in; Water Spider Family. **b** *Pirate Spider, *Pirata piratica:* 8 mm; body with downy hair; hides with feet resting on water, detects prey by vibrations on surface, runs out over surface to catch it. **c** *Dolomedes fimbriatus:* ♂ 12 mm, ♀ 20 mm; body brown with yellowish white edges. **b** and **c** belong to the Swamp Spider Family. **d** *Tetragnatha extensa:* 17 mm; 8 eyes in two rows, body small; Orb-web Spider Family. All live by water.

The Water Boatman or Backswimmer and *Corixa punctata* are water-dwellers belonging to the Water Boatman Families; they swim by rowing movements of the legs, and rise to the surface to breathe. The Water Measurer or Water Gnat, the Great Pond Skater and the Water Cricket are bugs which run only on the surface of the water, the Water Cricket only on running water. *Podura aquatica* is a Springtail, found in groups in quiet spots on the surface.

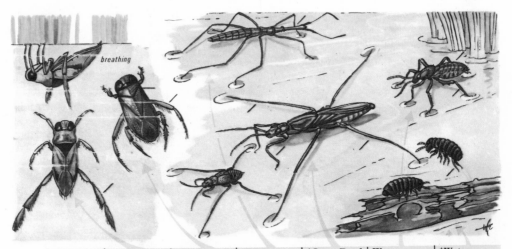

breathing

	*Water Boatman	*Lesser Water Boatman	*Water Measurer	*Great Pond Skater	Water Cricket	*Water Springtail
Scientific Name	*Notonecta glauca*	*Corixa punctata*	*Hydrometra stagnorum*	*Aquarius najas*	*Velia caprai*	*Podura aquatica*
Size	13–16 mm	Up to 14 mm	Up to 12 mm	♂ 13 mm	6–7 mm	Up to 1.5 mm
Distinguishing Features	Back wedge-shaped, light-coloured, hind legs very long, hairy; swims on its back; bites	Front of back with 15–16 transverse lines, middle legs the longest	Crawls slowly over water on six legs; part of head in front of eyes twice as long as that behind	Runs rapidly on the four hind legs, front legs hold the prey, ♀ larger	Legs short, belly thick, runs on six legs	Body plump, black, minute forked spring on abdomen

a *Crayfish, *Astacus fluviatilis:* up to 20 cm, ♀ somewhat smaller; spawning time 5–6; pointed spike on forehead, red areas at the leg joints. **b** *Cambarus affinus:* up to 20 cm; 5–6; similar to **a**, but with dark red transverse bands on the abdominal segments; introduced from America. Both are long-tailed decapod crustaceans of the River Crayfish Family. They live in still and running water, especially where there is a high content of lime, necessary for the formation of the heavy shell. **a**, which is excellent to eat, is declining in numbers, possibly through water pollution and over-fishing in some areas. **b** lives in some rivers and lakes in NC Europe.

a **Mitten Crab,** *Eriocheir sinensis:* carapace
up to 7 cm long and 9 cm wide; pincers large,
covered with thick felty hair; originates from
China and has become widespread from the
Baltic to the Atlantic coast of France (recorded
once from Britain, but not established there),
in still or running water. b **River Crab,**
Potamon fluviatile: carapace up to 5 cm long
and wide; edge of forehead smooth, slightly
curved; clear streams in the Mediterranean
region. c ***Apus,*** *Triops cancriformis:* up to
10 cm total length; 4—11; large carapace;
widespread but rare, found in shallow pools;
in Britain only ♀ usually found.

Atyaephyra desmaresti comes from the Mediterranean region and has been introduced into
Holland and the Rhineland. Water Lice and Freshwater Shrimps are common everywhere;
Asellus cavaticus and *Niphargus puteanus* live in wells, caves and underground streams, the latter
also in springs. The Water Louse and *Asellus cavaticus* belong to the Water Louse Family, the
Freshwater Shrimp and *Niphargus puteanus* to the Freshwater Shrimps. Fish Lice are parasitic
on many fish, frequently infesting the gill areas.

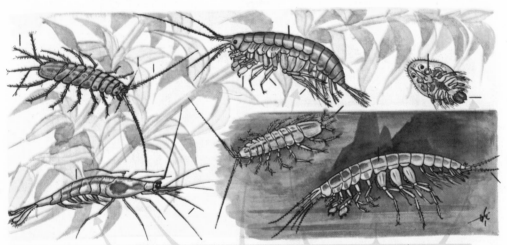

		*Water Louse		*Freshwater Shrimp		*Fish Louse
Scientific Name	*Atyaephyra desmaresti*	*Asellus aquaticus*	**Asellus cavaticus*	*Gammarus pulex*	*Niphargus puteanus*	*Argulus foliaceus*
Size	Up to 20 mm	Up to 25 mm	5–8 mm	♂ 20 mm	♂ 30 mm	♀ up to 8.5 mm
Distinguishing Features	Body transparent, narrow, pincers on 1st and 2nd pairs of walking legs	Body flat, one pair of long and one of short antennae	Body transparent, tail-bristles short, no eyes	♀ 15 mm; body laterally flattened; swims or moves about on its side	♀ 18 mm; body transparent, with long tail fork; occurs in caves or wells	Body plate-like, abdomen two-lobed, lower jaws form two suckers

a *Lepidurus apus:* up to 6 cm with fork;
carapace large, oval; found in snow-melt
pools. b **Fairy Shrimp,** *Branchipus schaef-
feri:* up to 11.5 mm; 5–9; two short and two
long antennae. c **Brine Shrimp,** *Artemia
salina:* 8–11 mm; antennae short, eyes stalked;
swims upside-down; found in salt-lakes,
where the concentration of salt may be higher
than in sea-water; once occurred in the British Isles but now probably extinct there.
d ***Opossum Shrimp,*** *Mysis relicta:* up to
20 mm long; eyes stalked, carapace broader
at rear. All these species are rare although
relatives of **d** are very common in the sea.

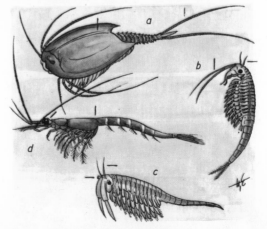

a *Medicinal Leech, *Hirudo medicinalis:* 3.5 cm; six reddish lengthwise stripes; bloodsucker on mammals. b *Horse Leech, *Haemopis sanguisuga:* 3.5 cm; ten eyes, back darkly spotted; eats small animals. Both are members of the Jawed Leech Family, which are widespread in ponds, lakes and ditches; the Medicinal Leech is now rare in Britain. c *Piscicola geometra:* up to 5 cm; body round, suckers circular. d *Glossiphonia complanata:* up to 3 cm; two dark lengthwise stripes along the top. c and d belong to the Sucker Leech Family, which feed on fishes, snails or worms. All leeches are capable of great elongation when moving.

Tubifex tubifex, Stylaria lacustris and *Eiseniella tetraëdra* are members of the Earthworm Order. The commonest is *Tubifex tubifex,* which is often found in thousands on muddy beds. *Stylaria lacustris* swims freely in water. Many different kinds of Flatworms are found in freshwater; the species illustrated live on plants or under stones and may be distinguished by their colour and by the number and arrangement of their eyes.

Scientific Name	*Tubifex tubifex	*Stylaria lacustris	Eiseniella tetraëdra *Square-tailed Worm	*Dendrocoelum lacteum	*Polycelis cornuta	*Planaria gonocephala
Size	Up to 8 cm	Up to 1.8 cm	3–5 cm	Up to 2.5 cm	Up to 2 cm	2.5 cm
Distinguishing Features	Head in the mud, rear end waves about in the water (breathing)	Head drawn out into a long 'tongue', pair of eye-spots	Middle and rear parts of body four-angled, clitellum long	Body milk-white, head with short moveable tentacles, two black eyes	Colour varied, head with two awl-like tentacles, many marginal eyes	Head triangular, two kidney-shaped eyes

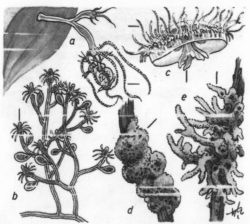

a *Common Hydra, *Hydra vulgaris:* up to 1 cm; body grey, tentacles retractable. b *Cordylophora caspia:* 5 cm; colony with many branching tubes. c *Craspedacusta sowerbyi:* up to 1.9 cm; resembles a small jellyfish. These are Coelenterates related to familiar sea-shore creatures (pages 174–6); like them, they feed on smaller animals which they subdue with poisonous stings. d *River Sponge, *Ephydatia fluviatilis:* body often pale in colour when not exposed to light. e *Pond Sponge, *Euspongilla lacustris:* body with finger-like projections. d and e are Sponges which form encrusting growths on plants, wood or stones in the water.

Sea and Shore

In this section are included plants and animals living in open water, in shallows, on rocky coasts and rock-pools, on sea-walls and other sea defences, along the high-water mark on sandy or gravelly shores by the open sea, on coastal sand-dunes, muddy shores with mudflats, salt-marshes and fens. As a result of the diversity of this environment a correspondingly rich plant and animal life has evolved along the sea-coasts, often specially adapted to the saline content of the sea water, which in the North Sea is from 30 to 33 per cent and in the western Baltic from 13 to 20 per cent. Thus, many salt-water plants are succulent, for example, the Common Glasswort and the Seablite. Because of the muddy and sandy deposits, different animals, particularly many shellfish, snails and worms, obtain their nourishment and make their homes in marshy places beside the sea, known as saltings. Flocks of shore birds, which nest on the shore, in the nearby dunes or on the fens, visit the saltings at low-tide for food.

In the foreground in the illustration there are, from left to right, an Oystercatcher, a Turnstone, a pair of Ringed Plovers and a Sheld-duck. Behind them are two Common Gulls, a Common Seal, a group of Dunlin in breeding plumage and, on the post, a Redshank. The ducks swimming on the sea are a pair of Eiders. Flying on the left of the picture are a number of Herring Gulls, and on the right several Terns, one of which, a Little Tern, is seen diving on its prey. Many sedentary animals, for example Bryozoans, Sea-squirts, Worms and Coelenterates, and many plants, especially Green, Brown and Red Algae (seaweed), grow in colonies on the coast, anchored on solid objects such as rocks and man-made sea defences.

133

a *Creeping Willow, *Salix repens:* shrub, 30–150 cm; stems creeping to erect, leaves silky beneath, capsules greyish-downy; 4–5; in most of Europe; Willow Family. b *Sea Buckthorn, *Hippophaë rhamnoides:* shrub, 1–5 m; willow-like, thorny, flowers dioecious, inconspicuous, fruit berry-like, orange-red; 3–5; widespread. c Narrow-leaved Oleaster, *Elaeagnus angustifolia:* shrub up to 8 m; thorny, leaves silvery-white beneath, fruit berry-like, reddish yellow; 5–6; Mediterranean region. Both belong to the Oleaster Family. d *Burnet Rose, *Rosa spinosissima:* prickly shrub, 10–40 cm; flowers usually cream-white, without bracts; 5–7; widespread; Rose Family.

The Toothed Melilot (Baltic coast and salty areas inland in N and E Europe) and the Sea Pea (dunes and shingle along the North Sea and Baltic) belong to the Pea Family. The Sweet Alison (a native of the Mediterranean region, widely naturalized elsewhere), the Sea Rocket (a drift-line plant of sandy and shingly shores), the Sea-kale (shores and cliffs along the Atlantic and Baltic coasts and round the Black Sea) and the Broad-leaved Pepperwort (salt-marshes and on wet sand throughout Europe, except the far north) belong to the Crucifer Family.

	Toothed Melilot	*Sea Pea	†Sweet Alison	*Sea Rocket	*Sea-kale	*Broad-leaved Pepperwort
Scientific Name	*Melilotus dentatua*	*Lathyrus maritimus*	*Lobularia maritima*	*Cakile maritima*	*Crambe maritima*	*Lepidium latifolium*
Longevity, Size	☉, 15–60 cm	♃, 20–50 cm	☉–♃, 9–30 cm	♃, 15–45 cm	♃, 40–60 cm	♃, 30–100 cm
Distinguishing Features; Flowering Time	Leaves pinnately trifoliate, closely and sharply serrate, flowers yellow; 5–9	Leaflets large, mostly 4-paired, stipules hastate, flowers purple to blue; 6–8	Stems much-branched, petals white, entire, fruits obovate, slightly hairy; 6–9	Leaves fleshy, simple or pinnately divided, flowers lilac to pink, fruits 2-jointed; 7–10	Cabbage-like leaves very large, long-stalked, glaucous, flowers white, fruits 2-jointed; 5–6	Basal leaves crenate-toothed, stem leaves entire or distantly toothed, fruits almost circular; 6–7

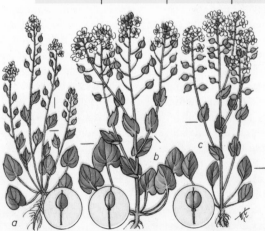

a *Danish Scurvy-grass, *Cochlearia danica:* ☉, 2–20 cm; basal leaves roundish or more or less triangular, heart-shaped at base, stem leaves ivy-like, usually stalked; 1–6. b *Common Scurvy-grass, *Cochlearia officinalis:* ☉–♃, 10–25 cm; basal leaves orbicular to kidney-shaped, heart-shaped at base, stem leaves coarsely toothed, clasping the stem; 5–8. c *Long-leaved Scurvy-grass, *Cochlearia anglica:* ☉–♃, 5–35 cm; basal leaves oblong or obovate, wedge-shaped at base, upper leaves heart-shaped at base, clasping the stem; 4–7. All are members of the Crucifer Family, found on sea-coasts.

a *Sea-holly, *Eryngium maritimum:* ♃, 30–60 cm; glaucous, leaves spinous-toothed, bracts broadly 3-lobed, spinous-serrate, flowers bluish, stalkless, in dense heads; 6–10; on sandy and shingle shores. **b** *Smallest Hare's-ear, *Bupleurum tenuissimum:* ☉, 10–50 cm; umbels with 1–4 rays, partial umbels with 4–5 flowers, bracts and bracteoles subulate; 7–9; in salt-marshes and waste places. **c** *Wild Celery, *Apium graveolens:* ☉, 30–100 cm; basal leaves simply pinnate, lobed and serrate, umbel with 6–12 rays, bracts and bracteoles absent; 6–10; in damp places near the sea, by rivers and ditches. All belong to the Carrot Family.

The Sea Pearlwort and the Dark-green Mouse-ear are locally common plants of sand-dunes, dune-slacks, rocks and sandy or stony places near the sea. The Sea Spurreys occur mainly in muddy and sandy salt-marshes. The Sea Sandwort is widespread on mobile sand and sandy shingle. All these species belong to the Pink Family. The Sea Beet, a member of the Goosefoot Family, is a local plant of sea-shores throughout Europe.

	*Sea Pearlwort	*Greater Sea Spurrey	*Sea Spurrey	*Sea Sandwort	*Dark-green Mouse-ear	*Sea Beet
Scientific Name	Sagina maritima	Spergularia media	Spergularia marina	Honkenya peploides	Cerastium atrovirens	Beta vulgaris subsp.maritima
Longevity, Size	☉, 2–12 cm	♃, up to 40 cm	☉, 2–20 cm	♃, 5–25 cm	☉–☉, 5–25 cm	☉, 20–80 cm
Distinguishing Features; Flowering Time	Sepals hooded, half-spreading in fruit, petals small, often absent; 5–8	Capsule 8–10 mm, seeds all with a broad scarious wing; 7–9	Capsule not exceeding 7 mm, seeds winged or not; 5–9	Leaves ovate, acute, very fleshy, yellowish green, flowers greenish white, clustered; 6–7	Bracts, bracteoles leafy, flowers usually tetramerous, sepals glandular-hairy, except at tip; 3–4	Basal leaves, long-stalked, inflorescence large, much-branched, flowers 2–4 per cluster; 6–9

a Bassia, *Bassia hirsuta:* ☉, up to 30 cm; leaves linear, mostly scabrous, flowers 1–2 in each leaf-axil; 8–9; rare, on sandy sea-shores in S and C Europe. **b** *Herbaceous Sea-blite, *Suaeda maritima:* ☉, 10–20 cm; leaves small, half-terete, acute and narrowed at base, fleshy; 7–9; common in salt-marshes and on sea-shores. **c** *Saltwort, *Salsola kali:* ☉, up to 60 cm; much-branched, leaves with spine at tip; 7–9; widespread on sandy shores. **d** *Common Glasswort, *Salicornia europaea:* ☉, 15–30 cm; leaves fleshy, opposite, the pairs fused along their margins and enveloping the stem; 8–9; common, in muddy salt-marshes. All belong to the Goosefoot Family.

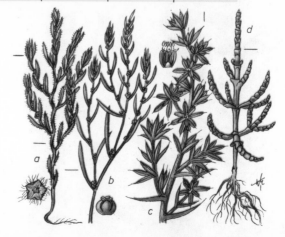

a *Stalked Sea Purslane, *Halimione ped-
unculata:* ☉, 3–30 cm; leaves silvery-mealy,
fruits long-stalked; 8–9. b *Common Sea
Purslane, *Halimione portulacoides:* a mealy
shrub, 40–100 cm; fruit stalkless, bracteoles
usually 3-lobed; 7–9. c *Frosted Orache,
Atriplex laciniata: ☉, 15–110 cm; mealy white
or almost silvery, bracteoles united up the
middle, hardened below; 8–9. d *Shore
Orache, *Atriplex littoralis:* ☉, 15–110 cm;
bracteoles 3-angled, toothed, united only at
base; 7–8. All are members of the Goosefoot
Family, found by the North Sea and Baltic;
a and **b** in salt-marshes and wet meadows,
c and **d** on sand and gravel.

The Sea Bindweed belongs to the Bindweed Family and is found on sandy and shingly sea-shores.
The Fragrant Toadflax occurs only on the Baltic coast and in S Russia; the Spiked Speedwell is
widespread, from S Scandinavia to C Spain, Italy and Greece, occurring in various types of
habitats, including sand-dunes. Both belong to the Figwort Family. The Sea Wormwood and the
Sea Aster are widespread. The Buttonweed is probably a native of S Africa, but is now widely
distributed in Europe.

	*Sea Bindweed	Fragrant Toadflax	*Spiked Speedwell	*Sea Wormwood	*Sea Aster	†Buttonweed
Scientific Name	*Calystegia soldanella*	*Linaria odora*	*Veronica spicata*	*Artemisia maritima*	*Aster tripolium*	*Cotula coronopifolia*
Longevity, Size	♃, 10–40 cm	☉, 15–60 cm	♃, 15–45 cm	♃, 30–70 cm	♃, 15–100 cm	☉–♃, 8–50 cm
Distinguishing Features; Flowering Time	Stem procumbent, leaves heart- to kidney-shaped, fleshy; 6–8	Leaves glaucous, flowers fragrant, in loose racemes, 16–18 mm long; 6–8	Stem pubescent in the upper part, leaves opposite, coarsely toothed; 7–9	Strongly aromatic, leaves white-downy, flower-heads bright yellow or orange; 8–9	Leaves fleshy, flower-heads in loose corymbs, ray-florets usually blue-purple; 7–9	Strongly aromatic, leaves deeply toothed to pinnatifid, heads with tubular florets; 7–8

a *Seaside Centaury, *Centaurium vulgare:*
☉–☉, 2–25 cm; basal leaf-rosette, corolla-tube
nearly as long as calyx; 7–8; local, on dunes
and sandy places, N and W Europe; Gentian
Family. b *Sea Pink or Thrift, *Armeria
maritima:* ♃, 6–20 cm; leaves fleshy, flowers
pink, in solitary terminal head; 5–7; coastal
salt-marshes, rocks and cliffs, also on mountains inland. c *Sea-lavender, *Limonium
vulgare:* ♃, 15–45 cm; inflorescence corymbose, spikelets crowded into spikes; 8–9;
muddy salt-marshes. Both belong to the Sea-
lavender Family. d *Sea Milkwort, *Glaux
maritima:* ♃, 10–30 cm; leaves small, fleshy;
6–8; usually on sea-shores; Primrose Family.

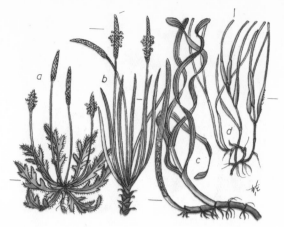

a *Buck's-horn Plantain, *Plantago coron-opus:* ⊙-♃, 2–20 cm; leaves pinnatifid or toothed, hairy; 6–9; on sandy and gravelly soil, most common near the sea. **b** *Sea Plantain, *Plantago maritima:* ♃, 5–60 cm; leaves linear; 6–10; in salt-marshes and grassy places near the sea, also by mountain streams. Both belong to the Plantain Family. **c** *Common Eel-grass** or **Grass-wrack,** *Zostera marina:* ♃, 30–40 cm; flowering stems branched, leaves 3–7 mm wide, sheaths entire; 5–6. **d** *Dwarf Eel-grass,** *Zostera nana:* ♃; flowering stems unbranched, leaves 1–2 mm wide, notched, sheaths split; 5–7. **c** and **d** belong to the Eel-grass Family and grow on muddy shores.

The Sand Sedge grows on sandy shores all round Europe, except the far north, the French Sedge mainly on the North Sea and Baltic. The Salt-marsh Sedge, the Dotted Sedge and the Distant Sedge are found on dunes, salt-marshes and fens along the Baltic and North Seas and on many North Sea islands. The Bottle Sedge is widely distributed throughout Europe, occurring in wet peaty places, also near the sea. All are members of the Sedge Family.

	*Sand Sedge	French Sedge	*Salt-marsh Sedge	*Bottle Sedge	*Dotted Sedge	*Distant Sedge
Scientific Name	*Carex arenaria*	*Carex ligerica*	*Carex extensa*	*Carex rostrata*	*Carex punctata*	*Carex distans*
Longevity, Size	♃, 7–50 cm	♃, 7–40 cm	♃, 10–40 cm	♃, 25–90 cm	♃, 15–45 cm	♃, 20–80 cm
Distinguishing Features; Flowering Time	Far-creeping in straight lines, terminal spikes ♂, lower ♀, middle ones sometimes ♂ at top; 5–7	Spikes 4–7, usually all ♀ at the top, ♂ in the lower part of the inflorescence; 5–7	Grass-green, ♂ spike stalk-less, ♀ ones usually contig-uous, bracts very long; 7–8	Bluish green, ♂ spike 2–4, fruits long-beaked, inflated; 5	Yellowish-green, glumes reddish brown, fruits without ribs, dotted; 5–7	Greyish green, glumes green-ish brown, fruits distinctly ribbed; 5–6

a *Coiled Tassel-pondweed** or **Sea Ruppia** *Ruppia spiralis:* ♃, 1–25 cm; stalks of the inflor-escence spirally coiled; 8–10; brackish ditches near the sea; Tassel-pondweed Family. **b** *Sea Arrow-grass,** *Triglochin maritima:* ♃, 10 to 100 cm; stigmas 6, flowers in dense racemes; 5–8; salt-marshes and grassy places on rocky shores; Arrow-grass Family. **c** *Sea Rush,** *Juncus maritimus:* ♃, 5–120 cm; leaves thick, terete, sharply pointed; 8–10; salt-marshes. **d** *Baltic Rush,** *Juncus balticus:* ♃, 30 to 70 cm; far-creeping, in straight lines, base of stem with yellowish brown sheaths; 8–10; dune-slacks and other damp sandy places. Both belong to the Rush Family.

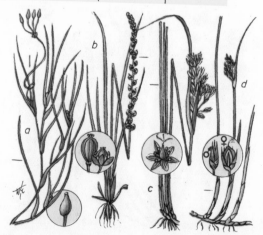

a *Mud Rush, *Juncus gerardii:* ♃, 5–70; rhizome far-creeping, stems stiffly upright, flattened below, nearly terete above; inflorescence loose, perianth nearly equalling the fruit; 6–9; widespread, in salt-marshes. **b Frog Rush,** *Juncus ranarius:* ☉, up to 20 cm; branches of inflorescence usually with 2 or 3 flowers; 6–9. **c *Dwarf Rush,** *Juncus pygmaeus:* ☉, 1–10 cm; flowers 1–5, in heads, capsule straw-coloured, pointed; 5–10; widespread, local. **d Flattened Rush,** *Juncus anceps:* ♃, 10–60 cm; inflorescence of numerous 3–6-flowered heads, stem and leaves strongly flattened; 7–8; W Mediterranean region, Atlantic Europe. All belong to the Rush Family.

Members of the Grass Family which are found along sea-coasts are illustrated below. The Reedlike Foxtail grows in salt meadows in W, N and E Europe, the other species in sandy places, often on dunes. The Marram-grass is widespread. The Lyme-grass grows in N and W Europe, the Sand Couch in W Europe, northwards to S Scandinavia, the Sand Cat's-tail or Sand Timothy from the Mediterranean region to S Scandinavia and the Curved Sea Hard-grass from the Mediterranean to S and E England.

	*Lyme-grass	*Marram-grass	*Sand Couch	Reedlike Foxtail	*Sand Cat's-tail	*Curved Sea Hard-grass
Scientific Name	*Elymus arenarius*	*Ammophila arenaria*	*Agropyron junceiforme*	*Alopecurus arundinaceus*	*Phleum arenarium*	*Parapholis incurva*
Longevity, Size	♃, 100–150 cm	♃, 60–100 cm	♃, 30–60 cm	♃, 60–125 cm	☉, 8–15 cm	☉, 15 cm
Distinguishing Features; Flowering Time	Rhizomatous, leaves bluish grey, spikelets usually in pairs 3–6-flowered, lemmas densely hairy; 6–8	Rhizomatous, leaves greyish green, inrolled, panicles spike-like, spikelets 1-flowered; 6–7	Rhizomatous, leaves densely and minutely hairy on ribs above, axis of the spike fragile; 6–8	Panicle spike-like, lemma awned on back just below the middle, shorter than the glumes; 5–7	Panicle spike-like, up to 4 cm long, narrowed at the base, lemma about ⅓ length of glumes; 6–7	Spikes rigid, curved, spikelets 1-flowered, in the hollows in the spike-axis; 5–6

a *Reflexed Salt-marsh-grass, *Puccinellia distans:* ♃, 15–50 cm; lower branches of panicle deflexed; 6–10; widespread. **b *Common Salt-marsh-grass,** *Puccinellia maritima:* ♃, 30–100 cm; branches of panicle usually erect; 6–9; W Europe. Both belong to the Grass Family, grow in salt-marshes. **c *Sea Club-rush,** *Scirpus maritimus:* ♃, 15–120 cm; stems 3-angled, rough towards the top; 6–8; widespread. **d *Brown Club-rush** or **Narrow Blysmus,** *Blysmus rufus:* ♃, 3–40 cm; leaves involute, rush-like; 5–6; N and W Europe. **e *Dwarf Spike-rush,** *Eleocharis parvula:* ♃, 2–8 cm; leaves setaceous, channelled, spikelet greenish; 7–9; widespread. All belong to the Sedge Family.

a **Sea Medick**, *Medicago marina:* ♃, 10 to
40 cm; plant woolly-downy; 4–7; Pea Family.
b ***Horned-poppy**, *Glaucium flavum:* ⊙-⊙,
30–50 cm; leaves glaucous, flowers yellow;
5–8. c **†Red Horned-poppy**, *Glaucium corni-
culatum:* ⊙, 15-50 cm; petals red or orange,
with a black, white-margined spot at the base;
5–8. b and c belong to the Poppy Family. d
Caper Bush, *Capparis spinosa:* ♃, up to
100 cm; shrub-like, leaves ovate, fruits known
as capers; 7–8; Caper Family. All these plants
grow on sandy shores or cliffs in the Mediterranean region.

The Three-horned Stock is a member of the Crucifer Family which grows on sea-shores in
southern parts of the Mediterranean region. The Land Caltrops (Bean-caper Family) occurs in
sandy places, along roadsides and on waste ground; the Purple Spurge and the Sea Spurge
(Spurge Family) are widespread; the Shrubby Glasswort (Goosefoot Family) prefers damp,
salty muddy places; and the Silky Catchfly (Pink Family) is a local plant of sandy shores.

	Three-horned Stock	Land Caltrops	*Purple Spurge	*Sea Spurge	Shrubby Glasswort	Silky Catchfly
Scientific Name	*Matthiola tricuspidata*	*Tribulus terrestris*	*Euphorbia peplis*	*Euphorbia paralias*	*Salicornia fruticosa*	*Silene sericea*
Longevity, Size	⊙, 10–40 cm	⊙, 10–130 cm	⊙, 5–25 cm	♃, 30–60 cm	♃, up to 40 cm	♃, 40–70 cm
Distinguishing Features; Flowering Time	Flowers purple, fruits 4–10 cm long, with three horns; 7–8	Flowers small, yellow, fruit separating into 5 woody spiny carpels; 5–10	Plant procumbent, leaves and bracts not differing, stipules present; 5–10	Plant upright, leaves and bracts differing, stipules absent; 3–8	Branches jointed, leaves reduced, flowers in stalked spikes; 9–10	Flowers large, petals pink, notched; 5–6

a **Sea Squill** or **Sea Onion**, *Urginea maritima:* ♃, 15–120 cm; bulb very large, up to
2 kg, flowers white; 9–12; sand, rocks and
dry hills near the sea; Lily Family. b **Sea-
daffodil** or **Mediterranean Lily**, *Pancratium
maritimum:* ♃, 30–40 cm; flowers white,
fragrant, corona with 2-toothed segments;
7–9; on coastal sands; Daffodil Family.
c **Posidonia**, *Posidonia oceanica:* ♃, 20 to
40 cm; submerged form up to 30 m; flowers
in head-like inflorescences; 10; grows in the
sea; Posidonia Family. d ***Hare's-tail**,
Lagurus ovatus: ⊙, 10–30 cm; panicle spike-
like, dense, very softly hairy, bristly; 5–6; dry
places near the sea; Grass Family. All are
natives of the Mediterranean region.

a *Sea Grass, *Enteromorpha compressa:* up to 30 cm; plants tubular, compressed, up to 1 cm wide, narrowed at base. **b** *Sea Lettuce, *Ulva lactuca:* up to 25 cm; plants with broad lobes, having wavy margins. **c** *Bryopsis, *Bryopsis plumosa:* up to 10 cm; plant without transverse cell-walls, being branched into two rows of pinnate filaments. **d** *Acrosiphonia, *Acrosiphonia arcta:* up to 8 cm; uniaxial filaments branch freely, producing, in addition to the ordinary branches, small hooks and coils which unite filaments in groups. All belong to the Green Algae and occur in the North Sea, in some cases also in the Baltic.

Of the Brown Algae in the table, the Bladder Wrack and Spiral Wrack are particularly common throughout Europe on rocks, stones and wood along sea-coasts. The other species are chiefly or exclusively found on rocky shallows.

	*Bladder Wrack	*Spiral Wrack	*Serrated Wrack	*Cuvie	*Tangle	*Sea Belt
Scientific Name	*Fucus vesiculosus*	*Fucus spiralis*	*Fucus serratus*	*Laminaria hyperborea*	*Laminaria digitata*	*Laminaria saccharina*
Size	Up to 100 cm	Up to 30 cm	Up to 60 cm	Up to 150 cm	Up to 300 cm	Up to 400 cm
Distinguishing Features	Plants with pairs of air vesicles, conceptacles ♂ or ♀ (dioecious)	Plants without air vesicles, each conceptacle with ♂ and ♀ reproductive bodies (monoecious)	Plants sharply serrate, up to 5 cm wide, thallus without air vesicles, dioecious	Lamina wide, split at the ends, stipe (stalk) compressed, base of lamina heart-shaped	Lamina split into linear strap-like segments, leathery	Lamina ribbon-like, leathery, up to 30cm wide, shining brown, undulate at or near margins

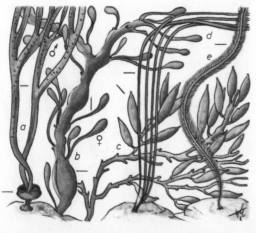

a *Sea Thong, *Himanthalia elongata:* up to 300 cm when reproductive; vegetatively a button-like structure 4 cm across, conceptacles ♂ or ♀, then reproductive parts belt-shaped, branched. **b** *Knotted Wrack, *Ascophyllum nodosum:* up to 150 cm; air vesicles large, conceptacles stalked, round or oval, dioecious. **c** *Sea Oak, *Halidrys siliquosa:* up to 200 cm; air vesicles pod-shaped, mucronate. **d** *Sea Lace, *Chorda filum:* up to 300 cm; fronds cord-like, up to 5 mm thick. **e** *Hairy Chorda, *Chorda tomentosa:* up to 100 cm; plant densely hairy. All belong to the Brown Algae.

a *Carragheen or Irish Moss, *Chondrus crispus:* 15 cm; frond-clusters fan-shaped, tough, leathery, violet-red to dark purple-brown. b *Purple Laver, *Porphyra umbilicalis:* up to 15 cm wide; lamina leaf-like, thin, often split, violet-red. c Common Phyllophora, *Phyllophora brodiaei:* up to 15 cm; lobes of the lamina deep red, leathery, stalked. d Red Phyllophora, *Phyllophora crispa:* up to 15 cm; similar to the latter, but lamina more uniformly wide. All these species belong to the Red Algae, and are found in the North Sea, particularly near Heligoland, at times also in the Baltic.

Of the Red Algae shown in the table, the Cockscomb and Plumaria are only found in the North Sea, chiefly on rocky shallows. The other species live also in the W Baltic; Hildenbrandia is found on flat beaches covering stones, Corallina (a calcareous seaweed: its cell walls store up calcium carbonate) and Furcellaria occur in greater depths.

	Hildenbrandia	*Delesseria	*Cockscomb	*Plumaria	*Furcellaria	*Corallina
Scientific Name	Hildenbrandia prototypus	Delesseria sanguinea	Plocamium vulgare	Plumaria elegans	Furcellaria fastigiata	Corallina officinalis
Size	Up to 15 cm	Up to 15 cm	Up to 25 cm	Up to 10 cm	Up to 25 cm	Up to 10 cm
Distinguishing Features	Skin-like, blood-coloured to brownish red, forming smooth and firm crusts on stones	Delicate plants, leaf-like, with thick midrib and lateral veins, crimson-red	Tips of branchlets comblike, somewhat cartilaginous, rose-red	Branches in one plane, plumose segments in two rows, brownish red to blackish	Fronds forked, cartilaginous, blackish, ♂ tips of branches yellow, ♀ club-shaped	Branches opposite, calcareous, 1–2 mm thick, club-shaped

a *Membranoptera, *Membranoptera alata:* up to 10 cm; terminal segments 2-lobed. b *Pepper Dulse, *Laurencia pinnatifida:* up to 10 cm; plants cartilaginous, flat, branched. c *Common Red Ceramium, *Ceramium rubrum:* up to 15 cm; plants jointed, tips pincer-shaped. d Halarachnion, *Halarachnion ligulatum:* 15 cm; plant strap-shaped, ligulate-fringed at the margins. All belong to the Red Algae, and are found in the North Sea, a and c also in the W Baltic.

a Polar Bear, *Thalarctos maritimus:* ♂ up to 2.5 m + 10 cm, ♀ up to 1.85 m + 10 cm; coat yellowish white; swims very well and can dive for up to two minutes; ♀ hibernates in holes in the snow, in which from 1–3 cubs are born in February or March; a carnivore of the Bear Family. **b Walrus,** *Odobenus rosmarus:* ♂ 3–4.5 m, ♀ up to 3 m; body yellowish brown, upper canines very long, longer on the ♂ than the ♀, hind feet can turn forwards; swims well and can dive for up to 10 minutes and to a depth of 30 m; belongs to the same group of carnivores as the Seals and Sea-lions. Both live among the pack-ice and drift-ice of the Arctic Ocean.

Of the seals in the table only the Grey or Atlantic Seal and the Common Seal breed round Britain, the Grey Seal mainly on the west and north coasts; all the others are only seen occasionally. The Ringed, Bearded, Harp or Greenland Seals, and the Hooded Seal or Bladdernose live among the drift-ice, the Ringed and Grey Seals on cliffs and rocky coasts and also in the central and northern parts of the Baltic. Young seals are born singly; they are large, and are soon able to swim and to care for themselves.

	*Common Seal	Ringed Seal	Harp Seal	Bearded Seal	*Grey Seal	Hooded Seal
Scientific Name	*Phoca vitulina*	*Phoca hispida*	*Phoca groenlandica*	*Erignathus barbatus*	*Halichoerus grypus*	*Cystophora cristata*
Size	Up to 1.9 m	Up to 1.8 m	Up to 2.2 m	Up to 3.1 m	Up to 3.3 m	Up to 2.35 m
Distinguishing Features	Back with dark spots on a light background, white vibrissae	Light rings on dark background, brown vibrissae	♂ with long saddle-like mark on back, ♀ browner, saddle smaller, pups white	Skin brown, upper lip with very long light-coloured vibrissae	Skin colour mostly grey with black spots, ♀ usually with larger spots than ♂, pups white	Body light grey, head and flippers black, ♂ with inflatable nasal organ

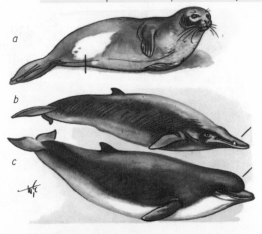

a Monk Seal, *Monachus monachus:* 3.8 m; light patch on side of body; inhabits the coasts of the Mediterranean and Black Seas but has, however, been almost exterminated. **b Sowerby's Whale,** *Mesoplodon bidens:* 4.9 m; head small, long pointed 'beak'. **c Bottle-nosed Whale,** *Hyperoodon ampullatus:* ♂ up to 9 m, ♀ up to 7.5 m; conspicuously protuberant forehead; said to be able to dive for from 1–2 hours and to a depth of 1300 m. **b** and **c** are Toothed Whales of the N Atlantic; Sowerby's Whale is also found in the Mediterranean. They feed on medium-sized fishes and on squid, which they seize and swallow whole.

a Sperm Whale, *Physeter catodon:* ♂ up to 18.5 m, ♀ up to 9 m; head very large, right-angled, single blowhole near end of snout on left side, back fin resembles small humps. **b *Common Dolphin,** Delphinus delphis:* up to 2.4 m; body very slender, with different coloured bands along the side, beak very pointed. **c *Bottle-nosed Dolphin,** Tursiops truncatus:* up to 3.7 m; upper parts dark, under parts light-coloured, lower jaw longer than upper jaw. **d White Whale** or **Beluga,** *Delphinapterus leucas:* up to 4.3 m; no pronounced beak, adult animals white. All are Toothed Whales, widespread throughout the world, except the White Whale, which is exclusively polar.

Except for the N Atlantic Biscayan Whale, which is a Right Whale, the animals below are Rorquals; they have a world-wide distribution and may in summer reach European coastal waters, especially off Norway, Spitzbergen and the White Sea, in schools of 3–20 or more. All, including the Biscayan Whale, are Baleen Whales, with plates of baleen or whalebone through which they filter plankton food from the water. The Blue Whale is probably the largest creature that has ever lived.

	Common Rorqual or Fin Whale	Lesser Rorqual or Piked Whale	Sei Whale	Blue Whale	Humpback Whale	Biscayan Whale
Scientific Name	*Balaenoptera physalus*	*Balaenoptera acutorostrata*	*Balaenoptera borealis*	*Balaenoptera musculus*	*Megaptera novaeangliae*	*Balaena glacialis*
Size	Up to 24.5 m	Up to 9 m	Up to 18.3 m	24.5–30.5 m	Up to 15 m	Up to 18 m
Distinguishing Features	Upper parts grey, under parts white	Broad white transverse band on pectoral fin; the smallest Baleen Whale	Wavy border between colouring of back and belly, dorsal fin large	Uniformly bluish grey with light spots, dorsal fin very small	Tubercles on head and on edge of the very long pectoral fins	Forehead with horny, warty plate, no dorsal fin; slow-moving, very rare

a *Killer Whale, Orcinus orca:* ♂ up to 9.2 m, ♀ up to 4.6 m; very large dorsal fin, white patch over eyes; a powerful aggressive animal hunting in packs, preying mainly on warm-blooded creatures, including other whales. **b False Killer,** *Pseudorca crassidens:* ♂ up to 5.6 m, ♀ up to 5 m; uniformly black, glossy; feeds mainly on cuttlefish and medium-sized fishes. **c *Common Porpoise,** Phocoena phocoena:* up to 1.8 m; upper parts black, under parts white; the commonest whale in British waters. **d Narwhal,** *Monodon monoceros:* up to 4.9 m; ♂ with a tusk up to 2.5 m long; usually found in polar waters. All are Toothed Whales which regularly visit European coastal waters.

a *****Black-throated Diver**, *Gavia arctica:* 58.5–68.5 cm; crown grey, back checkered with white; migrant. **b** *****Red-throated Diver**, *Gavia stellata:* 53–61 cm; head grey, throat dark red, bill slender, tilted up slightly; partial migrant. **c Great Northern Diver** or **Loon**, *Gavia immer:* 68.5–81.5 cm; head black, back uniformly figured with white, bill black, strong, straight; migrant. **d White-billed Diver**, *Gavia adamsii:* 68.5–81.5 cm; similar to **c**, but bill yellowish; migrant. All belong to the Diver Family. Almost entirely helpless on land, they nest close to the shore of inland waters in the far north; in winter they move south along the coasts.

All the Geese shown below nest in colonies on the ground in the tundra, in Iceland and the far north. The Pink-footed Goose also nests on rocky cliffs along rivers, the Snow Goose in N Greenland, in NE Siberia and in the north of N America. In winter these species come further south, which is when they are seen along sea-coasts, often in very large flocks, the Snow Goose as a rare vagrant.

	*White-fronted Goose	*Lesser White-fronted Goose	*Pink-footed Goose	Snow Goose
Scientific Name	*Anser albifrons*	*Anser erythropus*	*Anser brachyrhynchus*	*Anser hyperboreus*
Size	66–76 cm	53.5–66 cm	61–76 cm	63.5–76 cm
Distinguishing Features	Black belly-stripes, adult geese with white patch on forehead, bill reddish; migrant	Similar to White-fronted Goose, but with yellow iris, white forehead patch of adult larger, bill reddish; migrant	Neck dark, bill small, black and red, rarely with some white on forehead; migrant	Plumage white, wing tips black. bill and feet reddish; partial migrant

a *****Manx Shearwater**, *Procellaria puffinus:* 35.5 cm; upper parts black, under parts white; migrant from the coasts of Brazil to the N Atlantic. **b Cory's Shearwater**, *Puffinus kuhlii:* 46 cm; bill yellow; partial migrant as far north as the Mediterranean. **c Great Shearwater**, *Procellaria gravis:* 46 cm; upper tail-coverts white; migrant. **d Sooty Shearwater**, *Procellaria grisea:* 40.7 cm; body entirely dark; migrant. **c** and **d** are two S Atlantic species which may occasionally be seen off European coasts. Shearwaters nest colonially in burrows or crevices on inaccessible coasts and islands. They are helpless on land and normally fly to and from their nests only at night.

a *Leach's Petrel, *Oceanodroma leucorhoa:* 20 cm; tail forked, rump white; flitting flight; migrant. **b** *Storm Petrel, *Hydrobates pelagicus:* 15 cm; rump white, feet black, tail square-ended; partial migrant. **c** *Fulmar Petrel, *Fulmarus glacialis:* 47 cm; nape thick, bill heavy, nasal tubes prominent, gull-like appearance; lays eggs on exposed cliffs; partial migrant. All belong to the Tubenose Family whose members all have nostrils enclosed in tubes along the top of the bill, and which includes the shearwaters, petrels, fulmars, and in the Southern Hemisphere the albatrosses. All are exclusively marine. Those shown breed along the coasts of Britain and Iceland, **b** also on Mediterranean islands.

The Ruddy Sheld-duck nests in S Spain and the S Balkans and is a rare vagrant elsewhere in Europe. The other birds illustrated below are Geese. The Barnacle Goose and the Brent Goose nest in the rocky tundra and on Arctic islands and are common winter visitors along more southerly sea-coasts. The Red-breasted Goose also inhabits the coastal regions of the tundra but occurs only as a vagrant over most of Europe. Canada Geese came originally from N America and live in Europe in a feral state.

	*Barnacle Goose	*Brent Goose	*Canada Goose	Red-breasted Goose	Ruddy Sheld-duck
Scientific Name	*Branta leucopsis*	*Branta bernicla*	*Branta canadensis*	*Branta ruficollis*	*Casarca ferruginea*
Size	58–68 cm	56–61 cm	91–102 cm	53–56 cm	63 cm
Distinguishing Features	Face and rump white, neck, breast and tail black; migrant	Head, neck and breast black, white spot on neck; migrant	White chin-patch, head and neck black, breast whitish brown; partial migrant	Conspicuous head markings, breast chestnut-brown, flanks white; migrant	Plumage rust-red, head light-coloured, ♂ with black band round neck; partial migrant

a *Sheld-duck, *Tadorna tadorna:* 61 cm; broad fox-coloured band across chest, bill red, that of ♂ with knob; in winter, one of the most easily recognized shore birds; partial migrant, nests in burrows along European coasts. **b** Barrow's Goldeneye, *Bucephala islandica:* 46 cm; ♂ with white crescent patch on face, ♀ similar to that of the Goldeneye (page 112); resident only in Iceland but occurs very rarely elsewhere. **c** Steller's Eider, *Polysticta stelleri:* 46 cm; ♂ under parts rusty yellow, black side-spot, green patch on back of head, ♀ dark brown; partial migrant. All are Sea Ducks which nest on northern coasts.

a Marbled Duck, *Anas angustirostris:* 38 cm; dappled plumage, dark eye-stripe, ♂ with small tuft on nape; migrant, nests on overgrown freshwater lakes in the Mediterranean region. **b *Scaup Duck,** *Aythya marila:* 48.5 cm; ♂ white in the centre, front and hind end black, ♀ with white spot at base of bill; migrant, breeds on Norwegian and Icelandic inland lakes and migrates to North Sea coasts in winter. **c Harlequin Duck,** *Histrionicus histrionicus:* 43 cm; harlequin markings; resident, nests gregariously near rapids in Iceland; when feeding, moves in close packs; likes rough water. **a** is a surface-feeding duck, **b** and **c** diving Sea Ducks.

All the birds shown below are Sea Ducks which obtain their food primarily by diving. They nest in the tundra, by lakes or on moors in the north, the Scoter in remote parts of N Scotland. In winter they move further south. The Eider Ducks breed on coasts further south and are well known on the Farne Islands. Surf Scoters and King Eiders are rare vagrants, the former from N America and the latter from the Arctic.

	*Long-tailed Duck	*Velvet Scoter	*Common Scoter	Surf Scoter	*Eider	King Eider
Scientific Name	*Clangula hyemalis*	*Melanitta fusca*	*Melanitta nigra*	*Melanitta perspicillata*	*Somateria mollissima*	*Somateria spectabilis*
Size	♂ 53 cm	56 cm	48 cm	53 cm	58 cm	56 cm
Distinguishing Features	♀ 40 cm; ♂ body checkered, tail pointed, ♀ face white; migrant	♂ black with white wing-patch, ♀ brownish with white wing-patch; migrant	♂ plumage black, bill with yellow spot, ♀ brownish, crown dark; migrant	♂ with white spot on forehead and on nape, ♀ without white on wings; migrant	♂ upper parts white, under parts black, breast cream-coloured, ♀ with brown bands; resident	♂ front white, rear black, upper mandible enlarged, ♀ with reddish bands; partial migrant

a *Gannet, *Sula bassana:* 91.5 cm; wing tips black; makes spectacular dives to catch fish, sometimes from 100 feet up; Gannet Family; nests in vast colonies or gannetries in a few places along rocky coasts of Britain, Iceland and Norway; largest British sea-bird. **b *Cormorant,** *Phalacrocorax carbo:* 91.5 cm; chin, cheeks and thigh-patch white. **c *Shag,** *Phalacrocorax aristotelis:* 76 cm; greenish black, crest on head. **d Pygmy Cormorant,** *Phalacrocorax pygmaeus:* 48.5 cm; head dark brown, with crest; native to the Balkans, living usually on inland waters. **b, c** and **d** are partial migrants of the Cormorant Family and nest on cliff-ledges or in bushes.

a Pallas's Sand-grouse, *Syrrhaptes para-doxus:* 35–40 cm; belly black, centre tail feathers long; partial migrant, inhabits sandy semi-deserts and occasionally visits Europe in flocks; Sand-grouse Family. **b *Rock Dove,** *Columba livia:* 33 cm; two black wing-bands; resident on cliffs, sea and inland; the ancestor of all domestic pigeons, which resemble it closely if they return to the wild; Pigeon Family. **c Lesser Kestrel,** *Falco naumanni:* 30 cm; similar to Kestrel, but ♂ with un-spotted upper parts; migrant. **d Eleonora's Falcon,** *Falco eleonorae:* 38 cm; plumage slate-grey; resident. **c** and **d** belong to the Birds-of-Prey Family and nest on cliffs in the Mediterranean region.

Of the Waders illustrated below, the Ringed and the Kentish Plover nest along European coasts on sandy beaches, the former northwards from Belgium, the latter southwards but including the Kent coast. Turnstones breed on northern coasts and are met with as passage migrants or summer residents along all W European coasts. The Dotterel and the Grey Plover inhabit the tundra, the Dotterel also dry mountain meadows in the Alps and the Scottish Highlands.

	*Ringed Plover	*Kentish Plover	*Dotterel	*Grey Plover	*Turnstone
Scientific Name	*Charadrius hiaticula*	*Charadrius alexandrinus*	*Charadrius morinellus*	*Charadrius squatarola*	*Arenaria interpres*
Size	19 cm	16 cm	21.5 cm	28 cm	23 cm
Distinguishing Features	Young with a brown, adult a black breast-band, white neck-band, legs orange yellow; partial migrant	Dark spot on side of breast, legs and bill blackish; partial migrant	White stripe **over** eyes, belly brown with white stripe; migrant	Under parts of summer plum-age black, above speckled grey, under parts of winter plumage light; migrant	Head black and white, black breastband, rust-coloured back, upper parts of winter plumage dark; migrant

a White-tailed Eagle, *Haliaëtus albicilla:* 68–91 cm; tail short, wedge-shaped, white, head light brown; feeds on fish, sometimes plunging into water for them, small mammals, birds up to duck size, and on carrion; partial migrant, nests on rocky crags and in tall trees along the Baltic coast, in Norway, in the north of the U.S.S.R. and in the Balkans, now ex-tinct in Britain. **b Gyr Falcon,** *Falco rusti-colus:* 52–56 cm; similar to Peregrine Falcon (page 55), but without facial markings; flies with slower, more silent wing-beats than **a**; many different geographical types exist; resident, nests on rocky crags in the north. Both are Birds of Prey.

a ***Avocet,** *Recurvirostra avosetta:* 43 cm; bill with upward curve, body white, upper head and nape black, back with two broad black lengthwise bands; partial migrant. b ***Oystercatcher,** *Haematopus ostralegus:* 43 cm; head, neck and back black, under parts white, bill and feet red; a noisy bird common on beaches throughout the summer, it feeds on sand-burrowing animals, never on oysters; partial migrant. Both are Waders which lay their eggs on the ground, with little in the way of nesting material. The avocet has recently re-established itself as a breeding bird in Britain on the Suffolk coast.

The Red-necked Phalarope belongs to the Phalarope Family, the other birds shown below are Waders. The Dunlin, the commonest shore wader, nests on moors and marshes in N Europe, the Knot and the Phalarope in the tundra, the Curlew-sandpiper in arctic regions of Asia, the Purple Sandpiper in hilly tundra areas, the Redshank on meadowlands almost throughout Europe. All have a lighter winter plumage without the red of the summer feathers. They are seen on migration on estuaries and sea-shores in very large numbers.

	*Dunlin	***Knot**	***Curlew-sandpiper**	***Purple Sandpiper**	***Redshank**	***Red-necked Phalarope**
Scientific Name	*Calidris alpina*	*Calidris canutus*	*Calidris testacea*	*Calidris maritima*	*Tringa totanus*	*Phalaropus lobatus*
Size	17.5 cm	25.5 cm	19 cm	20 cm	28 cm	18 cm
Distinguishing Features	In summer with large black patch on belly, bill long, slightly curved; partial migrant	Body plump, in summer head and under parts red; migrant	Under parts of display plumage rust-brown, rump white, bill with downward curve; migrant	Body plump, upper parts slate-grey in winter, belly white, legs yellow; partial migrant	Back, rump and trailing edge of wings white, legs and base of bill red; partial migrant	In summer throat white, rust-coloured band on sides of neck; migrant

a ***Bar-tailed Godwit,** *Limosa lapponica:* 38 cm; bill slightly upturned, tail barred. b ***Sanderling,** *Crocethia alba:* 20.5 cm; winter plumage very light-coloured, shoulders black. c ***Little Stint,** *Calidris minuta:* 13.5 cm; in summer brown, in winter grey. All are Waders, and migrants which nest in the tundra; they are winter visitors on W and S European coasts, where they are often seen together in huge flocks. d **Cream-coloured Courser,** *Cursorius cursor:* 23 cm; black and white eye-stripe; plover-like in general movements but a very good runner; resident; Courser Family, normally found in N Africa but is a vagrant as far as Britain.

a *Little Gull, Larus minutus:* 28 cm; the smallest gull, head pitch black in display plumage; partial migrant, breeds in colonies along the whole eastern coast of the Baltic, also often on inland marshes. **b** *Glaucous Gull, Larus hyperboreus:* 66–81.5 cm; plumage white, bill large; partial migrant; can be confused with **c** *Iceland Gull, Larus glaucoides:* 56–66 cm; wings white, bill small, young with brown-striped plumage; partial migrant. All breed in colonies on islands in the far north and are winter residents along coasts further south. The Iceland Gull is rare south of Scandinavia. All belong to the Gull Family.

Gulls are the commonest coastal birds. The Lesser Black-backed, the Common, the Herring and the Black-headed Gulls breed in colonies along N European coasts, occasionally also by inland rivers and lakes. Great Black-backed Gulls tend to breed close to the sea, though they may come inland during the winter, when all species move further south. At this time the Black-headed Gull has only a dark spot behind the eye; in this plumage it is seen as a familiar scavenger in many towns.

	*Great Black-backed Gull	*Lesser Black-backed Gull	*Herring Gull	*Common Gull	*Black-headed Gull	Audouin's Gull
Scientific Name	*Larus marinus*	*Larus fuscus*	*Larus argentatus*	*Larus canus*	*Larus ridibundus*	*Larus audouinii*
Size	74 cm	53 cm	56 cm	40 cm	38 cm	50 cm
Distinguishing Features	Back and wings black, legs flesh-coloured, head with brown stripes in winter; partial migrant	Similar to Great Black-backed Gull, but smaller, legs yellow; partial migrant	Back and wings grey, legs flesh-coloured, young birds brown; partial migrant	Similar to Herring Gull but much smaller, legs and bill greenish; partial migrant	In summer, head chocolate-brown, in winter white, bill and legs red; partial migrant	Bill red with black band, legs olive-green; a deep-sea bird, nests on Mediterranean islands

a Mediterranean Gull, *Larus melanocephalus:* 39 cm; primary feathers pure white, head black in summer. **b** Slender-billed Gull, *Larus genei:* 43 cm; head white in summer. Both breed in colonies on islands and along river-banks on the coasts of the Mediterranean. **c** Ivory Gull, *Pagophila eburnea:* 44.5 cm; plumage entirely white, legs black; breeds in the Arctic. **d** *Kittiwake, Rissa tridactyla:* 40 cm; wing tips completely black, breeds on sheer cliffs round England, Norway and Heligoland; the only gull to build a substantial nest, of mud and grass; a migrant which travels as far as the coasts of Brazil in winter.

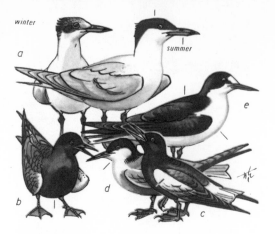

a Caspian Tern, *Hydropogne caspia:* 53.5 cm; crown and sides of head black; largest of the terns, almost gull-like in flight, distinguished by heavy bill; migrant, breeds along the sandy coasts of the Baltic. **b Black Tern,** *Chlidonias niger:* 24 cm; plumage blackish; migrant, builds floating nests on inland lakes. **c White-winged Black Tern,** *Chlidonias leucopterus:* 23.5 cm; body black, shoulders white; migrant, E Europe. **d Whiskered Tern,** *Chlidonias hybrida:* 25 cm; cheeks and neck white; migrant, SW Europe. **e Sooty Tern,** *Sterna fuscata:* 40.5 cm; upper parts black, under parts white; a visitor from the tropics. All belong to the Tern Subfamily.

The Roseate Tern nests exclusively by the sea, usually with Arctic or Common Terns. All the other terns illustrated below nest along the coasts and occasionally also inland. The Gull-billed Tern is mainly a Mediterranean species, although it also breeds on the Danish coasts. Terns mostly lay their beautifully camouflaged eggs on the bare sand or shingle and do not make any nest. The newly hatched chicks are also camouflaged, and are further protected by the density of the breeding colony.

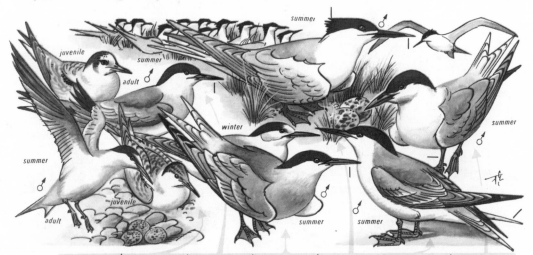

	*Little Tern	*Common Tern	*Arctic Tern	*Sandwich Tern	*Roseate Tern	Gull-billed Tern
Scientific Name	*Sterna albifrons*	*Sterna hirundo*	*Sterna macrura*	*Sterna sandvicensis*	*Sterna dougallii*	*Gelochelidon nilotica*
Size	24 cm	35.5 cm	38 cm	41 cm	38 cm	38 cm
Distinguishing Features	Forehead white, bill yellow with black tip, crown of young ash-grey; migrant	Bill orange-red with black tip, young birds with white fore-head; migrant	Bill blood-red without black tip, forehead white in winter plumage; migrant	Crest on back of head, bill black with yellow tip; migrant	Over half of bill black, tail long, deeply forked; migrant	Bill powerful, short and quite black, legs black; migrant

a *Long-tailed Skua, *Stercorarius longicaudus:* 53.5 cm; centre tail feathers very long and pointed. **b Pomarine Skua,** *Stercorarius pomarinus:* 51 cm; centre tail feathers blunt. **c *Great Skua,** *Stercorarius skua:* 61 cm; tail with two small points. **d *Arctic Skua,** *Stercorarius parasiticus:* 46 cm; centre tail feathers of medium length, pointed. All belong to the Skua Family and nest in colonies on moorlands of far N Europe. Skuas look like big brown gulls, to which they are related. They are pirate birds, chasing other birds and forcing them to give up the fish they have caught. They are very aggressive when nesting.

a Shore Lark, *Eremophila alpestris:* 16.5 cm; striking head markings with 'horns'; migrant, Lark Family. **b *Snow Bunting,** *Plectrophenax nivalis:* 16.5 cm; plumage chiefly white; large flocks flying high may look almost like drifting snowflakes; partial migrant. **c Lapland Bunting,** *Calcarius lapponicus:* 15 cm; conspicuous head and nape markings; migrant. **b** and **c** belong to the Finch Family. They nest in the far north and winter mainly along coasts further south. **d Richard's Pipit,** *Anthus richardi:* 18 cm; breast clearly striped, claw on hind toe very long; migrant, breeds in Asia, visiting Europe as a passage migrant; Pipit Family.

The birds shown below belong to the Auk Family. They are black and white sea-birds which can swim and dive well. When standing auks hold themselves upright. Their short wings move very fast, giving an impression of rather feeble flight; in fact, they travel much further than the gulls and many larger birds. The Common and Black Guillemots, the Razorbill and the Puffin all breed on suitable cliffs round Britain, the Puffin in burrows, the rest on cliff ledges, the Guillemot in the most exposed places.

	*Puffin	*Common Guillemot	Brünnich's Guillemot	*Razorbill	*Little Auk	*Black Guillemot
Scientific Name	*Fratercula arctica*	*Uria aalge*	*Uria lomvia*	*Alca torda*	*Plautus alle*	*Uria grylle*
Size	30.5 cm	42 cm	42 cm	41 cm	20 cm	34 m
Distinguishing Features	Bill large, triangular, colourful, in summer cheeks white, in winter dull grey; migrant	Head and neck black, in winter black stripe on white cheeks; partial migrant	Bill thick, with light-coloured line along sides, large head-cap in winter; partial migrant	Bill thick, with white marking, white eye-stripe in summer; partial migrant	Body small, bill very short, winter plumage with more white; partial migrant	Plumage black with large white patch on wings. winter plumage much lighter; partial migrant

a Loggerhead Turtle, *Caretta caretta:* up to 1 m; legs and feet like fins, carapace on back with five pairs of main shields. **b Green Turtle,** *Chelonia mydas:* up to 1.4 m; carapace on back with four pairs of costal shields, forelegs generally with only one claw. **c Luth** or **Leathery Turtle,** *Dermochelys coriacea:* up to 2 m; carapace consists of small bony plates, skin leathery. **a** and **b** are Sea Turtles, **c** is a Leathery Turtle. All live in the warm oceans and are only rarely found as far north as the Mediterranean; there are occasionally records of all these species found stranded on British coasts.

a *European Anchovy, *Engraulis encrasi-cholus:* up to 20 cm; 5–6; upper jaw more than three-quarters of the head length. b *Pilchard* or *Sardine, Sardina pilchardus:* up to 30 cm; 6–7; gill-covers striped. Both live in the Mediterranean and may travel as far as the North and Irish Seas. c *Herring, Clupea harengus:* up to 35 cm; 3–5 and 9–10; pelvic fins behind leading edge of dorsal fins. d *Sprat, Clupea sprattus:* up to 17 cm; 5–6; pelvic fins in front of dorsal fins. e *Allis Shad, Alosa alosa:* up to 71 cm; 3–5; black spot behind gill-covers; spawns in rivers. All belong to the Herring Family, living in the Atlantic, North Sea and Baltic.

Sea fishes of the Hake and Cod Families are described below. The Atlantic Cod and the Haddock are among the most commercially valuable fishes of the N Atlantic waters, the Cod also being found in the Baltic. The Poor Cod is the smallest but the most widespread of the family, being found from N Scandinavia to the Mediterranean. The Bib or Pout occurs only in more southerly waters. The Haddock is commonest further north, while the Whiting also has a very wide distribution.

	*European Hake	*Atlantic Cod	*Bib	*Poor Cod	*Haddock	*Whiting
Scientific Name	Merluccius merluccius	Gadus morhua	Trisopterus luscus	Trisopterus minutus	Melanogrammus aeglefinus	Odontogadus merlangus
Size; Spawning	125 cm; 4–7	80–150cm; 2–5	30 cm; 1–4	25 cm; 3–6	50–80 cm; 2–5	50 cm; 2–6
Distinguishing Features	2nd dorsal fins and anal fin very long, back part higher, lower jaw longer than upper jaw	Lateral line light-coloured, barbel large, back and sides with dark spots	Body high, with small black dots or with four dark transverse lines	Eyes very large, 1st dorsal fin pointed, back yellowish brown, sides dark-spotted	Lateral line dark, dark spot above pectoral fins	Lateral line bent below 2nd dorsal fin, dark spot at base of pectoral fins

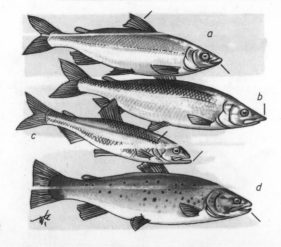

a *Coregonus lavaretus:* up to 50 cm; 10–12; mouth small, dorsal fin short, nose only slightly protruding; Baltic. This species is a salt-water form of a fish which also occurs in upland waters (page 299). b *Houting, Coregonus oxyrhynchus:* up to 50 cm; 10–12; nose very prominent, dark; North Sea. c *Smelt* or *Sparling, Osmerus eperlanus:* up to 33 cm; 3–4; mouth large, lateral line short; smells of cucumber. d *Sea Trout, Salmo trutta trutta* up to 100 cm; 11–3; mouth terminal, body compressed; northern waters. All belong to the Salmon Family and spawn in rivers.

a *Snake Pipe-fish, *Entelurus aequoreus:* up to 60 cm; 6–7; caudal fin very small. **b** *Straight-nosed Pipe-fish, *Nerophis ophidion:* about 15 cm; 5–8; no caudal fin. **c** *Broad-nosed Pipe-fish, *Syngnathus typhle:* 28 cm; 4–8; snout small, high. **d** *Great Pipe-fish, *Syngnathus acus:* 40 cm; 6–8; snout slender, rounded. **e** Pipe-fish, *Syngnathus rostellatus:* 16 cm; 6–8; snout half length of head. **f** Mediterranean Seahorse, *Hippocampus guttulatus:* 16 cm; 5–8; prehensile tail. All are feeble swimmers and seek the protection of seaweed in the lower tidal and offshore zones. They inhabit the Atlantic coasts and the North Sea, **b, c** and **e** also the Baltic, **f** the Mediterranean.

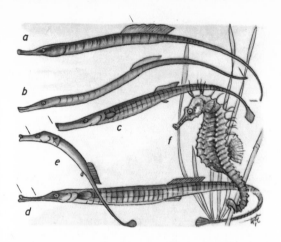

The Blue Whiting occurs along W European coasts, from the Arctic to the Mediterranean, but not in the North Sea. The Pollack extends to the west coast of Portugal, the Coal-fish or Saithe and the Common Ling to the Bay of Biscay, the Four-bearded Rockling to the English Channel and the Baltic; the Blue Ling occurs only along the Norwegian coast. Rocklings live over soft sea-beds, the other species over stony ones, mostly at a considerable depth. All belong to the Cod Family.

	*Blue Whiting	*Coal-fish	*Pollack	*Common Ling	Blue Ling	*Four-bearded Rockling
Scientific Name	*Micromesistius poutassou*	*Pollachius virens*	*Pollachius pollachius*	*Molva molva*	*Molva dipterygia*	*Rhinonemus cimbrius*
Size; Spawning	To 50 cm; 3–5	Up to 1 m;1–4	Up to 1 m; 2–5	Up to 2 m; 3–6	Up to 1.5 m	To 35 cm; 2–8
Distinguishing Features	Caudal fin deeply forked, lateral line brownish, back bluish grey, 1st anal fin very long	End of caudal fin concave, lateral line straight, light-coloured, back dark green	Lower lip protruding, 1st anal fin very long, back brownish yellow	Barbel long, forward dorsal fin short, rear one long, upper jaw protruding	Jaws the same length, eyes very large, barbel short	One barbel on lower jaw, three on upper jaw, 1st dorsal fin of free rays

a *Moray Eel or **Murry,** *Muraena helena:* up to 1.5 m; body eel-like; lives in warm seas, rarely as far north as Britain. **b** *Conger Eel, *Conger conger:* up to 3 m; 5–6; dorsal fin commences far forwards; feeds on many other fishes and on octopus; one of the largest fishes caught off the sea-shore. **c** *Garfish, *Belone belone:* up to 1 m; 5–6; jaws bill-like; sometimes caught for food, bones bright green. **d** *Skipper, *Scomberesox saurus:* up to 40 cm; 5–6 finlets. **e** *Fifteen-spined Stickleback, *Spinachia vulgaris:* 15 cm; 4–7; 14–17 spines on back. All live in European seas and give their names to the families to which they belong.

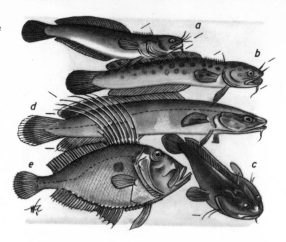

a *Five-bearded Rockling, *Ciliata mustela*: 25 cm; 1–6; one barbel on lower jaw, four on upper. **b** *Three-bearded Rockling, *Gaidropsaurus vulgaris*: 60 cm; 2–6; one barbel on lower jaw, two on upper. **c** *Lesser Forkbeard, *Raniceps raninus*: 30 cm; 6–8; pectoral fin with two long rays. **d** *Torsk or Tusk, *Brosme brosme*: 1 m; 4–6; dorsal and anal fins very long. All inhabit the Atlantic coasts, **b** also the Mediterranean, and are members of the Cod Family. **e** *John Dory, *Zeus faber*: 70 cm; 6–8; 1st dorsal fin with long spiny rays; widespread from the Mediterranean to Ireland.

All the fishes illustrated below are predaceous species which are found in the Mediterranean and at times also along the Atlantic coasts of Europe, the Bass and Meagre regularly in the English Channel, the Atlantic Horse Mackerel or Saurel and the Red Mullet as far as the North Sea. Apart from the Meagres, which are closely related, each of these species belongs to a separate family.

	*Bass	*Atlantic Horse Mackerel	Meagre	Brown Meagre	*Red Mullet	Orange Scorpion Fish
Scientific Name	Morone labrax	Trachurus trachurus	Argyrosomus regius	Sciaena umbra	Mullus surmuletus	Scorpaena scrofa
Size; Spawning	Up to 1m; 5–8	To 50 cm; 5–8	Up to 2.3 m	Up to 60 cm	To 45 cm; 6–7	Up to 30.5 cm
Distinguishing Features	Gill-covers with two strong spikes, lateral line blackish, anal fin with three spines	Lateral line with scale-like plates, 1st anal fin with two spines, back dark green	1st dorsal fin with 10–11 spines	Upper side dark brown, fins brown or black, 2nd ray of anal fin much thickened	Pink colour, usually with 3–5 yellow stripes along each side, chin with two long barbels	Head with protuberances, body reddish, brown-spotted, fine spines connected to poison glands

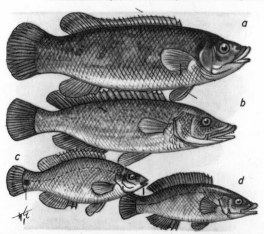

a *Ballan Wrasse, *Labrus bergylta*: up to 45 cm; 5–8; pectoral and pelvic fins orange-red. **b** *Labrus viridis*: 40 cm; 4–7; back greenish with blue dots. **c** *Corkwing Wrasse, *Crenilabrus melops*: up to 25 cm; 7–9; there are many colour varieties of this fish, but all have a black spot at the base of the caudal fin. **d** *Goldsinny, *Ctenolabrus rupestris*: up to 18 cm; 5–8; black spot on top of tail. All have a long dorsal fin, which is partly spiny, and thick lips which fold inside the mouth; they belong to the Wrasse Family and are widespread along the coast from the Mediterranean to the North Sea and occasionally as far as the W Baltic.

a *Greater Sand-eel, *Ammodytes lanceolatus:* up to 30 cm; 5–8; back brownish or yellowish green, underside silvery. **b *Lesser Sand-eel,** *Ammodytes tobianus:* up to 20 cm; 5–6 and 8–10; back green, sides and belly silvery. Both belong to the Sand-eel Family. **c *Greater Weever,** *Trachinus draco:* up to 45 cm; 6–8; 1st dorsal fin black, caudal fin blackish, other fins yellow. **d *Lesser Weever,** *Trachinus vipera:* up to 20 cm; 5–9; back reddish with dark spots. Both belong to the Weever Family. All are widespread along the Atlantic coasts and in the North Sea, **a** and **b** also in the Baltic. **c** and **d** have poisonous spines which can give a very painful sting.

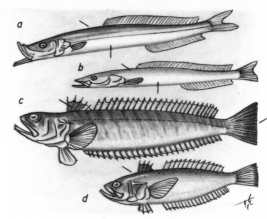

The Dolphin (not to be confused with the sea-mammal of the same name), the Blue-finned Tuna and the Swordfish are fast-swimming predaceous fishes found mainly in the warmer waters of the world. The related Mackerel extends further north and is caught in large numbers in the N Atlantic. The Dolphin is never found in British waters, but the Tuna and Swordfish may occur there as summer vagrants.

	*Common Mackerel	**Dolphin**	**Blue-finned Tuna**	**Swordfish**	***Dragonet**	***Spotted Dragonet**
Scientific Name	*Scomber scombrus*	*Coryphaena hippurus*	*Thunnus thynnus*	*Xiphias gladius*	*Callionymus lyra*	*Callionymus maculatus*
Size; Spawning	To 50 cm; 6–7	To 1 m; 8–9	To 5 m; 8–10	To 4 m; 4–7	30.5 cm; 2–8	♂ 14 cm; 2–8
Distinguishing Features	Dark transverse bands on back, five finlets on top and below tail in front of caudal fin	Body colour very variable, dorsal fin very long, extends from top of head	Nine finlets on each side of tail in front of caudal fin, back dark blue, belly white	Upper jaw prolonged to form a long sword	♀ up to 25 cm, belly milk-white, ♂ belly yellowish, both with large fins	♀ up to 11 cm, with brown band over back, ♂ with row of spots on 2nd dorsal fin

a *Black Goby, *Gobius niger:* 14 cm; 5–8; back brownish, belly yellowish white. **b *Painted Goby,** *Gobius pictus:* 5 cm; 5–8; sides yellowish with five dark spots. **c *Common Goby,** *Pomatoschistus microps:* 11 cm; 4–8; back scales with black border. **d *Transparent Goby,** *Aphia minuta:* 7 cm; 5–8; completely transparent. **e *Crystallogobius linearis:* 48 cm; 3–4; like **d,** but with 3–5 small spots along the side. All belong to the Goby Family and are active fishes which live in tidal pools; if left stranded, they are capable of jumping across the sand to find water.

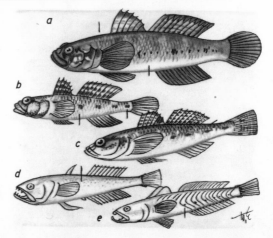

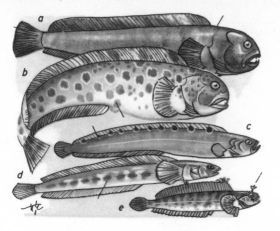

a *****Wolf Fish,** *Anarhichas lupus:* 1.75 m; 11–1; grey, with 10–12 inconspicuous transverse bands. **b Smaller Wolf Fish,** *Anarhichas minor:* up to 2 m; 11–1; reddish yellow with numerous dark brown spots. Both belong to the Wolf Fish Family. **c** *****Gunnel,** *Centronotus gunellus:* 30.5 cm; 11–1; 9–13 eye-spots along the dorsal fin; eggs are laid in a clump on the shore and are guarded by the parent fish, even through low-tide; Butterfish Family. **d** *****Band Fish,** *Lumpenus lampretaeformis:* 41 cm; 12–1; 8–9 longish spots along the centre of each side; Band Fish Family. **e** *****Yarrell's Blenny,** *Chirolophis galerita:* up to 15 cm; 10–12; orbital tentacles on forehead; Blenny Family. All inhabit northern waters.

Atherina hepsetus, the Sand Smelt and the Thick-lipped Mullet are widespread in the Mediterranean, the Sand Smelt extending through the English Channel and Zuyder Sea as far as N Scotland, the Thick-lipped or Grey Mullet as far as the southern North Sea. The Viviparous Blenny is a common fish living near the sea-bottom in seaweed areas from Scandinavia to the Bay of Biscay. The Butterfly Blenny and the Blenny or Shanny mainly inhabit the Mediterranean, but occur as far north as British coasts.

		*Viviparous Blenny	Thick-lipped Mullet	*Sand Smelt	*Butterfly Blenny	*Blenny
Scientific Name	*Atherina hepsetus*	*Zoarces viviparus*	*Chelon labrosus*	*Atherina presbyter*	*Blennius ocellaris*	*Blennius pholis*
Size; Spawning	10–15 cm; 6–8	45.5 cm; 12–2	To 66 cm; 5–6	To 15 cm; 6–8	To 15 cm; 5–7	To 15 cm; 5–7
Distinguishing Features	Eyes very large, body silvery grey, back darker	With 10–20 oblique bands along dorsal fin and back, belly whitish	Mouth small, upper lip very thick, two widely separated dorsal fins	2nd dorsal fin notched, back transparently grey-green, sides and belly white	Orbital tentacle on forehead branched, eye-spot on forward dorsal fin	Colouring very variegated, on a greenish base with brown spots

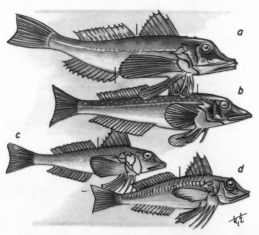

a *****Tub Gurnard,** *Trigla hirundo:* 76 cm; 6–10; upper side reddish. **b** *****Gurnard,** *Trigla gurnardus:* 51 cm; 4–8; back and sides slate-grey. **c** *****Streaked Gurnard,** *Trigla lineata:* 33 cm; 6–7; back and sides bluish grey. **d Red Gurnard,** *Trigla cuculus:* 30.5 cm; 4–8; obliquely elongated scales along lateral line. All belong to the Gurnard Family and are commercially valuable fish, **a** caught in summer, **b** throughout the year in the North Sea, **c** and **d** in the Mediterranean and occasionally as far north as Scotland. Gurnards use their long spines to stir up the sand for food.

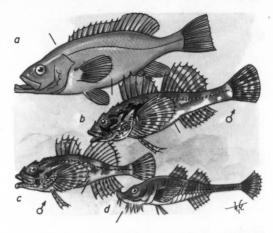

a Norway Haddock, *Sebastes viviparus:* 76 cm; 4–5; body red, belly lighter; viviparous; Scorpion Fish Family; a carnivorous fish of northern waters. **b Short-spined Sea Scorpion** or **Father-lasher,** *Cottus scorpius:* ♂ 30 cm, ♀ smaller; 12–2; skin scaleless, ♂ during spawning time with brightly spotted belly, ♀ with reddish yellow belly. **c Long-spined Sea Scorpion,** *Cottus bubalis:* 18 cm; 1–4: during spawning time ♂ with cherry-red belly covered with brownish spots. **d *Armed Bullhead** or **Pogge,** *Agonus cataphractus:* 20 cm; 1–4; lower jaw with numerous barbels. **b** and **c** are Bullheads; common, especially in the north and west; **d** uncommon, mainly by river-mouths, harbours in the north-east.

All the species illustrated below are native to the Mediterranean, where the Blotched Picarel and the Sea Bream are among the commonest fishes. The latter is also found along the Atlantic coasts as far as England and into the North Sea. All are much prized in Mediterranean countries as their flesh is delicious.

	Blotched Picarel	*Sea Bream	Two-banded Bream	Gilt-head Bream	Dentex	Painted Comber
Scientific Name	Maena vulgaris	Pagellus centrodontus	Sargus vulgaris	Chrysophris aurata	Dentex vulgaris	Serranus scriba
Size; Spawning	Up to 25 cm	50 cm; 12–1	Up to 30 cm	50–60 cm	Up to 1 m; 6	Up to 30 cm
Distinguishing Features	Body lead-coloured, with dark length-wise stripes, black spot behind pectoral fins	Body orange-red, dark spot over pectoral fins, caudal fin red	Tail black and yellow, nape blackish	Yellow spot on forehead, red spot on gill-covers	Caudal fin large, sickle-shaped, dark, back bluish grey, sides yellowish coppery	Body reddish, with 7 wide, blackish blue trans-verse bands, belly and fins yellowish

a *Lumpsucker, *Cyclopterus lumpus:* ♂ 35 cm, mainly red, ♀ 50 cm, mainly blue; 1–4; high, lumpy back, with rows of tubercles along body, whole surface of body rough, large sucker disc on underside; ♂ looks after young; Lumpsucker Family. **b *Common Sea-snail,** *Liparis liparis:* 15 cm; 11–2; pelvic fins fused to form a sucker disc on belly, two pairs of nostrils. **c *Montagu's Sea-snail,** *Liparis montagui:* 8 cm; 2–4; similar to **b**, but with one pair of nostrils. Both belong to the Sea-snail Family. All inhabit the Atlantic coasts and the North Sea, **a** and **b** also the Baltic.

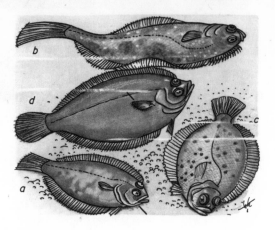

a *Long Rough Dab, *Hippoglossoides platessoides:* up to 30 cm; 1–5; long mouth cleft, very rough scales. **b** *Brill, *Scophthalmus rhombus:* up to 60 cm; 3–7; height: length = 2:3; skin smooth; left-eyed. **c** *Dab, *Limanda limanda:* up to 40 cm; 3–4; skin rough, lateral line describes an arch over the pectoral fin. **d** *Witch, *Glyptocephalus cynoglossus:* up to 50 cm; 5–7; body length 3 to 4 times height, right pectoral fin blackish. All belong to the Flatfish Family and live in the North Sea and, with the exception of **d**, the W Baltic. **a, c** and **d** lie on the left side and have the right eye uppermost.

The Flounder lives in the lower reaches of large rivers in N Europe, the other species illustrated in the North Sea and Icelandic waters; the Plaice also lives in the Baltic. All are commercially valuable Flatfishes, especially the Sole and Turbot. The Halibut is the largest of the native species. All lie either on the right or left side of their bodies, and are then left- or right-eyed respectively.

	*Plaice	*Flounder	*Lemon Sole	*Halibut	*Turbot	*Sole
Scientific Name	*Pleuronectes platessa*	*Platichthys flesus*	*Microstomus kitt*	*Hippoglossus hippoglossus*	*Scophthalmus maximus*	*Solea solea*
Size; Spawning	To 60 cm; 1–3	40–50 cm; 2–4	To 50 cm; 4–8	Up to 2 m; 3–5	Up to 1 m; 4–7	To 50 cm; 5–7
Distinguishing Features	Skin smooth, upper side and fringe of fins with orange spots; right-eyed	Similar to Plaice, but more slender, skin very rough; $^1/_3$ left-, $^2/_3$ right-eyed	Head small, lateral line straight, tail short; right-eyed	Body grey-brown, long, caudal fin concave, lateral line strongly curved; right-eyed	Body almost circular, upper side with hard bony tubercles; left-eyed	Gap between dorsal, anal and caudal fins, mouth very small; right-eyed

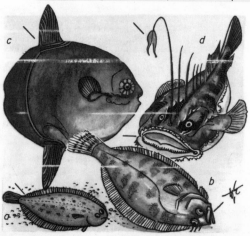

a *Solenette, *Buglossidium luteum:* up to 12 cm; 6–7; black rays at intervals in fringe of fins; right-eyed. **b** *Megrim, *Lepidorhombus whiffiagonis:* up to 60 cm; 5–6; mouth cleft large, oblique, lateral line strongly curved above the pectoral fin; left-eyed. **c** Common Ocean Sunfish, *Mola mola:* up to 2.5 m; dorsal and anal fins very high and pointed; found mainly in tropical waters. **d** *Angler, *Lophius piscatorius:* up to 2 m; head and mouth very large, first dorsal fin ray forms a 'fishing line', with which the fish, lying hidden on the sea-bed, lures small prey towards its mouth.

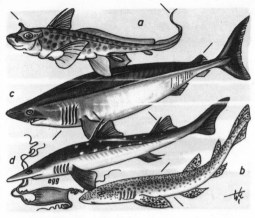

a *Rabbit Fish, *Chimaera monstrosa:* up to 1 m; 4–8; tail long and tapering, single erectile appendage on forehead; related to the sharks; Chimaera Family, found in the northern North Sea. **b *Rough Hound** or **Lesser Spotted Dogfish,** *Scylliorhinus canicula:* up to 1 m; 9–2; body greyish red, black-spotted, underside yellowish white. **c *Atlantic Mackerel Shark,** *Isurus nasus:* up to 4 m; 3–5; 1st dorsal fin large, 2nd very small, gill openings large, all in front of the 1st dorsal fin. **d *Common Spiny Dogfish,** *Squalus acanthias:* up to 1 m; 5–8; spine in front of both dorsal fins; viviparous. **b, c** and **d** are common Sharks found in the N Atlantic and North Sea.

Some of the Sharks illustrated below are widespread and regularly, some even commonly, met with in the North Sea. The Greenland Shark lives only in northern waters. Blue Sharks are principally found in the Mediterranean but produce their young off the coast of Cornwall. With the exception of the egg-laying Greenland Shark all are viviparous. All are edible, but of little commercial value. The flesh of the Common Spiny Dogfish (illustration upper right on this page) is called Rock Salmon.

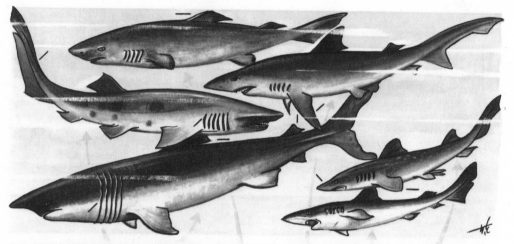

	Six-gilled or Brown Shark	*Basking Shark	Greenland Shark	*Blue Shark	*Tope	*Stellate Smooth-hound
Scientific Name	*Hexanchus griseus*	*Cetorhinus maximus*	*Somniosus microcephalus*	*Carcharius glaucus*	*Galeorhinus galeus*	*Mustelus asterias*
Size; Spawning	Up to 5 m	Up to 12 m	Up to 7 m	6–7 m	Up to 1 m; 6–9	Up to 1 m; 11
Distinguishing Features	Six gill openings on each side, tail 1/8 of body length	Gill openings very long; swims very slowly when feeding (on plankton)	No anal fin, dorsal fins without spines; egg-laying	Body very slender, upper side blue, pectoral fins sickle-shaped	Body grey, snout long, 2nd dorsal and anal fins of similar size	Body grey with light dots, pectoral fins short and wide, snout pointed and slender

a *Common Skate, *Raja batis:* up to 2.5 m long, 1.5 m wide; 2–4; snout long and pointed, skin smooth. **b *Thornback Ray,** *Raja clavata:* ♂ up to 76 cm, ♀ up to 125 cm; 2–4; upper and under sides with spines. **c Starry Ray,** *Raja asterias:* up to 50 cm; skin with fine spines, rough. **d Common Sting Ray,** *Dasyatis pastinaca:* up to 2.5 m; tail with spine. All belong to the Ray Order, related to the Sharks; they live on the sea-bed, feeding mainly on molluscs, along the Atlantic coasts and in the North Sea, **d** in the Mediterranean. **e *Sea Lamprey,** *Petromyzon marinus:* up to 1 m; 3–5; back marbled; a primitive jawless fish of the Lamprey Subclass, parasitic on other fishes.

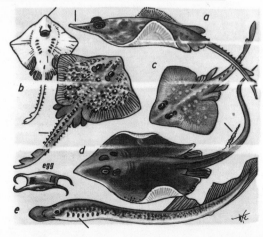

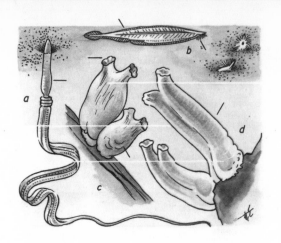

a **Acorn Worm,* *Balanoglossus clavigerus:* 50 cm; head with club-shaped proboscis, very soft-bodied. **b** **Lancelet* or **Amphioxus,** *Branchiostoma lanceolatum:* 6 cm; fish-like shape, mouth round with finger-like projections; burrows in sand, leaving head and top ¹/₃ of body projecting. **c** **Ascidiella scabra:* 8 cm; body sack-shaped, with gelatinous tunic and large siphons; common on rock and shells on the lower shore. **d** **Sea Vase,* *Ciona intestinalis:* up to 12 cm; bodies cylindrical, yellowish white; often numerous, especially on pier-supports and on buoys. **c** and **d** are Sea-squirts occurring in the N Atlantic and the Baltic. All these species are primitive Chordates.

Bryozoans or Sea Mats are small, inconspicuous, but highly complex animals which form numerous large, sessile colonies. Sometimes these colonies form a crusty covering to seaweed or shells, sometimes they grow like leaves or small trees. Numerous species are widespread; species closely related to Hornwrack and *Crisia eburnea* are cosmopolitan. *Membranipora membranacea* and *Flustra securifrons* are found from the Arctic to the Adriatic; the others are all also native to the Baltic.

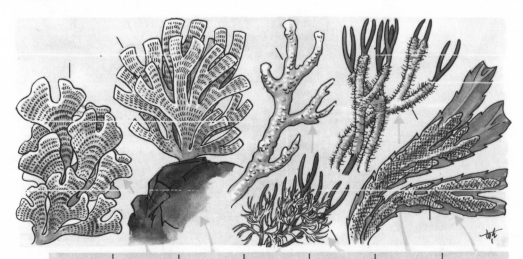

	*Hornwrack					
Scientific Name	*Flustra foliacea*	**Flustra securifrons*	**Alcyonidium gelatinosum*	**Crisia eburnea*	**Membranipora pilosa*	**Membranipora membranacea*
Size	Up to 20 cm	Up to 15 cm	Up to 50 cm	Up to 2.5 cm	0.8 mm thick	1 mm thick
Distinguishing Features	Colonies in leaf-shaped lobes with rounded corners, seaweed-like	Colonies in linear lobes with blunted ends	Colonies gelatinous, branching like a tree, sponge-like, slimy	Cells cylindrical, mostly with a long spine, colonies branching like a tree	Colonies form a bark-like covering with rectangular tracery	Colonies form a small-meshed covering with numerous fine bristles

a **Gooseberry Sea-squirt,* *Dendrodoa grossularia:* up to 15 mm; bodies red, with two prominent siphons; dense masses of individuals may become fused to common bases; found on the lower shore. **b** **Golden Star Sea-squirt,* *Botryllus schlosseri:* individual animal up to 2.5 mm; from 6–20 grouped in a star-like colony; common on the lower shore, especially in late summer. **c** *Cynthia papillosa:* 12 cm; tunic a beautiful red, tuberous. **d** **Clavelina lepadiformis:* up to 3 cm; usually orange in colour. All are Sea-squirts; **a, b** and **d** live in the Baltic and on some Atlantic coasts, including Britain, **c** in the Mediterranean.

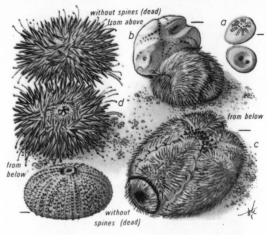

a *Green Sea Urchin, *Echinocyamus pusillus:* up to 1 cm; body ovate, flattened; lives at a depth of 10–50 m. b *Sea Potato, *Echinocardium cordatum:* 4 cm long, 3 cm wide; body heart-shaped when seen from above. c *Purple Heart Urchin, *Spatangus purpureus:* up to 12 cm long and 10 cm wide; body broadly heart-shaped, vaulted on top, flat below; 5–900 m. a–c are Irregular Sea Urchins which live in burrows. d *Purple-tipped Sea Urchin, *Psammechinus miliaris:* 2–4 cm; flattened sphere-shaped, olive-green to bluish; a Regular Sea Urchin, surface-dwelling. All are widespread from Scandinavia southwards, mainly on rocky shores, d also in the W Baltic, c in the Mediterranean.

The Common Starfish is widespread in the North Sea and the W Baltic down to a depth of 400 m. The Common Sunstar lives in the North Sea and the Baltic where the sea-bed is firm, at a depth of up to 50 m, the Burrowing Starfish buried in sand at up to 1000 m. Brittle-stars live on muddy sand. Starfishes feed mainly on molluscs, Brittle-stars are generally scavengers.

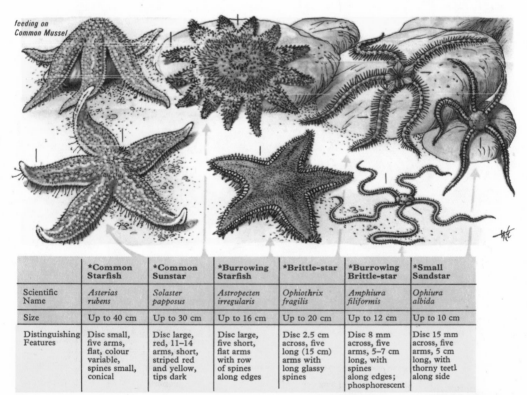

feeding on Common Mussel

	*Common Starfish	*Common Sunstar	*Burrowing Starfish	*Brittle-star	*Burrowing Brittle-star	*Small Sandstar
Scientific Name	Asterias rubens	Solaster papposus	Astropecten irregularis	Ophiothrix fragilis	Amphiura filiformis	Ophiura albida
Size	Up to 40 cm	Up to 30 cm	Up to 16 cm	Up to 20 cm	Up to 12 cm	Up to 10 cm
Distinguishing Features	Disc small, five arms, flat, colour variable, spines small, conical	Disc large, red, 11–14 arms, short, striped red and yellow, tips dark	Disc large, five short, flat arms with row of spines along edges	Disc 2.5 cm across, five long (15 cm) arms with long glassy spines	Disc 8 mm across, five arms, 5–7 cm long, with spines along edges; phosphorescent	Disc 15 mm across, five arms, 5 cm long, with thorny teeth along side

a *Edible Sea Urchin, *Echinus esculentus:* up to 12 cm; spherical, underside flat; lives on hard surfaces at a depth of up to 1200 m, from Scandinavia to Portugal. A scale-worm may often be found living among the spines of this species. b *Violet Sea Urchin, *Sphaerechinus granularis:* 15 cm; hemispherical, spine tips white; found on firm beaches. c *Paracentrotus lividus:* 6 cm; conical, spines long; lives in rocky hollows, large numbers often occurring together. a–c are widespread Regular Sea Urchins. d *Dorocidaris papillata:* 4–4.5 cm; spines thick, up to 9 cm long; a Pencil Urchin found in the Mediterranean.

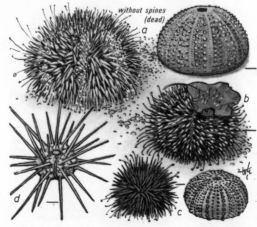

without spines (dead)

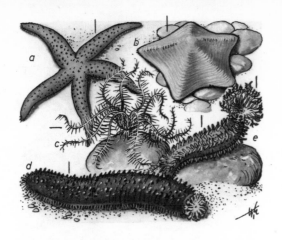

a *Echinaster sepositus:* up to 25 cm; arms thick, vermilion, skin without spines. b **Anseropoda placenta:* up to 20 cm; body almost paper-thin; 10–600 m deep. Both are Starfishes. c **Mediterranean Feather-star,** *Antedon mediterranea:* 15 cm; ten arms with many branches; a Feather-star, related to the Starfishes. d *Holothuria tubulosa:* up to 30 cm; body gherkin-shaped. e **Cucumaria planci:* 15 cm; with feathery tentacles. d and e are Sea-cucumbers, related to Starfishes, which live on muddy sea-beds. All except b and e are restricted to the Mediterranean, but comparable species occur in more northerly waters.

The Little Cuttle and *Sepia elegans* live on sandy and gravelly sea-beds, mainly in the Mediterranean; the remaining species illustrated below occur along the Atlantic coasts and in the North Sea, Forbes' Squid and the North Sea Squid also at times in the W Baltic, although they do not occur inshore. The egg capsules of the latter, which form large clusters, are spawned in July. All are Cephalopods.

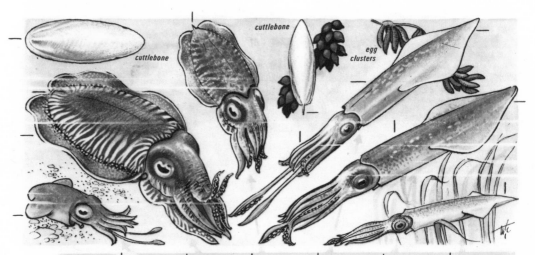

	*Little Cuttle	*Common Cuttlefish		*Common Squid	*Forbes' Squid	*North Sea Squid
Scientific Name	*Sepiola atlantica*	*Sepia officinalis*	**Sepia elegans*	*Loligo vulgaris*	*Loligo forbesi*	*Alloteuthis subulata*
Size	3–6 cm	Up to 50 cm	15 cm	Up to 50 cm	Up to 150 cm	13 cm
Distinguishing Features	Body short and wide, lateral fins roundish, two very long tentacles	Body flat, with border of lateral fins, tail-spine of cuttlebone short, 8 short 2 long tentacles	Tail-spine of cuttlebone long, projecting beyond the skin	Body light-coloured, cigar-shaped, with 8 short and 2 long tentacles, rhombic swimming fins	Arms 1/2 total length, triangular fins	Arms 1/2 total length, skin silvery grey, transparent, with dark spots, fins narrow, short

a ***Common Octopus,** *Octopus vulgaris:* 20–30 cm; eight long arms each with two rows of suckers; body colour can change rapidly. b ***Musk Octopus,** *Eledone moschata:* up to 40 cm; eight arms each with a single row of suckers. c **Paper Nautilus,** *Argonauta argus:* ♂ 1 cm, ♀ 20 cm; shell, which is the brood-chamber for the eggs, boat-shaped, paper-thin. All are Cephalopods of the Octopus Suborder. a and c live in the Mediterranean; a is the commonest species found along the coasts and a favourite food throughout the Mediterranean countries, extending north as far as the coasts of Great Britain, especially after a mild winter; b is a northern species.

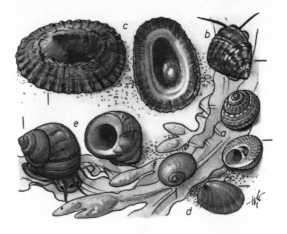

a *Grey Top Shell, Gibbula cineraria:* up to 1.8 cm; shell top-shaped. **b** *Common Top Shell, Calliostoma conuloide:* up to 3 cm; conical, marbled. All Top Shells have heavy mother-of-pearl layers which may show on the surface. **c** *Common Limpet, Patella vulgata:* up to 5.5 cm; strong radial ribs. **d** *Blue-rayed Limpet, Patina pellucidum:* up to 2 cm; cup-shaped, with blue stripes. **e** *Common or Edible Periwinkle, Littorina littorea:* 2–3 cm; pointed. **f** *Flat Periwinkle, Littorina littoralis:* up to 1.5 cm; blunt. There are four species of periwinkle on the shore, clearly zoned according to their height above the low-water mark. All common from Scandinavia to the Mediterranean.

All the species illustrated below are Carnivorous Sea-snails, which feed on other shells or barnacles. They search out their prey using their siphon, probably as a scent organ; they kill and eat them by boring through the shell into the flesh with their rasp-like tongues. The two species of *Murex* are found in the Mediterranean, the others all live further north.

	*Common Whelk	*Spindle Shell	*Sting Winkle			*Dog Whelk
Scientific Name	*Buccinum undatum*	*Neptunea antiqua*	*Ocenebra erinacea*	*Murex brandaris*	*Murex trunculus*	*Nucella lapillus*
Size	Up to 12 cm	Up to 20 cm	6–6.5 cm	Up to 10 cm	Up to 8 cm	3–4 cm
Distinguishing Features	Shell thick-walled, with undulating, grooved whorls, eggs in parchment-like capsules; 10–5	Last whorl of shell very rounded, aperture wide	Shell spindle-shaped, thick-walled, about seven whorls, with scaly ribs	Shell with long spines, siphon tube very long, edge of aperture dentate	Shell with brown bands and short spines, siphon short	Shell ovate, often with black or yellow bands, lip thick, dentate

a *Cypraea pyrum:* 4 cm; shell brownish golden. **b** *Pelican's Foot, Aporrhais pespelecani:* 5 cm; outer lip finger-shaped; burrows in muddy gravel offshore. **c** *Tower Shell, Turritella communis:* 5 cm; shell with about 15 whorls. **d** *Common Wentletrap, Clathrus clathrus:* 3–4 cm; shell with tall ridges. **e** *Large Necklace Shell, Natica catena:* 4 cm; shell globose. **f** *Common Necklace Shell, Natica nitida:* 1.5 cm; 5–7 whorls. **a** is found in the Mediterranean, the rest are widespread in European waters. **e** and **f** are burrowing carnivores which feed like the species described in the table above; both have very polished shells.

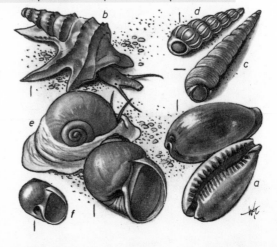

a *Netted Dog Whelk, *Nassarius reticulatus:* 2–3 cm; shell cone-shaped, eight whorls with ornamental transverse ridges. b *Thick-lipped Dog Whelk, *Nassarius incrassatus:* up to 1.5 cm; short, forked, without appendages. c *Turreted Conelet, *Lora turricula:* 2 cm; whorls set back like steps; a Dog Whelk. d *Hydrobia ulvae:* 0.5 cm; shell with eight whorls, the body one as large as the other seven. e *Needle Shell, *Bittium reticulatum:* 9–12 mm; shell with fine lattice markings. All are common sea-snails; d is so numerous in some muddy areas that the whole surface of the mud looks granular. a and b are carnivorous, feeding mainly on mussels and barnacles.

Tonna galea lives on muddy and gravelly sea-beds below 30 m; the remaining species shown below are found in the upper shore zone, where they live among seaweed or burrow in the sand. The Ormer or Ear Shell, which occurs as far north as the Channel Islands, is found on rocks and harbour jetties; it is very good to eat, and the beautiful shell is valuable. All are found in the Mediterranean.

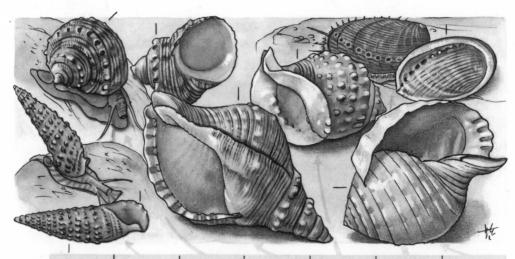

		Turban Shell			*Ormer	Tun Shell
Scientific Name	Cerithium vulgatum	Bolma rugosa	Tritonium nodiferum	Cassidaria echinophora	Haliotis lamellosa	Tonna galea
Height	Up to 7 cm	6–7 cm	Up to 40 cm	Up to 11 cm	6–8 cm	Up to 25 cm
Distinguishing Features	Shell thick-walled, conical, rough, edge of aperture dentate	Outside of shell rough, with knobs, inside porcelain-like with calcium covering	Largest Mediterranean sea-snail, shell thick-walled, body whorl very large	Few whorls, edge of aperture thickened, polished	Shell flat, only twisted at the upper end, with deep mother-of-pearl sheen	Body whorl very large, barrel-shaped, shell with lengthwise fluting

a †Slipper Limpet, *Crepidula fornicata:* up to 5 cm; shell dish-shaped, with a plate inside; introduced from America; has become a pest in oyster-beds, where they smother the oysters. b *Keyhole Limpet, *Fissurella costata:* up to 5 cm; shell cup-shaped, with hole for breathing tube. c *Sea Hare, *Aplysia punctata:* up to 8 cm; body with internal shell, changes colour. d *Tusk Shell, *Dentalium cutalis:* 5 cm; burrowing; shell like an elephant's tusk. e *Chiton or Coat-of-mail Shell, *Lepidochitona cinereus:* 2 cm; with eight articulated shell-plates; can roll up to protect itself against battering by the waves, but normally attached to rocks like limpets.

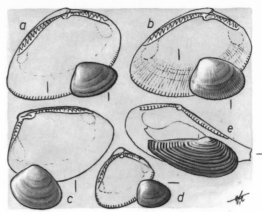

a *Common Nut Shell, *Nucula nucleus:* 12 mm; teeth uniform, ventral shell edge crenate, valve concentrically striped. **b** *Shining Nut Shell, *Nucula turgida:* 13 mm; similar to **a**, but valve also radially striped. **c** *Thin Nut Shell, *Nucula tenuis:* 12 mm; similar to **a**, but ventral shell edge smooth. **d** *Nucula nucleus* var. *tumidula:* 6 mm; shell high, concentrically striped only. **e** *Beaked Leda, *Nuculana minuta:* 14 mm; valve with two edges. All live on European Atlantic coasts, burrowing well below the low-water mark. The Nut Shells feed through a small mouth as they burrow; the toothed edge of the foot grasps fragments of sand, etc., and pulls the shell along. Leda Shells are filter-feeders.

Malletia obtusa lives in deeper water (up to 600 m); the Dog Cockle on hard sea-beds in the English Channel and along the Atlantic coasts, commonly in large colonies; the Noah's Ark and Milky Ark Shells from the North Sea to the Mediterranean. The last two species belong to the Boat Shell Family. The Marbled Crenella is widespread, and the Black Crenella inhabits northern waters; both belong to the Mussel Family.

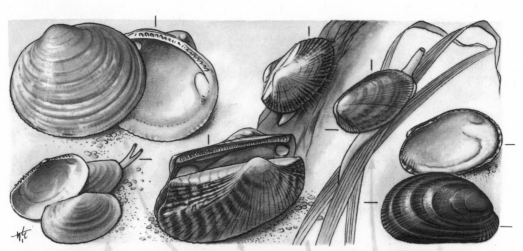

		*Dog Cockle	Noah's Ark Shell	*Milky Ark Shell	*Marbled Crenella	*Black Crenella
Scientific Name	*Malletia obtusa*	*Glycymeris glycymeris*	*Arca noae*	*Arca lactea*	*Musculus marmoratus*	*Musculus niger*
Length of Shell	Up to 13 mm	6–10 cm	5–8 cm	1.4 cm	1.7 cm	3.5 cm
Distinguishing Features	Shell oval, thin, transparent, with fine, concentric stripes, siphons long, grow together	Shell thick, almost circular, teeth numerous	Shell thick-walled, strongly ribbed, inequilateral	Valves milk-white, lattice-work sharply defined	About 16 ribs on front of valve, 25 at back; often in sea-squirts or shelter of other shells	Shell rather flat, with about 12 ribs at front and 50–60 at back

a *Common Mussel, *Mytilus edulis:* up to 8 cm; inside of valve white with blue edge; found, often in great numbers, on rocks and breakwaters, where the tide brings a plentiful supply of food, which they filter from the water. **b** *Queen Scallop, *Chlamys opercularis:* 9 cm; valve with 18–22 ribs. **c** *Variegated Scallop, *Chlamys varia:* 4–6 cm; shell with about 30 ribs, ears unequal. **d** *Saddle Oyster, *Anomia ephippium:* 3 cm; lower valve with hole for byssus; a Jingle Shell. **e** *Flat or **Native Oyster, *Ostrea edulis:* 12 cm; chalky, laminated shell. All the species shown here are common bivalves, many of which, including **a**, may contain small pearls.

a *Heart Cockle, *Glossus humanus:* up to 12 cm; valves concentrically striped; depths greater than 4 fathoms. b *Iceland Cyprina,* *Arctica islandica:* up to 11 cm; valves very large, strong, dark colour, teeth large (a characteristic of shallow-burrowing bivalves). c *Rayed Artemis, *Dosinia exoleta:* up to 5 cm; valves round, with fine concentric ribs. d *Smooth Artemis, *Dosinia lupinus:* up to 3.5 cm; valves round, with very fine stripes. c and d are Venus Shells of N European waters, where they burrow in sand, d often to some depth, at low-water mark and beyond; they are occasionally found as far south as the Mediterranean; b occurs in the Baltic.

The Elliptical Astarte is a shallow-burrowing species found off Northern coasts. Most of the Cockles illustrated will be found only as empty shells, for they burrow below low-water mark. The Common Cockle, however, occurs in huge numbers on many sandy beaches and is widely gathered for food; it is also the main food of the Oystercatcher (page 148). The Rusty Montacute Shell is found only in the burrows of the Sea Potato (page 161), or sometimes between its spines.

	*Elliptical Astarte	*Rusty Montacute Shell	*Common Cockle	*Prickly Cockle	*Banded Cockle	*Norwegian Cockle
Scientific Name	Astarte elliptica	Montacuta ferruginosa	Cerastoderma edule	Acanthocardia echinata	Cardium ovale	Laevicardium norvegicum
Length of Shell	Up to 3 cm	Up to 9 mm	Up to 5 cm	Up to 7 cm	Up to 1.5 cm	3–6 cm
Distinguishing Features	Valves elongated, flattened, with 20–40 large concentric ribs	Valves twice as long as high, bluish to violet, fragile	Valve with about 24 thick ribs; may be very numerous on middle and lower shore	Valves large, obliquely blunted at edge, about 20 spiny ribs	Valves thin, about 25 regular, delicate, radial ribs	Valves thick, higher than long, about 40 only slightly defined ribs

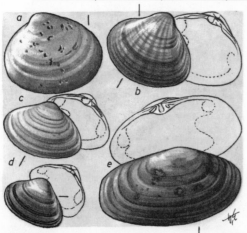

a *Mactra corallina plistoneerlandica:* up to 7 cm; shell thick, concentrically striped; found only as a fossil of the Pleistocene Period, in Holland. b *Rayed Trough Shell, *Mactra corallina cinerea:* up to 6 cm; valves with colourful radial stripes. c *Thick Trough Shell, *Spisula solida:* up to 6 cm; valve thick-walled, oval. d *Cut Trough Shell, *Spisula subtruncata:* up to 3 cm; valve triangular. e *Common Otter Shell, *Lutraria lutraria:* up to 13 cm; valve longish, external skin brown. These are members of the two families known as 'gapers' because the shells cannot close completely; they burrow in sandy mud.

a *Blunt Tellin, *Tellina crassa:* 5 cm; shell thick, mantle cavity deep. b *Baltic Tellin, *Macoma balthica:* 2.2 cm; valve broadly triangular, yellow, green, red or brown. c *Macoma calcarea:* 5 cm; shell elongated; Baltic, rare in the North Sea. d *Bean Tellin, *Tellina fabula:* 2.2 cm; right valve with very fine oblique ribs. e *Thin Tellin, *Tellina tenuis:* 2.5 cm; valve broadly oval, thin, concentrically banded. All Tellin Shells are deep burrowers living mainly towards low-water mark and beyond, sometimes in very great numbers. The shells often have unequal valves connected by a very strong ligament, which causes them to open out like butterfly wings after death.

The American Piddock is a Borer introduced in European seas. All the other species illustrated are Venus Shells. The Pullet Carpet Shell is common on muddy gravel in quiet, deepish water, the Carpet Shell is known only as a fossil from deposits of the Ice Age. Venus Shells are widespread to a depth of more than 50 m on sandy bottoms in the North Sea and along the Atlantic coasts into the Mediterranean. As seen in the fossil example, shells are often attacked by boring sponges.

	*Pullet Carpet Shell	Fossil Carpet Shell	*Striped Venus	*Warty Venus	*Oval Venus	†American Piddock
Scientific Name	*Venerupis pullastra*	*Venerupis senescens*	*Venus striata*	*Venus verrucosa*	*Venus ovata*	*Petricola pholadiformis*
Length of Shell	Up to 6.5 cm	Up to 7 cm	Up to 3.5 cm	3–5 cm	9–12 mm	6.5 cm
Distinguishing Features	Shell rhomboidal, with delicate radial and concentric stripes	Valves with coarse concentric stripes, rounded at front and hind ends	Valves basically triangular, with close, concentric, sharp ridges	Valves with concentric ridges forming tubercles	Valves rounded, with lattice sculpturing through 50 radial and 20–25 concentric stripes	Valves with radial ribs and concentric stripes, front ribs rasp-like

a *Wavy Venus, *Mysia undata:* 3 cm; mantle cavity large; common in fine sand. b *Banded Wedge Shell, *Donax vittatus:* 3 cm; shell highly polished, colour variable; found in sand at about low-water mark. c *Faroe Sunset Shell, *Gari fervensis:* 5 cm; lattice sculpturing on posterior part of shell; shell highly polished inside; commonest in the north. d *Peppery Furrow Shell, *Scrobicularia plana:* 5.5 cm; shell thin, oval. e *White Furrow Shell, *Abra alba:* 3.8 cm; valves thin. f *Glossy Furrow Shell, *Abra nitida:* 1.5 cm; long and oval. Furrow Shells normally live in mud below the tide-line, especially in estuaries or in less salty water.

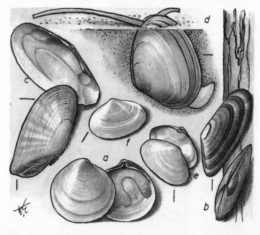

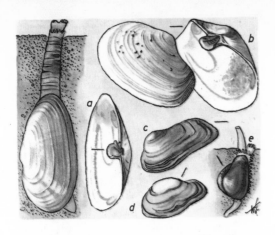

a *Sand Gaper, *Mya arenaria:* 12 cm; shell rounded at hind end, but shape and thickness very variable; wide range of habitats. b *Blunt Gaper, *Mya truncata:* 7 cm; similar to a, but valve with straight hind edge. c *Arctic Rock Borer, *Saxicava arctica:* 2 cm; shell with two keel-like edges. d *Wrinkled Rock Borer, *Saxicava rugosa:* 5 cm; shell very irregularly formed. The Rock Borers make holes in offshore rocks. e *Basket Shell, *Aloides gibba:* 1.3 cm; valves very dense, of unequal size; lives in the North Sea. c and d can only be distinguished with certainty in the young stages; later their form depends on the habitat.

The Norwegian Rock Borer is found along the Danish, British and Icelandic coasts, the Common, Oval and White Piddocks on the Atlantic coasts and, with the exception of the Common Piddock, also in the W Baltic. All bore dwelling-holes or tubes in wood, chalk, peat or firm clay; the Shipworm bores only in wood. The Papery Lantern Shell is common in the North Sea, the Atlantic and the Mediterranean.

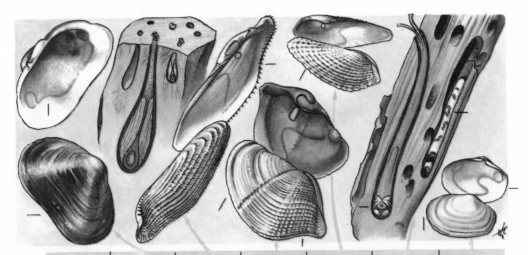

	*Norwegian Rock Borer	*Common Piddock	*Oval Piddock	*White Piddock	*Shipworm	*Papery Lantern Shell
Scientific Name	*Panopea norvegica*	*Pholas dactylus*	*Zirfaea crispata*	*Barnea candida*	*Teredo navalis*	*Thracia phaseolina*
Length of Shell	Up to 8 cm	Up to 15 cm	Up to 8 cm	Up to 7 cm	9 mm	Up to 3 cm
Distinguishing Features	Shell thick, elongated, upper and lower edges almost parallel	Front end of valve elongated like a finger, rasp-like; phosphorescent	Front of valve spiny, hind part concentrically striped	Valves with radial, spiny ribs, rasp-like, especially at front end	Valve up to 9 mm long, bores holes up to 8 mm wide, 20 cm long, calcareous lining	Valves unequal, brittle, front end roundish, hind end blunted

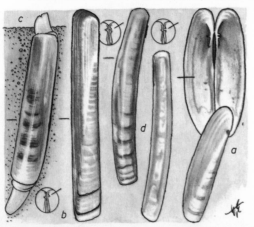

a *Transparent Razor Shell, *Cultellus pellucidus:* 3.9 cm long, 1 cm wide; shell thin, greenish white. b *Pod Razor Shell, *Ensis siliqua:* 20 cm long, 2.5 cm wide; shell straight. c *Grooved Razor Shell, *Solen marginatus:* 12.5 cm long, 2.1 cm wide; edges parallel. d *Sword Razor Shell, *Ensis ensis:* 9.3 cm long, 1.2 cm wide; shell slightly curved; height:length = 1:8. All live in vertical holes on sandy shores. Although dead shells may often be found, it is rare to catch a live Razor Shell, as they can dig into the sand faster than most people can.

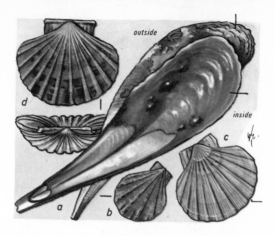

a Fan Mussel, *Pinna nobilis:* 80 cm; shell externally rough, internally with a mother-of-pearl sheen. **b *Seven-rayed Scallop,** *Chlamys septemradiatus:* up to 4.5 cm; shell roundish, with 5–9 broad, flat ribs; Atlantic coasts. **c *Great Scallop** or **Clam,** *Pecten maximus:* up to 13 cm; 'ears' perfectly symmetrical, shell with 14–17 wide ribs; Atlantic coasts. **d Pilgrim's Scallop,** *Pecten jacobaeus:* 15 cm; shell thin, large-ribbed; lives on flat Mediterranean shores. Scallops live at the lowest level of the shore, and beyond. They swim by clapping the valves of their shells together. The edge of the mantle has many tentacles, some bearing opalescent eyes.

The Spiny Lobster or Langouste lives on rocky bottoms from the Mediterranean as far north as Cornwall, the Lobster on rocky bottoms as far as Norway. The Norway Lobster or Dublin Bay Prawn is found in deep water, the Common Hermit Crab in littoral areas in general. Prideaux's Hermit Crab is found in water up to 150 m deep, and *Eupagurus anachoretus* lives on rocks and gravelly sea-beds in the Mediterranean. All are long-tailed walking forms of Decapod Crustaceans.

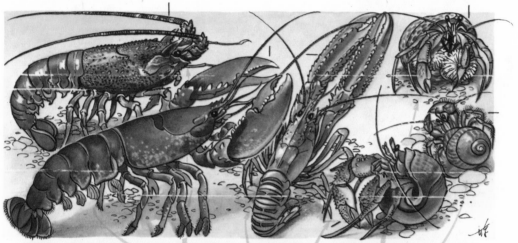

	*Lobster	*Spiny Lobster	*Norway Lobster	*Common Hermit Crab	*Prideaux's Hermit Crab	
Scientific Name	*Homarus gammarus*	*Palinurus elephas*	*Nephrops norvegicus*	*Eupagurus bernhardus*	*Eupagurus prideauxi*	*Eupagurus anachoretus*
Size	Up to 50 cm	Up to 50 cm	♂ 18 cm	Up to 10 cm	Up to 8 cm	Up to 4 cm
Distinguishing Features	1st walking legs with large pincer for crushing, and smaller one for seizing prey	1st pair of walking legs has grasping claws without pincers, antennae very long, powerful	♀ 14 cm; pincer-bearing limbs very long, angled, light red-brownish	Pincers unequal, larger protects shell aperture, hind part of body soft-skinned	Pincers long; almost always lives in symbiosis with a sea anemone, *Adamsia palliata*	Body with vivid bright colouring, legs with long hairs

a *Green Squat Lobster, *Galathea squamifera:* body up to 8 cm; dark brownish green; under stones on the lower shore of North Sea and Atlantic coasts. **b *Palaemon adspersus:** up to 7 cm; rostrum on forehead with 5–6 teeth on top, three teeth underneath. **c *Prawn,** *Palaemon squilla:* up to 5 cm; rostrum on forehead with 7–9 teeth on top, three teeth underneath; flat places from the Mediterranean to Norway and the Baltic. **d *Shrimp,** *Crangon crangon:* up to 7 cm; no rostrum, but sharp point between eyes; lives on sand all round Europe. All are long-tailed swimming forms; they are camouflaged by their lack of colouring. Shells inflexible and shed periodically with growth.

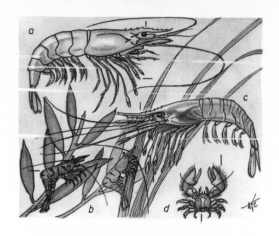

a Red Prawn, *Parapenaeus longirostris:* 12–13 cm; rostrum on forehead long and pointed; Mediterranean. **b *Chameleon Prawn,** Hippolyte varians:* up to 1.5 cm; back of body humped, first pair of legs short and thick, second pair long and thin. This animal gets its name from its ability to change colour; although abundant, it is often missed because it matches its background perfectly. **c** **Palaemon xiphias:* 5–7 cm; rostrum on forehead very long, concave. **b** and **c** are long-tailed swimming forms, extending to the W Baltic from the southern North Sea. **d *Grey Porcelain Crab,** Porcellana platy-cheles:* carapace about 1 cm wide; pincers thickly haired.

Ilia nucleus and *Dorippe lanata* live in the Mediterranean among sea-grass, on rocky bottoms or in shingle. The Sponge Crab, so called because it is always associated with a sponge, is a mainly Mediterranean species, but a few are found as far north as Britain. Hairy Crabs and Pea Crabs are found along North Sea and Atlantic coasts. The Slender-legged Crab extends into the W Baltic. All are short-tailed Crustaceans. With the exception of the Sponge Crab they are very small (under 3 cm).

		*Sponge Crab		*Slender-legged Crab	*Hairy Crab	*Pea Crab
Scientific Name	*Ilia nucleus*	*Dromia vulgaris*	*Dorippe lanata*	*Macropodia rostrata*	*Pilumnus hirtellus*	*Pinnotheres pisum*
Carapace	Up to 3 cm	Up to 15 cm	2–2.5 cm	Up to 2 cm	Up to 2.4 cm	♂ 4.5, ♀ 12 mm
Distinguishing Features	Body almost spherical, eyes and antennae situated well forward	Body strongly arched, cover-ed with dense, short bristles, pincers very powerful	Body reddish yellow, round-ish, pincers small, 1st and 2nd pairs of walking legs very long	Carapace triangular, rostrum long, pointed, legs long; camou-flages itself with seaweed	Carapace highly arched, broader than long	Carapace spherical, eyes degenerate, skin thin, soft, ♀ found in mussels, ♂ free-living

a *Edible Crab, Cancer pagurus:* carapace up to 30 cm wide; front edge of shell crenated, pincer tips black; found mainly on rocky shores under stones and seaweed, larger specimens below the tide-line. **b *Shore Crab,** Carcinus maenas:* carapace up to 10 cm; edge of forehead with five teeth on each side; the commonest British crab. **c *Spider Crab,** Hyas araneus:* carapace up to 10.5 cm, ovate, 1st pair of legs with pincers; camouflages itself with seaweed; widely distributed but not usually very common. All are short-tailed Crustaceans living in the North Sea and on Atlantic coasts, the Shore Crab and the Spider Crab also in the W Baltic.

a *Portunus hastatus:* 3–4 cm; two long and powerful spikes on each side of carapace, pincer legs long and strong. **b** *****Swimming Crab**, *Macropipus holsatus:* carapace about 4 cm long, hairless, edge of forehead with five equally large teeth on each side. **c** *****Velvet Crab**, *Macropipus puber:* carapace up to 12 cm long; edge of forehead with 6–8 teeth on each side; the most aggressive rock-pool crab, if disturbed it will hold its claws out in an attacking posture. All are swimming crabs with swimming plates on the last pair of walking legs. All live in the Mediterranean, **b** and **c** also in the North Sea and Atlantic. All are eaten in Mediterranean countries.

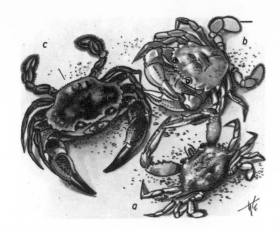

The Crustaceans shown below are widespread in European coastal waters. *Orchestia gammarella* and *Talitrus saltator* live on shingly or sandy beaches, while *Corophium volutator*, a Burrowing Shrimp, digs holes for itself in muddy shallows. *Idotea baltica* eats plants, Pennant's Skeleton Shrimp or Screw small animals. Both are widespread in the North Sea and the Baltic. *Praunus flexuosus* is an Opossum Shrimp which lives in coastal regions and is an important food for fish.

		*Sandhopper			*Chameleon Shrimp	*Pennant's Skeleton Shrimp
Scientific Name	*Orchestia gammarella	Talitrus saltator	*Corophium volutator	*Idotea baltica	Praunus flexuosus	Caprella linearis
Size	Up to 17 mm	Up to 16 mm	6 mm	Up to 30 mm	Up to 30 mm	♂ 32 mm
Distinguishing Features	Both the first two pairs of thoracic legs with pincers, end joint of 2nd pair of legs enlarged	Only 2nd pair of thoracic legs with pincers, jumps from 20–30 cm	Eyes dark red, ♂ with very long 2nd antennae	Body flattened, seven pairs of legs, tail plate with three spines	Eight pairs of legs, carapace and abdomen delicately transparent	♀ 14 mm, body wine-red, eyes bright red, ♂ very slender

Barnacles are included among the Crustaceans because, although the adult forms are unlike the other members of the group, the larval stages are very similar. The Stalked Barnacles, which live on wood, include **a** *****Lepas hillii:* stalk up to 10 cm long; **b** *****Goose Barnacle**, *Lepas anatifera:* similar to **a**, but with stalk up to 30 cm long; **c** *****Lepas fascularis:* shell up to 3.5 cm; grooved. The Acorn or Rock Barnacles include **d** *****Balanus balanoides:* up to 1 cm high and 2 cm wide; generally diamond-shaped overall; a more northern species, found on the middle shore; **e** *****Balanus crenatus:* up to 3.4 cm high and 1.9 cm wide; found on underside of overhanging rocks, in less exposed places than **c**.

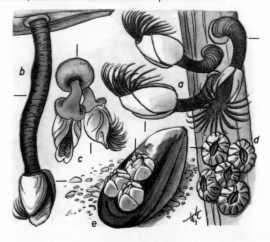

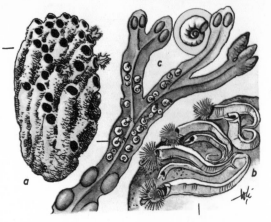

a **Sabellaria spinulosa:* up to 4 cm long; builds tubes up to 30 cm long and about 5 mm in diameter out of grains of sand cemented together; lives in large colonies, often forming reef-like banks. **b** **Pomatoceros triqueter:* up to 5 cm; semicircular wreath of tentacles, red, blue or yellow; builds long, triangular calcareous tubes. **c** **Spirorbis borealis:* 3 mm; lives in small, post-horn-shaped calcareous tubes, attached to seaweed or stones. All are tube-living Polychaetes (Bristle-worms) living in European seas. The tubes are often found, but the worms emerge only when covered with water, returning rapidly at unusual movement or if a shadow crosses them.

Five crustaceans and one spider, *Garypus beauvoisi*, are described below. All live in the Mediterranean. The Great Sea-slater is related to woodlice, the remainder are long-tailed Crustaceans. With the exception of the Great Sea-slater and *Aristeomorpha foliacea* (lower depths below 250 m), which live along rocky coasts, all live on muddy bottoms, on flat beaches or, like *Garypus beauvoisi*, under piles of seaweed thrown up along the shore.

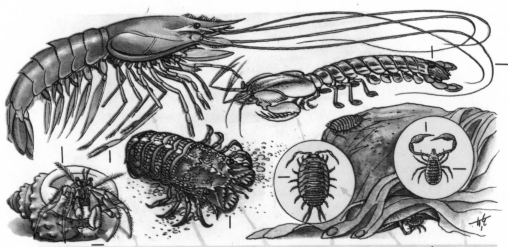

			*Squat Lobster	*Mantis Shrimp	*Great Sea-slater	
Scientific Name	*Diogenes pugilator*	*Aristeomorpha foliacea*	*Scyllarus arctus*	*Squilla mantis*	*Ligia oceanica*	*Garypus beauvoisi*
Size	Up to 3 cm	♂ 30 cm	Up to 10 cm	Up to 20 cm	Up to 3 cm	Up to 6 cm
Distinguishing Features	Body small, 2nd antennae short, feather-like, colouring varied, left pincer very large	♀ 20 cm, with long, pointed rostrum, ♂ with short, serrated rostrum	Body dark brown, plump and tough, outer antennae widened like leaves	Body light-coloured, tail-segment with two dark spots, front legs prehensile	Body dotted with grey, antennae long, uropods with two long pointed processes	Four pairs of legs, one pair of pincers, skin looks finely grained

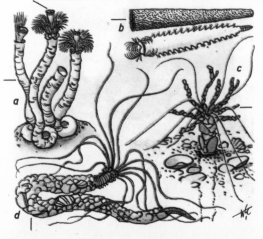

a **Serpula vermicularis:* round tube 7–10 cm long, slightly larger towards mouth, showing growth rings; lives offshore but often cast up on beach, especially on Great Scallop Shells (page 169); North Sea and Atlantic coasts. **b** **Pectinaria coreni:* up to 10 cm; delicate cigar-shaped tubes made up of grains of sand of uniform size; Atlantic coasts, North Sea and Baltic. **c** **Lanice conchilega:* up to 30 cm; tube encrusted with fragments of shell and gravel, protrudes about 5 cm from ground; in sand and shingle on lower shore, N European coasts. **d** *Polymnia nebulosa:* up to 30 cm; twisted tubes of sand and shingle; Mediterranean. All are Polychaetes (Bristle-worms).

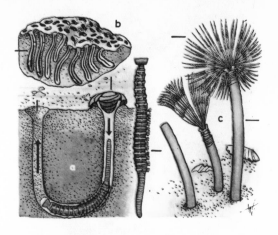

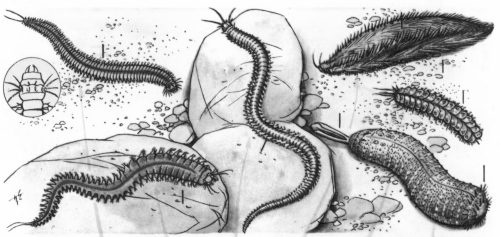

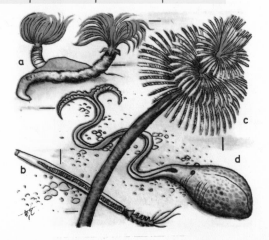

a *Lugworm, *Arenicola marina:* 10–20 cm; greenish or yellow-black, with 13 pairs of blood-red gill tufts along the middle of the body; makes worm casts and a funnel-like hollow 10–15 cm away with a U-shaped tube between them; difficult to dig up complete, but taken by fishermen as the best bait for sea fish. b *Polydora ciliata:* up to 2 cm; bores U-shaped tubes up to 2 mm in diameter in rocks. c *Peacock Worm, *Sabella pavonina:* up to 30 cm; living tubes soft, vertical, protruding about 10 cm from mud, double crown of tentacles from two semi-circular lobes. All are common round the coasts of Britain and much of Europe.

The worms shown below can all be found in the North Sea and the Baltic. *Nereis* and *Eunice,* which are Ragworms, are predaceous, feeding on many kinds of small animals including the tentacles of the tube-worms shown above. The Sea Mouse and the related Scale Worm are mainly scavengers. *Echiurus* is a browser, feeding by means of its extensile proboscis; unlike *Bonellia* (at bottom of page), to which it is related, the males and females lead separate existences.

				*Sea Mouse	*Scale Worm	
Scientific Name	*Nereis pelagica	*Nereis diversicolor	*Eunice harassi	Aphrodite aculeata	Gattyana cirrosa	*Echiurus echiurus
Size	Up to 10 cm	Up to 10 cm	20–25 cm	Up to 10 cm	2.5–5 cm	Up to 12 cm
Distinguishing Features	Body segments numerous, with hairy parapodia; on rocky shores	Body brownish, antennae small; digs irregularly branched holes in estuarine mud	Body segments numerous, parapodia with red gill tufts, middle antennae longest	Body short and wide, with two rows of bristles along the side, many fine bristles on back	Body brown, with 15 pairs of transparent scales on back	Body limbless, head with spathulate proboscis

a *Protula intestinum:* diameter of tube 10 to 12 mm; double crown of tentacles, blood-red, tubes calcareous. b *Hyalinoecia tubicola:* tubes horny, 5–7 cm long, 2–4 mm thick; animal wanders around with tube. c *Spirographis spallanzanii:* up to 50 cm; in hard parchment-like tube, spiral crown of tentacles. d *Bonellia viridis:* ♀ 15 cm, with forked head lobes, ♂ 1–2 mm; the animal illustrated is the female, the male being a minute parasitic form; tentacles always extended (cf. *Echiurus,* above). a is a Mediterranean species, the others may also be found further north.

a *Corymorpha nutans:* 5–6 cm; bell pointed, with one tentacle. **b** *Sarsia tubulosa:* 5.5 cm; mouth stalk and four tentacles blue. **c** *Med-usa, Leuckartiara octona:* 15 cm; bell with spherical bulge. **d** *Luminous Jellyfish, Pelagia noctiluca:* 5–6 cm; eight tentacles round edges, mouth lobes very long, with frilled edges; rare. All are True Jellyfish found in the Atlantic, North Sea and the W Baltic. **e** *By-the-wind-sailor, Velellá vel-ella:* 1–5 cm; blown along by the wind by means of its gas-filled bladder; often lives in colonies on the surface of the sea; a Mediter-ranean Siphonophore, which may reach south-west coasts of Britain.

The White or Moon Jelly, the Compass Jellyfish, the Blue Hairy Jellyfish, the Red or Arctic Jellyfish and *Rhizostoma pulmo* are True Jellyfish. They live in open water in the North Sea and the Atlantic; the White Jelly alone is more numerous in the Baltic, *Rhizostoma pulmo* is also found in the Mediterranean. The Portuguese Man-o'-war is a warm-water Siphonophore which occasionally gets blown into northern waters.

	*White Jelly	*Compass Jellyfish	*Blue Hairy Jellyfish	*Red Jellyfish		*Portuguese Man-o'-war
Scientific Name	*Aurelia aurita*	*Chrysaora hysoscella*	*Cyanea lamarckii*	*Cyanea capillata*	*Rhizostoma pulmo*	*Physalia physalia*
Disc Diameter	30–40 cm	Up to 30 cm	Up to 35 cm	Up to 1 m	Up to 60 cm	20–30 cm
Distinguishing Features	Umbrella violet, reddish or yellowish, sexual organs of ♂ whitish, of ♀ reddish	Umbrella shallowly arched, with 16 brown, forked stripes, sexual organs white, yellow or red	Umbrella flat, sexual organs, enteron and gastric pouches cornflower blue	Similar to previous, but yellowish brown to reddish yellow, tentacles up to 2 m long	Umbrella hemispherical-ly vaulted, with blue lobes around edge	Large, gas-filled bladder, tentacles many yards long, powerful stinging cells; dangerous

a *Craterolophus tethys:* up to 2 cm; attached, with four pairs of tentacles around the edge; a Stalked Jellyfish. **b** *Leucothea multicornis:* 20–40 cm; yellowish brown, with gelatinous lobes; Mediterranean and further north. **c** *Sea-gooseberry, Pleurobrachia pileus:* 2 cm; body slightly ovoid. **d** *Bolinopsis infun-dibulum:* up to 15 cm; body pear-shaped. **e** *Beroë ovata:* up to 1.2 cm; body cylin-drical. **b, c, d** and **e** are Comb-jellies found in European seas. In some years, they may be swept into shallow water in large numbers; unlike other Coelenterates, they do not catch their prey using sting-cells.

a * **Dahlia Sea Anemone**, *Tealia felina*:
5cm long, up to 7 cm thick; column red, green
or pink, tentacles barred with white, very thick,
in five circles round the mouth; lives low on
beach. b *Aiptasia diaphana*: 3–5 cm diameter; tentacles rusty yellow, unable to contract. c *Snakelocks Sea Anemone**, *Anemo-
nia sulcata*: 4 cm high; tentacles 5 cm long, unable to contract; green colour due to many
minute plants which live in its tissues in symbiosis. d *Wartlet** or **Gem Sea Anemone**,
Bunodactis verrucosa: up to 5 cm high; with
vertical rows of warts; lives in rock-crevices
and holes. All live from the Mediterranean
northwards along the Atlantic coasts.

Calliactis parasitica may live in symbiosis with Hermit Crabs. The other species of Sea Anemones
illustrated are found on firm sea-beds on rocks, breakwaters, mussels, etc., in the North Sea; the
Beadlet Anemone and *Actinia cari* also in the Baltic and the Mediterranean. *Sagartiogeton
undatus* occasionally digs itself into the sand.

	*Beadlet Anemone			*Parasitic Anemone		
Scientific Name	*Actinia equina*	*Actinia cari*	*Diadumene luciae*	*Calliactis parasitica*		*Sagartiogeton undatus*
Height	Up to 3 cm	4–6 cm diam.	Up to 1.4 cm	7 cm		Up to 12 cm
Distinguishing Features	Tentacles more slender than those of *Urticina felina*, column red, green or yellow	Mostly green with dark transverse lines, tentacles short, retractable	5 mm thick, 8–20 orange vertical stripes, tent-acles up to 2.5 cm, unable to contract	Column min-utely corrugat-ed above, warts below, yellowish with purple-brown stripes	Illustrated here is another form of *Calliactis parasitica*, on a hermit crab's shell	Tentacles very long, pendent, column red, yellow or brown, with vertical stripes

a **Vestlet**, *Cerianthus membranaceus*: up to
20 cm; tentacles long, white; Mediterranean.
b *Plumose Sea Anemone**, *Metridium senile*:
up to 13 cm; tentacles very delicate and
numerous, giving a feathery appearance, many
colour varieties. c *Cereus pedunculatus*: 5 cm;
over 700 tentacles. d **Dead Men's Fingers**,
Alcyonium glomerulatum: up to 15 cm; column
cushion-like, lobed, colour variable, a soft
coral with colonial polyps; Mediterranean.
e **Red Coral**, *Corallium rubrum*: colony-form-
ing, with red calcareous skeleton; Mediterranean; this species, which is the origin of
precious coral, has become very rare almost
everywhere through over-collection.

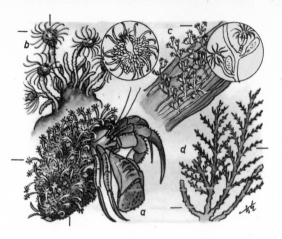

a *Hydractinia echinata:* 6 mm high; wreath of tentacles almost doubled, spines between the polyps. **b** *Oaten-pipes Hydroid,* *Tubularia larynx:* up to 7 cm; tentacles in two circles, lower one with about 20, upper one with 14–20 tentacles; on buoys, piers, etc., below tide-level. **c** *Obelia geniculata:* up to 4 cm; single polyps arranged alternately giving zigzag appearance; medusae with 16–20 tentacles; on weeds. **d** *Herring-bone Polyp,* *Halecium halecium:* up to 10 cm; colonies fan-shaped, centre stem sturdy. These are Sea Firs found on the Atlantic coasts, in the North Sea, and more rarely in the W Baltic; occasionally also in the Mediterranean.

Sea Firs are colonial relatives of the Sea Anemones. The Sea Oak lives on the Atlantic coasts, in the North Sea and the Baltic, *Eudendrium ramosum* on seaweed or rocks in the Mediterranean. The remaining species are chiefly found in the North Sea; the Squirrel's Tail covers extensive areas in saltings; *Hydrallmania falcata* prefers oyster-beds; *Abietinaria abietina* attaches itself to rocks and mussel shells.

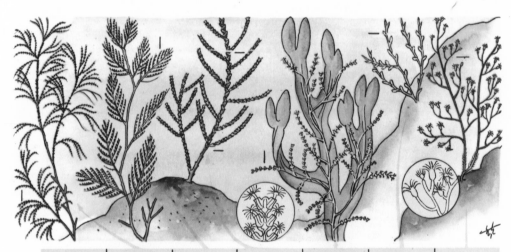

	*Squirrel's Tail			*Sea Oak		
Scientific Name	*Sertularia cupressina*	*Hydrallmania falcata*	*Abietinaria abietina*	*Dynamena pumila*	*Sertularella polyzonias*	*Eudendrium ramosum*
Size	Up to 45 cm	Up to 45 cm	Up to 30 cm	Up to 5 cm	Up to 5 cm	5–10 cm
Distinguishing Features	Colonies large, bushy, polyps arranged in two rows	Stems spirally twisted, cups in rows along the branches	Colonies sturdy, on one plane, stalk simple, branches alternate	Colonies usually unbranched, creeping, polyps opposite; lives on Fucus	Colonies with few branches, polyps barrel-shaped immediately below joints	Polyp colony axial, polyps without cup-shaped hydrotheca

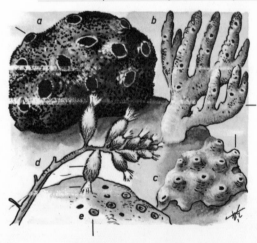

a Turkey or Toilet Sponge, *Euspongia officinalis:* up to head size; skeleton horny; collected commercially in the Mediterranean. **b** *Haliclona oculata:* up to 30 cm; stems like antlers. **c** *Bread-crumb Sponge, Halichondria panicea:* up to 10 cm; oscula (large pores through which water is pumped out during feeding) tower-shaped; forms encrusting masses on rock, the bases of seaweed fronds, etc. **d** *Sycon raphanus:* 3–4 cm; with spicules. **e** *Sulphur Sponge, Cliona celata:* round bore-holes 2–3 mm in diameter; a Boring Sponge which will bore into limestone or shells, especially oysters, which it often reduces to a crumbly texture.

Meadows and Pastureland

Meadows are treeless grassy tracts which may be either natural or artificial. Natural meadows are of two main types: water-meadows along river-banks, where periodic flooding prevents tree colonization, and alpine meadows above the tree-line. Artificial meadows (pastureland) have no trees and shrubs because of continuous mowing and grazing. The characteristic plants of all meadows and pasturelands are perennial grasses, which not only survive repeated cropping, but are strengthened and made even denser by it. With the exception of clover, the farmer considers all other plants growing on meadows and pastureland as weeds which reduce the yield of his hay. But for most people it is just because of the brilliant variety of flowers that meadows are so attractive. Distinction is made according to the nature of the soil between lush meadows, with a high hay yield, and poor meadows, with a low yield. Wet meadows often consist predominantly of sedges, which are not eaten by cattle. The crop from such reed-meadows is often used for bedding for cattle. Meadows which are mown alternate between an abundance and a paucity of vegetation. This periodic reduction of ground cover has a considerable effect upon animal life, but some birds and mammals have adapted themselves to the habitat. During flowering time a host of insects lives and feeds in meadows. The animal populations of many meadow areas have been much reduced recently by sprays used to destroy weeds which are the food of many specialized feeders, or directly by insecticides. Of the mammals specialized for meadow-life, many undergo great fluctuations of population. The Field Vole in Britain tends to have population cycles of 4 years. It may reach plague numbers of up to 400 animals per acre, after which a crash occurs and numbers are very low again.

a Many-flowered Crowfoot, *Ranunculus polyanthemos:* ♃, 25–130 cm; basal leaves usually deeply trifid, flower-stalks bristly, furrowed; 5–7; C and N Europe. **b †Winter Aconite**, *Eranthis hyemalis:* ♃, 4–15 cm; stem leaves 3, arranged in a whorl just beneath flower, flowers solitary; 2–3; a native of S Europe. **c Isopyrum**, *Isopyrum thalictroides:* ♃, 10–30 cm; leaves bluish green, 2-ternate, flowers pentamerous, solitary; 4–5; C Europe. **d †Purple Clematis**, *Clematis viticella:* a woody climber, 3–4 m; perianth-segments 4, blue or purple, hairy at margins; 6–8; a native of S Europe. All belong to the Buttercup Family; **b** and **d** are naturalized in many parts of Europe as escapes.

The Lesser Celandine or Pilewort and the three buttercups described below are common and widespread. The Globe Flower occurs in moorland meadows, wet pastures, scrub and woods throughout Europe, but only on mountains in the south. The Stinking Hellebore is a local plant of dry, stony slopes, woods and scrub in SW Europe, extending northwards to Britain and N Germany, and southwards to Switzerland and S Italy. All belong to the Buttercup Family.

	*Lesser Celandine	*Meadow Buttercup	*Creeping Buttercup	*Bulbous Buttercup	*Globe Flower	*Stinking Hellebore
Scientific Name	*Ranunculus ficaria*	*Ranunculus acris*	*Ranunculus repens*	*Ranunculus bulbosus*	*Trollius europaeus*	*Helleborus foetidus*
Longevity, Size	♃, 5–30 cm	♃, 30–100 cm	♃, 15–60 cm	♃, 5–50 cm	♃, 5–70 cm	♃, 15–100 cm
Distinguishing Features; Flowering Time	Basal leaves heart-kidney-shaped, sometimes with bulbils in leaf-axils, sepals 3, petals 8–12; 3–4	Basal leaves 5–7-lobed, long-stalked, receptacle glabrous, fruits with a short beak; 5–10	Stem with stolons, basal leaves 3-lobed to pinnate, receptacle hairy, sepals 5; 5–8	Stem tuberous (corm-like) at base, sepals 5, strongly reflexed; 5–8	Stem un-branched, perianth-segments 5–10, forming a globular flower; 5–6	Stem leafy, lower leaves evergreen, pedate, bracts entire, perianth-segments bell-shaped; 3–4

a Narrow-leaved Meadow-rue, *Thalictrum simplex:* ♃, 20–120 cm; basal leaves 2–3-pinnate, leaflets lobed or toothed or entire; 6–7. **b †French Meadow-rue**, *Thalictrum aquilegifolium:* ♃, 30–150 cm; filaments as wide as anthers, lilac or white; 5–7; E and C Europe and on mountains in the south. **c *Lesser Meadow-rue**, *Thalictrum minus:* ♃, 15 to 150 cm; basal leaves 3–4-ternate, leaflets irregularly lobed or toothed; 5–7; widespread. **d Shining Meadow-rue**, *Thalictrum lucidum:* ♃, 60–120 cm; flowers upright, in rather dense clusters; 6–8; C and E Europe. All belong to the Buttercup Family and occur in moorland meadows.

a *Yellow Marsh Saxifrage, *Saxifraga hirculus:* ♃, 10–40 cm; stalks of lower leaves sheathing, sepals reflexed and long-hairy at base; 7–9; widespread, on moors; Stonecrop Family. b *Grass of Parnassus, *Parnassia palustris:* ♃, 15–45 cm; basal leaves long-stalked, stem leaf 1, stalkless, clasping stem; 7–9; widespread, in marshes and fens; Parnassus-grass Family. c *Bur Medick, *Medicago minima:* ☉, 5–30 cm; leaflets hairy, pod sub-globose, in a spiral of 2–7 turns, spiny; 4–7; widespread, in sandy and gravelly places; Pea Family. d *Dropwort, *Filipendula vulgaris:* ♃, 15–80 cm; roots with ovoid tubers, leaves pinnate; 5–7; widespread; Rose Family.

The Tormentil, the Common Lady's Mantle and the Common Avens or Herb Bennet are common on meadows, in woods and on scrubland, the Tormentil particularly in heath meadows. The Water Avens and the Great Burnet are widespread in meadows, the Water Avens also occurs in high alpine meadows and in wet and swampy woods. The Salad Burnet is found on grassland and scree. All belong to the Rose Family.

	*Tormentil	*Common Lady's Mantle	*Water Avens	*Common Avens	*Great Burnet	*Salad Burnet
Scientific Name	Potentilla erecta	Alchemilla vulgaris	Geum rivale	Geum urbanum	Sanguisorba officinalis	Sanguisorba minor
Longevity, Size	♃, 5–40 cm	♃, 10–50 cm	♃, 30–50 cm	♃, 25–50 cm	♃, 40–120 cm	♃, 10–40 cm
Distinguishing Features; Flowering Time	Root-stock with reddish flesh, stipules palmate, petals 4; 5–8	Leaf-stalks longer than 5 cm, leaf-blade 7–11-lobed, stamens 4; 5–9	Stipules small, flowers nodding, reddish; 4–5	Stipules large, flowers upright, petals light yellow; 5–10	Leaves with 3–7 pairs of leaflets, flowers in dense spikes or heads, dull crimson; 6–9	Leaves with 4–12 pairs of leaflets, flowers in globose heads, green, often purple-tinged; 5–6

a *Sickle Medick, *Medicago falcata:* ♃, 30 to 60 cm; flowers in head-like racemes, pods usually sickle-shaped; 5–9. b *Black Medick, *Medicago lupulina:* ☉-♃, 5–50 cm; leaflets hairy, flowers small, in head-like racemes, pod 1-seeded, black when ripe; 5–9. c *Zig-zag Clover, *Trifolium medium:* ♃, 7–70 cm; leaflets very finely toothed, heads 2–3 cm long, reddish purple, calyx-tube glabrous; 6–8. d *Sulphur Clover, *Trifolium ochroleucon:* ♃, 15–50 cm; heads about 2 cm long, whitish yellow, calyx-tube hairy; 6–7. All are widespread members of the Pea Family found in dry meadows and along roadsides.

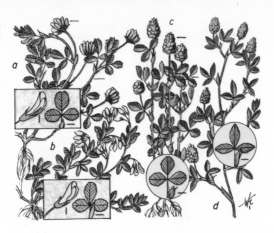

a *Lesser Yellow Trefoil, *Trifolium dubium:* ⊙-⊙, 10–30 cm; stem slender, heads 10–20-flowered, flower-stalks stout, shorter than the calyx-tube; 5–10; widespread. **b** *Slender Yellow Trefoil, *Trifolium micranthum:* ⊙, 2–10 cm; stem very slender, heads 2–6-flowered, flower-stalks slender, equalling the calyx-tube; 5–7; in S, W and C Europe. **c** *Hop Trefoil, *Trifolium campestre:* ⊙-⊙, 5–30 cm; terminal leaflet with a longer stalk than in the lateral leaflets; 6–9; widespread. **d** †Large Hop Trefoil, *Trifolium aureum:* ⊙, up to 40 cm; all leaflets short-stalked; 6–8; mainly in C Europe. All are members of the Pea Family, occurring in meadows.

The Red Clover and the White Clover are widespread in meadows, the latter also in poor grassland and by roadsides. The Soft Clover grows locally on dry pastureland and in sandy fields, the Rough Clover in dry places on shallow or sandy soils, and the Mountain Clover in dry meadows and open woodlands in hilly districts. The Strawberry Clover grows in marshy meadows, particularly on saline ground, or in grassy places on heavy clay soils. All belong to the Pea Family.

	*Red Clover	*Soft Clover	*Rough Clover	*Strawberry Clover	Mountain Clover	*White Clover
Scientific Name	*Trifolium pratense*	*Trifolium striatum*	*Trifolium scabrum*	*Trifolium fragiferum*	*Trifolium montanum*	*Trifolium repens*
Longevity, Size	♃, 10–40 cm	⊙-⊙, 5–30 cm	⊙, 3–20 cm	♃, 8–30 cm	♃, 20–60 cm	♃, 3–25 cm
Distinguishing Features; Flowering Time	Stipules 3-angled, bristle-pointed, flowers pink-purple or whitish, calyx 10-ribbed; 6–9	Leaflets hairy, heads ovoid, enfolded in stipules of subtending leaves, petals pale pink; 5–8	Lateral veins of leaflets forward curved, thickened towards the margins, petals whitish; 5–7	Stems creeping, rooting at the nodes, stipules with subulate points, flowers purplish; 6–9	Stem clothed with silky woolly hairs, leaflets with short prickly teeth; 5–8	Stems creeping, rooting at the nodes, stipules long-pointed, flowers white, rarely pink; 5–9

a *Kidney Vetch, *Anthyllia vulneraria:* ♃, 5–50 cm; stem leaves pinnate, calyx more or less woolly, inflated; 5–9; widespread in dry places. **b** †Dragon's Teeth, *Tetragonolobus maritimus:* ♃, 10–30 cm; flowers 25–30 mm long, solitary, pod winged; 5–7; a native of S Europe, has become naturalized in many places. **c** Common Birdsfoot-trefoil, *Lotus corniculatus:* ♃, 10–45 cm; stem sharply angled, flowers 2–6 in each head; 5–9; widespread. **d** Yellow Lupin, *Lupinus luteus:* ⊙, 15–70 cm; leaves palmate, with 5–9 leaflets, flowers in whorls; 6–9; occurs in the western part of the Mediterranean region. All these species belong to the Pea Family.

a Hairy Milk-vetch, *Oxytropis pilosa:* 2↓, 15–30 cm; white-hairy, flowers pale yellow, in globose heads; 6–8; hillocks and grassy places, SE, C and southern N Europe. **b Yellow Milk-vetch,** *Astragalus cicer:* 2↓, 20 to 80 cm; flowers pale yellow, in long-stalked racemes; 6–8; grassy places, thickets, roadsides, SE and C Europe. **c *Purple Milk-vetch,** *Astragalus danicus:* 2↓, 5–16 cm; flowers bluish purple, in upright, crowded heads on leafless stalks; 5–6; local, C and southern N Europe. **d *Meadow Vetchling,** *Lathyrus pratensis:* 2↓, 30–120 cm; scrambling, leaves with 1 pair of leaflets and a tendril, flowers 1–12 in each cluster; 5–8; widespread. All belong to the Pea Family.

The Swamp Violet is a rare plant of moorland meadows of C, SE and southern N Europe. Marsh and Heath Violets are widespread, the former in marshes and wet heaths, the latter in drier habitats. The Peat Violet is common on moorland meadows in N and EC Europe. The Fen Violet occurs in fens, on margins of pools and in flat moorland, from S Scandinavia southwards to Switzerland. The Dwarf Violet is a local plant of poor meadows, marshes and fens in SE, C and N Europe, northwards to Sweden. All belong to the Violet Family.

	Swamp Violet	*Marsh Violet	Peat Violet	*Fen Violet	Dwarf Violet	*Heath Violet
Scientific Name	*Viola uliginosa*	*Viola palustris*	*Viola epipsila*	*Viola persicifolia*	*Viola pumila*	*Viola canina*
Longevity, Size	2↓, 10–15 cm	2↓, 5–25 cm	2↓, 6–12 cm	2↓, 6–25 cm	2↓, 1–10 cm	2↓, 5–30 cm
Distinguishing Features; Flowering Time	Leaf-stalk winged, leaf-blade ovate-heart-shaped, crenate; 4–6	With a long creeping rhizome, bracteoles in middle of flower-stalk, leaves 2–6, basal; 6–7	With a long creeping rhizome, bracteoles in upper third of flower-stalk, leaves 2, basal; 5	Leaf-stalk winged in the upper part, leaves triangular, lanceolate, spur very short; 5–7	Leaf-stalk broadly winged, leaves lanceolate, stipules large; 5–6	Leaves long-stalked, stipules rather thick, 5–10 cm long, nearly entire or toothed; 4–6

a †Goat's Rue or **French Lilac,** *Galega officinalis:* 2↓, 40–100 cm; leaves pinnate, with 11–17 leaflets, flowers bluish white; 7–8; SE and C Europe; Pea Family. **b *Lady's Smock,** *Cardamine pratensis:* 2↓, 15–50 cm; leaves pinnate, anthers yellow; 4–6; widespread; Crucifer Family. **c *Meadow Cranesbill,** *Geranium pratense:* 2↓, 30–70 cm; leaves palmately 5–7-lobed; 6–8; widespread; Cranesbill Family. **d *Purging Flax,** *Linum catharticum:* ⊙, 3–30 cm; stem slender, leaves opposite; 6–8; widespread. **e Narrow-leaved Flax,** *Linum tenuifolium:* 2↓, 10 to 70 cm; leaves alternate, flowers pink; 6–7; dry meadows, thickets and scree, Mediterranean region and C Europe; Flax Family.

a* Wild Carrot, *Daucus carota:* ⊙, 25–80 cm;
bracts ternate or pinnatifid, umbel flat or
convex, flowers white, central one often red;
6–10. **b *Burnet-saxifrage,** *Pimpinella saxifraga:* ♃, 25–80 cm; leaves simply pinnate,
uppermost stem leaves small, with sheath-like
stalks, bracts and bracteoles absent; 6–10.
c *Hogweed, *Heracleum sphondylium:* ♃,
60–120 cm; stem angled, furrowed, rough,
with short hairs, flowers white, outer ones
extremely unequal; 5–10. All are members of
the Carrot Family, growing widespread in
meadows and pastureland, **b** chiefly on dry
turf and hillocks, **c** also by hedges, roadsides
and in woods.

The Cambridge Parsley is widespread from N and C Europe southwards to France, Italy and
the N Balkans. The Marsh Angelica and the Cnidium occur in E, SE and C Europe, the latter
also in N Europe, the Wild Angelica in lowland and mountain districts throughout Europe, but
rarely in the south. These four species grow mainly in fens and damp meadows. The Spignel-
meu is a plant of grassy places in mountain districts in N, C and W Europe, the Annual or
Steppe Moon Carrot of SE and C Europe. All belong to the Carrot Family.

	*Cambridge Parsley	Marsh Angelica	Wild Angelica	Cnidium	*Spignel-meu	Annual Moon Carrot
Scientific Name	*Selinum carvifolia*	*Angelica palustris*	*Angelica sylvestris*	*Cnidium dubium*	*Meum athamanticum*	*Seseli annuum*
Longevity, Size	♃, 30–150 cm	♃, 50–120 cm	♃, 50–150 cm	⊙, 30–60 cm	♃, 15–60 cm	⊙–♃, 3–80 cm
Distinguishing Features; Flowering Time	Stem ridged, leaves 2–3-pinnate, segments mucronate; 7–8	Stem ridged, leaves 3–4-pinnate, segments blunt, with short cartilaginous tips; 7–8	Stem terete, striate, leaves 2–3-pinnate, segments sharply serrate, stalks deeply channelled; 7–9	Leaves 2-pinnate, with linear segments, bracteoles numerous, subulate; 7–10	Leaves 3–4-pinnate, segments capillary, usually whorled, flowers yellowish white; 5–7	Bracteoles longer than the partial umbels, flowers white or reddish; 7–8

a *Hog's Fennel, *Peucedanum officinale:* ♃,
60–120 cm; leaves 3 to 6 times ternately
divided, flowers small, pale yellow; 7–9; on
banks near the sea, in meadows and thickets,
in C and W Europe and the Balkans. **b *Milk
Parsley,** *Peucedanum palustre:* ♃, 50–150 cm;
stem hollow, strongly ridged, bracts and
bracteoles lanceolate; 7–8; widespread, in
fens, marshes, moors and thickets. **c Pepper
Saxifrage,** *Silaum silaus:* ♃, 60–90 cm;
leaves 2–3 pinnate, segments entire or pinnatisect, with spiny tips, flowers greenish yellow;
5–9; common in meadows and on grassy banks
in most of Europe, rare in the Mediterranean
region. All belong to the Carrot Family.

a *****Chalk Milkwort,** *Polygala calcarea:* ♃, 5–20 cm; portion of stem below rosette leafless, flowers 6–7 mm; 4–6; grassy places on calcareous soils. **b** **Tufted Milkwort,** *Polygala comosa:* ♃, 8–35 cm; flowers usually pinkish violet, in many-flowered loose racemes with a terminal tuft of long bracts; 5–7; dry meadows and hillocks in most of Europe. **c** *****Bitter Dwarf Milkwort,** *Polygala amara:* ♃, 3–15 cm; rosette leaves larger than stem leaves; 5–8; widespread, in damp mountain pastures. All belong to the Milkwort Family. **d** *****Leafy Spurge,** *Euphorbia esula:* ♃, 30–80 cm; umbel many-rayed, leaf-tips finely toothed; 6–8; widespread, but local, pastures, woods, stream-sides; Spurge Family.

The Racemose Dock and the Curled Dock grow in marshy meadows and along river-banks; the sorrels in meadows, damp, grassy places, stony pastureland and in sandy fields; the Bistort or Snake Weed in damp meadows, particularly in moorland; the Water-pepper in wet meadows mainly on the banks of ditches and lakes, also in shallow water in ponds and ditches. All are common and widespread members of the Dock Family.

	Racemose Dock	*Curled Dock	*Sheep's Sorrel	*Common Sorrel	*Bistort	*Water-pepper
Scientific Name	*Rumex thyrsiflorus*	*Rumex crispus*	*Rumex acetosella*	*Rumex acetosa*	*Polygonum bistorta*	*Polygonum hydropiper*
Longevity, Size	♃, 30–60 cm	♃, 50–100 cm	♃, 5–15 cm	♃, 30–100 cm	♃, 30–100 cm	☉, 8–100 cm
Distinguishing Features; Flowering Time	Inflorescence dense, bright red, ochrea toothed or split; 6–8	Leaf-margins usually undulate and strongly crisped, stalk flat on upper surface; 5–7	Leaves small, narrow, hastate, the lower lobes spreading, flowers dioecious; 5–7	Basal leaves long-stalked, arrow-shaped, flowers dioecious; 6–8	Leaves broadly ovate, often heart-shaped at base, flowers small, pink, in dense stout spike; 5–7	Leaves with a peppery taste, lanceolate, ochrea not or shortly fringed; 7–9

a Bavarian False-flax, *Thesium bavarum:* ♃, 30–70 cm; leaves 3–7 mm wide, 3–5-veined; 5–7; rocky slopes, edges of woods, C Europe. **b Pyrenean False-flax,** *Thesium pyrenaicum:* ♃, 10–50 cm; leaves 3-veined, flowers with 3 bracts; 5–7; mountain meadows, bushy slopes and open woods in C and W Europe. **c Bractless False-flax,** *Thesium ebracteatum:* ♃, 7–30 cm; flowers with 1 bract; 5–6; on grassy hillocks, wood-meadows in E and C Europe. **d Beaked False-flax,** *Thesium rostratum:* ♃, 15–30 cm; much-branched at base, with sterile and fertile stems, flowers with 1 bract; 4–5; stony meadows and sunny slopes in mountain districts of C Europe. All belong to the Sandalwood Family.

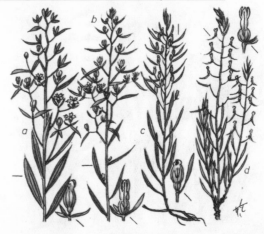

a *Ragged Robin, *Lychnis flos-cuculi:* ♃, 30–100 cm; petals rose-red, cleft into 4 narrow lobes; 5–8; common in damp meadows, marshes and wet woods. b †German Pink, *Dianthus carthusianorum:* ♃, 2–70 cm; flowers up to 10 in each head, petals purplish; 6–8; C and S Europe, on rocks and pastures. c *Maiden Pink, *Dianthus deltoides:* ♃, 5–50 cm; stem short hairy, petals rose with pale dots and a dark basal band; 6–9; widespread, in dry grassy places. d Fringed Pink, *Dianthus superbus:* ♃, 20–80 cm; petals pale pink to purple, pinnately narrowly lobed; 6–9; rare, in thickets, wood-meadows and flat moorland in most of Europe. All belong to the Pink Family.

The Curtis's Mouse-ear, the Field Mouse-ear and the Jagged Chickweed are generally widespread in Europe; the latter is doubtfully native in Britain, known now from Surrey. The Sand Pink occurs in dry turf, sandy fields, pine woods, and on heaths and dunes, the Bog Stitchwort in marshy meadows and along river-banks, the Common Mouse-ear in dry meadows, rocky pastureland and sandy fields, also in mountains up to 2500 m. All belong to the Pink Family.

	Sand Pink	*Jagged Chickweed	*Bog Stitchwort	*Curtis's Mouse-ear	*Common Mouse-ear	*Field Mouse-ear
Scientific Name	*Dianthus arenarius*	*Holosteum umbellatum*	*Stellaria alsine*	*Cerastium semidecandrum*	*Cerastium holosteoides*	*Cerastium arvense*
Longevity, Size	♃, 10–30 cm	☉, 5–30 cm	♃, 10–40 cm	☉, 3–20 cm	☉–♃, 10–35 cm	♃, 10–30 cm
Distinguishing Features; Flowering Time	Flowers solitary or few, fragrant, petals white, the limb laciniate beyond middle, bearded; 6–8	Flowers 3–15 in each umbel-like cyme, white or pale pink, fruit-stalks deflexed; 3–5	Leaves bluish green, fruit-stalks at first reflexed, then upright; 5–6	Petals 2–5 mm long, sepals glandular hairy, with broad scarious margins; 3–5	Petals 6–7 mm long, sepals hairy, with narrow scarious margins; 5–10	Flowers large, leaves linear, fruit-stalks upright; 4–6

a *Annual Knawel, *Scleranthus annuus:* ☉–☉, 2.5-25 cm; sepals acute with narrow scarious margins, petals absent; 3–10; widespread in dry sandy and gravelly places and meadows. b Tartarian Catchfly, *Silene tatarica:* ♃, 2–30 cm; leaves lanceolate, acute, inflorescence with 1–3-flowered branches; 7–9; sandy river-banks and grassy places in the U.S.S.R and NE Europe, extending to NE Germany. c Nottingham Catchfly, *Silene nutans:* ♃, 25–70 cm; flowers in a loose one-sided panicle; 6–8; widespread but local. d Spanish Catchfly, *Silene otites:* ☉–♃, 20–60 cm; flowers dioecious, petals entire; 5–8; sunny hillocks, pastures, dunes and pine woods, in S, SE and C Europe.

a *Bladder Campion, *Silene vulgaris:* ♃, 20–100 cm; petals deeply cut, calyx a purplish or yellowish net-veined bladder, leaves bluish green; 5–9. b *Knotted Pearlwort, *Sagina nodosa,* ♃, 5–15 cm; flowers pentamerous, petals twice as long as sepals, stem with 'knots' (clusters of the short blunt linear leaflets in leaf-axils); 5–8. c *Bog Sandwort, *Minuartia stricta:* ♃, 5–20 cm; flowers 1–3 on each stem, petals shorter than sepals. d †Five-stamened Spurrey, *Spergula pentandra:* ⊙, 5–20 cm; stamens 5; 4–5. All belong to the Pink Family and occur in meadows, c particularly in high flat moorland, on wet rocks and on scree on mountains of N and C Europe, d in sandy pastures and on heaths.

The members of the Gentian Family shown below grow in dry meadows, moorland pastures and on flat moors. The Marsh Gentian and the Autumn Gentian are widespread, but local, occurring throughout Europe except in the south. The Crosswort Gentian is a rare plant of S, C and N Europe, the Milkweed Gentian of S and C Europe (Alps). The Early Gentian grows locally in mountain areas of C Europe. The Greater Field Gentian is uncommon, growing in C, W and N Europe.

	Crosswort Gentian	*Marsh Gentian	Early Gentian	*Greater Field Gentian	*Autumn Gentian	Milkweed Gentian
Scientific Name	*Gentiana cruciata*	*Gentiana pneumonanthe*	*Gentianella praecox*	*Gentianella germanica*	*Gentianella amarella*	*Gentiana asclepiadea*
Longevity, Size	♃, 15–50 cm	♃, 15–40 cm	⊙, 15–45 cm	⊙, 3–45 cm	⊙, 3–30 cm	♃, 15–70 cm
Distinguishing Features; Flowering Time	Leaves fused in pairs by the greater part of their bases, flowers usually tetra-merous; 7–10	Flowers 1–7, terminal or axillary, corolla with 5 green lines on the outside; 7–10	Stem branched in the upper half, flowers numerous, lilac; 6–10	Stem branched above, corolla much exceed-ing the calyx; 5–10	Corolla 9–18 mm long, violet, rarely yellowish, with 4 or 5 teeth; 6–10	Flowers blue, rarely yellow-ish white, 1–3 in each leaf-axil, flower-stalks 2–10 mm long; 7–9

a *Common or Lesser Centaury, *Centaurium erythraea:* ⊙, 2–50 cm; leaves in a basal rosette, flowers slightly stalked or stalkless, forming a more or less dense corymb-like cyme; 7–9. b–c *Slender Centaury, *Centaurium pulchellum:* ⊙, 2–15 cm; basal leaf-rosette absent, stem usually much-branched, with dichotomous widely spreading branches; 6–10. d Marsh Felwort, *Swertia perennis:* ♃, 12-70 cm; upper part of stem with 4 winged angles; 7–9. All are members of the Gentian Family growing in meadows or other grassy places, though b is often found near the sea.

a *Brookweed,** *Samolus valerandi:* ♃, 15 to 50 cm; flower-stalks long, with a tiny lanceolate bract about the middle; 6–9; local, marshy meadows and ditches. **b *Creeping Jenny,** *Lysimachia nummularia:* ♃, 10–50 cm; creeping, leaves gland-dotted, flowers solitary; 5–7; widespread, moist grassy places. Both belong to the Primrose Family. **c †Estoril Thrift,** *Armeria pseudarmeria:* ♃, 30 to 50 cm; leaves limp, flowers pale pink; 6–7; rare, dry grassy places and pine woods of the W Mediterranean region and C Europe; Thrift Family. **d †Upright Bugle,** *Ajuga genevensis:* ♃, 5–30 cm; upper bracts longer than flowers; 8–9; dry grassy places, widespread but local; Thyme Family.

The Common Bugle and the Common Self-heal are widespread and common, the Large-flowered Self-heal local, in meadows, on dry turf and at the edges of woods. The Cut-leaved Self-heal is a native of the Mediterranean region, S and C Europe, growing in pastures, meadows and on stony slopes. The Wood Clary is a common plant of dry grassy places and open woods in C, E and SE Europe. The Meadow Clary occurs locally in meadows and thickets of S and C Europe, naturalized elsewhere. All belong to the Thyme Family.

	*Common Bugle	*Common Self-heal	Large-flowered Self-heal	†Cut-leaved Self-heal	Wood Clary	*Meadow Clary
Scientific Name	*Ajuga reptans*	*Prunella vulgaris*	*Prunella grandiflora*	*Prunella laciniata*	*Salvia nemorosa*	*Salvia pratensis*
Longevity, Size	♃, 4–50 cm	♃, 5–60 cm	♃, 6–35 cm	♃, 5–30 cm	♃, 30–90 cm	♃, 15–70 cm
Distinguishing Features; Flowering Time	Stoloniferous, stem hairy on 2 opposite sides, lower bracts resembling stem leaves; 4–6	Flowers bluish violet, 7–15 mm long, with a straight tube, in small heads; 5–10	Flowers bluish violet, 20–25 mm long, with a bent tube, in large heads; 6–8	Densely hairy, upper leaves pinnatifid, flowers usually cream white; 6–8	Bracts usually violet, acuminate, flowers blue, rarely red or white; 6–7	Flowers large, blue, sometimes red or white, leaves ovate, heart-shaped at the base; 6–8

a *Lesser Skullcap,** *Scutellaria minor:* ♃, 7–25 cm; corolla small, 6–8 mm long; 7–8; damp grassy places, widespread but local. **b Pot Marjoram,** *Origanum vulgare:* ♃, 25–80 cm; bracteoles purple, longer than calyx, calyx with nearly equal teeth, corolla 2-lipped; 7–9; widespread, pastures, hedgebanks and scrub. Both belong to the Thyme Family. **c *Blue Jacob's Ladder,** *Polemonium caeruleum:* ♃, 20–50 cm; flowers blue, corolla rotate; 6–9; local, grassy slopes, screes and rock-ledges in N and C Europe; Jacob's Ladder Family. **d *Common Comfrey,** *Symphytum officinale:* ♃, 20–120 cm; flowers pink or white; 5–7; widespread and frequent, damp grassy places; Borage Family.

a *Common Yellow-rattle, *Rhinanthus
minor:* ☉, 10–60 cm; corolla-tube straight,
15 mm long; 5–7; widespread and common
in grassy places. **b** *Greater Yellow-rattle,
Rhinanthus serotinus: ☉, 12–60 cm; corolla-
tube curved upwards, 20 mm long; 5–7; common in cornfields, less common in meadows
and on sandhills. **c** Narrow-leaved Yellow-
rattle, *Rhinanthus aristatus:* ☉, 10–100 cm;
bracts with awn-like teeth at the base; 8–10;
in mountain meadows of C Europe. **d** Long-
hairy Yellow-rattle, *Rhinanthus alectorolo-
phus:* ☉, 15–80 cm; calyx white-woolly; 5–9;
common, in thickets, meadows and fields of
C Europe. All are semi-parasites of the Figwort Family.

With the exception of the Purple Mullein, the plants shown below are widespread in meadows,
on bushy slopes and in open woodlands in most of Europe. The Irish Eyebright occurs in stony
pastures on scree and rocks and in open woods in mountain areas of Europe, from Gotland to
the Balkans, Corsica and S Spain. The Purple Mullein is a native of S, SE, E and C Europe,
growing in steppe meadows. All belong to the Figwort Family.

	*Meadow Eyebright	*Irish Eyebright	*Upright Eyebright	*Woodland Eyebright	*Common Cow-wheat	†Purple Mullein
Scientific Name	*Euphrasia rostkoviana*	*Euphrasia salisburgensis*	*Euphrasia brevipila*	*Euphrasia nemorosa*	*Melampyrum pratense*	*Verbascum phoeniceum*
Longevity, Size	☉, 4–50 cm	☉, 5–25 cm	☉, 2–40 cm	☉, 7–15 cm	☉, 10–30 cm	♃, 15–90 cm
Distinguishing Features; Flowering Time	Calyx with glandular hairs, shorter than corolla-tube, flowers white, upper lip violet; 5–10	Stem leaves with 4–10 teeth, calyx glabrous, flowers white, upper lip blue; 6–8	Bracts ovate, usually with 8–14 awned teeth, flowers lilac or white with a lilac upper lip; 5–10	Stem slender, much-branch-ed, flowers small, white, lower lip spotted with yellow; 8–10	Bracts with long, awn-like teeth, flowers yellow, racemes one-sided; 6–9	Flowers dark violet, long-stalked, leaves soft-hairy beneath; 5–6

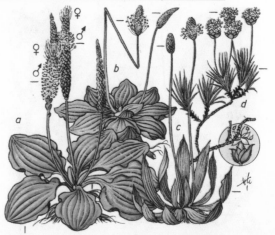

a *Great Plantain, *Plantago major:* ♃,
10–70 cm; leaves broadly ovate, abruptly nar-
rowing into a long stalk, spikes up to 16 cm
long; 5–11. **b** *Hoary Plantain, *Plantago
media:* ♃, 15–60 cm; leaves gradually narrowed into a short stalk, spikes usually only
3–6 cm long; 5–10. **c** *Ribwort, *Plantago
lanceolata:* ♃, 15 to 50 cm; leaves lanceolate,
5-veined; 6–10. **d** †Shrubby Plantain,
Plantago sempervirens: ♃, 10–40 cm; stem
branched, spikes nearly globose; a native
of the western part of S Europe. All are
members of the Plantain Family.

a ***Lady's Bedstraw**, *Galium verum:* ♃, 15–80 cm; leaves 8–12 in each whorl; 6–10. b ***Hedge Bedstraw**, *Galium mollugo:* ♃, 20–60 cm; stem 4-angled, leaves 1-veined, 6–8 in a whorl, corolla-lobes pointed; 6–8. c **⁺Northern Bedstraw**, *Galium boreale:* ♃, 20–50 cm; stem rigid, 4-angled, leaves 3-veined, 4 in a whorl; 6–8; N and C Europe, southwards to N Italy. All are widespread common members of the Bedstraw Family, occuring in grassland, c also on rocky slopes, stream-sides and scree. d **Elder-leaved Valerian**, *Valeriana sambucifolia:* ♃, 30–100 cm; leaves with 7–11 leaflets, flowers reddish to white; 6–8; damp grassy places, widespread in C Europe; Valerian Family.

The Marsh Valerian is widespread in damp meadows and flat moors; the Common and Broad-fruited Cornsalads grow in grassy places and cultivated fields. All three belong to the Valerian Family. The Hare-bell, the Spreading Bellflower and the Rampion Bellflower belong to the Bellflower Family; the first two are widespread in meadows, hedgebanks and woods, mainly in N and C Europe, the latter is a native of the Mediterranean region and C Europe, growing in meadows and thickets.

	*Marsh Valerian	***Common Cornsalad**	***Broad-fruited Cornsalad**	***Hare-bell**	***Spreading Bellflower**	**†Rampion Bellflower**
Scientific Name	*Valeriana dioica*	*Valerianella locusta*	*Valerianella rimosa*	*Campanula rotundifolia*	*Campanula patula*	*Campanula rapunculus*
Longevity, Size	♃, 8–50 cm	☉, 7–30 cm	☉, 15–30 cm	♃, 15–45 cm	☉-♃, 30–60 cm	♃, 30–100 cm
Distinguishing Features; Flowering Time	Stem leaves usually pinnat-ifid, basal leaves ovate, flowers di-oecious; 5–6	Basal leaves spathulate, stem leaves oblong, fruits compressed; 4–5	Resembling previous spec-ies, but fruits ovoid, sterile cells together larger than fertile one; 4–5	Radical leaves long-stalked, suborbicular, upper stem leaves narrowly linear, stalk-less; 6–9	Inflorescence with spreading branches, corolla-lobes about as long as tube, acute, spreading; 5–7	Inflorescence with short, up-right branches, corolla similar to that of previous species; 5–8

a ***Common Sheepsbit**, *Jasione montana:* ☉, 10–50 cm; without stolons, leaves with undulate margins; 6–9; widespread in grass-land, on heaths, cliffs and shingle. b **Perennial Sheepsbit**, *Jasione perennis:* ♃, 3–60 cm; with stolons, leaves flat; 7–8; woods and sandy heaths of C and Atlantic Europe. c ***Ivy-leaved Bellflower**, *Wahlenbergia hederacea:* ♃, up to 30 cm; creeping, flowers solitary, long-stalked; 6–8; damp moorland, heaths and open woods of W and C Europe. d **Round-headed Rampion**, *Phyteuma orbi-culare:* ♃, 5–70 cm; stigmas usually 3; 5–9; meadows, flat moorland and pastures in S and C Europe. All belong to the Bellflower Family.

a *Small Cudweed, *Filago minima:* ⊙, 2 to 30 cm; silky hairy, heads 3–6, in small clusters; 6–10; widespread. b *Irish Fleabane, *Inula salicina:* ♃, 20–80 cm; leaves more or less glabrous, outer involucral bracts lanceolate, glabrous; 6–8; widespread, in meadows, thickets and on rocky slopes. c †British Fleabane, *Inula britannica:* ♃, 70–100 cm; leaves softly hairy below, outer involucral bracts linear, hairy; 7–11; damp meadows, ditches and river-banks in S, C and N Europe. d Mountain Arnica, *Arnica montana:* ♃, 30–60 cm; basal leaves in a rosette, heads large; 6–9; common on moorland, heaths and rocky slopes in mountain areas of C and N Europe. All belong to the Daisy Family.

The Yarrow, the Sneezewort, the Common Carline-thistle and the Common Ragwort are widespread and common in meadows and pastureland in most of Europe; the carline-thistles grow also on barren and sunny hills. The Great Carline-thistle, which is usually stemless, occurs in S, SE and C Europe, the Moorland Ragwort in marshy meadows, fen ditches, and on river-banks in N and C Europe. In Britain it was recorded from E Anglia, Lincoln and Sussex, but now is apparently extinct. All belong to the Daisy Family.

	*Yarrow	*Sneezewort	Great Carline-thistle	*Common Carline-thistle	*Common Ragwort	*Moorland Ragwort
Scientific Name	*Achillea millefolium*	*Achillea ptarmica*	*Carlina acaulis*	*Carlina vulgaris*	*Senecio jacobaea*	*Senecio palustris*
Longevity, Size	♃, 15–50 cm	♃, 30–60 cm	♃, up to 10 cm	⊙, 20–60 cm	♃, 30–100 cm	♃, 25–100 cm
Distinguishing Features; Flowering Time	Leaves 2–3 times pinnate, ultimate segments linear-subulate, ray-florets white or pink; 6–10	Leaves linear-lanceolate, serrate, stalkless, inflorescence loose, ray-florets white; 6–10	Stem usually very short, head solitary, large, inner involucral bracts silvery white; 7–8	Stem upright, heads 2–5 or more in a corymb, inner involucral bracts straw-coloured; 7–9	Leaves lyrate, with large terminal lobe, outer fruits glabrous, central ones hairy; 7–8	Yellowish green, stem stout, hollow, woolly-hairy, stem leaves half-clasping the stem; 6–7

a Annual Fleabane, *Erigeron annuus:* ⊙, 50–120 cm; ray-florets about twice as long as the disc-florets, pappus 2-rowed, outer bristles much shorter; 6–10; a native of N America, naturalized in many places in Europe. b *Wayside Cudweed, *Gnaphalium uliginosum:* ⊙, 9–25 cm; stem with white woolly hairs, clusters of heads overtopped by leaves at their base, involucral bracts brown; 6–10; widespread, in damp places. c *Jersey Cudweed, *Gnaphalium luteo-album:* ⊙, 5 to 40 cm; clusters of heads not overtopped by leaves at their base, involucral bracts straw-coloured; 6–10; in sandy fields in most of Europe, except the north. All belong to the Daisy Family.

a *Saw-wort, *Serratula tinctoria:* ♃, 10 to
100 cm; heads small, cylindrical, loosely
corymbose, florets all tubular, purple; 7–9;
widespread, in open grassland, clearings, and
at the margins of woods. **b** *Daisy, *Bellis
perennis:* ♃, 3–20 cm; leaves in a rosette,
heads with ray and disc florets; 3–10. **c** *Oxeye Daisy, *Chrysanthemum leucanthemum:* ♃,
up to 50 cm; leaves toothed to serrate, heads
solitary with ray and disc florets; 6–7; widespread. **d** *Common Dandelion, *Taraxacum officinale:* ♃, 15–70 cm; milky sap, scape
hollow, heads with ligulate florets, fruits with
beak and pappus; 3–9; widespread and common in grassy and waste places. All belong to
the Daisy Family.

Members of the Daisy Family having heads with ligulate florets are described below. The Common Cat's-ear and the Hairy Hawkbit are widespread in meadows, heaths and open woodlands.
The other species are common but local plants of meadows and grassy places, growing throughout Europe, except the Purple Vipersgrass, which occurs in SE and C Europe, in pasturelands
and heaths on calcareous soils.

	*Common Cat's-ear	*Hairy Hawkbit	*Autumn Hawkbit	*Goatsbeard	Purple Vipersgrass	*Common Vipersgrass
Scientific Name	*Hypochoeris radicata*	*Leontodon taraxacoides*	*Leontodon autumnalis*	*Tragopogon pratensis*	*Scorzonera purpurea*	*Scorzonera humilis*
Longevity, Size	♃, 25–80 cm	☉–♃, 3–30 cm	♃, 6–70 cm	☉, 30–60 cm	♃, 25–75 cm	♃, 10–30 cm
Distinguishing Features; Flowering Time	Leaves sinuate-toothed, scape usually with a solitary head, outer ligules deeply tooth-ed; 5–9	Outer florets grey-violet beneath, inner fruits with a feathery papp-us, outer with scaly cup; 7–8	Scape usually with several heads, all fruits with a single row of feathery hairs; 6–11	Scapes enlarg-ed below heads, fruits with beak and big pappus of feathery hairs; 5–8	Leaves 3-angled, striate, florets wine-red; 5–6	Scape woolly, leafless, usually with a solitary head, involucre woolly below; 5–6

a †Beaked Hawksbeard, *Crepis vesicaria:*
☉, 30–50 cm; heads in corymbs, fruits with
a distinct beak, outer florets with red stripes
beneath; 5–6; locally common, on waysides
and in grassy and waste places. **b** *Rough
Hawksbeard, *Crepis biennis:* ☉, 60–120 cm;
leaves pinnately lobed, fruit narrowed upwards, not beaked; 5–9; locally frequent, in
pastures, by waysides and in waste places.
c Meadow Hawkweed, *Hieracium caespit-
osum:* ♃, 30–80 cm; heads clustered; 5–8; on
grasslands in most of Europe. **d** †Tall Hawkweed, *Hieracium praealtum:* ♃, 30–120 cm;
upper heads in a dense corymb; 5–7; in grassy
habitats in most of Europe. All belong to
the Daisy Family.

a *Meadow Saffron, *Colchicum autumnale:* ♃, 5–30 cm; flowers solitary, perianth-segments united below into a long tube; poisonous; 8–9; in leaf 5–7; damp meadows and woods, in S, SE and C Europe. **b Two-leaved Squill,** *Scilla bifolia:* ♃, 10–30 cm; basal leaves 2, broadly linear, racemes 2–12-flowered; 3–4; meadows and open woodland, in S and C Europe. **c *Autumnal Squill,** *Scilla autumnalis:* ♃, 7–20 cm; leaves 5–6, flowering scape leafless; 8; grasslands in the Mediterranean region and C Europe. **d †Daylily,** *Hemerocallis lilioasphodelus:* ♃, 60 to 120 cm; flowers funnel-shaped; 6; mainly in S, SE and C Europe. All belong to the Lily Family.

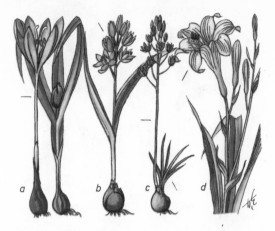

The Field Garlic is common on grassy hills and in scrubland; the other species shown below are found locally in grassy places and meadows. The Angled Garlic occurs in C Europe; the Round-headed Leek is a Mediterranean species extending northwards to Belgium, CW Germany and C Russia, rare in Britain. The Sweet-smelling Garlic grows in S Europe and the southern part of C Europe. All belong to the Daffodil Family.

	*Chive	***Crow Garlic**	***Round-headed Leek**	**Angled Garlic**	**Sweet-smelling Garlic**	***Field Garlic**
Scientific Name	*Allium schoenoprasum*	*Allium vineale*	*Allium sphaerocephalon*	*Allium angulosum*	*Allium suaveolens*	*Allium oleraceum*
Longevity, Size	♃, 15–45 cm	♃, 30–90 cm	♃, 30–70 cm	♃, 30–60 cm	♃, 30–50 cm	♃, 30–80 cm
Distinguishing Features; Flowering Time	Leaves and scape slender, terete, filaments without teeth, flowers pink; 4–7	Leaves subcylindric, slightly grooved, hollow, spathe 1-valved, falling off, flowers purple; 6–8	Leaves subcylindric, grooved, hollow, flowers purple, filaments with a very narrow teeth; 6–8	Stem sharply angled, leaves up to 6 mm wide, sharply keeled, 5-veined beneath; 7–8	Leaves flat, keeled beneath, inflorescence almost globose; 7–8	Inflorescence often with bulbils, much shorter than the leaf-like segments of the spathe; 7–8

a *Spiked Star-of-Bethlehem, *Ornithogalum pyrenaicum:* ♃, 50–100 cm; perianth-segments pale yellow; 6–8; in meadows, woods and scrub of S, C and W Europe. **b *Common Star-of-Bethlehem,** *Ornithogalum umbellatum:* ♃, 10–30 cm; inflorescence a corymbose raceme; 5–8; Mediterranean region, extending northwards to Sweden. **c Narrow-leaved Star-of-Bethlehem,** *Ornithogalum gussonei:* ♃, 8–15 cm; basal leaves linear; 4–6; Mediterranean region and C Europe. **d †Drooping Star-of-Bethlehem,** *Ornithogalum nutans:* leaves upright, flowers drooping; 4–5; S and C Europe. All belong to the Lily Family; **b, c** and **d** grow in grassy places.

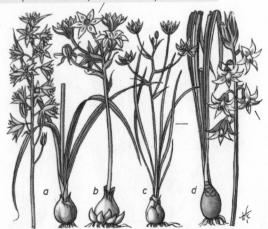

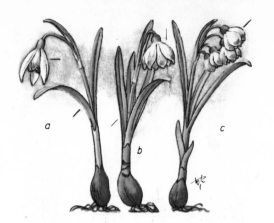

a ★Snowdrop, *Galanthus nivalis:* ♃, 7–20 cm; leaves mostly 2, basal, linear, inner perianth-segments short, with a green spot; 1–3; widespread. **b ★Spring Snowflake,** *Leucojum vernum:* ♃, 8–30 cm; leaves 3–5, scape usually with a solitary flower, perianth-segments 6, of almost equal length; 2–4; on hills of S and C Europe, and in damp scrub and on hedge-banks of NW Europe. **c ★Loddon Lily,** *Leucojum aestivum:* ♃, 30–50 cm; resembling **b**, but scape with 3–6 flowers; 4–5; wet meadows and thickets, in S, C and NW Europe. All are rare members of the Daffodil Family, growing in damp meadows, scrubland and woods.

The Fritillary is a widespread local plant of damp meadows and pastures. The Wild Tulip, (S Europe, naturalized elsewhere) occurs in woodland meadows, orchards, parks and vineyards. The Yellow-stars-of-Bethlehem grow mostly in grasslands and woods; the Meadow Yellow-star is widespread, the others are local plants. The Spathed Yellow-star occurs in Atlantic and C Europe, the Small Yellow-star in S, C and E Europe, the Bohemian Yellow-star in SE and C Europe, on sunny hillocks and in sandy steppe. All belong to the Lily Family.

	Spathed Yellow-star-of-Bethlehem	Bohemian Yellow-star-of-Bethlehem	Meadow Yellow-star-of-Bethlehem	Small Yellow-star-of-Bethlehem	*Fritillary	†Wild Tulip
Scientific Name	*Gagea spathacea*	*Gagea bohemica*	*Gagea pratensis*	*Gagea minima*	*Fritillaria meleagris*	*Tulipa sylvestris*
Longevity, Size	♃, 12–20 cm	♃, 3–8 cm	♃, 4–30 cm	♃, 7–15 cm	♃, 10–35 cm	♃, 40–80 cm
Distinguishing Features; Flowering Time	Radical leaves mostly 2, subcylindric, hollow, flower-stalks glabrous; 4–5	Radical leaves mostly 2, bluish green, almost thread-like, flower-stalks hairy; 3–4	Radical leaves usually 1, linear, stem leaves fringed, flower-stalks glabrous; 4–5	Radical leaves usually 1, narrowly linear, 1–2 mm wide, bulbs of unequal size; 3–4	Leaves grooved, flowers usually solitary, purple to creamy white, checkered; 4–5	Stem usually with solitary flower, perianth-segments yellow with a hairy tip; 4–6

a ★Common Asparagus, *Asparagus officinalis:* ♃, 30–180 cm; leaves scale-like, cladodes in clusters, needle-like, berries red; 6–8; sandy pastures, hillocks and grassy sea-cliffs, in the E Mediterranean region and in C and NW Europe; some forms cultivated as vegetables, and naturalized in waste places; Lily Family. **b ★Wild Daffodil,** *Narcissus pseudonarcissus:* ♃, 15–30 cm; perianth-segments 6, pale yellow, corona deep yellow, trumpet-like; 3–4; damp woods and grasslands of C, W and NW Europe; Daffodil Family. **c †Purple Crocus,** *Crocus purpureus:* ♃, 4–8 cm; flowers white or violet, usually solitary; 3–4; mountain meadows of C and S Europe; Iris Family.

a ***Spiked Sedge,** *Carex spicata:* ♃, 20 to 80 cm; leaves 3–4 mm wide, fruit 4.5–5 mm long; 5–6; widespread, in marshes, beside ponds and in grassland. **b** ***Oval Sedge,** *Carex ovalis:* ♃, 8–50 cm; leaves 2–3 mm wide; spikes 4–7, ♂ at base, fruits winged; 5–6; in rough grassy places, widespread but local. **c** ***Star Sedge,** *Carex echinata:* ♃, 10–45 cm; fruits spreading starwise; 5–6; widespread and frequent in bogs and marshes. **d** ***Downy-fruited Sedge,** *Carex filiformis:* ♃, 25–60 cm; ♀ spikes 1–2, shortly cylindrical, ♂ spikes usually stalked, fruits downy; 4–5; reed-swamp and damp grassland, C and N Europe, rare in the south. All belong to the Sedge Family.

The gladioles shown below grow locally in damp and swampy meadows and in damp thickets, the Swamp Gladiole in C Europe, the Meadow Gladiole in E and C Europe. The Siberian Iris is a rare plant of damp and swampy meadows, found in most of Europe. The remaining species are local plants of woodland meadows; the Grass-leaved Iris in S and C Europe, the Leafless Iris and the Variegated Iris in E and C Europe. All belong to the Iris Family.

	Swamp Gladiole	Meadow Gladiole	Siberian Iris	Grass-leaved Iris	Leafless Iris	Variegated Iris
Scientific Name	*Gladiolus palustris*	*Gladiolus imbricatus*	*Iris sibirica*	*Iris graminea*	*Iris aphylla*	*Iris variegata*
Longevity, Size	♃, 20–45 cm	♃, 30–50 cm	♃, 30–80 cm	♃, 15–30 cm	♃, 15–50 cm	♃, 80–100 cm
Distinguishing Features; Flowering Time	Spikes with 2–6 distant flowers, capsule with 6 weak furrows; 6–7	Spikes with 5–10 almost contiguous flowers, capsule notched at tip, with rounded angles; 7	Scape hollow, 2–4-flowered, leaves about 5 mm wide, ovary 3-angled; 5–6	Scape solid, compressed, with two sharp edges, much shorter than leaves, 1–2-flowered; 5–6	Scape without leaves in the upper part, flowers violet, bearded; 5	Spathes inflated, outer perianth-segments whitish yellow, inner ones golden yellow; 6

a ***Long-stalked Yellow Sedge,** *Carex lepidocarpa:* ♃, 20–60 cm; ♀ spikes from 2–4, somewhat distant, stalkless, or lower ones shortly stalked, ♂ spike 1, usually long-stalked; 5–7; widespread. **b Tufted Sedge,** *Carex juncella:* ♃, 20–70 cm; tufted, ♀ spikes 2–3, rather distant, the lower distinctly stalked; 4–6; N and C Europe. **c** ***Common Sedge,** *Carex nigra:* ♃, 5–40 cm; stem sharply 3-angled, spikes short, upright; 5–8. **d** ***Brown Sedge,** *Carex disticha:* ♃, 20 to 80 cm; terminal spike ♀, intermediate ♂ and lower ♀; 5–6. All are common members of the Sedge Family, growing mainly in marshy meadows.

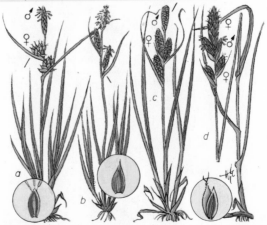

a **Barley Sedge**, *Carex hordeistichos:* ♃, 10–20 cm; stem overtopped by the flat, leaf-like bracts, ♀ spikes 3–4; 4–6; local, in S, SE and C Europe. b ***Buxbaum's Sedge**, *Carex buxbaumii:* ♃, 10–50 cm; spikes 3–5, club-shaped, terminal spike ♀ in upper part, ♂ below; 4–5; widespread, but local. c ***Glaucous Sedge**, *Carex flacca:* ♃, 8–50 cm; leaves 2–6 mm wide, ♂ spikes 1–2; 5–6; widespread and common. d ***Carnation Sedge**, *Carex panicea:* ♃, 15–40 cm; lower bract leaf-like, closely sheathing, ♂ spikes upright, ♀ distant, few-flowered; 5–6; widespread and common. All belong to the Sedge Family and occur in meadows, moorland and scrubland.

The grasses illustrated below all have spike-like panicles. The Crested Dog's-tail, the Meadow Foxtail and the Timothy-grass are widespread and common in meadows, pastures and sandy places throughout Europe. The Crested Hair-grass is also widespread, occurring in dry grassland. The Pyramidal Hair-grass is a frequent plant of dry turfs and open scrubland in N and C Europe. The Marsh Foxtail grows in moist places throughout Europe. All belong to the Grass Family.

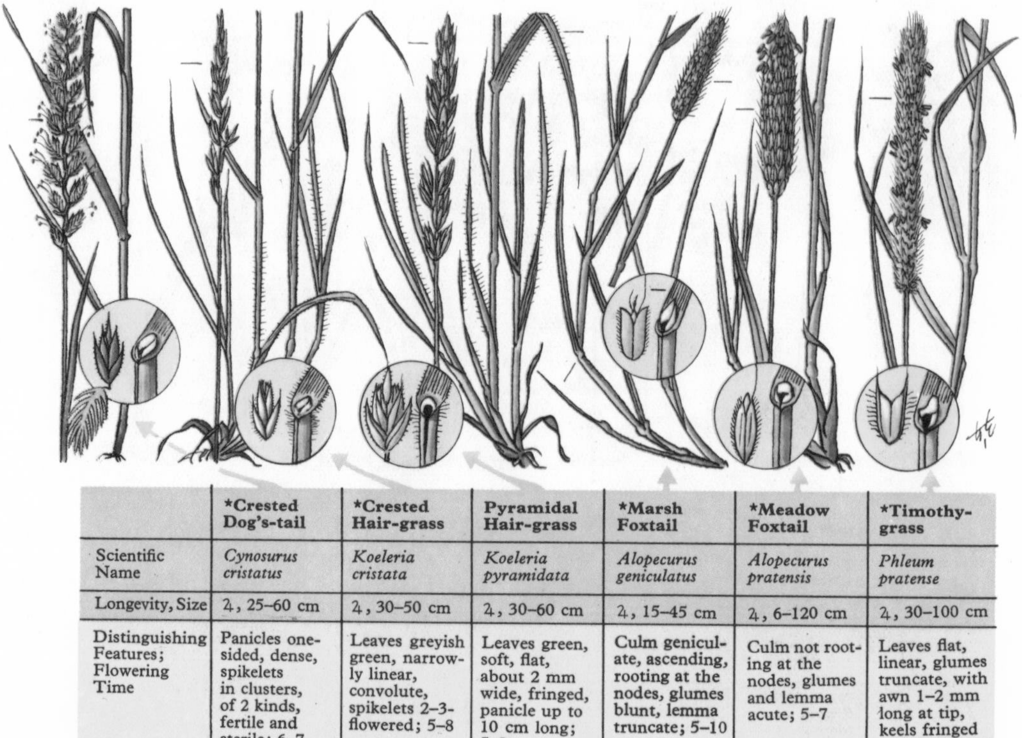

	*Crested Dog's-tail	*Crested Hair-grass	Pyramidal Hair-grass	*Marsh Foxtail	*Meadow Foxtail	*Timothy-grass
Scientific Name	*Cynosurus cristatus*	*Koeleria cristata*	*Koeleria pyramidata*	*Alopecurus geniculatus*	*Alopecurus pratensis*	*Phleum pratense*
Longevity, Size	♃, 25–60 cm	♃, 30–50 cm	♃, 30–60 cm	♃, 15–45 cm	♃, 6–120 cm	♃, 30–100 cm
Distinguishing Features; Flowering Time	Panicles one-sided, dense, spikelets in clusters, of 2 kinds, fertile and sterile; 6–7	Leaves greyish green, narrowly linear, convolute, spikelets 2–3-flowered; 5–8	Leaves green, soft, flat, about 2 mm wide, fringed, panicle up to 10 cm long; 5–8	Culm geniculate, ascending, rooting at the nodes, glumes blunt, lemma truncate; 5–10	Culm not rooting at the nodes, glumes and lemma acute; 5–7	Leaves flat, linear, glumes truncate, with awn 1–2 mm long at tip, keels fringed with hairs; 5–9

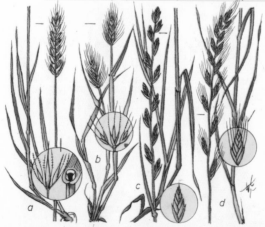

a ***Meadow Barley**, *Hordeum secalinum:* ♃, 30–80 cm; glumes awn-like; 6–7. b ***Sea Barley**, *Hordeum marinum:* ☉, 10–40 cm; glumes of the lateral spikelets dissimilar, one bristle-like, the other broadly winged below; 5–8; along sea-coasts. c ***Perennial Rye-grass**, *Lolium perenne:* ♃, 30–60 cm; spikelets with their edges fitting into hollows in the axis, with 1 glume (except terminal spikelet), lemma awnless; 6–10. d †**Italian Rye-grass**, *Lolium multiflorum:* ☉-☉, 30 to 90 cm; resembling **c**, but lemma usually awned; 6–8; a native of C and S Europe. All are members of the Grass Family, widespread and common in grasslands and meadows.

a *Mat-grass, *Nardus stricta:* ♃, 15–20 cm;
leaves bristle-like, stiff, spikes one-sided,
slender, spikelets 1-flowered, narrow, finely
pointed; 5–6. **b** *Chalk False-brome, *Brachypodium pinnatum:* ♃, 60–120 cm; inflorescence spike-like, leaves rigid, awn much
shorter than lemma; 6–7. **c** *Yorkshire Fog,
Holcus lanatus: ♃, 30–100 cm; leaves and leaf-
sheaths densely hairy, awn scarcely projecting,
finally hooked; 6–8. **d** *Oat-grass, *Arrhe-
natherum elatius:* ♃, 50–150 cm; lower floret
usually ♂, with an awn from the back in the
lower third, the upper ♂, usually awnless; 6–7.
All are members of the Grass Family, widespread and common in grasslands, **a** sometimes on high ground.

The grasses shown below are widespread and common throughout Europe. The Red Fescue,
the Creeping Bent and the Velvet Bent occur in lowland meadows, hill and mountain grassland,
open woodland, and in salt-marshes and on dunes; the Meadow Fescue grows in meadows,
pastures and by roadsides; the Tall Fescue in reed meadows, on banks of rivers, lakes and
streams and in pastures, the Common Bent in lowland grasslands, on heaths, moorland, pastures
and waste ground. All belong to the Grass Family.

	*Red Fescue	*Meadow Fescue	*Tall Fescue	*Creeping Bent	*Common Bent	*Velvet Bent
Scientific Name	*Festuca rubra*	*Festuca pratensis*	*Festuca arundinacea*	*Agrostis stolonifera*	*Agrostis tenuis*	*Agrostis canina*
Longevity, Size	♃, 30–70 cm	♃, 40–100 cm	♃, 60–120 cm	♃, 26–50 cm	♃, 30–75 cm	♃, 30–70 cm
Distinguishing Features; Flowering Time	Leaves about 2 mm wide, spikelets reddish violet, in a panicle 6–15 cm long; 6–10	Auricles of leaves hairless, panicle com-pact, lemmas awnless; 6–7	Auricles of leaves with hairs, panicle spreading, lemmas short-awned; 5–7	Stoloniferous, ligule up to 6 mm long, panicle open in flower, fin-ally con-tracted; 6–8	Tufted, ligule up to 2 mm long, panicle open and very loose; 6–8	Leaf-blades pointed, ligule pointed, 2–4 mm long, panicle usually open, loose, pa-lea minute; 6–8

a *Common Meadow-grass, *Poa pratensis:*
♃, 15–90 cm; creeping slender rhizomes,
ligules short; 5–6; meadows, pastures, roadsides. **b** *Rough Meadow-grass, *Poa triv-
ialis:* ♃, 50–90 cm; creeping leafy stolons,
ligules long, pointed; 6–7; damp meadows,
pond and stream margins, waste and cultivated land. **c** *Cock's-foot, *Dactylis glomerata:*
♃, 30–125 cm; leaves keeled, ligules long,
pointed, panicle with short-stalked compressed spikelets crowded at ends of branches;
5–6; meadows, roadsides, waste ground.
d *Quaking-grass, *Briza media:* ♃, 30 to
50 cm; spikelets broad, purplish, on slender
stalks; 5–9; meadows and grassy places. All
widespread members of the Grass Family.

a *Yellow Oat-grass, *Trisetum flavescens:*
♃, 30–80 cm; leaves hairy above, spikelets
usually yellowish, lemma with 2 bristle points
at tip, awned; 5–6. b *Meadow Oat-grass,
Helictotrichon pratense: ♃, 30–100 cm; leaf-
sheaths glabrous, leaves stiff, glaucous; 5–8.
c *Downy Oat-grass, *Helictotrichon pubescens:* ♃, 30–120 cm; leaf-sheaths, at least the
lower, hairy, leaves flat, soft; 5–7. d †Canary-
grass, *Phalaris canariensis:* ☉, 20–50 cm;
glumes strongly winged, fertile lemma hairy,
with 2 small sterile lemmas at base; 5–10;
Mediterranean region, naturalized elsewhere.
All belong to the Grass Family; a, b and c
are widespread and common in meadows.

The Hairy Brome is widespread and frequent in open woodland, woodland meadows, at edges
of woods, in hedgerows and on roadsides. The other species shown below grow in grasslands,
cultivated fields, on roadsides, hillocks and waste ground. The Awnless Brome prefers sandy and
stony soils, the Upright Brome well-drained calcareous soils. The Soft Brome is widespread
and common, the other species are found in scattered localities throughout Europe, sometimes
being frequent. All belong to the Grass Family.

	†Awnless Brome	*Upright Brome	†Field Brome	*Soft Brome	*Smooth Brome	*Hairy Brome
Scientific Name	*Bromus inermis*	*Bromus erectus*	*Bromus arvensis*	*Bromus mollis*	*Bromus racemosus*	*Bromus ramosus*
Longevity, Size	♃, 30–80 cm	♃, 30–120 cm	☉, 25–90 cm	☉–☉, 20–50 cm	☉, 30–60 cm	♃, 45–180 cm
Distinguishing Features; Flowering Time	Rhizomes extensively creeping, leaves flat, hairless, lemmas blunt, awnless; 6–7	Densely tufted, basal leaves inrolled, panicle short, with erect branches; 5–6	Panicle loose, with widely spreading branches, anthers 3–4.5 mm long; 6–7	Leaves and leaf-sheaths green, hairy, lemma 8–9 mm long, usually hairy; 5–6	Leaves and sheaths yellowish green, hairy, lemmas thicker, hairless; 5–6	Leaf-sheaths with spreading or reflexed hairs, panicle large, with nodding branches; 5–7

a *Tufted Hair-grass, *Deschampsia ces-
pitosa:* ♃, 50–150 cm; tufted, leaves flat, with
translucent veins, lemma with short awn from
near base; 6–7. b *Purple Small-reed,
Calamagrostis canescens: ♃, 60–100 cm; leaves
hairy above, lemma with very short awn; 7–8.
c *Wood Small-reed, *Calamagrostis epi-
geios:* ♃, 100–150 cm; leaves not hairy above,
glumes narrower, more pointed, lemma with
long awn; 7–8. d *Heath-grass, *Sieglingia
decumbens:* ♃, 10–60 cm; leaf-sheaths with
ring of hairs at mouth, lemma with 3-toothed
apex; 6–7. All belong to the Grass Family;
widespread and common; a and d in moorland, meadows and heath, b and c in damp
woodlands.

a *Early Purple Orchid, *Orchis mascula:* ♃, 15–60 cm; flowers purple, lip paler, deeply 3-lobed; 4–6. b *Frog Orchid, *Coeloglossum viride:* ♃, 10–30 cm; basal leaves 2–3, ovate, lip 3.5–6 mm long, parallel-sided, hanging vertically, 3-lobed near tip; 5–8; especially on calcareous soils. c *Lesser Butterfly Orchid, *Platanthera bifolia:* 20–70 cm; leaves usually 3 cm wide, flowers yellowish white, spur slender, almost horizontal; 5–7. d *Greater Butterfly Orchid, *Platanthera chlorantha:* ♃, 40–60 cm; flowers greenish white, spur curved; 5–7. All are widespread but local members of the Orchid Family, growing in meadows, occasionally also in woods.

The orchids illustrated below are found in scattered localities throughout Europe. They are often rare and local, growing in meadows, pastures, on grassy slopes, hillsides, on field-borders and banks, usually on chalk and limestone. The Fly Orchid and the Pyramidal Orchid occur also in woods, copses and in scrub. The Fly Orchid is found in mountainous areas up to 1600 m, the Musk Orchid up to 1800 m. All belong to the Orchid Family.

	*Fly Orchid	*Bee Orchid	*Early Spider Orchid	*Late Spider Orchid	*Musk Orchid	*Pyramidal Orchid
Scientific Name	Ophrys insectifera	Ophrys apifera	Ophrys sphegodes	Ophrys fuciflora	Herminium monorchis	Anacamptis pyramidalis
Longevity, Size	♃, 15–30 cm	♃, 20–50 cm	♃, 12–40 cm	♃, 15–30 cm	♃, 8–30 cm	♃, 20–60 cm
Distinguishing Features; Flowering Time	Lip 3–lobed, middle lobe deeply bifid, downy, dark purplish brown with bluish markings; 5–6	Lip resembling a humblebee, 5-lobed, velvety, dark brown with yellow markings; 6–7	Lip convex, nearly entire, broad, purplish brown with yellowish markings; 5–6	Lip flat, usually entire, with hook-like tooth, velvety, dark brown with greenish markings; 5–6	Leaves 2–3, oblong or lanceolate, flowers very small; 5–6	Spike dense, conical, flowers purple, lip 3-lobed; 6–7

a *Lizard Orchid, *Himantoglossum hircinum:* ♃, 30–80 cm; stem angled, flowers greenish, smelling strongly of goats; 5–6; rare, on calcareous soil in S and C and NW Europe. b *Marsh Helleborine, *Epipactis palustris:* ♃, 10–80 cm; lip with reddish veins; 8–9; locally frequent, usually in fens and dune-slacks. c *Autumn Lady's Tresses, *Spiranthes spiralis:* ♃, 7–20 cm; stem with bracts and lateral basal rosette of leaves, flowers in spirally twisted dense spike; 8–10; rare, in moist meadows and hilly pastures. d *Summer Lady's Tresses, *Spiranthes aestivalis:* ♃, 15–35 cm; stem leafy, flowers in spirally twisted loose spike; 7–8; rare, marshy ground, S and C Europe. All Orchid Family.

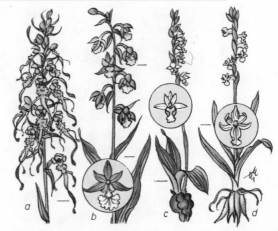

a *Soldier Orchid, *Orchis militaris:* ♃,
20–40 cm; lip with linear, curved basal lobes
and broad central lobe, divided into 2 segments, with a small tooth between them;
5–6; rare. **b Three-toothed Orchid,** *Orchis
tridentata:* ♃, 15–30 cm; lip with dark violet
dots, toothed; 3–6; rare. **c *Burnt-tip Orchid,** *Orchis ustulata:* ♃, 6–40 cm; flowers
blackish when unopened, lip dotted with red
purple; 5–6; rare. **d *Green-winged Orchid,** *Orchis morio:* ♃, 7–30 cm; lip wide,
3-lobed, crenulate, spur cylindrical; 4–6;
meadows and pastures. All are members of
the Orchid Family; **a, c** and **d** occur in grassy
places in most of Europe, **b** in S and C Europe.

Most of the orchids illustrated below are widespread and common in meadows and on grassy
hills. The Bug Orchid grows in S and C Europe, the Elder-scented Orchid in S and C Europe,
northwards to Scandinavia (sometimes local and rare), the Traunsteiner's Orchid in moorland
meadows in the Alps, the southern Black Forest, C, E and NE Europe. All belong to the Orchid
Family.

	*Spotted Orchid	***Broad-leaved Orchid**	**Bug Orchid**	**Elder-scented Orchid**	***Traunstein-er's Orchid**	***Fragrant Orchid**
Scientific Name	*Dactylorhiza fuchsii*	*Dactylorhiza majalis*	*Orchis coriophora*	*Dactylorhiza sambucina*	*Dactylorhiza traunsteineri*	*Gymnadenia conopsea*
Longevity, Size	♃, 15–70 cm	♃, 10–40 cm	♃, 15–40 cm	♃, 10–40 cm	♃, 15–60 cm	♃, 10–60 cm
Distinguishing Features; Flowering Time	Stem solid, leaves 6–10, spreading, mostly brown-spotted, lip 3-lobed; 6–8	Stem thick, hollow, lip slightly lobed, inflorescence dense; 5–6	Spike cylind-rical, flowers purple, often spotted, smel-ling of bugs; 5–7	Flowers purple or yellow, smelling of elders, margin of lip crenate; 4–5	Stem slender, central lobe of lip blunt, lateral lobes finely crenul-ate; 6–8	Lip bluntly 3-angled, spur about twice as long as the ovary, flowers scented; 7–8

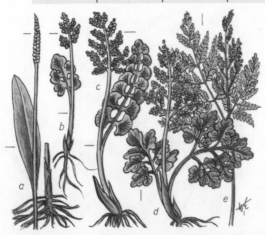

a *Adder's Tongue Fern, *Ophioglossum
vulgatum:* ♃, 5–25 cm; leaf entire; 6–7;
widespread, but local. **b Simple Moonwort,**
Botrychium simplex: ♃, 5–15 cm; sterile blade
below middle of leaf; 6; rare, N and C Europe.
c *Common Moonwort, *Botrychium lunaria:* ♃, 8–25 cm; sterile blade about middle
of leaf; 6–7; widespread, but local. **d †Multi-
fid Moonwort,** *Botrychium multifidum:* ♃,
5–20 cm; leaf-segments stalked; 7–9; local,
N and C Europe. **e Virginian Moonwort,**
Botrychium virginianum: ♃, 15–50 cm; leaf-
segments nearly stalkless; 7–8; local, E and
EC Europe, westwards to Sweden and the
Tyrol. These ferns belong to the Adder's
Tongue Family; meadows, heath, woodland.

a †Damascus Fennel-flower or **Love-in-a-mist,** *Nigella damascena:* ⊙, 20–45 cm; flowers pale blue, with an involucre of much dissected leaves; 4–6. **b French Anemone,** *Anemone coronaria:* ♃, 25–35 cm; leaves 2-ternate, segments deeply lobed, flowers red, blue or white; 3–4. **c †Blue Anemone,** *Anemone apennina:* ♃, 15–30 cm; perianth-segments 10–18, sky blue; 3–4. **d Star Anemone,** *Anemone hortensis:* ♃, 15–40 cm; leaves palmately divided or lobed, flowers usually purple; 1–4. All belong to the Buttercup Family and grow in stony pastureland, cultivated fields and on dry hills in the Mediterranean region.

All the plants shown below are natives of the Mediterranean region, where they occur in stony pastureland and grassy places, the Bitumen Scurvy-pea also being found on rubbish-dumps, the Silvery Birdsfoot Trefoil on sandy shores and the Purple Viper's Bugloss on cultivated fields. The Sicilian Rue belongs to the Rue Family, the Bitumen Scurvy-pea, the Hairy Dorycnium, and the Silvery Birdsfoot-trefoil to the Pea Family, and the Buglosses to the Borage Family.

	Sicilian Rue	Bitumen Scurvy-pea	Hairy Dorycnium	Silvery Birdsfoot-trefoil	*Purple Viper's Bugloss	Italian Bugloss
Scientific Name	*Ruta chalepensis*	*Psoralea bituminosa*	*Dorycnium hirsutum*	*Lotus creticus*	*Echium plantagineum*	*Echium italicum*
Longevity, Size	♃, 30–70 cm	♃, up to 50 cm	♃, 20–60 cm	♃, 10–30 cm	⊙, 30–100 cm	♃, 50–100 cm
Distinguishing Features; Flowering Time	With a strong smell, leaves somewhat fleshy, dotted, flowers greyish yellow; 4–7	Leaves glandular-dotted, flowers bluish violet, pods ovoid, hairy; 5–7	Plant with greyish white hairs, flowers reddish white, keel white or pink; 5–7	Stem weak, woody below, flowers yellow, pods glabrous, narrow, not or slightly curved; 3–4	Plant with soft spreading hairs, flowers purple, finally bluish violet; 3–7	Plant with stiff spreading hairs, flowers reddish or pale violet; 4–7

a Amethystine Sea-holly, *Eryngium amethystinum:* ♃, 50–100 cm; plant with a steely blue sheen, umbel head-like; 7–10; Carrot Family. **b Mediterranean Mullein,** *Verbascum sinuatum:* ♃, 50–100 cm; flowers yellow, filaments purple, woolly; 5–7; Figwort Family. **c Brush-grass,** *Chrysopogon gryllus:* 50–100 cm; spikelets with golden red hairs at the base; 5–8. **d †Great Quaking-grass,** *Briza maxima:* ⊙, 30–60 cm; spikelets very large, nodding; 4–5. **c** and **d** belong to the Grass Family. All these species are natives of the Mediterranean region, occurring mainly in meadows and other grassy places.

a * **Brown Hare,** *Lepus europaeus:* 54.4 cm + 10 cm; ears long, black-tipped, upper side of tail black; a powerful long-distance runner. b *Rabbit, *Oryctolagus cuniculus:* 40 cm + 7 cm; ears short, without black tips, tail white. Both belong to the Rabbit Family, and are widespread throughout Europe, including in woods, but not in mountainous areas, a not in the Iberian Peninsula and the north, b not in E, N and SE Europe. Rabbits usually live socially in burrows, rarely straying far outside; the hare is a solitary animal living above ground. c **Steppe Pika,** *Ochotona pusilla:* 15 cm + 0 cm; coat greyish brown, ears white-edged; lives in burrows, U.S.S.R.

The Great Jerboa or Earth Hare and the Northern Three-toed Jerboa, rodents of the Jerboa Subfamily, live in holes which they dig in the ground on the steppes of the SW U.S.S.R. The Voles live in shallow runs in the ground in meadows and cultivated land. The Northern Root Vole and the Common Vole occur throughout continental Europe, except in Scandinavia and the extreme south, the Northern Vole in Scandinavia and E Europe. The only one living in Britain (but not in Ireland) is the Short-tailed or Field Vole.

	Northern Root Vole	Common Vole	Northern Vole	*Short-tailed Vole	Great Jerboa	Northern Three-toed Jerboa
Scientific Name	Pitymys subterraneus	Microtus arvalis	Microtus oeconomus	Microtus agrestis	Allactaga major	Dipus sagitta nogai
Size	11 cm + 4 cm	11 cm + 3.5 cm	13 cm + 5 cm	10.5 cm + 4 cm	18 cm + 26 cm	17 cm + 21 cm
Distinguishing Features	Upper side dark grey, ears very short, almost completely hidden in coat	Coat smooth, short-haired, tail of almost uniform colour, outside of ear very hairy	Coat dark brown, ears very small, almost entirely hidden, tail rather long	Coat long-haired, rough, tail very short, out-side of ears slightly hairy	Ears large, as long as the head, hind legs four times longer than the forelegs	Ears small, forelegs very short; entrance to burrow oval

a *Stoat,* *Mustela erminea:* 29.5 cm + 11 cm; in summer upper side of coat reddish brown, underside whitish, in winter may be white, tail always with black tip. Families of stoats sometimes stay together through the summer and hunt as packs. b *Weasel,* *Mustela nivalis:* ♂ 20 cm + 6 cm, ♀ 18 cm + 5 cm; coat similar to a, but back and underside colourings separated by a very irregular line, tail without black tip; changes to winter coat in N Europe only. c **Dwarf Weasel,** *Mustela minuta:* up to 19.5 cm + 5.2 cm; straight line between brown of back and white of underside. All are members of the Weasel Family, living in holes in places with a lot of cover; they feed mainly on rodents.

a ***Montagu's Harrier,** *Circus pygargus:*
41–47 cm; ♂ with black wing-bands, rump
light grey, belly and upper legs brown-
streaked, ♀ with white spot on rump;
migrant.
b ***Hen Harrier,** *Circus cyaneus:* 43–51 cm;
♂ and ♀ with conspicuous white spot on rump,
♂ without wing-bands, belly and upper legs
not streaked; partial migrant. Both are Birds
of Prey native to large areas of C, W and E
Europe, **b** also in N Europe, where they nest
on the ground in fields, marshy meadows and
moors. All harriers hold their wings in a V in
gliding flight; in spring they make acrobatic
display flights. The ♀ is fed by the ♂ as she
incubates her eggs.

With the exception of the Corncrake, a member of the Rail Family, and the Snowy Owl, all the
birds illustrated are Waders. Lapwings and Corncrakes are native throughout large areas of
Europe, where they nest in meadows, although the latter is becoming very rare in Great Britain.
The Black-tailed Godwit and the Ruff breed in marshes and meadows in N and C Europe. The
Snowy Owl nests in the tundra, the Slender-billed Curlew on marshy steppes around the Volga
and in the Urals.

	*Corncrake	***Lapwing**	***Ruff** (♂) or Reeve (♀)	***Black-tailed Godwit**	Slender-billed Curlew	Snowy Owl
Scientific Name	*Crex crex*	*Vanellus vanellus*	*Philomachus pugnax*	*Limosa limosa*	*Numenius tenuirostris*	*Nyctea scandiaca*
Size	27 cm	30.5 cm	♂ 34.5 cm	41 cm	41 cm	53.5–66 cm
Distinguishing Features	Upper parts rusty brown, dark-streaked, below yellow-brown, bill and feet yellow; migrant	Throat and breast black, long crest, throat of young white; partial migrant	♀ 20.5 cm; males vary in colouring in summer, with neck-ruff, ♀ inconspicuous; migrant	In summer breast rusty brown, tail white, tip black, legs long; migrant	Flanks with heart-shaped spots, crown without streaks; migrant	Plumage of mature bird snow-white, of younger animals with dark bars, head large; migrant

a White Wagtail, *Motacilla alba alba:* 18 cm;
plumage of ♂ and ♀ black and white; partial
migrant. **b *Pied** or **Water Wagtail,** *Motacilla alba yarellii:* 18 cm; back black; partial
migrant; British subspecies, the commonest
form is illustrated; usually seen near water
but often also on lawns. **c *Grey Wagtail,**
Motacilla cinerea: 18 cm; back grey; partial
migrant. **d Blue-headed Wagtail,** *Motacilla
flava flava:* 16.5 cm; back olive-green; migrant. **e *Yellow Wagtail,** *Motacilla flava
flavissima:* 16.5 cm; very yellow; migrant, the
British subspecies. All belong to the Pipit
Family and nest in holes or (**d** and **e**) on the
ground.

a White-winged Lark, *Melanocorypha leucoptera:* 18 cm; wings with wide, white band;
migrant, SE Russia. **b Little Bunting,** *Emberiza pusilla:* 13 cm; crown and cheeks chestnut-brown; Finch Family; migrant, N Russia.
Both nest on the ground on grassy steppes.
c *Starling, *Sturnus vulgaris:* 21.5 cm;
plumage with metallic sheen, finely spotted;
partial migrant. **d Spotless Starling,** *Sturnus
unicolor:* 21.5 cm; darker than Starling, without spots; resident. Both are noisy, aggressive
birds which nest in holes in trees. **c** is common
throughout Europe with the exception of the
south-west, where it is to some extent replaced by **d.**

The Whitethroat and the Warblers nest close to the ground in thick scrubland, the Aquatic
Warbler principally in sedges. The Wheatear, a member of the Thrush Family, builds its nest
in holes in walls, heaps of stones or rabbit burrows, the Meadow Pipit under tufts of grass and
heather. The River Warbler and the Aquatic Warbler are E and S European species, the other
birds illustrated occur throughout large areas of Europe, although the Icterine Warbler does not
normally occur in Britain.

	Icterine Warbler	*Whitethroat	River Warbler	Aquatic Warbler	*Meadow Pipit	*Common Wheatear
Scientific Name	*Hippolais icterina*	*Sylvia communis*	*Locustella fluviatilis*	*Acrocephalus paludicola*	*Anthus pratensis*	*Oenanthe oenanthe*
Size	13 cm	13.5 cm	13 cm	13 cm	14 cm	14 cm
Distinguishing Features	Upper parts olive-coloured, under parts lemon, legs bluish; migrant	Throat white, under parts light reddish, ♂ head light grey, ♀ brownish; migrant	Upper parts dark olive-brown, breast with pale streaks; migrant	Head with yellowish crown-stripe and a dark stripe on each side; migrant	Plumage with vivid brown streaks, edges of tail white, spur large; partial migrant	Rump and sides of tail white, ♂ in summer with grey back; migrant

a Black-eared Wheatear, *Oenanthe his-
panica:* 14 cm; ♂ in two colour varieties, either
with a black throat (**a**) or black ear-coverts
only (**a₁**), ♀ very much like Common Wheatear; migrant, Mediterranean region. **b Black
Wheatear,** *Oenanthe leucura:* 14 cm; plumage of ♂ and ♀ black, rump white; migrant,
SE Rumania, Spain, Portugal and S France.
c Pied Wheatear, *Oenanthe leucomela:* 13 cm;
♂ throat and back black; resident, Spain,
Portugal, S France. All belong to the Thrush
Family. Wheatears make their nests in holes
among rocks; the Black Wheatear often
camouflages the entrance with a pile of peb-
bles.

a Black-veined White Butterfly, *Aporia crataegi:* 6.5 cm; 6–7; wings white, with black veins running to outer edge; lays 150–200 eggs on hawthorns and sloes; once common in Great Britain, now extinct there. **b *Large White Butterfly,** *Pieris brassicae:* 6.5 cm; 4–6 and 7–9; two black spots on upper side of fore wings of ♀, on underside of those of ♂; eggs mainly on cabbages. **c Small White Butterfly,** *Pieris rapae:* 4.5 cm; 4–9; similar to **b**, but black wing-tips smaller. **b** and **c** are migrants. **d Green-veined White Butterfly,** *Pieris napi:* 4.3 cm; 5 and 8–9; tips of fore wings blackish, those of ♀ with one or two black spots; eggs on Garlic Mustard. All belong to the Whites Family.

The Camberwell Beauty, which is a rare migrant to Britain, lays eggs on birches, willows and poplars, *Euphydryas maturna* on Devilsbit Scabious and plantains, the other species on nettles. The Peacock sometimes lays its eggs on wild hops and the Comma on currant and gooseberry bushes and on elms. All belong to the Tortoiseshell Family and are common in large areas of Europe. Species occurring in Britain have two flight periods: an early one consisting of overwintering or migrant adults, the later one of their offspring.

	*Peacock	*Red Admiral	*Small Tortoiseshell	*Camberwell Beauty	*Comma	
Scientific Name	*Nymphalis io*	*Vanessa atalanta*	*Aglivis urticae*	*Nymphalis antiopa*	*Polygonia c-album*	*Euphydryas maturna*
Size; Flying	6.5 cm; 7–9	6 cm; 7–9	5.5 cm; 7–10	7.5 cm; 7–9	5.5 cm; 7–10	4.5 cm; 5–7
Distinguishing Features	Wings brownish red, with black spots, each with a large eye-spot	Wings black, fore wings with a brick-red transverse band and white spots	Wings fox-coloured, three black spots on front edge of each fore wing	Wings dark velvet–brown, with yellow, more rarely white, margins	Wings brown-ish yellow, with dark spots, with C on the under-side of each hind wing	Wings dark brown, with row of light yellow spots along outer edge

a *Orange Tip, *Anthocharis cardamines:* 4.5 cm; 4–5; ♀ fore wings white, tips greyish black, those of ♂ half orange; eggs on Lady's Smock; hibernates in chrysalis stage. **b *Brimstone,** *Gonepteryx rhamni:* 5.5 cm; 3–4 and 7–8; all four wings with small orange spot, ♀ paler; eggs on Common and Alder Buckthorn; hibernates in adult stage. **c *Clouded Yellow,** *Colias croceus:* 5 cm; 8–9; wings yellowish red, with marginal band. **d *Pale Clouded Yellow,** *Colias hyale:* 4.5 cm; 5 and 8–9; wings with delicate red margin; rare in Britain, where the winter usually kills the hibernating caterpillars. All are meadow-living members of the Whites Family.

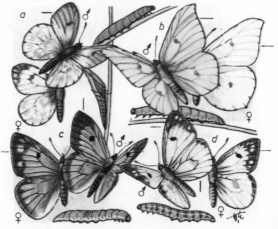

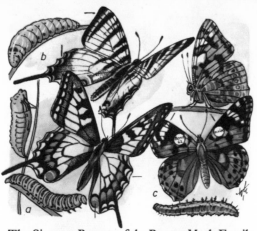

a *Swallowtail, *Papilio machaon:* 8 cm; 4–5 and 7–8; wings yellow with wide, black, yellow-spotted edges, hind wings with reddish yellow eye-spot; eggs on plants of the Parsley Family; in Britain found only in E Anglia. **b Scarce Swallowtail,** *Iphiclides podalirius:* 8 cm; 5–6 and 7–8; similar to **a,** but black margin only on outer edge, blue moon-shaped spots on hind wings; eggs on sloes, pear and apple trees. **c *Painted Lady,** *Vanessa cardui:* 5.5 cm; 5–6 and 7–9; wings yellowish red, with black and white spots; migrant (shown here bearing wing-labels for migration checks); eggs on thistles, milfoils and nettles. **a** and **b** belong to the Swallowtail Family, **c** to the Tortoiseshell Family.

The Six-spot Burnet, of the Burnet Moth Family, lays its eggs on clover and vetches; the Hornet Clearwing, which mimics a large wasp, on poplars; the Garden Tiger (Tiger Moth Family) on many garden plants; the Emperor Moth (Emperor Moth Family) on sloes, hornbeams and numerous other plants. The Red Underwing (caterpillars on poplars and willows) and the Large Yellow Underwing (caterpillars on sorrel, cabbages, auricula and other plants) belong to the Noctuid Family.

	*Six-spot Burnet	*Hornet Clearwing	*Garden Tiger	*Emperor Moth	*Red Underwing	*Large Yellow Underwing
Scientific Name	*Zygaena filipendulae*	*Sesia apiformis*	*Arctia caia*	*Saturnia pavonia*	*Catocala nupta*	*Noctua pronuba*
Size; Flying	3.5 cm; 6–8	4.5 cm; 5–6	7 cm; 7–8	♀ 7 cm; 4–5	8 cm; 8–9	5.5 cm; 6–7
Distinguishing Features	Fore wings green, with three pairs of red spots, hind wings red	Wings transparent, with brown veins and brown front edge, head yellow	Fore wings brown with white lines, hind wings reddish yellow with blue spots	♂ 5.5 cm; wings purple-grey, each with a yellow-edged eye-spot and a dark band	Hind wings vermilion, with two uneven black bands	Hind wings yellow with black band, fore wings mottled brown; (recorded at other times)

a *Small Heath, *Coenonympha pamphilius:* 5 cm; 5–10; wings ochre with a dark margin; caterpillars on soft grasses; hibernates in caterpillar stage. **b *Meadow Brown,** *Maniola jurtina:* 5–6 cm; 6–9; ♀ fore wings with white-centred eye-spot; probably the commonest British butterfly, may be seen almost throughout the summer, flying in dull weather as well as sunshine; caterpillars on grasses. **c** *Erebia medusa:* 4 cm; 5–7; wings of ♂ with three eye-spots, those of ♀ with five. All belong to the Browns Family. **d** *Chrysophanus hippothoe:* 3 cm; 5–7; ♂ reddish golden, ♀ blackish brown and reddish yellow; Blues Family.

a *Codling Moth, *Laspeyresia pomonella:*
2.8 cm; 5–7; fore wings with rust-red transverse
lines; an orchard pest, caterpillars live in
apples; a Tortrix Moth. b *Goat Moth, *Cossus
cossus:* up to 9.5 cm; 6–7; wings ash-grey,
underside lighter, fore wings with many transverse bands; strong, goat-like smell; caterpillars take 3–4 years to develop, feeding on
the wood of elm, ash or willow; Goat Moth
Family. c *Aciptilia pentadactylus:* 2.3 cm;
7–8; fore wings with two, hind wings with
three slits, white; Plume Moth Family.
d *Small Ermine Moth, *Hyponomeuta
malinellus:* 2 cm; fore wings white with black
dots; caterpillars live communally in webs,
feeding on spindle-tree.

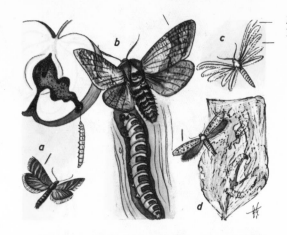

All humblebees (or bumblebees) have plump and corpulent bodies covered with a dense hairy.
coat. Like bees they possess a sting (which they rarely use) and pollen brushes and baskets,
With their long (16–22 mm) tongues humblebees gather nectar from flowers which have long
tubes or spurs. All the species illustrated are native throughout large parts of Europe. Earth
Small Garden and Large Red-tailed Humblebees build their nests in the ground, the others
under grass and moss.

	*Earth Humblebee	*Common Carder Bee	*Small Garden Humblebee	*Large Red-tailed Humblebee	Early Humblebee	*Moss Carder Bee
Scientific Name	Bombus terrestris	Bombus agrorum	Bombus hortorum	Bombus lapidarius	Bombus pratorum	Bombus muscorum
Size	♀ 2.5 cm	♀ 2 cm	♀ 2.3 cm	♀ 2.5 cm	♀ 1.8 cm	♀ 2.2 cm
Distinguishing Features	♂ 2 cm; body black, with 2 yellow transverse bands, tip of abdomen white	♂ 1.5 cm; head and back brownish red, abdomen with 2 yellow transverse bands, tip reddish	♂ 2 cm; body black with 3 yellow transverse bands, tip of abdomen white	♂ 1.8 cm; body black, tip of abdomen red, hairy coat smooth, long, velvety	♂ 1.3 cm; body black with 2 yellow transverse bands, tip of abdomen yellowish	♂ 1.6 cm; coat with short hairs, yellowish to reddish, lighter on the sides

a *German Wasp, *Vespa germanica:* 2 cm;
5–9; head-shield with three black spots, body
with a lot of yellow. b *Hornet, *Vespa crabro:*
♀ 3 cm, ♂ 3.4 cm; 6–9; head much widened
behind the eyes. Both build their nests in the
ground or in dark hiding-places. c *Polistes
gallicus:* 2 cm; 5–9; abdomen narrow. d *Vespa media:* 2.5 cm; 6–9; hind edge of head with
three eye-spots; builds grey hanging nests in
bushes. Wasps build nests of paper which
they prepare by chewing up wood. The cells
of the nest are arranged in horizontal layers;
in them the grubs are fed on the flesh of other
animals. True Wasps fold their wings into
long creases over their bodies.

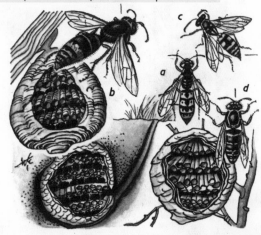

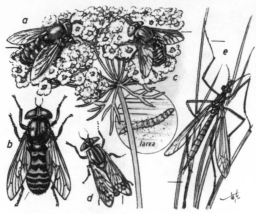

a *****Hoverfly**, *Syrphus lunulatus:* 12 mm; 6–8; abdomen with six light-yellow crescentic patches; adults feed on nectar, larvae on aphids; Hoverfly Family. **b** *****Horse Fly**, *Tabanus bovinus:* 20–25 mm; 5–9; wings transparent, of uniform colour, abdomen with light spots on back, ♀ with piercing mouthparts. **c** *****Thunder Fly** or **Gold-eye**, *Chrysops caecutiens:* up to 10 mm; wing with dark transverse band. **d** *****Clegg** or **Rain Fly**, *Haematopota pluvialis:* up to 10 mm; 6–9; wings with white spots. **b**, **c** and **d** are bloodsuckers of the Horse Fly Family. **e** *****Common Crane Fly** or **Daddy-long-legs**, *Tipula oleracea:* up to 25 mm; 6–9; legs very long; Crane Fly Family; the larvae are pests.

The illustration below shows flies whose larvae are parasitic in domestic animals and Red Deer. The route taken through the host's body by the developing larvae is indicated. These parasites may be serious pests to the animals they infest. The Black Spiny Fly is also parasitic in its larval stage. The Green Bottle is a scavenger, the larvae feeding only on the flesh of dead animals, the adult on nectar.

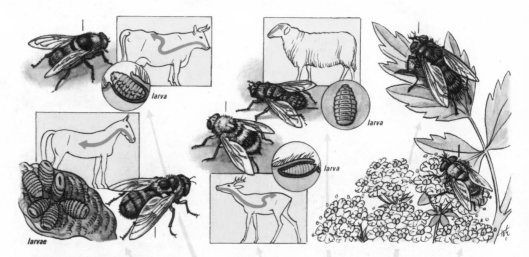

larva
larva
larva
larvae

	*****Common Horse Bot-fly	*****Ox Warble Fly	*****Deer Warble Fly	*****Sheep Bot-fly	*****Black Spiny Fly	*****Green Bottle
Scientific Name	*Gastrophilus intestinalis*	*Hypoderma bovis*	*Hypoderma diana*	*Oestrus ovis*	*Echinomyia grossa*	*Lucilia caesar*
Size; Flying	12–15 mm; 6–9	14–16 mm; 6–7	15 mm; 5–6	10–12 mm; 8–9	25 mm; 6–9	12 mm; 6–9
Distinguishing Features	Wings glass-clear with grey transverse bands; eggs on horse hair	Body covered with dense black and yellow hairs; eggs spindle-shaped; on cattle hair	Body sturdy, like a humblebee, front of abdomen light, dark in the centre	Body brown, end of abdomen hairy, checkered; pupation in the ground	Body black, with thick spiky bristles, head and wing-base reddish yellow	Body shining golden green; eggs on flesh and open wounds

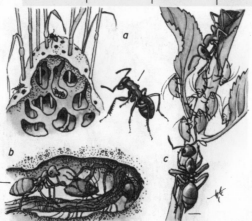

a *****Black Ant**, *Lasius niger:* 3–5 mm; body blackish brown; feeds on small animals, seeds, and honeydew milked from plant lice kept in the nest or placed on growing leaves in springtime. **b** *****Yellow Meadow Ant**, *Lasius flavus:* 3–5 mm; body uniformly yellow; nest oriented E–W, the east end being occupied; collects root aphid eggs in autumn and keeps them underground until hatching in spring, then cultivates the adults for honeydew. **c** *****Red Ant**, *Myrmica rubra laevinoides:* 4–5 mm; reddish yellow, poisonous sting on end of abdomen. All are common and widespread members of the Ant Family.

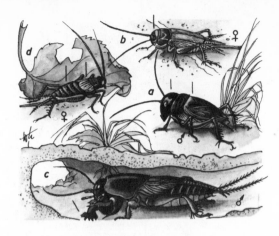

a *Field Cricket, Gryllus campestris:* 20 to 30 mm; head black; wings yellow at base, ♀ with ovipositor 11–14 mm long. **b** *House Cricket, Acneta domestica:* ♂ 19 mm, ♀ 21 mm; head brown with yellow spots, ♀ with ovipositor 11–14 mm long. **c** *Mole Cricket, Gryllotalpa gryllotalpa:* ♂ and ♀ 60–65 mm; first pair of legs with wide digging 'shovels'; rare in Britain. **d** Wood Cricket, *Nemobius silvestris:* ♂ 9 mm, ♀ 10–11 mm; 6-9; body dark brown with light spots, fore wings very short, ♀ with ovipositor 10–11 mm long. All except **c** belong to the Cricket Family, **c** to the Mole Cricket Family, which live in holes in the ground. Crickets chirp by rubbing together rough areas on the wings.

The Blue-winged Grasshopper, *Psophus stridulus* and the White-lined Grasshopper are common Short-horned Grasshoppers, found on meadows and pastureland throughout C Europe, *Psophus stridulus* particularly on lush mountain meadows. The Wart-biter and the two species of *Tettigonia* illustrated are Bush Crickets. All three species spend a lot of time resting on bushes, where they live chiefly on insects; they are native throughout C Europe.

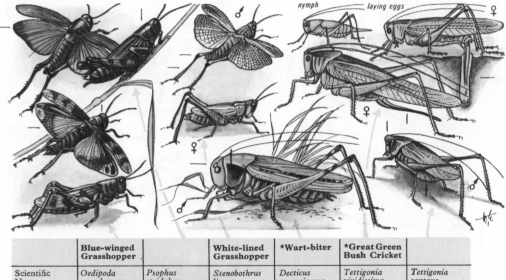

	Blue-winged Grasshopper		White-lined Grasshopper	*Wart-biter	*Great Green Bush Cricket	
Scientific Name	*Oedipoda coerulescens*	*Psophus stridulus*	*Stenobothrus lineatus*	*Decticus verrucivorus*	*Tettigonia viridissima*	*Tettigonia cantans*
Size	♂ 22, ♀ 27 mm	♂ 24, ♀ 30 mm	♂ 19, ♀ 24 mm	♂ 36, ♀ 45 mm	♂ 34, ♀ 36 mm	♂ 26, ♀ 28 mm
Distinguishing Features	Head yellowish brown, hind wings blue with wide black transverse band	Body blackish, hing wings red with black tips	Body green, ♀ with yellow transverse lines, hind wings colourless, tibia red or brown	Body green or brown, with 'horse head', front of thorax with brown spot on side	Fore wings grey, hind wings colourless, transparent, ♀ with long sheathed ovipositor	Body yellowish brown, antennae very long, ovipositor 23–30 mm long

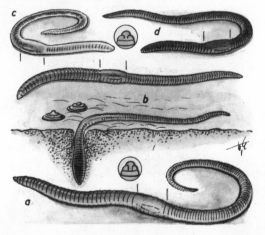

a *Lumbricus herculeus:* up to 36 cm; clitellum from 32nd to 37th segment. **b** *Lumbricus rubellus:* up to 12 cm; clitellum from 27th to 32nd segment. **c** *Allolobophora rosea:* up to 6 cm; body transparent. **d** **Brandling,** *Eisenia foetida:* up to 19 cm; each segment with a purple transverse stripe. The Brandling is a favourite bait worm for fishermen. All are widespread members of the Earthworm Group; **a** and **c** live in the ground (**a** in S Europe), **b** in rotting leaves and **d** in dung and compost heaps. **a** feeds on leaves which it pulls back into its burrow, the other species by eating earth as they burrow through it, extracting any foodstuffs in their digestive systems.

a Tarentula, *Tarentula fasciiventris:* 3–5 cm; dark transverse bands on abdomen. **b European Black Widow,** *Latrodectes tredecimguttatus:* up to 1 cm; 13 blood-red spots on abdomen. **c** *Euscorpius flavicaudus:* up to 4 cm; body blackish brown, abdomen with poisonous sting which reaches and kills its prey when the abdomen is twisted upwards and forwards. **d** *Buthus cocitanus:* up to 8 cm; very similar to **c,** but body yellowish brown. Both are True Scorpions found in the Mediterranean region. All the species figured here have a painful bite or sting, the Black Widow being very poisonous, although unless disturbed they are not usually aggressive.

All the insects in the table live on stony fields and among bushes in the Mediterranean region, the Praying Mantis (Mantis Family) also in warm places as far north as S Germany. The Stick Insect and the two locusts, which belong to the Grasshopper Family, eat plants, the other species prey on animals. Italian Locusts periodically appear as pests in Italy; the Egyptian Locust does not occur in swarms in Europe.

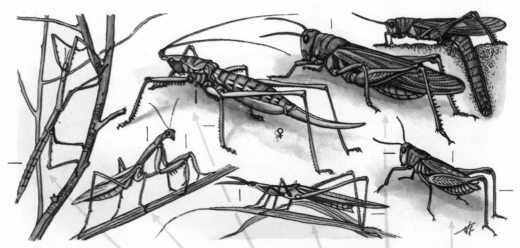

	Stick Insect	Praying Mantis	Bush Cricket		Egyptian Locust	Italian Locust
Scientific Name	*Bacillus rossii*	*Mantis religiosa*	*Saga serrata*	*Acrida nasuta*	*Anacridium aegyptium*	*Calliptamus italicus*
Size	Up to 9 cm	Up to 7 cm	♂ 60, ♀ 66 mm	Up to 7 cm	Up to 7 cm	Up to 3 cm
Distinguishing Features	Body stick-like, wingless, legs long and slender, antennae short	Fore legs prehensile, black spot on inside of femur, pronotum very long	Hind legs very long, thorax segments with 2 spines on underside, legs spiny	Head long, conical, jumping legs slender and very long, antennae flattened	Wings long, keel of pronotum crenate, body brown, finely spotted	Tibia red, fore wings striped, head roundish

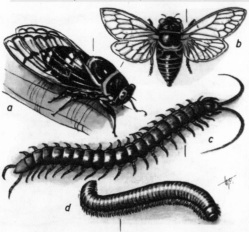

a *Cicada plebeja,* up to 5 cm; pronotum and elytra with yellow rear edge. **b** *Tibicen haematodes:* up to 4 cm; base of wings with orange-red veins. Both are Cicadas which are related to plant bugs, but produce a chirping noise like grasshoppers by vibrating a drum-like organ called the tymbal; only the ♂ makes a noise but the ♀, unlike most insects, can hear. **c** *Scolopendra cingulata:* up to 10 cm; 21 somites, each with one pair of legs; a Centipede. **d** *Pachyiulus flavipes:* up to 6 cm; legs yellowish, with two pairs to each somite; a Millipede found in the Mediterranean region.

Field, Garden and Park

Man has made far-reaching changes to nature by cultivating the land and laying out fields and meadows, gardens and parks. This has changed the original appearance of the land, and also its plant and animal life. Where formerly there were forests there are now wide expanses of cultivated fields with cereal and rootcrops and all kinds of fodder. Many native plants have disappeared, while some have adapted themselves to the changed conditions, and a number of alien plants brought in by man or by natural means have become naturalized; this new population now flourishes on such places as ploughed fields, footpaths, roadsides, rubbish-dumps, hedgerows, fences, and walls. Numerous animals, too, seek the proximity of human habitation. Many find their way into houses, out-buildings and gardens, for example, rats, many species of mouse, hedgehogs, weasels, polecats and martens. Hares and rabbits live in fields and meadows, and in some regions wild pigs and deer come out of the forest for food. Sparrows, swallows, swifts, storks, kestrels, jackdaws and different species of owl nest in or on houses; tits, thrushes, finches and many other birds inhabit gardens and parks.

a †Forking Larkspur, *Delphinium consolida:* ○, 20–40 cm; spur almost straight, fruit glabrous; 5–8; widespread, in fields and waste places. **b †Field Fennel-flower,** *Nigella arvensis:* ○, 7–30 cm; flowers pale blue, carpels united only below the middle; 7–9; native of Mediterranean region, naturalized elsewhere. Both belong to the Buttercup Family. **c *Fingered Saxifrage,** *Saxifraga tridactylitis:* ○, 2–18 cm; stem leafy, petals 2–3 mm; 4–6; local, on walls and sandy soil. **d *Irish Mossy Saxifrage,** *Saxifraga rosacea:* ⚇; 4–20 cm; stem with 3–9 flowers; 5–7; local, on mountains of NW and C Europe, also in Ireland. Both belong to the Saxifrage Family.

The Corn Crowfoot and the Summer Pheasant's-eye are widespread in cultivated fields; the latter, however, is a casual. The other species grow in scattered localities on clayey or calcareous fields, the Spring Pheasant's-eye also in heath meadows, on sunny hillocks and in pine woods, the Mousetail especially in damp habitats and in places which have been trampled by cattle, and in orchards. All belong to the Buttercup Family.

	*Corn Crowfoot	*Hairy Buttercup	†Spring Pheasant's-eye	Scarlet Pheasant's-eye	†Summer Pheasant's-eye	*Mousetail
Scientific Name	*Ranunculus arvensis*	*Ranunculus sardous*	*Adonis vernalis*	*Adonis flammea*	*Adonis aestivalis*	*Myosurus minimus*
Longevity, Size	○, 15–60 cm	⚇, 5–40 cm	⚇, 15–60 cm	○, 15–50 cm	○, 15–70 cm	○-⚇, 1–12 cm
Distinguishing Features; Flowering Time	Stem upright, flowers small, sulphur-yellow, fruits 4–8, large, spiny; 5–7	Basal leaves deeply 3-lobed, middle lobe stalked, sepals reflexed; 5–9	Leaves 2- or 3-pinnate, thread-like, flowers solitary, large, yellow, 3–7 cm wide; 4–5	Petals deep scarlet, rarely yellow, calyx hairy, fruits with black tips; 6–8	Leaves 2- or 3-pinnate, calyx glabrous, petals 5–8, red or yellow, fruits 4-angled; 5–7	Basal rosette of narrowly linear leaves, fruits in long spike resembling a mouse's tail; 4–6

a †Houseleek, *Sempervivum tectorum:* ⚇, 20–50 cm; rosette-leaves densely fringed on margins, flowers pale red; 7–9; in most of Europe, sometimes as an escape from gardens. **b †Rock Stonecrop,** *Sedum reflexum:* ⚇, 13–35 cm; leaves with small broad point at tip; 6–8; rocks and screes, widespread in C Europe, local elsewhere, often naturalized. **c †Insipid Stonecrop,** *Sedum sexangulare:* ⚇, 2–15 cm; leaves with spur at base; 7–8; widespread, but local, also on old walls. **d *Common Stonecrop** or **Wall-pepper,** *Sedum acre:* ⚇, 4–15 cm; leaves pointed, imbricate, with burning taste; 5–7; widespread. All belong to the Stonecrop Family, and grow mainly in sandy fields.

a Reddish Stonecrop, *Sedum rubens:* ⊙, 5–15 cm; glandular hairy above; 5–6; rare, fields and vineyards, S, W and C Europe; Stonecrop Family. **b *Common Agrimony,** *Agrimonia eupatoria:* ♃, 20–80 cm; leaves grey-hairy beneath; 6–9; widespread, common. **c Hairy Agrimony,** *Agrimonia pilosa:* ♃, 20–80 cm; leaves with stiff hairs on veins beneath; 6–8; uncommon, roadsides and thickets, E and EC Europe. **d *Parsley Piert,** *Aphanes arvensis:* ⊙, 1–30 cm; flowers in dense leaf-opposed clusters; 5–10; common, arable land, bare grassland. **b, c** and **d** Rose Family. **e †Birthwort,** *Aristolochia clematitis:* ♃, 20–80 cm; leaves heart-shaped; 5–6; S, C and W Europe; Birthwort Family.

The Silverweed, the Creeping Cinquefoil, the Hoary Cinquefoil and the Spring Cinquefoil are widespread and common on roadsides, dry places and in stony pastureland. The Silverweed prefers highly nutritive soils. The Small Cinquefoil occurs in dry meadows in lowlands and in mountain areas of the Balkans and C Europe, the Small-flowered Cinquefoil in scattered localities, in N, W and C Europe, mainly in dry meadows, sometimes in open woodlands. All belong to the Rose Family.

	*Silverweed	*Creeping Cinquefoil	*Hoary Cinquefoil	*Spring Cinquefoil	Small Cinquefoil	†Small-flowered Cinquefoil
Scientific Name	Potentilla anserina	Potentilla reptans	Potentilla argentea	Potentilla tabernaemontani	Potentilla pusilla	Potentilla thuringiaca
Longevity, Size	♃, 10–30 cm	♃, 10–40 cm	♃, 15–30 cm	♃, 8–30 cm	♃, up to 20 cm	♃, 15–30 cm
Distinguishing Features; Flowering Time	Leaves pinnate, with large and small leaflets, silky beneath, flowers solitary, rarely 2; 5–8	Leaves palmately 3–7-lobed, flowers long-stalked, usually solitary; 6–8	Leaves white-downy beneath, usually palmate with 5 leaflets, flowers small; 6–8	Leaves palmate, long-hairy, inflorescence 3–5-flowered, fruit-stalks curved downwards; 3–4	Plant with 3–10-rayed star-like hairs, central ray distinctly longer; 3–5	Stem slender, shortly hairy, flowers 1–2 cm wide, fruit-stalks curved upwards; 5–7

a *Spiny Rest-harrow, *Ononis spinosa:* ♃, 30–60 cm; stems usually spiny, with 2 lines of hairs, pod as long or longer than calyx; 6–9; widespread in rough grassy places. **b *Common Rest-harrow,** *Ononis repens:* ♃, 30–60 cm; stems usually unarmed, hairy all round; 6–9; widespread and common, in grassland. **c Yellow Rest-harrow,** *Ononis natrix:* ♃, 20–50 cm; plant densely glandular hairy; 5–7; usually rare, S and C Europe. **d Goat Rest-harrow,** *Ononis arvensis*: ♃, 30–60 cm; stem usually without glandular hairs, flowers pale red, rarely white; 7–8; rare, pastures and roadsides in E and C Europe. All belong to the Pea Family and grow in dry places.

a *Haresfoot Trefoil, *Trifolium arvense:* ♃, 3–45 cm; calyx with dense soft hairs; 5–7; widespread, common. b †Lucerne, *Medicago sativa:* ♃, up to 100 cm; flowers about 8 mm, calyx-stalk shorter than calyx-tube; 6–7; native to Mediterranean region, cultivated, naturalized in many places. c *Toothed Medick, *Medicago polymorpha:* ☉, 5–60 cm; wings longer than the keel, pods flat, in spiral of 1¹⁄₂–4 turns, with double row of unequal hooked spines; 5–7; S and C Europe. d *Birdsfoot, *Ornithopus perpusillus:* ☉, 3–50 cm; flowers whitish, standard violet-veined; 5–7; widespread, but local. All belong to the Pea Family and grow in sandy fields and along roadsides.

Melilots are widespread and common on embankments, roadsides, edges of fields and in waste places, introduced in many places. The Sand Milk-vetch occurs on heaths, sandy hillocks and in pine woods of E and C Europe, the Common Crown-vetch in meadows and bushy places of S and C Europe, naturalized elsewhere, the Mountain Crown-vetch in pastures, sunny calcareous slopes, dry woods and scrub of C, EC and SE Europe and the Crimea. All belong to the Pea Family.

	†White Melilot	†Common Melilot	†Golden Melilot	Sand Milk-vetch	†Common Crown-vetch	Mountain Crown-vetch
Scientific Name	*Melilotus alba*	*Melilotus officinalis*	*Melilotus altissima*	*Astragalus arenarius*	*Coronilla varia*	*Coronilla coronata*
Longevity, Size	☉, 30–150 cm	☉, 30–100 cm	♃, 100–150 cm	♃, 10–40 cm	♃, 30–120 cm	♃, 30–70 cm
Distinguishing Features; Flowering Time	Flowers white, standard longer than the wings, pods glabrous; 5–8	Standard and wings of almost equal length, pods hairy, blunt, brown when ripe; 5–9	Standard and wings of almost equal length, pods hairy, sharp, black when ripe; 7–9	Leaflets linear, racemes with 3–7 violet or whitish flowers; 6–7	Leaflets 6–12 pairs, stipules free, flowers pink, white and violet; 5–9	Leaflets 3–6 pairs, stipules fused, flowers yellow; 5–7

a Serradella, *Ornithopus sativus:* ☉-♃, 10–60 cm; bracts shorter than the flowers, flowers white or pink; 5–7; SW Europe, widely cultivated as a fodder plant. b *Sainfoin, *Onobrychis viciifolia:* ♃, 30–60 cm; flowers bright pink or red, pods tubercled on lower margin, 1-seeded; 5–7; local, in meadows, pastures and fields of SE Europe. c Lentil, *Lens culinaris:* ☉, 15–50 cm; pods flat, broad, 1–2-seeded; 5–7; a native of the E Mediterranean region. d †False Acacia, *Robinia pseudoacacia:* tree up to 27 m; flowers fragrant, in hanging racemes; 5–6; a native of N America. All are members of the Pea Family, widely cultivated and naturalized.

a *Yellow Vetch, *Vicia lutea:* ⊙, 10–60 cm; climbing, flowers pale yellow, pods hairy; 5–6; widespread, but local. **b** †Sand Vetch, *Vicia villosa:* ⊙, 30–60 cm; stem and leaves hairy; 5–8; S, C and E Europe. **c Lentil Tare,** *Vicia ervilia:* ⊙, 20–60 cm; leaves without tendrils, flowers pink, racemes 2–4-flowered; 6–8; S Europe. **d †Common Vetch,** *Vicia sativa:* ⊙, 15–90 cm; climbing, flowers large, with pink standard and purple wings, solitary or in pairs; 5–9; probably a native of W Asia. All are members of the Pea Family, occurring in fields, among cereal crops, in meadows and on roadsides, introduced and naturalized elsewhere.

The Bush Vetch and the Tufted Vetch are widespread and common in cultivated fields, poor meadows and on roadsides; the Hairy Tare and the Smooth Tare are more local, being found in the same types of habitat, and also in bushy places. The One-flowered Vetch is a native of the Mediterranean region, the Earth-nut Pea of C and S Europe, both growing in fields and hedges, and naturalized in other parts of Europe. All belong to the Pea Family.

	*Bush Vetch	*Tufted Vetch	One-flowered Vetch	*Hairy Tare	*Smooth Tare	†Earth-nut Pea
Scientific Name	*Vicia sepium*	*Vicia cracca*	*Vicia articulata*	*Vicia hirsuta*	*Vicia tetrasperma*	*Lathyrus tuberosus*
Longevity, Size	♃, 30–100 cm	♃, 20–150 cm	⊙, 20–70 cm	⊙, 20–70 cm	⊙, 15–60 cm	♃, 60–120 cm
Distinguishing Features; Flowering Time	Climbing, leaflets 4–8 pairs, racemes nearly stalkless, 2–5-flowered, flowers pale purplish; 5–6	Scrambling, leaflets 6–10 pairs, racemes with stalks 2–10 cm long, with many blue flowers; 6–7	With tendrils, stipules of different shape, racemes with 1–2 white or pale blue flowers; 4–6	Trailing, racemes 1–4-flowered, flowers dirty white or purplish, pod hairy, usually 2-seeded; 6–7	Trailing, racemes 1–2-flowered, flowers pale blue, pod glabrous, 4-seeded; 5–7	Scrambling, roots with small tubers, leaflets 1 pair, flowers scented, large, crimson; 6–7

a *Yellow Vetchling, *Lathyrus aphaca:* ⊙, up to 100 cm; scrambling, stipules leaf-like, hastate at base; 5–7; local, dry places, in S, C and W Europe. **b** *Grass Vetchling, *Lathyrus nissolia:* ⊙, 30–90 cm; stipules very small, phyllodes grass-like; 6–8; local, grassy and bushy places, mainly in S and C Europe. **c †Hairy Vetchling,** *Lathyrus hirsutus:* ⊙-⊙, 30–100 cm; pods with dense silky hairs; 6–8; S and C Europe, naturalized elsewhere. **d Sweet Pea,** *Lathyrus odoratus:* ⊙, 80 to 160 cm; flowers large, sweet-smelling, in various colours; 6–8; Mediterranean region, cultivated and naturalized in many other parts. All are members of the Pea Family, often growing in cornfields.

a *Field Poppy, *Papaver rhoeas:* ☉, 30 to
80 cm; capsule almost globose, glabrous,
stigma-rays 8–12; 5–7; common. b *Long-
headed Poppy, *Papaver dubium:* ☉, 30 to
60 cm; capsule obovoid-oblong, glabrous,
stigma-rays 4–9; 5–7; common. c *Pale
Poppy, *Papaver argemone:* ☉, 15–30 cm;
capsule narrowly obovoid-oblong, with few
erect bristles, stigma-rays 4–6; 5–7; common.
d *Bristly Poppy, *Papaver hybridum:* ☉,
15–60 cm; capsule globose, densely covered
with yellowish white bristles, stigma-rays
5–8; 5–7; rare. All are members of the Poppy
Family, occurring in arable fields and waste
places in most of Europe.

The fumitories shown below are mainly found in cultivated fields and waste places. The Common Fumitory and the Pale Fumitory are widespread, the other species grow in scattered
localities and are uncommon or rare. The Beaked Fumitory occurs in C and SE Europe, the
Dense-flowered in S, W and C Europe, the Dark Fumitory in S and C Europe, extending
eastwards to the Ukraine, and the Ramping Fumitory in S, W and C Europe. All belong to the
Poppy Family.

	*Common Fumitory	Beaked Fumitory	*Dense-flowered Fumitory	Dark Fumitory	*Pale Fumitory	*Ramping Fumitory
Scientific Name	*Fumaria officinalis*	*Fumaria rostellata*	*Fumaria densiflora*	*Fumaria schleicheri*	*Fumaria vaillantii*	*Fumaria capreolata*
Longevity, Size	☉, 7–50 cm	☉, 15–50 cm	☉, 30–90 cm	☉, 15–30 cm	☉, 15–30 cm	☉, 30–90 cm
Distinguishing Features; Flowering Time	Bracts half as long as fruit-stalks, corolla 7–9 mm, fruit broader than long, wrinkled; 5–10	Bracts ²/₃ as long as fruit-stalks, corolla 7–9 mm, fruit subglobose, keeled, nearly smooth; 6–8	Bracts exceed fruits-stalks, corolla 6–7 mm, fruit sub-globose, keel-ed, wrinkled; 6–11	Bracts ³/₄ as long as fruit-stalks, corolla 5–6 mm, fruit subglobose, keeled, weakly wrinkled; 6–9	Bracts ¹/₂ as long a fruit-stalks, corolla 5–6 mm, fruit subglobose, wrinkled; 6–9	Climbing, co-rolla 10–14 mm, creamy white, with blackish tips and wings of upper petal; 6–9

a †Opium Poppy, *Papaver somniferum:* ☉,
10–100 cm; flowers violet to white; 6–8;
Mediterranean region, naturalized elsewhere.
b *Small-flowered Fumitory, *Fumaria
parviflora:* ☉, up to 30 cm; flowers usually
white, 5–6 mm long; 6–9; local, S and C
Europe, northwards to Britain. c *Wall
Fumitory, *Fumaria muralis:* ☉, 20–80 cm;
flowers purple, with blackish red tips; 6–9;
rare, W Europe. d *Greater Celandine,
Chelidonium majus: ♃, 30–70 cm; with bright
yellow latex, flowers in umbels, fruits pod-
like capsules; 5–9; widespread and common
in hedgerows and by walls. All are members
of the Poppy Family, occurring, except d, in
arable land and waste places.

a *Black Mustard, *Brassica nigra:* ⊙, 30 to 80 cm; leaves lyrate-pinnatifid, with a large terminal lobe, sepals erect, fruits appressed to stem; 6–9; widespread in S and C Europe. **b *Wild Cabbage,** *Brassica oleracea:* ⊙-4, 50–150 cm; flowers sulphur-yellow, large, 12–26 mm long, sepals erect, fruits spreading; 5–9; on maritime coasts of Atlantic Europe, Mediterranean and Adriatic regions. **c †Turnip,** *Brassica rapa:* ⊙-⊙, 60–120 cm; sepals horizontally spreading, upper stem leaves clasping the stem; 4–9; widespread. All are cultivated plants of the Crucifer Family, found also as escapes, occurring in arable land and waste places.

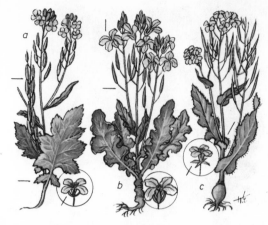

The Hairy Mustard is a native of C and SW Europe, found also in the Alps, the Watercress-leaved Mustard of SW Europe, the Wallflower Cabbage of W Europe, mainly in the mountains; all are widely naturalized on arable and waste land. Wall-rockets are locally common in similar situations, and on walls; the Rod-like Wall-rocket is a native of S Europe, the Common Wall-rocket or Stinkweed of S and C Europe. Both are naturalized elsewhere. The Perennial Wall-rocket occurs in most of Europe. All belong to the Crucifer Family.

	†Hairy Mustard	†Watercress-leaved Mustard	†Wallflower Cabbage	*Perennial Wall-rocket	†Rod-like Wall-rocket	†Common Wall-rocket
Scientific Name	*Erucastrum gallicum*	*Erucastrum nasturtiifolium*	*Rhynchosinapis cheiranthos*	*Diplotaxis tenuifolia*	*Diplotaxis viminea*	*Diplotaxis muralis*
Longevity, Size	⊙, 10–60 cm	4, 20–110 cm	⊙, 20–60 cm	4, 30–80 cm	⊙, 15–25 cm	⊙-4, 12–60 cm
Distinguishing Features; Flowering Time	Sepals erect, petals pale or golden yellow, fruits curving upwards, stalkless above sepal-scars; 5–9	Sepals spread horizontally, petals yellow, fruits spreading, stalked above sepal-scars; 5–8	Sepals erect, fruits 4–7 cm long, spreading horizontally, with a long beak; 6–10	Leaves pinnate, with 7–11 linear leaflets, stinking, lower flower-stalks as long as fruit; 5–10	Leaves confined to a basal rosette, petals 3–4 mm long, outer stamens sterile; 6–9	Resembling the previous species, but petals at least 4–5 mm long, outer stamens fertile; 6–9

a *Wild Radish, *Raphanus raphanistrum:* ⊙, 20–60 cm; petals yellow or white, fruit-pods jointed, sepals upright; 6–8; widespread, common. **b *Charlock** or **Wild Mustard,** *Sinapis arvensis:* ⊙, 30–70 cm; leaves stiffly hairy, fruits with conical beak 10 mm long; widespread, common. **c †White Mustard,** *Sinapis alba:* ⊙, 25–80 cm; upper stem leaves stalked, fruits with flattened beak 15 mm long; 6–9; Mediterranean region, cultivated and naturalized elsewhere. **d †Flixweed,** *Descurainia sophia:* ⊙-4, 10–90 cm; flowers pale yellow, fruits curved upwards; 5–7; widespread, locally common. All these plants of the Crucifer Family occur as weeds in arable and waste land and on roadsides.

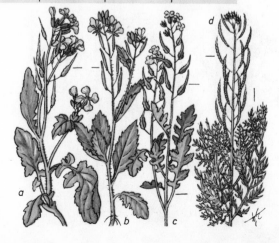

a Calepina, *Calepina irregularis:* ☉, 30 to 100 cm; upper leaves clasping stem, flowers small, white; 5–6; local, S, C and W Europe. **b †Steppe Cabbage,** *Rapistrum perenne:* ☉-♃, 30–80 cm; fruit tapering into a beak; 6–7; C and E Europe. **c †Hybrid Cabbage,** *Rapistrum rugosum:* ☉, 20–60 cm; fruit abruptly contracted into a beak; 5–10; S Europe. **d †Hare's-ear Cabbage,** *Conringia orientalis:* ☉, 15–80 cm; petals 10–13 mm long, yellowish white, fruit 4-angled; 5–7; Mediterranean region. All are members of the Crucifer Family, found mainly as weeds in arable and waste land; all may occur as casuals or be widely naturalized.

The Common Pepperwort, the Narrow-leaved Pepperwort, the Hoary Cress and the Common Wart-cress are widespread and sometimes frequent in most of Europe, occuring in dry pastures, on walls, banks, roadsides, in cultivated fields and waste places. The Tall Pepperwort, a native of the Mediterranean region growing usually on rocky hills, and the Garden Cress, which is cultivated as a salad plant, are found as casuals in many places. All belong to the Crucifer Family.

	Common Pepperwort	†Tall Pepperwort	†Garden Cress	†Narrow-leaved Pepperwort	†Hoary Cress	*Common Wart-cress
Scientific Name	*Lepidium campestre*	*Lepidium graminifolium*	*Lepidium sativum*	*Lepidium ruderale*	*Cardaria draba*	*Coronopus squammatus*
Longevity, Size	☉-☉, 5–80 cm	♃, 40–70 cm	☉, 30–60 cm	☉, 5–50 cm	♃, 30–90 cm	☉, 2–30 cm
Distinguishing Features; Flowering Time	Densely hairy, upper leaves clasping stem, fruits with small white scale-like vesicles; 5–7	Stem branched above, basal leaves toothed or pinnately lobed, fruits small, 2.5–4 mm ovoid; 6–7	Leaves glabrous, glaucous, basal ones lyrate, toothed, fruits 5–6 mm long, winged; 6–9	Stem usually much-branched, stinking, petals usually absent, stamens usually 2; 5–11	Stem leaves with auricles at the base, clasping stem, flowers white, fruits wider than long; 4–7	Flowers white, in short racemes, fruits apiculate, ridged or warty, kidney-shaped; 6–10

a †Woad, *Isatis tinctoria:* ☉, 50–140 cm; flowers yellow, numerous, fruits flattened, oblong, 1-seeded, drooping; 5–7; most of Europe. **b *Wild Candytuft,** *Iberis amara:* ☉, 5–25 cm; petals white or lilac, of unequal length; 7–8; locally common, dry hillsides and cornfields in S and W Europe, naturalized elsewhere. **c *Rock Hutchinsia,** *Hornungia petraea:* ☉, 3–10 cm; leaves pinnate, flowers white; 4–6; rare, usually on limestone rocks in S, W and C Europe. **d Salt-cress,** *Hymenobolus procumbens:* ☉, 2–15 cm; flowers white, fruit elliptical to obovate; 4–5; frequently near the sea, mainly in S Europe. All belong to the Crucifer Family.

a †Ball Mustard, *Neslia paniculata:* ○, 15–80 cm; leaves clasping stem, fruits spherical; 5–7; native of S Europe, a casual elsewhere. **b †Crested Cabbage**, *Bunias erucago:* ○-○, 30–60 cm; fruits with 4 irregularly crested wings; 5–7; a native of S Europe, naturalized in most other parts. **c *Perfoliate Pennycress**, *Thlaspi perfoliatum:* ○, 6 to 40 cm; fruits 4–6 mm long, style short; 4–6; widespread but local. **d Mountain Pennycress**, *Thlaspi montanum:* ♃, 10–30 cm; mat-forming, style exceeding the notch; 4–5; C Europe. All belong to the Crucifer Family; the first three occur in arable fields, waste land and grassy places, **d** on cliff-ledges, scree, open scrub and grassland.

The Field Pennycress and the Shepherd's Purse are widespread and common plants of cultivated fields, waste places and waysides. The Shepherd's Cress grows in sandy arable fields and often also on dunes, mainly in W and C Europe, the Alpine Pennycress on the mountains of C and S Europe, and in Britain, the Smooth Buckler-mustard mainly in mountain areas of S and C Europe. The Honesty is a native of SE Europe, cultivated and naturalized elsewhere. All belong to the Crucifer Family.

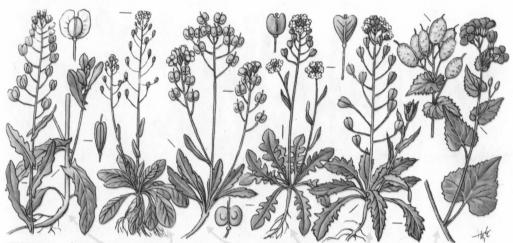

	*Field Pennycress	*Alpine Pennycress	†Smooth Buckler-mustard	*Shepherd's Cress	*Shepherd's Purse	†Honesty
Scientific Name	*Thlaspi arvense*	*Thlaspi alpestre*	*Biscutella laevigata*	*Teesdalia nudicaulis*	*Capsella bursa-pastoris*	*Lunaria annua*
Longevity, Size	○, 12–70 cm	○-♃, 5–30 cm	♃, 20–50 cm	○, 8–15 cm	○, 2–80 cm	♃, 30–100 cm
Distinguishing Features; Flowering Time	Stem angled, stem leaves arrow-shaped at the base, clasping stem, fruits almost orbicular; 4–6	Petals white, rarely pink, fruits usually narrowly obcordate; 4–6	Leaves stiff-hairy, flowers bright yellow, fruits with 2 strongly flattened, valves; 5–7	Leaves in a basal rosette, mostly lyrate-pinnatifid, flowers white; 4–5	Leaves in a basal rosette, deeply pinnatifid to entire, fruits 3-angled, notched above; 2–11	Upper leaves stalkless, fruits large, flat, almost circular; 4–6

a †Golden Alison, *Alyssum saxatile:* ♃, 10–30 cm; grey-hairy, fruits roundish, glabrous; 4–5; SE and C Europe. **b †Small Alison**, *Alyssum alyssoides:* ○-♃, 5–25 cm; grey-hairy, fruits almost circular, hairy; 4–9; in most of Europe, introduced and naturalized in the north. **c Mountain Alison**, *Alyssum montanum:* ♃, 5–30 cm; plant greyish green, style about 2 mm long; 4–5; in most of Europe. **d †Hoary Alison**, *Berteroa incana:* ○, 30–35 cm; petals deeply bifid, fruits with star-like hairs; 6–10; E, C and N Europe. All are members of the Crucifer Family, growing on arable and waste land and in grassy fields.

a *Wall Whitlow-grass, *Draba muralis:*
☉-☉, 15–40 cm; flowers white, stem leaves
more than 3, half-clasping stem; 5–7. **b**
*Common Whitlow-grass, *Erophila verna:*
☉, 2–15 cm; fruits oblanceolate or elliptical;
2–5. **c** *Inflated-podded Whitlow-grass,
Erophila spathulata: ☉, 1–20 cm; leaves
minutely hairy above, with forked and star-
like hairs, fruits nearly spherical; 2–5.
d *Early Whitlow-grass, *Erophila praecox:*
☉, 1–20 cm; leaves coarsely hairy above, with
simple and some forked hairs, fruits shortly
obovoid; 2–5. All belong to the Crucifer Family and are widespread and local on rocks,
walls and in dry places in most of Europe.

The Hairy Bitter-cress, the Early Winter-cress and the Sand Rock-cress are widespread and
common on cultivated fields, by waysides, and on waste land in most of Europe. The other
species shown below grow on stream-banks, in hedges and on arable and waste land; the Small-
flowered Bitter-cress and the Common Winter-cress in most of Europe, the Small-flowered
Landcress in E, C and N Europe. All belong to the Crucifer Family.

	Small-flowered Bitter-cress	*Hairy Bitter-cress	†Early Winter-cress	*Small-flowered Landcress	*Common Winter-cress	Sand Rock-cress
Scientific Name	*Cardamine parviflora*	*Cardamine hirsuta*	*Barbarea intermedia*	*Barbarea stricta*	*Barbarea vulgaris*	*Cardaminopsis arenosa*
Longevity, Size	☉, 7–40 cm	☉, 3–25 cm	☉, 15–70 cm	☉, 25–100 cm	☉, 20–130 cm	☉-☉, 10–50 cm
Distinguishing Features; Flowering Time	Leaves pinnate, stem flexuous, fruit-stalks spreading; 5–9	Stamens 4, fruits upright, over-topping the flowers; 5–6	Basal leaves with 3–5 pairs of lobes, upper stem leaves pinnate-ly divided; 4–5	Basal leaves with 1–3 pairs of lobes, upper-most stem leaves simple, fruits appress-ed to stem; 4–6	Basal leaves with 5–9 pairs of lobes, uppermost stem leaves simple, fruits upright; 4–7	Flowers white or reddish, 7–11 mm long, leaves with forked hairs; 4–6

**a Upright Rock-cress, *Arabis recta:* ☉,
10–40 cm; fruits scarcely thicker than their
stalks; 4–5; widespread. **b Night-scented
Rocket, *Hesperis tristis:* ☉, 30–60 cm; flowers purple-red or white, fruits curved; 5–6;
E and C Europe, a rare escape from cultiva-
tion. **c *Thale Cress, *Arabidopsis thaliana:* ☉,
6–30 cm; stem-leaves stalkless, fruits linear;
4–5; widespread. **d †Tumbling Mustard,
Sisymbrium altissimum: ☉, 25–100 cm; uppermost leaves divided into linear or thread-like
segments, flowers pale yellow, sepals spreading; 5–7; E and C Europe, naturalized elsewhere. All belong to the Crucifer Family and
occur in waste land, hedgerows and grassy
places, **c** also on walls and banks.

a †Rigid Rocket, *Sisymbrium strictissimum:* ♃, 50–200 cm; leaves entire or toothed, hairy beneath, fruits up to 6 cm; 6–8; C and E Europe. **b *Hedge Mustard,** *Sisymbrium officinale:* ⊙, 25–70 cm; fruits 10–15 mm, stiffly upright, appressed to axis; 5–10; widespread. **c †False London Rocket,** *Sisymbrium loeselii:* ⊙-⊙, 30–90 cm; fruits curved upwards, twice as long as their stalks; 6–7; E and C Europe. **d †London Rocket,** *Sisymbrium irio:* ⊙, 15–60 cm; fruits several times longer than their stalks, overtopping the flowers; 5–6; S Europe. All are members of the Crucifer Family, introduced and established in other parts of Europe, growing on waysides and in waste places.

The Common Treacle-mustard is widespread and common on arable and waste land and by waysides. The Hawkweed Treacle-mustard (E, C and N Europe), the Scented Treacle-mustard (C Europe) and the Hawksbeard Treacle-mustard (SE and C Europe) grow on dry and sunny hillocks and stony slopes, the Fallow Treacle-mustard (E, SE and C Europe) on walls and on arable and waste ground. The Wallflower in a native of the E Mediterranean region, widely cultivated and established as a garden escape. All belong to the Crucifer Family.

	†Common Treacle-mustard	Hawkweed Treacle-mustard	Scented Treacle-mustard	Fallow Treacle-mustard	Hawksbeard Treacle-mustard	†Wallflower
Scientific Name	*Erysimum cheiranthoides*	*Erysimum hieraciifolium*	*Erysimum odoratum*	*Erysimum repandum*	*Erysimum crepidifolium*	*Cheiranthus cheiri*
Longevity, Size	⊙, 10–120 cm	⊙, 25–125 cm	⊙-⊙,30–70 cm	⊙, 15–40 cm	⊙, 20–80 cm	⊙-♃,10–90cm
Distinguishing Features; Flowering Time	Hairs of the leaves predominantly 3-branched, fruits 12–27 mm long; 5–9	Hairs of the leaves as in previous species, fruits 4-angled, appressed to the axis; 6–8	Flowers sweet-scented, flower-stalks shorter than sepals, fruits 2–6 cm long, 4-angled; 6–7	Hairs of the leaves 2-branched, fruits 4.5–10 cm long, spreading horizontally; 4–7	Basal leaves in a rosette, fruits thicker than their stalks, stiff-hairy; 4–7	Flowers yellow or brownish, fragrant, fruits 2.6–6 cm long, hairy; 5–6

a †Small-fruited Camelina, *Camelina microcarpa:* ⊙, 10–80 cm; stems and leaves densely hairy, fruits 5–7 mm, with slightly convex valves; 5–7; S and C Europe. **b †Gold of Pleasure,** *Camelina sativa:* ⊙, 10–80 cm; stems and leaves usually glabrous, fruits 7–9 mm, with strongly convex valves; 5–7; E Europe. Both are members of the Crucifer Family, found as weeds in corn, flax and lucerne fields. **c Dyer's Rocket** or **Weld,** *Reseda luteola:* ⊙, 20–120 cm; flowers tetramerous; 6–8. **d Wild Mignonette,** *Reseda lutea:* ⊙-♃, 20–60 cm; flowers usually hexamerous; 6–8. Both belong to the Mignonette Family, and are widespread and locally common in arable and waste land.

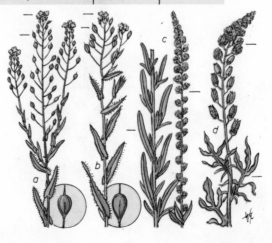

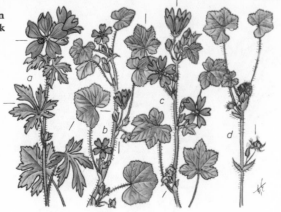

a *Musk Mallow, *Malva moschata*: ♃, 30–80 cm; leaves deeply divided into 5–7 palmate segments, flowers pink, rarely white; 6–11. **b** *Dwarf Mallow, *Malva neglecta*: ☉-♃, 7–70 cm; flowers 1.8–2.5 cm wide, fruit-stalks bent downwards; 5–11. **c** *Common Mallow, *Malva sylvestris*: ♃, 30–60 cm; flowers 2.5–4 cm wide, fruit-stalks upright; 6–11. **d** †Small Mallow, *Malva pusilla*: ☉, 15–50 cm; petals and calyx about the same length; 7–9. All belong to the Mallow Family and are widespread and usually common in waste land, grassy places, pastures, hedge-banks and by roadsides; **a**, **b** and **c** in most of Europe, **d** in C and N Europe.

The Hairy Violet and the Heartsease are widespread on cultivated and waste land, in grassy places, and open woodlands, the White Violet in hedges and thickets in mountain areas of S and C Europe; Violet Family. The Common St John's Wort is common throughout Europe, the Trailing St John's Wort in W and C Europe; both occur by waysides, at edges of cultivated fields, in grassland and open woods, the rare Elegant St John's Wort in dry, sunny places, pastures and hillocks in S, SE and C Europe; St John's Wort Family.

	*Hairy Violet	White Violet	*Heartsease	*Common St John's Wort	*Trailing St John's Wort	Elegant St John's Wort
Scientific Name	*Viola hirta*	*Viola alba*	*Viola tricolor*	*Hypericum perforatum*	*Hypericum humifusum*	*Hypericum elegans*
Longevity, Size	♃, 15–40 cm	♃, 10–40 cm	☉-♃, 10–45 cm	♃, 20–60 cm	♃, 2–30 cm	♃, 15–30 cm
Distinguishing Features; Flowering Time	Leaves long-stalked, regularly crenate at margins, flowers violet, blue or white; 3–4	Flowers white or violet, with yellowish spur, ovaries hairy; 3–4	Stipules pinnate, flowers yellow, violet or pink, or of these colours in combination; 5–10	Stem with 2 raised lines, leaves with translucent glandular dots, sepals entire; 6–8	Stem procumbent, 2-angled, hollow, sepals of unequal size, entire; 6–9	Stem 2-angled in the upper part, with black glands, leaves half-clasping the stem; 6–7

a Thuringian Mallow, *Lavatera thuringiaca*: ♃, 50–120 cm; flowers 5–8 cm wide; 7–10; uncommon, meadows and scrubland of SE and C Europe. **b** †Long-hairy Mallow, *Althaea hirsuta*: ☉-☉, 15–60 cm; flowers lilac, 2.5 cm wide; 7–9; arable and waste land, Mediterranean region and C Europe, naturalized elsewhere. Both belong to the Mallow Family. **c** Thymelea, *Thymelaea passerina*: ☉, 15–40 cm; flowers small; 7; dry hillocks, arable and waste land, Mediterranean region and C Europe; Daphne Family. **d** †Common Evening-primrose, *Oenothera biennis*: ☉, 40–100 cm; stem leaves blunt; 6–9; a native of N America, naturalized in many places, in sandy situations; Willow-herb Family.

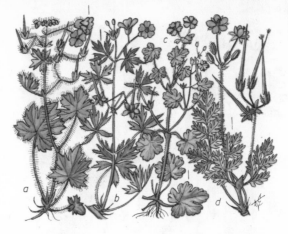

a *Dovesfoot Cranesbill, *Geranium molle:* ☉-☉, 5–40 cm; plant with dense long soft hairs, petals deeply notched, carpels glabrous, seeds smooth; 5–10. **b *Cut-leaved Cranesbill,** *Geranium dissectum:* ☉, 8–70 cm; carpels hairy, seeds pitted; 5–10. **c *Round-leaved Cranesbill,** *Geranium rotundifolium:* ☉, 6 to 40 cm; petals entire, carpels hairy, seeds pitted; 6–10. **d *Common Storksbill,** *Erodium cicutarium:* ☉, up to 60 cm; petals bright rosy purple, often with blackish spot at base, inflorescence umbel-like; 4–7. All belong to the Cranesbill Family, and are widespread and common in arable and waste land and by roadsides in most of Europe.

The Yellow Flax (Flax Family) occurs in meadows and open scrubland in E, SE and C Europe All the other plants below belong to the Carrot Family. The Upright Hedge-parsley is widespread, growing in hedges and grassy places and on roadsides; the other species are uncommon, growing on arable and waste land, in vineyards and dry meadows, the Spreading Hedge-parsley in S, W and C Europe, the Great Bur-parsley and the Orlaya in S and C Europe, the Small Bur-parsley in most regions.

	Yellow Flax	*Upright Hedge-parsley	*Spreading Hedge-parsley	†Great Bur-parsley	†Small Bur-parsley	Orlaya
Scientific Name	*Linum flavum*	*Torilis japonica*	*Torilis arvensis*	*Turgenia latifolia*	*Caucalis platycarpos*	*Orlaya grandiflora*
Longevity, Size	⍉, 20–60 cm	☉, to 130 cm	☉, 30–90 cm	☉, 10–60 cm	☉, 8–30 cm	☉, up to 1m
Distinguishing Features; Flowering Time	Stem angled in the upper part, glabrous, flowers yellow, in a cymose inflorescence; 6–7	Bracts 5 or more, fruits with hooked spines; 6–8	Bracts 1 or absent, fruits with curved but not hooked spines; 7–8	Leaves simply pinnate, petals bifid, unequal, white, red or reddish brown; 5–7	Leaves 2–3-pinnate, petals deeply notched, flowers white or reddish; 5–7	Leaves 2–3-pinnate, outer flowers with petals 5–8 mm long; 7–8

a *Hemlock, *Conium maculatum:* ☉-☉, 50–200 cm; with a smell of mice, stem furrowed, purple-spotted; poisonous; 6–9; widespread. **b †Longleaf,** *Falcaria vulgaris:* ⍉, 25–80 cm; leaves 1–2-ternate, segments narrow, sickle-shaped; 7–10; C and S Europe. **c *Caraway,** *Carum carvi:* ☉, up to 100 cm; leaves 2–3-pinnatisect, lower pair of segments of partial leaflet appressed to primary axis of leaf, fruits strongly scented; 4–7; widespread. **d *Field Eryngo,** *Eryngium campestre:* ⍉, 10–90 cm; heads yellowish, almost spherical, leaves, bracts and bracteoles spiny; 7–9; S, W and C Europe. All belong to the Carrot Family; arable and waste land, dry grassy places, waysides.

a *Rough Chervil, *Chaerophyllum temulentum:* ⊙-⊙, 30–120 cm; root elongate, stem red-spotted, with stiff hairs, bracteoles hairy; 6–7. **b Tuberous-rooted Chervil**, *Chaerophyllum bulbosum:* ⊙-♃, 50–200 cm; root tuberous, stem glabrous or with scattered hairs on leaf-bases, bracteoles glabrous; 6–8. **c *Bur Chervil**, *Anthriscus caucalis:* ⊙, 50–100 cm; fruit with spine-like bristles, flowers small; 5–6. **d *Cow Parsley**, *Anthriscus sylvestris:* ⊙, 15–150 cm; umbels 7–15-rayed, fruit smooth or with bristly tubercles, very shortly beaked; 4–8. All are members of the Carrot Family, widespread in waste and grassy places, by hedgerows and at edges of woods.

The Fool's Parsley and the Wild Parsnip are widespread and common, the former as a weed of cultivated ground, the latter on roadsides and in grassy and waste places. The Knotted Hedge-parsley occurs on dry banks and arable land in S and W Europe, the Great Hartwort in hedgerows, on roadsides and river-banks, and on arable and waste land in S and SC Europe. The Horse-fennel (uncommon, SE and C Europe) and the Moon Carrot (widespread but local, most of Europe) occur on dry hillocks and in open scrubland. All belong to the Carrot Family.

	*Knotted Hedge-parsley	*Fool's Parsley	*Wild Parsnip	†Great Hartwort	Horse-fennel	*Moon Carrot
Scientific Name	*Torilis nodosa*	*Aethusa cynapium*	*Pastinaca sativa*	*Tordylium maximum*	*Seseli hippomarathrum*	*Seseli sibirica*
Longevity, Size	⊙, 10–35 cm	⊙, 7–125 cm	⊙, 30–100 cm	⊙, 30–120 cm	♃, 30–90 cm	♃, 30–120 cm
Distinguishing Features; Flowering Time	Umbels nearly stalkless, outer fruits with straight spreading spines, inner tuberculed; 4–9	Leaves ternately 2-pinnate, bracteoles 3, on outer side of partial umbels, deflexed; poisonous; 6–10	Umbels with 8–12 rays of unequal length, stem furrowed; smelling of carrot; 7–8	Stem ridged, hollow, rays thick, 5–15, bristly, fruits with thickened border, bristly; 6–8	Basal leaves multi-pinnatifid, bracteoles fused, forming cup; 7–8	Stem somewhat ridged, calyx-teeth long, subulate; 7–9

a *Shepherd's Needle, *Scandix pectenveneris:* ⊙, 8–50 cm; umbels with 1–3 rays, fruit subcylindric with a very long beak up to 6 times as long as the fruit; 5–6; widespread but local, in arable land. **b *Thorowwax**, *Bupleurum rotundifolium:* ⊙, 10–50 cm; upper leaves perfoliate, bracts absent; 6–7; local, in cornfields, mainly in S and C Europe. **c *Sickle Hare's-ear**, *Bupleurum falcatum:* ♃, 30–100 cm; stem leaves tapering at the base, lower leaves stalked, bracts 2–5; 7–10; on waste land and hedgebanks in scattered localities throughout Europe. All belong to the Carrot Family.

a †**False Bishop's Weed,** *Ammi majus:* ☉, 20–100 cm; stem leaves 2–3-pinnatisect, bracts 3-lobed or pinnatisect; 6–10; a native of S Europe, introduced elsewhere. b *****Great Earth-nut,** *Bunium bulbocastanum:* ♃, 30 to 100 cm; stem with a thick globose underground tuber at the base; 6–7; C and W Europe. c *****Honewort,** *Trinia glauca:* ♃, up to 50 cm; dioecious, glaucous, glabrous, root with fibrous remains of stalks at the top, basal leaves 2–3-pinnatisect, ♂ umbels with rays of unequal length, flat-topped, ♀ with rays of unequal length. All are rare members of the Carrot Family growing in cultivated fields, pastureland and dry short grassland.

The Roman Nettle is a native of S Europe, found as a casual elsewhere. The Small Nettle and the Stinging Nettle are widespread and common, mainly on cultivated or waste land and near buildings. Both Pellitories-of-the-wall occur in cracks of old walls and rocks and in waste places, the former widely distributed but local, the latter common in S Europe, rare in C Europe All belong to the Nettle Family. The Annual Mercury (Spurge Family) grows in waste places and as a garden weed in most of Europe.

	†Roman Nettle	*Small Nettle	*Stinging Nettle	*Upright Pellitory-of-the-wall	Branched Pellitory-of-the-wall	*Annual Mercury
Scientific Name	*Urtica pilulifera*	*Urtica urens*	*Urtica dioica*	*Parietaria diffusa*	*Parietaria ramiflora*	*Mercurialis annua*
Longevity, Size	☉, up to 80 cm	☉, 30–60 cm	♃, 30–125 cm	♃, 30–90 cm	♃, up to 70 cm	☉, 10–80 cm
Distinguishing Features; Flowering Time	Leaves coarsely serrate, ♀ flowers in long-stalked, spherical heads; 6–10	Lower leaves shorter than their stalks, plant monoecious; 5–11	Lower leaves longer than their stalks, plant dioecious; 6–10	Stem simple, short-hairy, leaves large, oblong, shining; 6–9	Stem branched, decumbent, leaves small, ovate; 5–10	Stem bluntly 4-angled, branched, flowers dioecious, in many-flowered spikes; 5–10

a *****Sun Spurge,** *Euphorbia helioscopia:* ☉, 5–40 cm; leaves and bracts very blunt, upper stem leaves larger than lower; 4–11. b †**Cypress Spurge,** *Euphorbia cyparissias:* ♃, 10 to 50 cm; with long-creeping rhizome, leaves narrowly linear, 1–3 mm wide; 4–7. c *****Broad Spurge,** *Euphorbia platyphyllos:* ☉, 20–60 cm; leaves deeply heart-shaped at the base, often hairy beneath, smelling of mice; 6–9. All are members of the Spurge Family, and are widespread in most of Europe, growing mainly as weeds in gardens, cultivated fields and waste land, often as garden escapes.

a **Dwarf Spurge*, *Euphorbia exigua*: ☉, 3–30 cm; leaves linear, stalkless, glaucous, up to 4 mm wide, with pointed tips; 5–11. **b** **Sickle Spurge**, *Euphorbia falcata*: ☉, 8–40 cm; leaves lanceolate, up to 5 mm wide; 6–10. **c** **Petty Spurge*, *Euphorbia peplus*: ☉, 10–30 cm; leaves ovate-orbicular, stalked, green, fruit a winged capsule; 6–11. All are members of the Spurge Family, growing as weeds in gardens and cultivated fields and on waste ground; the first two species are widespread and common throughout Europe, the last is an uncommon plant of S and C Europe.

The members of the Dock Family shown below are widespread and common or local throughout Europe. The Redleg and Pale Persicaria grow on cultivated and waste land, and beside ponds and ditches; the Knotgrass on roadsides, between paving stones and in waste places; the Black Bindweed on arable and waste land, and in gardens; the Copse Bindweed, which is rarer, in thickets and damp hedgerows. The Tartarian Buckwheat, a native of C Asia which has been introduced, is found as a weed on arable and waste land.

	*Redleg	**Pale Persicaria*	**Knotgrass*	**Black Bindweed*	**Copse Bindweed*	**Tartarian Buckwheat**
Scientific Name	*Polygonum persicaria*	*Polygonum lapathifolium*	*Polygonum aviculare*	*Polygonum convolvulus*	*Polygonum dumetorum*	*Fagopyrum tataricum*
Longevity, Size	☉, 15–100 cm	☉, 30–120 cm	☉, 5–100 cm	☉, up to 100 cm	☉, up to 200 cm	☉, 25–75 cm
Distinguishing Features; Flowering Time	Leaves with a dark spot, ochreae with long hairs, perianth-segments and flower-stalks glandless; 7–10	Only uppermost ochreae with few short hairs, perianth-segments and flower-stalks glandular; 7–10	Stem branched, usually prostrate, ochreae silver, irregularly cleft, flowers in leaf-axils; 5–9	Stem slender, angled, twining, flower-stalks in fruit 1–2 mm, jointed above the middle; 7–10	Similar to previous, flower-stalks jointed below middle, outer perianth-segments wide-winged; 7–9	Leaves triangular, usually wider than long, flowers greenish; 7–8

a **Fiddle Dock*, *Rumex pulcher*: ☉, 20 to 80 cm; leaves fiddle-shaped; 5–7; usually on sandy soils in S and W Europe. **b** **Broad Dock*, *Rumex obtusifolius*: ♃, 60–150 cm; basal leaves large, blunt, heart-shaped at base, hairy on veins beneath; 6–8; widespread and common, waste ground, hedgerows and margins of fields. **c** *†French Sorrel*, *Rumex scutatus*: ♃, 10–50 cm; leaves about as long as broad, the upper stalked; 5–6; S and C Europe. All belong to the Dock Family. **d** *†Feather Pink*, *Dianthus plumarius*: ♃, 30–60 cm; petals white or pink, cut almost to the middle; 4–7; calcareous mountains of EC Europe, naturalized elsewhere; Pink Family.

a *Fine-leaved Sandwort, *Minuartia hybrida:* ☉, 3–16 cm; plant loosely tufted, sepals equalling capsule; 5–7. b *Small Thyme-leaved Sandwort, *Arenaria leptoclados:* ☉, 2–20 cm; stem upright, leaves stalkless, sepals often slightly longer than the straight-sided fruit; 5–10. c *Childling Pink, *Petrorhagia prolifera:* ☉, 10–50 cm; flower-heads in involucre of membranous bracts; 6–10. d †Cow Basil, *Vaccaria pyramidata:* ☉, 20–70 cm; stem branched, inflorescence much-branched; 6. All belong to the Pink Family; a and b widespread, common, c and d local, uncommon, in arable and waste land, on walls, sunny hillocks and cliffs.

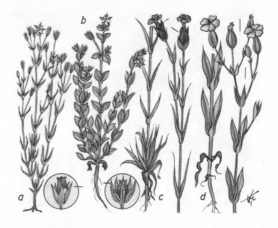

The Corn Cockle is widespread, but local, growing in cornfields. The Campions are widespread and common in cultivated fields, by waysides and in scrubland, the Red Campion being also found in meadows and clearings. The Soapwort is common in waste land, on roadsides and banks. The Sticky Sandwort occurs locally in cultivated fields and dry places in SE and C Europe. All these plants are members of the Pink Family.

	*Corn Cockle	*White Campion	*Red Campion	*Night-scented Campion	*Soapwort	Sticky Sandwort
Scientific Name	Agrostemma githago	Silene alba	Silene dioica	Silene noctiflora	Saponaria officinalis	Minuartia viscosa
Longevity, Size	☉, up to 70 cm	☉, 25–70 cm	♃, 30–60 cm	☉, 15–30 cm	♃, 15–70 cm	☉, 3–16 cm
Distinguishing Features; Flowering Time	Leaves with appressed white hairs, flowers large, solitary, petals purple; poisonous; 6–9	Stem with soft hairs, glandular-sticky above, flowers dioecious, capsule-teeth upright; 6–9	Stem with soft hairs, flowers red, dioecious, capsule-teeth rolled back; 4–9	Stem glandular, sticky, inflorescence forked, flowers hermaphrodite; 7–9	Leaves broadly ovate to elliptic, 5–20 mm wide, flowers flesh-coloured, in terminal corymbs; 6–9	Stem glandular-hairy, branched at the base, many-flowered, flowers white; 5–8

a *Common Chickweed, *Stellaria media:* ☉, 5–40 cm; stem terete, with single row of hairs; 3–10; a weed of arable and waste land. b *Greater Stitchwort, *Stellaria holostea:* ♃, 15–35 cm; stem 4-angled, petals cut to the middle; 4–6; woods and hedgerows. c *Lesser Stitchwort, *Stellaria graminea:* ♃, 8–40 cm; leaves fringed at base, corolla as long as calyx; 5–7; woods, heaths and grassland. d *Dwarf Chickweed, *Moenchia erecta:* ☉, 3–10 cm; flowers usually tetramerous; 4–5; in pastures, sandy and gravelly turf, and on cliffs and dunes near the sea. All are members of the Pink Family, widespread and common throughout Europe, except d which is an uncommon plant of S and C Europe.

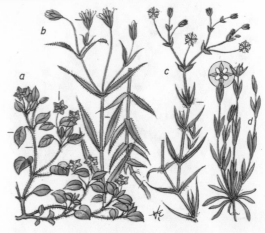

a *Sticky Mouse-ear, *Cerastium glomeratum:* ⊙-⊝, 5–25 cm; leaves yellowish green, with pointed tips; 3–9; widespread, common. **b *Smooth Rupture-wort,** *Herniaria glabra:* ♃, 5–30 cm; plant glabrous, with numerous prostrate shoots, calyx glabrous; 5–8; widespread, but local. **c †Hairy Rupture-wort,** *Herniaria hirsuta:* ♃, 5–20 cm; plant with dense hairs, calyx with spreading hairs; 7–9; mainly S and C Europe. **d Clustered Gypsophila,** *Gypsophila fastigiata:* ♃, 15 to 50 cm; stem sticky above; 6–8; SE and C Europe. All belong to the Pink Family and grow in sandy fields and short grassland, **d** also in sandy pine woods and on sunny hillocks.

The Catchflies occur in scattered localities in Europe, in cultivated fields and dry places, the Sweet William Catchfly in C, S and E Europe, widely naturalized elsewhere, the Small-flowered Catchfly in S and C Europe, and the Forked Catchfly in E and SE Europe, naturalized in many countries. The Corn Spurrey and the Red Spurrey are widespread and frequent in sandy cultivated fields, stony pastureland and waste land. The Field Spurrey is a rare cornfield weed. All belong to the Pink Family.

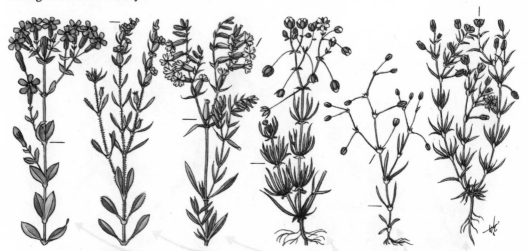

	†Sweet William Catchfly	*Small-flowered Catchfly	†Forked Catchfly	*Corn Spurrey	Field Spurrey	*Red Spurrey
Scientific Name	*Silene armeria*	*Silene gallica*	*Silene dichotoma*	*Spergula arvensis*	*Spergularia segetalis*	*Spergularia rubra*
Longevity, Size	⊙-⊝,10–60 cm	⊙, 10–45 cm	⊙, 20–100 cm	⊙, 10–30 cm	⊙, 2–10 cm	⊙, 3–30 cm
Distinguishing Features; Flowering Time	Stem slightly sticky above, upper leaves clasping the stem; 5–10	Flowers one-sided, in raceme-like monoaxial cymes, petals entire or notched; 6–8	Inflorescence forked, petals usually white, deeply bifid; 7–8	Leaves opposite, with axillary clusters of leaves, furrowed beneath, seeds narrowly winged; 6–10	Stem erect, leaves opposite, petals white, sepals with a short narrow point at tip; 6–7	Stem branched at the base, decumbent, petals rose-red, sepals without point at tip; 5–9

a *Mossy Pearlwort, *Sagina procumbens:* ♃, 2–5 cm; stem thread-like, sepals ovate; 5–9; a widespread and common member of the Pink Family, growing in grassy places on paths, banks and stream-sides. **b Hairy Summer Cypress,** *Kochia laniflora:* ⊙, 15–40 cm; perianth with 5 appendages; 8–10. **c Field Polycnemum,** *Polycnemum arvense:* ⊙, 2–30 cm; bracts as long as the perianth; 7–10. **d Great Polycnemum,** *Polycnemum majus:* ⊙, 10–20 cm; bracts longer than the perianth; 2–7. All belong to the Goosefoot Family and occur in S and C Europe, growing on sandy fields and hillocks, and in pastures.

a Sticky Goosefoot, *Chenopodium botrys:* ⊙, 15–60 cm; leaves and stem glandular-hairy, fragrant; 7–8. **b †Good King Henry,** *Chenopodium bonus-henricus:* ♃, 15–60 cm; inflorescence mostly terminal, narrow, leafless above; 4–10. **c *Stinking Goosefoot,** *Chenopodium vulvaria:* ⊙-⊙, 15–40 cm; plant mealy, inflorescences terminal or axillary, small, leafy; smelling of decaying fish; 5–9. **d *Many-seeded Goosefoot,** *Chenopodium polyspermum:* ⊙, 15–60 cm; leaves usually entire, inflorescence long, loose, with many axillary branched cymes; 8–9. All belong to the Goosefoot Family and grow in waste land; **a** in S and C Europe, **b**, **c** and **d** widespread in most of Europe.

All the members of the Goosefoot Family shown below are widespread and common or frequent in most of Europe, growing on waste ground, rubbish-dumps, barn-yards and in cultivated fields. The Oak-leaved Goosefoot is absent from the extreme north and from islands, and the Sowbane and the Red Goosefoot are rare in the Mediterranean region.

	†Upright Goosefoot	†Oak-leaved Goosefoot	†Sowbane	*Red Goosefoot	*Nettle-leaved Goosefoot	†Grey Goosefoot
Scientific Name	*Chenopodium urbicum*	*Chenopodium glaucum*	*Chenopodium hybridum*	*Chenopodium rubrum*	*Chenopodium murale*	*Chenopodium opulifolium*
Longevity, Size	⊙, 50–100 cm	⊙, 10–60 cm	⊙, 30–100 cm	⊙, 15–90 cm	⊙, 15–60 cm	⊙, 30–100 cm
Distinguishing Features; Flowering Time	Leaves with shallowly toothed margins, inflorescences axillary and terminal, upright; 7–9	Leaves sinuate, mealy-glaucous beneath, green above, inflorescences axillary and terminal; 7–10	Basal leaves heart-shaped at base, with large teeth, inflorescence cymose, often loose; 5–8	Leaves serrate-lobed to entire, inflorescence dense, leafy, with crowded small cymes; 7–9	Leaves coarsely toothed, inflorescences terminal and axillary, loose, leafy; 6–10	Leaves serrate-lobed to entire, inflorescence dense, leafy, with crowded small cymes; 7–9

a *Halberd-leaved Orache, *Atriplex hastata:* ⊙, up to 100 cm; fruit-bracteoles with short teeth on both sides; 6–9; widespread and common. **b Shining Orache,** *Atriplex nitens:* ⊙, up to 150 cm; leaves white beneath, fruit-bracteoles oblong-heart-shaped, net-veined; 7–9; E and C Europe. **c Long-leaved Orache,** *Atriplex oblongifolia:* ⊙, 30–90 cm; fruit-bracteoles entire, without teeth; 7–9; E, SE and C Europe. **d *Common Orache,** *Atriplex patula:* ⊙, 30–90 cm; fruit-bracteoles hastate; 7–10; widespread and common. All are members of the Goosefoot Family, growing in waste land, on rubbish-dumps, by roadsides and paths.

a **Fat Hen,* *Chenopodium album:* ☉, 20 to
150 cm; lower leaves shallowly toothed, the
upper entire, thin, glaucous; 7–10. **b** **Fig-
leaved Goosefoot,* *Chenopodium ficifolium:*
☉, 30–90 cm; middle lobe of leaves oblong,
coarsely toothed; 7–9. Both belong to the
Goosefoot Family, and are widespread and
common in most of Europe. **c** *†Common
Pigweed,* *Amaranthus retroflexus:* ☉, 3 to
100 cm, stem hairy, leaves rhombic-ovate,
flowers in conical spikes; 6–9. **d** *†Green
Pigweed,* *Amaranthus lividus:* ☉, 10–30 cm;
stem glabrous, leaves notched; 7–9. Both are
N American natives of the Amaranth Family,
naturalized throughout Europe, growing in
arable and waste land.

The Long-stalked Rock-jasmine (Primrose Family) grows in fields and pastures of E and C
Europe. The other plants below belong to the Bindweed Family, and are widespread throughout
most of Europe; the Field Bindweed as a common weed on cultivated and waste land, the
Great Bindweed in gardens, hedges and at edges of woods. The Dodders are parasitic on other
plants, the Flax Dodder on the Common Flax, the Common Dodder on furzes, Heather and
Thyme, the Greater Dodder on the Stinging Nettle and Hop.

	*Field Bindweed	***Great Bindweed**	**†Flax Dodder**	***Common Dodder**	***Greater Dodder**	**Long-stalked Rock-jasmine**
Scientific Name	*Convolvulus arvensis*	*Calystegia sepium*	*Cuscuta epilinum*	*Cuscuta epithymum*	*Cuscuta europaea*	*Androsace elongata*
Longevity, Size	♃, 20–75 cm	♃, 10–30 cm	☉	☉	☉	☉, 2–5 cm
Distinguishing Features; Flowering Time	Scrambling or climbing, leaves hastate, bracteoles small, distant from the calyx; 6–10	Climbing, flowers very large, with 2 large bracteoles, overlapping the calyx; 7–10	Stem twisting, flowers yellowish white, in dense clusters, corolla-tube inflated; 6–8	Stem twisting, scales in the throat of the corolla-tube large, closing tube, stamens exserted; 7–9	Stem twisting, scales in throat of corolla-tube small, not closing it, stamens included; 6–9	Corolla white with a yellow throat, calyx with star-like hairs, longer than corolla; 4–5

a Northern Rock-jasmine, *Androsace sep-
tentrionalis:* ☉, 5–15 cm; calyx glabrous,
shorter than corolla; 5–6; mainly in C and
N Europe. **b Great Rock-jasmine,** *Androsace maxima:* ♃, 2–10 cm; scape with simple
hairs, bracts leaf-like, longer than flower-
stalks, corolla white or reddish; 4; S and C
Europe. **c *Scarlet Pimpernel,** *Anagallis
arvensis:* ☉, 5–60 cm; corolla lobes fringed
with short hairs, red or blue; 6–10; widespread, common. **d *Chaffweed,** *Anagallis
minima:* ☉, 1–10 cm; flowers inconspicuous,
white or reddish, leaves with short point; 6–9;
widespread but local. All belong to the Primrose Family and grow mainly in cultivated and
waste land and pastures.

a **Small-flowered Navel-wort**, *Omphalodes
scorpioides*: ⊙, 10–30 cm; flowers blue,
throat-scales yellow; 4–6; woods, scrubland
and waste land of S and C Europe. b †**German Madwort**, *Asperugo procumbens*: ⊙,
20–70 cm; fruit-stalks recurved; 5–8; widespread but rare, in waste places and arable
land. c **Common Heliotrope**, *Heliotropium
europaeum*: ⊙, 20–30 cm; leaves soft-hairy,
flowers whitish, 2–4 mm wide; 7–9; a native
of S Europe, naturalized or casual elsewhere.
d †**Common Stitchseed**, *Lappula myosotis*:
⊙, 10–80 cm; stem weak, nutlets with hooked
spines on winged edges; 6–7; widespread, but
local, in dry waste and arable land. All belong
to the Borage Family.

The True Alkanet, the Hound's-tongue, the Small Bugloss and the Viper's Bugloss are widespread and locally common in arable and waste places, short grasslands, and on roadsides; the
Italian Alkanet, a native of the Mediterranean region, naturalized or a casual elsewhere, grows
on similar sites. The Wrinklenut, a S European plant, naturalized or a casual in C Europe,
grows at edges of fields or by roadsides. All belong to the Borage Family.

	†True Alkanet	Italian Alkanet	*Hound's-tongue	*Small Bugloss	*Viper's Bugloss	Wrinklenut
Scientific Name	*Anchusa officinalis*	*Anchusa italica*	*Cynoglossum officinale*	*Lycopsis arvensis*	*Echium vulgare*	*Nonnea pulla*
Longevity, Size	⊙, 20–100 cm	⊙, 40–60 cm	⊙, 40–100 cm	⊙-♃, 20–60 cm	⊙, 25–120 cm	♃, 12–40 cm
Distinguishing Features; Flowering Time	Upper leaves clasping stem, flowers red, later violet, in compound scorpioidal cymes; 5–9	Flowers sky-blue, only the lower flower-stalks with bracts; 5–9	Leaves thin, silky-hairy on both surfaces, corolla brown-ish red, rarely white; smelling of mice; 5–6	Plant bristly, leaves with undulate margins, flowers with white throat-scales; 5–10	Leaves long and narrow, corolla blue, rarely pink or white, about 15 mm long; 6–9	Leaves soft-hairy, entire, flowers dark reddish brown, rarely yellow, red or white; 5–8

a *****Changing Forgetmenot**, *Myosotis discolor*: ⊙, 8–30 cm; flowers yellow or white,
becoming blue and dark brown, corolla tube
twice length of calyx; 2–6. b *****Field Forgetmenot**, *Myosotis arvensis*: ⊙, 15–70 cm;
fruit-stalks as long as or longer than calyx;
5–7; c **Early Forgetmenot**, *Myosotis ramo-
sissima*: ⊙, 3–30 cm; fruit-stalks shorter than
calyx; 4–5. d *****Corn Cromwell**, *Lithospermum arvense*: ⊙, 10–30 cm; leaves faintly
veined, fruits wrinkled; 4–7. e *****Common
Cromwell**, *Lithospermum officinale*: ♃, 30 to
100 cm; leaves prominently veined, fruits
glabrous; 5–7; hedges and bushy places. All
belong to the Borage Family; widespread,
common, except **e**, in fields and by roads.

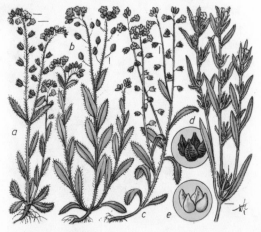

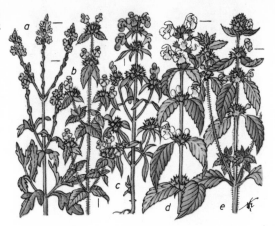

a *Vervain, *Verbena officinalis:* ☉, 30 to 100 cm; flowers small, in slender terminal spikes; 7–10; widespread and local, waysides and waste places, in most of Europe; Vervain Family. **b** †Red Hemp-nettle, *Galeopsis ladanum:* ☉, 5–70 cm; leaves 7–15 mm wide, 3–8 teeth on each side; 6–10. **c** *Narrow-leaved Hemp-nettle, *Galeopsis angustifolia:* ☉, 10–80 cm; leaves 2–5 mm wide, 1–4 teeth on each side; 6–10. **d** *Downy Hemp-nettle, *Galeopsis segetum:* ☉, 10–120 cm; corolla large, yellowish white; 7–8. **e** *Common Hemp-nettle, *Galeopsis tetrahit:* ☉, 20 to 150 cm; stem bristly, swollen at nodes, corolla purple; 7–10. All belong to the Thyme Family, common in arable and waste land.

The members of the Thyme Family illustrated below are generally found at the edges of cultivated fields, on village greens, by waysides and in hedgerows, sometimes also on dry turf. The Ground Ivy is widespread and common. The Large Hemp-nettle, the White Horehound and the Wild Cat-mint grow is scattered localities in most of Europe. The germanders are rare or uncommon plants of S and C Europe, growing mainly on calcareous ground; the Wall Germander also inhabits stony slopes and open scrubland.

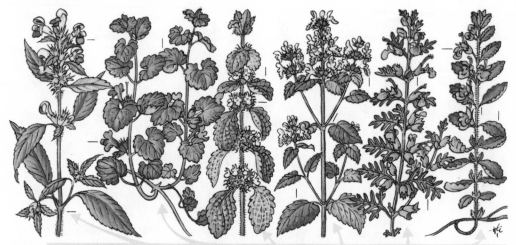

	*Large Hemp-nettle	*Ground Ivy	*White Horehound	*Wild Cat-mint	*Cut-leaved Germander	†Wall Germander
Scientific Name	*Galeopsis speciosa*	*Glechoma hederacea*	*Marrubium vulgare*	*Nepeta cataria*	*Teucrium botrys*	*Teucrium chamaedrys*
Longevity, Size	☉, up to 100 cm	♃, 2–15 cm	♃, 25–60 cm	♃, 10–100 cm	☉, 5–40 cm	♃, 10–40 cm
Distinguishing Features; Flowering Time	Corolla pale yellow, with a purple spot on lower lip, tube much longer than the calyx; 6–10	Leaves kidney-shaped, crenate, flowers bluish violet, in whorls in axils of leafy bracts; 4–6	Leaves orbicular, crenate, flowers white, hairy, calyx with 10 hooked teeth; 6–8	Leaves ovate, long-stalked, lower lip with red spots; fragrant; 6–11	Leaves pinnatifid, calyx waisted, pouched behind; unpleasant smell; 7–9	Leaves short-stalked, crenate, flowers purple, one-sided spike-like inflorescence; 7–9

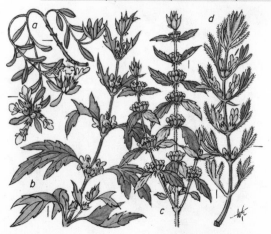

a Mountain Germander, *Teucrium montanum:* ♃, 5–40 cm; flowers in semi-spherical heads; 6–8; S and C Europe. **b** †Common Motherwort, *Leonurus cardiaca:* ♃, 30 to 100 cm; lower leaves palmately 3–7-lobed, lobes irregularly toothed; 6–9; scattered localities in most of Europe. **c** Biennial Motherwort, *Leonurus marrubiastrum:* ☉, 15 to 150 cm; leaves greyish-downy beneath; 7–8; SE and C Europe. **d** *Ground-pine, *Ajuga chamaepitys:* ☉, 4–50 cm; leaves deeply trifid, flowers yellow, solitary; 5–9; S and C Europe. All belong to the Thyme Family and grow mainly in cultivated fields, hedgerows, waste places and in open habitats in grassland.

a *Field Woundwort, *Stachys arvenis:* ☉,
5–70 cm; flowers pale red, with darker dots,
6 in each whorl, corolla longer than calyx;
6–10. b †Annual Woundwort, *Stachys
annua:* ☉-☉, 10–30 cm; flowers yellowish
white, spiny tips of calyx-teeth hairy; 6–10.
c †Upright Woundwort, *Stachys recta:* ♃,
20–40 cm; flowers pale yellow, 3–5 in each
whorl, spiny tips of calyx-teeth glabrous;
6–10. d *Downy Woundwort, *Stachys germanica:* ☉, rarely ☉ or ♃, 30–150 cm; plant
densely whitish-downy; 7–8. All belong to
the Thyme Family; a (widespread, locally
common) and b (S and C Europe) in
cultivated and waste land; c and d in dry
grassland, pasture, waste land, S and C Europe.

The Yellow Archangel (sometimes put into a separate genus) is common in woodlands; the
White Dead-nettle in hedgebanks, waste places and by roadsides; the Spotted Dead-nettle in
woodlands, hedgebanks, waste places and on river-banks and walls. The remaining species
inhabit cultivated and waste ground; the Henbit Dead-nettle and the Red Dead-nettle are common, but the Cut-leaved Dead-nettle, thought to be a hybrid between the Henbit Dead-nettle
and the Red Dead-nettle, is rare. All are widespread; Thyme Family.

	*Yellow Archangel	*White Dead-nettle	†Spotted Dead-nettle	*Henbit Dead-nettle	*Red Dead-nettle	*Cut-leaved Dead-nettle
Scientific Name	*Lamium galeobdolon*	*Lamium album*	*Lamium maculatum*	*Lamium amplexicaule*	*Lamium purpureum*	*Lamium hybridum*
Longevity, Size	♃, 10–60 cm	♃, 15–80 cm	♃, 20–130 cm	☉, 8–50 cm	☉, 5–40 cm	☉, 5–50 cm
Distinguishing Features; Flowering Time	Flowers golden yellow, lower lip of corolla 3-lobed, with well-developed lateral lobes; 5–6	Flowers white, corolla-tube slightly curved, with an oblique ring of hairs; 4–10	Flowers large, corolla-tube with transverse ring of hairs, lower corolla-lip dark-spotted; 3–10	Upper bracts stalkless, un-like leaves, corolla-tube long-exserted, glabrous within; 3–5	Bracts stalked, resembling the leaves, corolla-tube with con-spicuous ring of hairs; 3–5	Bracts stalked, resembling the leaves, corolla-tube without or with a faint ring of hairs; 3–8

a *Black Horehound, *Ballota nigra:* ♃,
50–100 cm; soft-hairy, with unpleasant smell;
4–7; widespread and common by roadsides
and on hedgebanks. b *Basil-thyme, *Acinos
arvensis:* ☉-♃, 5–60 cm; aromatic, flowers
bluish violet, up to 10 mm long; 6–9; widespread but local, arable fields, short grassland,
rocks. c *Corn Mint, *Mentha arvensis:* ♃,
10–45 cm; upper leaves clustered, flowers lilac,
in distant axillary whorls; 7–9; widespread and
common in arable fields, woods and by ponds.
d †Hyssop, *Hyssopus officinalis:* ♃, 50 to
150 cm; woody, aromatic, leaves linear-
lanceolate; 7–8; a native of S Europe, cultivated and naturalized in other parts. All
belong to the Thyme Family.

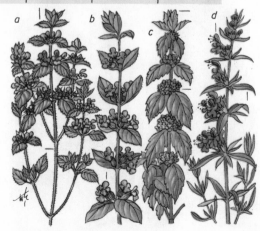

a †Ivy-leaved Toadflax, *Cymbalaria muralis:* ♃, 10–80 cm; flowers blue, with two yellow spots on palate; 6–8; a native of S Europe, naturalized in C and N Europe, common on old walls. **b *Sharp-leaved Fluellen,** *Kickxia elatine:* ☉, 10–40 cm; upper leaves hastate; 7–9; widespread, but usually local. **c *Round-leaved Fluellen,** *Kickxia spuria:* ☉, 3 to 50 cm; decumbent, flower-stalks woolly; 7–9; widespread, but rather local. **d Daisy-leaved Snapdragon,** *Anarrhinum bellidifolium:* ☉-♃, up to 70 cm; flowers pale violet, in racemes; 7; Mediterranean region, rare in C Europe. All belong to the Figwort Family; **b, c** and **d** grow in cultivated fields on light soils.

The Deadly Nightshade and the Winter-cherry grow in woods and thickets in S and C Europe, sometimes being found on waste ground. All the other species shown below grow in waste places, on rubbish-dumps, by roadsides and in sandy situations. The Black Nightshade is widespread and common. The Henbane and the Thorn-apple are less common, and sometimes very local and rare. The Yellow Nightshade is found in scattered localities in S and SC Europe. All belong to the Nightshade Family.

	*Deadly Nightshade	*Henbane	†Winter-cherry	*Black Nightshade	Yellow Nightshade	†Thorn-apple
Scientific Name	Atropa bella-donna	Hyoscyamus niger	Physalis alkekengi	Solanum nigrum	Solanum luteum	Datura stramonium
Longevity, Size	♃, 60–125 cm	☉-☉,30–80 cm	♃, 30–60 cm	☉, 30–70 cm	☉, 7–50 cm	☉, 30–150 cm
Distinguishing Features; Flowering Time	Leaves entire, flowers bell-shaped,stalked, nodding, berries black; very poisonous; 6–8	Leaves sinuate-coarsely toothed, flowers pale yellow, with violet veins; poison; 6–10	Leaves ovate, flowers whit-ish, nodding, calyx later orange-red; 5–8	Leaves ovate or rhombic, flowers white, berries black; 6–10	Plant woolly, flowers white, berries yellow, rarely red; 7–10	Leaves sinuate, flowers solit-ary, white, up to 7 mm, capsule with long sharp spines; 6–10

a Field Toadflax, *Linaria arvensis:* ☉, 15 to 20 cm; flowers pale blue, about 7 mm long; 6–10; S, SE, C and W Europe. **b *Toadflax,** *Linaria vulgaris:* ♃, 15–90 cm; flowers yellow with an orange-red palate, up to 33 mm long; 6–9; widespread and common. **c *Lesser Snapdragon,** *Misopates orontium:* ☉, 20 to 80 cm; leaves lanceolate, flowers usually pale red; 6–11; widespread, but local. **d *Small Toadflax,** *Chaenorhinum minus:* ☉, 5–60 cm; flowers with a spur about 9 mm long, in loose racemes; 6–9; widespread and common. All are common members of the Figwort Family, found in cultivated fields, by roadsides and on waste ground.

a *Field Cow-wheat, *Melampyrum arvense:* ⊙, 15–50 cm; bracts purple, lanceolate, pinnatifid, with long slender teeth; 6–9; widespread, but local and rare; Figwort Family.
b †Branched Broomrape, *Orobanche ramosa:* ⊙, 3–40 cm; stem branched, flowers pale yellow, 10–12 mm long, parasitic on tobacco and hemp; 8–10; S and C Europe.
c Sand Broomrape, *Orobanche arenaria:* ⊙-♃, 15–45 cm; flowers bluish violet, 25–35 mm long, lower lip hairy-lobed, parasitic on Mugwort (p. 238); 6–7; S and C Europe.
d *Amethyst-blue Broomrape, *Orobanche amethystea:* ⊙-♃, 20–40 cm; upper lip bifid; parasitic on Eryngo (p. 221); 6–7; S and W Europe. All belong to the Broomrape Family.

Mulleins belong to the Figwort Family. All the species shown below occur in stony, sandy and grassy places, by waysides, on embankments and on waste ground. The Dark Mullein and the Common Mullein are widespread and common; the Large-flowered Mullein is more local and uncommon. The Orange Mullein is found in scattered localities in S, W and C Europe; the Hoary Mullein is a very local plant of S and W Europe, the White Mullein of S and C Europe.

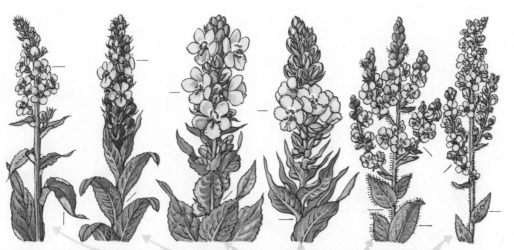

	*Dark Mullein	*Common Mullein	†Large-flowered Mullein	†Orange Mullein	*Hoary Mullein	*White Mullein
Scientific Name	*Verbascum nigrum*	*Verbascum thapsus*	*Verbascum thapsiforme*	*Verbascum phlomoides*	*Verbascum pulverulentum*	*Verbascum lychnitis*
Longevity, Size	⊙, up to 1.5 m	⊙, up to 1.8 m	⊙, up to 2 m	⊙, up to 2 m	⊙, up to 1.3 m	⊙, up to 1.5 m
Distinguishing Features; Flowering Time	Stem and leaves with star-like hairs beneath, hairs of filaments purple; 5–9	Stem and leaves with soft white wool, lower filaments glabrous or with few hairs; 7–9	Upper and middle stem leaves decurrent, crenate, flowers 30–50 mm wide; 7–8	Densely woolly, middle and upper stem leaves slightly decurrent, with nearly entire margins; 7–9	Stem terete, leaves mealy on both surfaces, flowers 14–20 mm wide; 7–8	Stem angled, leaves nearly glabrous above, mealy beneath, flowers 10–14 mm wide; 6–9

a *Thyme Speedwell, *Veronica serpyllifolia:* ♃, 3–30 cm; leaves entire or slightly crenate, flowers whitish, with blue veins; 4–5.
b *Wall Speedwell, *Veronica arvensis:* ⊙, 3–30 cm; leaves sessile or almost so, ovate, crenate, with crisped hairs; 4–10. **c †Breck Speedwell,** *Veronica praecox:* ⊙, 5–20 cm; leaves crenate, flowers blue; 3–6; S and C Europe. **d *Heath Speedwell,** *Veronica officinalis:* ♃, 10–30 cm; leaves short-stalked, flowers pale lilac, in dense spike; 5–8. All are widespread members of the Figwort Family, found mainly in cultivated fields and by waysides.

a *Green Field Speedwell,** *Veronica agrestis:* ☉, 3–10 cm; flowers pale blue with darker stripes, capsule with long glandular hairs; 3–10; widespread but uncommon, rare in the south. **b Prostrate Speedwell,** *Veronica prostrata:* ♃, 6–20 cm; leaves serrate, racemes compact at first; 4–6; S and C Europe. **c Dull Speedwell,** *Veronica opaca:* ☉, 6–30 cm; stem with spreading hairs, capsule densely downy; 3–10; N and C Europe. **d *Birdseye Speedwell,** *Veronica chamaedrys:* ♃, 5–40 cm; stem with long hairs in two rows on opposite sides; 5–8; widespread, common. All belong to the Figwort Family; **a** and **c** cultivated fields, gardens, **b** and **d** grassland, woods, hedges, pastures, roadsides.

The species of speedwell described below grow in cultivated fields, gardens, grassy places, meadows and on waste land. The Ivy Speedwell, the Common Field Speedwell (introduced from W Asia), and the Grey Field Speedwell are widespread and common throughout Europe. The other species occur in scattered localities, Dillenius's Speedwell in C Europe, confined to dry habitats. All belong to the Figwort Family.

	*Fingered Speedwell	*Spring Speedwell	Dillenius's Speedwell	*Ivy Speedwell	†Common Field Speedwell	*Grey Field Speedwell
Scientific Name	*Veronica triphyllos*	*Veronica verna*	*Veronica dillenii*	*Veronica hederifolia*	*Veronica persica*	*Veronica polita*
Longevity, Size	☉, 2–20 cm	☉, 5–20 cm	☉, 10–30 cm	☉, 3–30 cm	☉, 5–50 cm	☉, 3–30 cm
Distinguishing Features; Flowering Time	Leaves digitately 3–5-lobed, flowers blue, capsule with dense glandular hairs; 3–6	Flowers in loose racemes, nearly stalkless, blue, style short; 4–6	Flowers in elongate racemes, deep blue, style long; 4–5	Leaves ivy-like, with 5(-9) acute lobes, capsule spherical; 3–5	Leaves ovate, capsule net-veined, flowers blue, 8–12 mm wide, lobes of the capsule divergent; 3–10	Capsule glandular-hairy, style projecting beyond the notch at the top; 8–10

a Saw-leaved Speedwell, *Veronica teucrium:* ♃, 15–50 cm; flowers deep blue, in dense racemes; 5–7; thickets, pastures and roadsides, in S, W and C Europe; Figwort Family. **b †Fleawort Plantain,** *Plantago indica:* ☉, 7–60 cm; stem branched; 6–11; arable land and roadsides, in S and C Europe; Plantain Family; **c *Field Madder,** *Sherardia arvensis:* ☉, 3–35 cm; flower heads surrounded by involucre of 8–10 leaf-like bracts; 5–10; arable and waste land. **d *Crosswort,** *Cruciata chersonensis:* ♃, 15–70 cm; leaves hairy on the veins; 4–6; open woodlands, hedges and pastures and roadsides. Both are widespread and common members of the Bedstraw Family.

234

a *Small Goosegrass, *Galium tricornutum:*
⊙, 20–80 cm; flowers greenish white, in
threes, in stalked axillary cymes; 5–10.
b *Field Goosegrass, *Galium spurium:* ⊙,
30–100 cm; leaves in whorls of 6–10, flowers
only 1 mm wide; 5–9. Both are widespread
members of the Bedstraw Family, occurring
locally in arable land. c *Smooth-fruited
Cornsalad, *Valerianella dentata:* ⊙, 8–30 cm;
stem leaves with 1–2 teeth at base; 6–8.
d *Keeled Cornsalad, *Valerianella carinata:*
⊙, 7–25 cm; fruit nearly 4-angled in section,
with a deep groove. Both belong to the Valerian Family and grow in cultivated fields and
by waysides in S and C Europe.

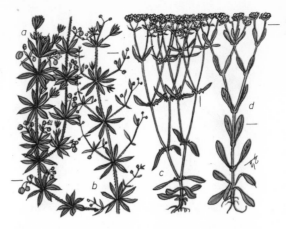

The Shepherd's Rod and the Wild Teasel are uncommon plants of woodlands, hedgebanks,
stream-banks, roadsides and pastures, the first in most parts, the second mainly in S and C
Europe. The Field Scabious is widespread and common in dry grassland, pastures and on
banks, the Devilsbit Scabious in marshes, fens, damp meadows and woods; all of these
belong to the Scabious Family. The bryonies, members of the Melon Family, are frequent in
hedges and bushy places, mainly in S and C Europe.

	*Shepherd's Rod	*Wild Teasel	*Field Scabious	*Devilsbit Scabious	White Bryony	*Red Bryony
Scientific Name	Dipsacus pilosus	Dipsacus fullonum	Knautia arvensis	Succisa pratensis	Bryonia alba	Bryonia dioica
Longevity, Size	⊙, 50–200 cm	⊙, 60–200 cm	♃, 20–120 cm	♃, 4–100 cm	♃, climbing	♃, climbing
Distinguishing Features; Flowering Time	Stem with spines on the angles, flower-heads about 2 cm wide, flowers pale yellow; 7–8	Stem spiny on the angles, flower-heads about 8 cm long, flowers pale lilac; 7–8	Receptacle without bracts, corolla usually 4-lobed, bluish lilac; 5–9	Rootstock ending abruptly, re-ceptacle with bracts; 7–9	Monoecious, calyx and corolla of equal length, berries black; 6–8	Dioecious, corolla longer than the calyx, berries scarlet; 6–7

a Downy Bellflower, *Campanula bononiensis:*
♃, 40–120 cm; flowers 10–19 mm long, leaves
irregularly doubly crenate; 7–10; northern
parts of S Europe and E and C Europe.
b †Creeping Bellflower, *Campanula ra-
punculoides:* ♃, 30–120 cm; raceme one-sided,
flowers 20–30 cm long, corolla-lobes fringed;
6–8; widespread and frequent in most of
Europe. c *Giant Bellflower, *Campanula
latifolia:* ♃, 50–120 cm; radical leaves soft-
hairy on both sides, flowers blue, purple or
white; 6–8; widely distributed but local
throughout Europe. All belong to the Bellflower Family and grow in bushy places, open
woodland and in hedges, sometimes also on
arable or waste land.

a Common Venus's Looking-glass, *Legousia speculum-veneris:* ⊙, 10–50 cm; flowers violet, calyx-teeth equal ovary; 6–8; S and C Europe. **b *Lesser Venus's Looking-glass,** *Legousia hybrida:* ⊙, 8–15 cm; flowers purplish red, calyx-teeth 1/2 length of ovary; 5–7; S, E, W and C Europe. Both belong to the Bellflower Family; local, arable and waste land. **c *Goldilocks,** *Crinitaria linosyris:* ♃, 30–60 cm; leaves 2 mm wide; 7–10; uncommon or rare, dry grassland, bushy places, limestone cliffs, S and C Europe. **d *Wall Lettuce,** *Mycelis muralis:* ♃, 20–150 cm; leaves thin, flowers 3–5; 7–9; widespread and common, on walls, rocks, occasionally in woodlands. Both belong to the Daisy Family.

The plants illustrated below belong to the Daisy Family. All are widespread in most of Europe, growing in cultivated fields, unbuilt areas, on waste land and by waysides, where they often are very abundant, particularly the Pineapple Weed, which sometimes forms dense carpets. Only the Yellow Chamomile and the Stinking Chamomile are somewhat rarer. The Pineapple Weed, probably introduced from NE Asia, has become naturalized and established throughout Europe. The Scentless Mayweed shown is the subspecies *inodorum*.

	*Scentless Mayweed	†Pineapple Weed	*Scented Mayweed	†Yellow Chamomile	*Stinking Chamomile	*Corn Chamomile
Scientific Name	*Tripleurospermum maritimum*	*Matricaria matricarioides*	*Matricaria recutita*	*Anthemis tinctoria*	*Anthemis cotula*	*Anthemis arvensis*
Longevity, Size	♃, 40–70 cm	⊙, 3–40 cm	⊙, 10–50 cm	♃,15–100 cm	⊙, 15–50 cm	⊙, 7–50 cm
Distinguishing Features; Flowering Time	Plant scentless, receptacle conical, solid, ray-florets 12–20; 6–10	Strongly aromatic, receptacle conical, hollow, ray-florets absent, disc-florets greenish yellow; 6–7	Plant strongly, pleasantly aromatic, receptacle conical, ray-florets about 15; 5–9	Ray-florets golden yellow, may be absent, receptacle hemispherical, scales cuspidate; 7–9	Ray-florets white, receptacle conical, scales subulate; 7–9	Bracts downy, ray-florets white, conical, scales cuspidate; 6–9

a Common Chamomile, *Chamaemelum nobile:* ♃, 10–40 cm; receptacle-scales oblong, blunt; 7–10; C and W Europe. **b Austrian Chamomile,** *Anthemis austriaca:* ⊙-⊙, 30–50 cm; receptacle-scales with long spiny tip; 6–8; C and northern parts of S Europe. **c Ruthenian Chamomile,** *Anthemis ruthenica:* ⊙, 15–60 cm; receptacle-scales toothed at tip; 6–9; SE and C Europe. **d Alpine Hawksbeard,** *Crepis alpestris:* ♃, 15–50 cm; heads solitary, large, 30–40 mm wide; 5–8; mountain areas of C Europe. All are uncommon members of the Daisy Family; **a** occurs in sandy places, pastures and by roadsides, **b** and **c** in arable and waste land, **d** in dry meadows and scrubland.

a *****Common Cudweed,** *Filago germanica:* ⊙, 7–40 cm; heads 10–30 in each cluster, bracts straight-pointed; 7–9; frequent, in S and C Europe. **b** †**Narrow Cudweed,** *Filago gallica:* ⊙, 4–20 cm; bracts woolly at the base; 6–8; rare, S and C Europe. **c** *****Broad-leaved Cudweed,** *Filago spathulata:* ⊙, 7–40 cm; bracts with recurved point; 7–9; rare, in S, SE and C Europe. **d** †**Field Cudweed,** *Filago arvensis:* ⊙, 7–60 cm; heads 2–7 in each cluster, bracts with woolly hairs extending to the tip; 7–9; widespread but uncommon, in S, C and N Europe. All belong to the Daisy Family and grow in cultivated fields and grassy and sandy places, dry pastures and by waysides.

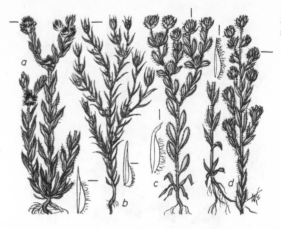

The Tansy, the Common Groundsel and the Sticky Groundsel are widespread and common; the other species shown below occur in scattered localities, in cultivated and arable land, sandy fields, vineyards and by waysides. The Corn Marigold is probably a native of the Mediterranean region and W Asia, naturalized elsewhere. The Field Marigold is an infrequent plant of S and C Europe. The Spring Groundsel is a native of SE Europe, well established in eastern C Europe. All belong to the Daisy Family.

	*Corn Marigold	†Tansy	†Field Marigold	*Common Groundsel	*Sticky Groundsel	Spring Groundsel
Scientific Name	*Chrysanthemum segetum*	*Chrysanthemum vulgare*	*Calendula arvensis*	*Senecio vulgaris*	*Senecio viscosus*	*Senecio vernalis*
Longevity, Size	⊙, 20–60 cm	♃, 50–120 cm	⊙, 10–40 cm	⊙, 5–40 cm	⊙, 10–50 cm	⊙, 10–60 cm
Distinguishing Features; Flowering Time	Leaves coarsely toothed or pinnatifid, half-clasping stem, ray-florets large, yellow; 6–8	Leaves 2-pinnatifid, heads flat, in corymbs, ray-florets absent; 7–9	Leaves oblong-lanceolate, heads 10–20 mm wide, later drooping, fruits spiny; 6–9	Leaves lobed to pinnatifid, toothed, ray-florets absent, bracts 21; 6–9	Plant very sticky, glandular-hairy, ray-florets revolute, pappus 3 times as long as fruits; 6–10	Leaves woolly, bracts 21, ray-florets 13, fruits hairy; 7–10

a *****Blue Fleabane,** *Erigeron acer:* ⊙-⊙, 10–100 cm; ray-florets yellowish, becoming reddish; 5–9; locally common throughout Europe. **b** †**Canadian Fleabane,** *Conyza canadensis:* ⊙-⊙, 10–100 cm; heads 3–5 mm wide, white or reddish; 6–10; a native of N America, well-established throughout Europe. **c** **Upright False Cudweed,** *Micropus erectus:* ⊙, 5–20 cm; heads in spherical clusters; 5–9; rare, sandy fields and sunny hillocks in S and C Europe and the Balkans. **d** *****Ploughman's Spikenard,** *Inula conyza:* ⊙-♃, 50–150 cm; marginal florets tubular or with very short ligule; 7–9; uncommon, SE and C Europe. All belong to the Daisy Family; dry grassland, rocky slopes, arable and waste land.

a †**Spiny Cocklebur,** *Xanthium spinosum:*
⊙, 15–70 cm; leaf-stalks with 1–2 trifid
yellow spines at base; 7–10. b †**Common
Cocklebur,** *Xanthium strumarium:* ⊙, 15 to
120 cm; leaves coarsely toothed to palmately
lobed; 7–10. c †**Small-flowered Galinsoga**
or **Gallant Soldier,** *Galinsoga parviflora:* ⊙,
6–80 cm; stem nearly glabrous, leaves stalked,
ovate, receptacle-scales usually trifid; 5–10.
d †**Hairy Galinsoga** or **Shaggy Soldier,**
Galinsoga ciliata: ⊙, 6–80 cm; stem hairy,
receptacle-scales finely toothed above; 4–10.
All are members of the Daisy Family introduced from America and now well established
on rubbish-dumps, waste and arable land and
in gardens.

All the members of the Daisy Family illustrated below are widespread and common throughout
Europe. They grow by waysides, on rubbish-dumps, waste land, dry meadows, pastures and in
gardens, the Welted Thistle and the Spear Thistle also being found in wet places in woods. The
Musk Thistle and the Dwarf Thistle prefer calcareous soils.

	*Musk Thistle	*Spiny Thistle	†Welted Thistle	*Spear Thistle	*Creeping Thistle	*Dwarf Thistle
Scientific Name	*Carduus nutans*	*Carduus acanthoides*	*Carduus crispus*	*Cirsium vulgare*	*Cirsium arvense*	*Cirsium acaulon*
Longevity, Size	⊙, 30–100 cm	⊙, 30–100 cm	⊙, up to 1 m	⊙, up to 1 m	♃, up to 1 m	♃, up to 30 cm
Distinguishing Features; Flowering Time	Heads usually solitary, droop- ing, up to 50 mm wide, bracts strongly reflexed, spine- tipped; 7–8	Leaf-lobes and wings of stem spiny, heads not closely clustered; 6–9	Stem usually naked just beneath heads, spines on wing and leaf-marg- ins weak, heads clustered; 7–9	Stem leaves decurrent, leaf-teeth with a long, yellow spine; 6–9	Stem much- branched, stem leaves not decurrent; 7–9	Stem with soli- tary, usually stalkless head, leaves in a basal rosette, spiny- toothed; 7–9

a ***Mugwort,** *Artemisia vulgaris:* ♃, 50 to
150 cm; leaves white-woolly beneath, the basal
ones lyrate-pinnatifid, auricled, stem leaves
2-pinnate, clasping the stem; 7–10; common.
b ***Breckland Mugwort,** *Artemisia campestris:* ♃, 30–90 cm; leaves 2–3-pinnate,
heads 2–4 mm long; 7–10; frequent. c
***Wormwood,** *Artemisia absinthium:* ♃,
60–120 cm; leaves silky-hairy, heads downy,
drooping, very aromatic; 7–9; infrequent. All
belong to the Daisy Family and are widespread in Europe, growing in grassy and waste
places, on rubbish-dumps, in hedgerows and
by waysides.

a *Great Burdock, *Arctium lappa:* ☉, 50–200 cm; lower leaves ovate-heart-shaped at the base, up to 50 cm long, involucral bracts with hooked tips, uniformly green; 7–8. **b *Lesser Burdock,** *Arctium minus:* ☉, 25–80 cm; lower leaves ovate-lanceolate, heart-shaped at the base, with sinuate margins, involucral bracts with reddish tips; 7–8. **c †Downy Burdock,** *Arctium tomentosum:* ☉, 40–100 cm; leaves greyish-downy beneath, involucral bracts with dense cobweb-like hairs; 7–9. All are common members of the Daisy Family, occurring in waste places, by waysides and, rarely, in woodland, throughout Europe.

Members of the Daisy Family, in which the marginal florets are ligulate, are described below. Most of them are widespread and common or locally common in most of Europe, growing by waysides, on sandy banks, waste land, heaths and in grassy places; the Smooth Cat's-ear also on dunes, the Hawkweed Ox-tongue on embankments and on scree by rivers. The Spider-seed, which is found in scattered localities in S, SE, W and C Europe, prefers calcareous soils.

	*Chicory	***Nipplewort**	***Swine's Succory**	***Smooth Cat's-ear**	***Hawkweed Ox-tongue**	***Spider-seed**
Scientific Name	*Cichorium intybus*	*Lapsana communis*	*Arnoseris minima*	*Hypochoeris glabra*	*Picris hieracioides*	*Arachnospermum laciniatum*
Longevity, Size	♃, 30–120 cm	☉, 20–90 cm	☉, 5–10 cm	☉, 10–30 cm	♃, 20–100 cm	☉, 20–40 cm
Distinguishing Features; Flowering Time	Stem branched, basal leaves usually roughly hairy, heads turning towards the sun; 7–9	Basal leaves with large terminal lobes, heads numerous, with a few ray-florets; 6–8	Scapes hollow, enlarging above, club-shaped beneath heads, heads 1–2, leaves fringed; 7–8	Leaves glabrous, ray-florets whitish beneath, short-ly toothed, pappus hairs in 2 rows; 7–9	Outer involucral bracts with bristles and short white hairs down central strip; 7–9	Stem branched, leaves deeply pinnatifid, heads solitary, florets sulphur-yellow; 7–8

a †Great Globe-thistle, *Echinops sphaero-cephalus:* ♃, 50–200 cm; stem branched, leaves pinnatifid, with spiny teeth, white-downy beneath; 7–8; in dry bushy places, open woods and on waste land. **b *Scotch Thistle,** *Onopordum acanthium:* ☉, 20–200 cm; stem with very broad spiny wings, heads solitary, large; 7–9; on waste land. **c Common Gum-succory,** *Chondrilla juncea:* ♃, 50–150 cm; stem with white bristly hairs in the lower part, basal leaves sinuate or almost pinnatifid, heads with ligulate florets; 7–9; in dry grassland and waste places. All are fairly common or uncommon members of the Daisy Family, growing mainly in S and C Europe.

239

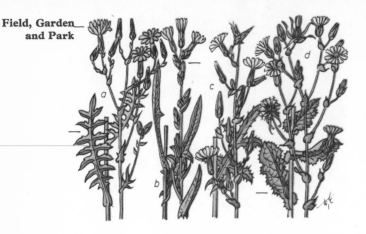

a Perennial Lettuce, *Lactuca perennis*: ♃,
20–60 cm; flowers blue, rarely white; 5–7;
rare, stony bushy slopes and rocks in S, SE
and C Europe. **b *Least Lettuce**, *Lactuca
saligna*: ☉-☉, 20–90 cm; upper stem leaves
linear, heads in a narrow panicle; 7–8. **c
*Prickly Lettuce**, *Lactuca serriola*: ☉-☉,
25–150 cm; stem leaves usually vertical, often
pointing north and south; 7–10. **d *Greater
Prickly Lettuce**, *Lactuca virosa*: ☉-☉,
50–150 cm; stem leaves usually horizontal,
spiny-fringed at margins; 7–9. All belong
to the Daisy Family; **b**, **c** and **d** grow mainly
on waste land, by roads, sometimes on walls,
in S and C Europe, naturalized elsewhere.

The French Hardhead and the Greater Knapweed, both widespread and common, and the
Spotted Knapweed, an infrequent plant of northern S and C Europe, grow by roadsides, in dry
meadows, hedgebanks, and on grassy and bushy slopes. The Cornflower, probably native in
much of Europe, occurs also as an introduced cornfield weed in many places. The Sow-thistles
are widespread and common on arable and waste land, the Corn Sow-thistle also on stream-
sides, drift-lines of marshes, and on banks. All belong to the Daisy Family.

	†French Hardhead	*Greater Knapweed	Spotted Knapweed	*Cornflower	*Corn Sow-thistle	*Smooth Sow-thistle
Scientific Name	*Centaurea jacea*	*Centaurea scabiosa*	*Centaurea maculosa*	*Centaurea cyanus*	*Sonchus arvensis*	*Sonchus oleraceus*
Longevity, Size	♃, 5–70 cm	♃, 30–100 cm	♃, 20–90 cm	☉, 15–80 cm	♃, 15–150 cm	☉, 20–90 cm
Distinguishing Features; Flowering Time	Upper leaves linear, append-ages of bracts rounded, with usually lacini-ate or fringed margins; 6–10	Leaves pin-natifid with entire or pin-natifid lobes, appendages of bracts comb-like; 6–10	Leaf segments narrowly lin-ear, downy, appendages of bracts with narrow seg-ments; 7–9	Stem leaves narrow, linear, outer florets large, bright blue, centre ones red-purple; 6–10	Stem usually simple, heads in loose cor-ymb, branches of inflores-cence glandu-lar-hairy; 6–10	Leaves with prickly teeth, stem leaves with pointed auricles, involucre not glandular;6–10

a *Prickly Sow-thistle, *Sonchus asper*:
☉-♃, 8–70 cm; leaf-margins prickly fringed,
stem leaves with rounded auricles; 6–10; a
widespread, common weed in gardens and on
arable and waste land. **b *Mouse-ear Hawkweed**, *Hieracium pilosella*: ♃, 3–40 cm; stem
leafless, with solitary head; 5–10; widespread
and common on moors, heaths and pastures,
rocks and roadsides. **c Wood Hawkweed**,
Hieracium sylvaticum: ♃, 25–50 cm; stem
usually with one leaf, basal leaves stalked;
5–6; common, woods, rocks and walls. **d
Hare's-ear Hawkweed**, *Hieracium bupleur-
oides*: ♃, 20–50 cm; stem with few heads,
basal leaves stalkless; 7–9; rare, rocks, scree,
in the Alps. All belong to the Daisy Family.

a †Tassel Hyacinth, *Muscari comosum:* ♃, 30–70 cm; raceme 8–20 cm long, topped by a cluster of upright, long-stalked purplish blue sterile flowers, fertile flowers brown; 5–6; fields, vineyards and grassy places in mountain areas. **b Grape Hyacinth,** *Muscari atlanticum:* ♃, 7–20 cm; flowers blue, leaves almost terete, 1–3 mm wide; 4–5; fields, vineyards, grassy places. **c Sky-blue Hyacinth,** *Muscari botryoides:* ♃, 10–30 cm; leaves 3–5 mm wide, flowers sky-blue; 4–5; woods, vineyards. **d *Neglected Hyacinth,** *Muscari neglectum:* ♃, 7–25 cm; leaves 3–5 mm wide, numerous, long, flowers blackish blue; 3–4; fields, grassy places. All are members of the Lily Family; mainly S and C Europe.

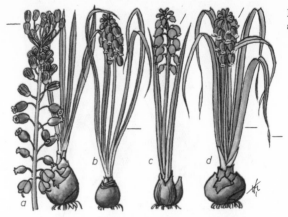

All the plants shown below belong to the Daffodil Family and grow mainly in cultivated fields, vineyards and grassy places, sometimes also in scrubland. The Welsh Leek, a native of SE Siberia, has become naturalized in many European countries. The Keeled Garlic, the Sand Leek, the Mountain Garlic and the Upright Garlic are widespread, but local or rare in most of Europe. The Round Garlic in found in scattered localities in S, SE and SC Europe.

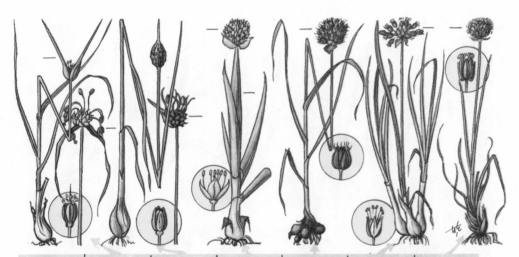

	†Keeled Garlic	*Sand Leek	†Welsh Leek	Round Garlic	Mountain Garlic	Upright Garlic
Scientific Name	*Allium carinatum*	*Allium scorodoprasum*	*Allium fistulosum*	*Allium rotundum*	*Allium montanum*	*Allium strictum*
Longevity, Size	♃, 30–60 cm	♃, 50–110 cm	♃, 40–100 cm	♃, 30–60 cm	♃, 20–40 cm	♃, 15–50 cm
Distinguishing Features; Flowering Time	Leaves always flat, slightly grooved, perianth-segments pink to dark violet, stamens exserted; 6–8	Leaves up to 15 mm wide, perianth-segments dark red, longer than the stamens; 6–7	Scape and leaves inflated, bulb rather small; 6–8	Leaves 3–6 mm wide, flat, umbel spherical, dense, without bulbils; 6–8	Leaves not keeled beneath, perianth-segments purplish violet, stamens exserted; 7–8	Bulb with a fibrous tunic, flowers purple, stamens nearly as long as perianth-segments; 6–8

a Woolly Yellow-star-of-Bethlehem, *Gagea villosa:* ♃, 7–15 cm; basal leaves usually 2; 3–4; uncommon, fields, grassy places and roadsides; Lily Family. **b *Black Bryony,** *Tamus communis:* ♃, twining; leaves deeply heart-shaped at base; 5–6; fairly common, margins of woods, scrub and hedgerows, in S, C and W Europe; Yam Family. **c †Saffron,** *Crocus sativus:* ♃, 8–30 cm; flowers violet, throat bearded at base; 9–11; a native of Mediterranean region, naturalized in C and W Europe; Iris Family. **d †Slender Rush,** *Juncus tenuis:* ♃, 15–30 cm; flowers in terminal panicle, overtopped by linear bracts; 6–9; a native of America, naturalized locally, on roadsides, waste land; Rush Family.

a *Round-fruited Rush, *Juncus compressus:*
♃, 10–70 cm; stem compressed, capsule sub-
globose; 6–9; widespread, but local, in fens,
by damp roadsides and rivers; Rush Family.
b *Spring Sedge, *Carex caryophyllea:* ♃,
5–25 cm; stem longer than leaves, bracts
bristle-like, shortly sheathing; 3–5; widespread, locally common, in dry grassland.
c Dwarf Sedge, *Carex humilis:* ♃, 3–15 cm;
leaves longer than stem, ♀ spike in sheathing
bracts; 3–4; rather rare, dry grassland and
open woods in C Europe. **d *Smooth Sedge,**
Carex laevigata: ♃, 50–100 cm; leaves
5–10 mm wide, ligule 10 mm long, all spikes
distant, ♀ spikes 3–4; 4–6; scattered, S, W
and C Europe. All belong to the Sedge Family.

The darnels are natives of the Mediterranean region, once common weeds of arable land, now
usually restricted to waste places. The Bearded Couch is locally common in woods and along
hedgerows. The Common Couch is a troublesome weed of cultivated fields and gardens,
growing also by roadsides, on waste land and sandy places near the sea. The Wall Barley is
widespread and common on waste ground, waysides and by walls. The Hard-grass occurs locally
on waste ground and by roadsides in S Europe. All belong to the Grass Family.

	†Common Darnel	Flax Darnel	*Bearded Couch	*Common Couch	*Wall Barley	Hard-grass
Scientific Name	*Lolium temulentum*	*Lolium remotum*	*Agropyron caninum*	*Agropyron repens*	*Hordeum murinum*	*Sclerochloa dura*
Longevity, Size	⊙, 30–80 cm	⊙, 30–60 cm	♃, 50–150 cm	♃, 20–150 cm	⊙, 15–40 cm	⊙, 2–20 cm
Distinguishing Features; Flowering Time	Spikelets with one edge against the axis, glume exceeding uppermost lemma; poisonous; 6–8	Similar to the previous species, but spikelets smaller, lemma awnless; 6–8	Plant tufted, spikelets with their broad side appressed to axis, lemmas long-awned; 6–7	Rhizomatous, spikelets falling entire at maturity, lemmas awnless or with short awn; 6–7	Spikelets 3 at each node of axis, glumes bristly, long-awned, some hair-fringed below; 6–9	Plant decumbent, spikelets compressed, with 3–6 florets; 5–7

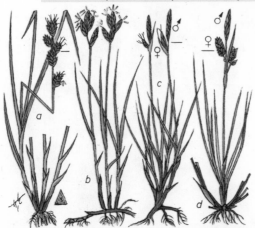

a *Tall Spiked Sedge, *Carex polyphylla:* ♃,
25–100 cm; ligule 1–2 mm, mature fruits
spreading or deflexed; 5–6; uncommon, dry
grassy places in C and N Europe. **b Early
Sedge,** *Carex praecox:* ♃, 10–25 cm; spikes
3–6, each ♂ below, ♀ at top; 4–6; uncommon,
dry meadows and grassy places in S and C
Europe. **c Lesser Sedge,** *Carex supina:* ♃,
8–20 cm; spikes contiguous, 1–3, each with
3–5 florets; 4–5; rare or uncommon, on dry
turf in S and C Europe. **d Shining Sedge,**
Carex liparocarpos: ♃, 8–20 cm; ♀ spikes
with up to 12 florets, shortly cylindrical; 4–5;
dry turf and sandy places, scattered, in S, SE,
E and C Europe. All belong to the Sedge
Family.

a †**Drooping Brome,** *Bromus tectorum:* ⊙, 30–80 cm; culms minutely hairy above, panicle dense, drooping to one side; 5–6; a native of Mediterranean region, widespread elsewhere. **b** *****Barren Brome,** *Bromus sterilis:* ⊙, 30–80 cm; culm smooth, panicle open, nodding, branches with 1 spikelet; 5–6; widespread, common. **c** †**Rye Brome,** *Bromus secalinus:* ⊙, 40–100 cm; lower leaf-sheaths usually hairless, spikelets disarticulating at maturity; 6–9; a common weed. **d** *****Meadow Brome,** *Bromus commutatus:* ⊙, 30–90 cm; panicles loose, lemmas obscurely nerved; 5–8; widespread, rather common. All belong to the Grass Family and grow mainly in arable and waste land, in most of Europe.

The Sweet Vernal-grass is widespread and common in dry meadows and pastures, also in open woodlands. The other species shown below grow on cultivated and waste land. The Yellow Bristle-grass and the Green Bristle-grass are widespread and common throughout Europe, the Rough Bristle-grass is also widely distributed but infrequent, the Short-awned Bristle-grass is rare, occuring in S and C Europe. The Annual Vernal-grass is a native of SW Europe, introduced elsewhere. All belong to the Grass Family.

	†Yellow Bristle-grass	†Rough Bristle-grass	Short-awned Bristle-grass	†Green Bristle-grass	*Sweet Vernal-grass	†Annual Vernal-grass
Scientific Name	*Setaria lutescens*	*Setaria verticillata*	*Setaria decipiens*	*Setaria viridis*	*Anthoxanthum odoratum*	*Anthoxanthum puelii*
Longevity, Size	⊙ ,10–40 cm	⊙, 25–60 cm	⊙, 20–70 cm	⊙, 15–60 cm	⚃, 30–50 cm	⊙, 10–25 cm
Distinguishing Features; Flowering Time	Panicle dense, bristles 5–10 beneath each spikelet, reddish yellow; 7–10	Panicle interrupted, bristles solitary or in pairs, with backward-pointing teeth; 7–10	Similar to the previous species, but bristles 3 mm long, with forward-pointing teeth; 7–10	Panicle dense, bristles 1–3 beneath each spikelet, greenish; 7–10	Panicle dense, culms unbranched, glumes thinly hairy; strongly scented with coumarin; 5–8	Panicle loose, culms branched, glumes hairless, slightly scented with coumarin; 5–6

a Common Beard-grass, *Bothriochloa ischaemum:* ⚃, 30–60 cm; spikes 3–5 cm long, in finger-like clusters of 5–10 at tip of culm; 8–9; frequent, stony roadsides and slopes in S, C and W Europe. **b** †**Cockspur-grass,** *Echinochloa crus-galli:* ⊙, 30–100 cm; panicles of few to many clustered racemes; 7–10; uncommon. **c** †**Smooth Finger-grass,** *Digitaria ischaemum:* ⊙, 8–50 cm; leaf-sheaths usually hairless, racemes usually 3; 7–10; rare or infrequent. **d** †**Hairy Finger-grass,** *Digitaria sanguinalis:* ⊙, 30–50 cm; leaf-sheaths usually hairy, racemes usually 5; 7–9; uncommon. All belong to the Grass Family; **b, c** and **d** are widespread weeds of arable and waste land.

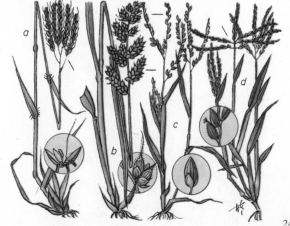

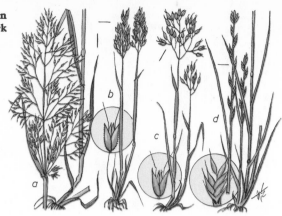

a ***Loose Silky-bent**, *Apera spica-venti:* ☉,
40–100 cm; panicle large, open, very delicate,
leaves pointed, sharp; 6–7; widespread, common. b ***Early Hair-grass**, *Aira praecox:* ☉,
3–10 cm; panicle dense, branches little longer than spikelets; 5–6; common, N, C and
W Europe. c ***Silvery Hair-grass**, *Aira
caryophyllea:* ☉, 6–15 cm; panicle loose,
branches spreading, much longer than spikelets; 5–7; frequent, S and C Europe. **d Delicate Nardurus**, *Nardurus tenellus:* ☉, 20 to
40 cm; spikelets shortly stalked, in simple
raceme; 5–7; rare, in S and C Europe. All
belong to the Grass Family and grow on
cultivated and waste land and in dry places.

The Slender Bristle-oat is a rare plant of dry meadows and roadsides in S and C Europe. The
other grasses shown below are widespread and usually common. The Sheep's Fescue grows on
heaths and moors; the Common Wild Oat on arable and waste land; the Annual Meadow-grass
usually in damp places, short grassland, on waste ground and by waysides; the Wood Meadow-
grass in woods, hedgerows and on old walls; the Flattened Meadow-grass on thin grassland, dry
banks, old walls and waste places. All belong to the Grass Family.

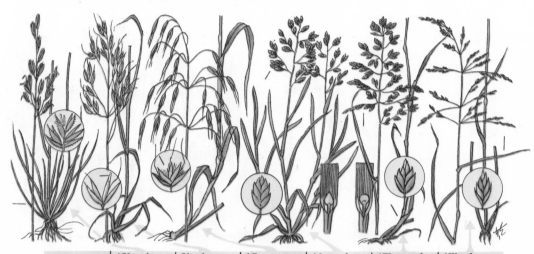

	*Sheep's Fescue	Slender Bristle-oat	†Common Wild Oat	*Annual Meadow-grass	*Flattened Meadow-grass	*Wood Meadow-grass
Scientific Name	*Festuca ovina*	*Ventenata dubia*	*Avena fatua*	*Poa annua*	*Poa compressa*	*Poa nemoralis*
Longevity, Size	♃, 15–60 cm	☉–♃, 50 cm	☉, 70–100 cm	☉–♃, 2–30 cm	♃, 20–50 cm	♃, 20–90 cm
Distinguishing Features; Flowering Time	Leaves hair- or bristle-like, leaf-sheaths split more than half-way when young; 5–7	Panicle up to 20 cm, lemma 2-toothed at tip, each tooth with a fine bristle; 6–7	Spikelets 2–3-flowered, lemmas stiffly hairy in lower half, awned from middle of the back; 6–8	Decumbent, lower panicle-branches later often reflexed, ligule 2–3 mm, lemma clearly veined; 2–11	Culm and leaf-sheaths compressed, ligule 1 mm, panicle narrow, lemma obscurely veined; 6–7	Ligule very short, panicle usually nodding, lemma obscurely veined; 5–7

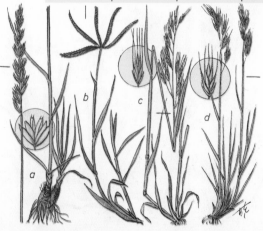

a **Sand Hair-grass**, *Koeleria glauca:* ♃,
30–50 cm; culm swollen at base, leaves greyish
green; 4–5; widespread, in scattered localities.
b **†Bermuda-grass**, *Cynodon dactylon:* ♃,
20–40 cm; spikes in cluster of 3–6 at tip of
culm; 5–6; widespread, in warmer areas.
c ***Rat's-tail Fescue**, *Vulpia myuros:* ☉,
10–50 cm; upper leaf-sheath reaching the
panicle, lower glume $\frac{1}{3}$ length of the upper;
5–10; frequent, S and C Europe. **d *Squir-
rel-tail Fescue**, *Vulpia bromoides:* ☉, 15 to
40 cm; leaf-sheath not reaching the panicle,
lower glume $\frac{1}{2}$ length of the upper; 5–8; widespread, locally common. All belong to the
Grass Family and occur in dry places.

a †**Small Eragrostis,** *Eragrostis minor:* ○, 15–50 cm; ring of hairs at junction of leaf-sheath and blade, spikelets often blackish violet; 7–9; Mediterranean region, naturalized or a casual elsewhere. **b** *****Early Sand-grass,** *Mibora minima:* ○, 3–9 cm; racemes spike-like, one-sided; 3–5; rare, SW and S Europe. **c** *****Grey Hair-grass,** *Corynephorus canescens:* ♃, 15–50 cm; plant greyish green, tufted, panicle silvery grey, awn of lemma club-shaped at tip; 6–8; widespread, local. **d** *****Slender Foxtail,** *Alopecurus myosuroides:* ○, 30–50 cm; upper leaf-sheaths inflated, glumes fused for $\frac{1}{3}$–$\frac{1}{2}$ their length; 4–5; widespread, uncommon. All belong to the Grass Family; waste and arable land.

The feather-grasses occur in S, SE, E and C Europe and are common only in steppe areas; the rare Cat's-tail on hillocks and arable land in S and C Europe. All belong to the Grass Family. The Monkey Orchid (Orchid Family) is a rare S and C European plant of grassy hills, bushy places and field borders. The Common Spleenwort, which is widespread and common, and the rare Breyne's Spleenwort, thought to be a hybrid between the Forked and Common Spleenworts, are ferns growing on rocks and walls. Both belong to the Polypody Family.

	Common Feather-grass	Hair-like Feather-grass	Rough Cat's-tail	*Monkey Orchid	*Common Spleenwort	*Breyne's Spleenwort
Scientific Name	*Stipa pennata*	*Stipa capillata*	*Phleum paniculatum*	*Orchis simia*	*Asplenium trichomanes*	*Asplenium breynei*
Longevity, Size	♃, 40–80 cm	♃, 40–90 cm	○, 15–30 cm	♃, 30–40 cm	♃, up to 30 cm	♃, 4–12 cm
Distinguishing Features; Flowering or Sporing Time	Awn up to 30 cm long, soft-hairy, hairs spreading; 5–6	Leaves bluish green, bristle-like, awn 10–25 cm long, hairless, rough; 7–8	Panicle spike-like, cylind-rical, 3–9 cm long, glumes 3-angled, inflated; 5–7 ⊙	Central lobe of lip with 2 long, narrow segments, hel-met whitish, rose-streaked or dotted; 5–6	Pinnae oval or oblong, short-stalked, crenate, falling off separately in autumn; 7–9	Pinnae 5–11, oblanceolate, wedge-shaped at base, toothed at tip; 7–9

a *****Wall Rue,** *Asplenium ruta-muraria:* ♃, up to 20 cm; indusium fringed; 6–7; widespread and common in most of Europe. **b** *****Rusty-back,** *Ceterach officinarum:* ♃, up to 20 cm; leaves densely scaly beneath, with overlapping scales; 7–9; common or local and rare in S, E and C Europe. **c** *****Brittle Bladder Fern,** *Cystopteris fragilis:* ♃, 10–40 cm; leaves tufted, 2–3-pinnate, delicate, spores prickly; 7–9; rather common, mainly on mountains in the south. **d Cretan Fern,** *Pteris cretica:* ♃, up to 100 cm; leaves with 2–9 pairs of pinnae; eastern Mediterranean region. All are ferns of the Polypody Family, found on old walls and on rocks.

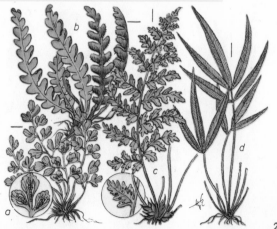

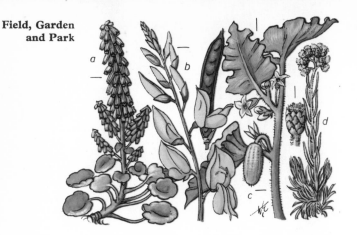

a *Wall Pennywort, *Umbilicus rupestris:* ⊙,
20–50 cm; flowers tubular, whitish green, in
dense simple or branched raceme; 4–5; Stonecrop Family. b †Spanish Broom, *Spartium
junceum:* shrub up to 5 m; branches rod-
shaped, green, pods grey-silky; 5–7; Pea
Family. c Squirting Cucumber, *Ecballium
elaterium:* ⊙, 50–100 cm; plant bluish green,
stiff-hairy, ripe fruit oblong, squirting its seeds
when touched; 3–9; Melon Family. d Italian
Everlasting, *Helichrysum italicum:* ♃, up to
30 cm; involucral bracts imbricate, brownish
straw-yellow; 5–9; Daisy Family. All grow in
cultivated and dry places in the Mediterranean
region; a also in W and C Europe, on rocks
and walls.

All the plants shown below are either trees or shrubs. Most of them grow in the Maquis, a type
of vegetation in the Mediterranean region composed of a large number of woody plants, often
having evergreen, leathery leaves. Such plants are: the Wild Olive (Olive Family), the Straw-
berry-tree, which can be a shrub (Heath Family), the Broad-leaved Mock-privet (subspecies
media is shown) (Olive Family), the Common Mastich-tree (Sumach Family), the Common
Myrtle (Myrtle Family) and the Sharp-leaved Asparagus (Lily Family).

	Wild Olive	*Strawberry-tree	Broad-leaved Mock-privet	Common Mastich-tree	Common Myrtle	Sharp-leaved Asparagus
Scientific Name	*Olea europaea* subsp. *oleaster*	*Arbutus unedo*	*Phillyrea latifolia*	*Pistacia lentiscus*	*Myrtus communis*	*Asparagus acutifolius*
Longevity, Size	Shrub, 1–3 m	Up to 10 m	Up to 8 m	Tree, 1–5 m	Shrub, 0.5–3 m	Climbing shrub
Distinguishing Features; Flowering Time	Branches thorny, flowers white, in racemes, drupes reddish black; 1	Bark reddish brown, shining above, flowers white or pink, berries red, edible; 1–2, in Ireland 9–12	Flowers green-ish white, berries bluish black, bark fissured; 3–6	Leaves glab-rous, leathery, flowers small, dioecious, berries red, later black; 3–7	Plant strongly scented, leaves with transluc-ent glandular dots, flowers white, berries blue-black; 6–8	Branches needle-like, flowers dioecious, greenish white, berries blackish; 8–9

a †Field Gladiolus, *Gladiolus segetum:* ♃,
60–90 cm; leaves 3–4; flowers large (3 cm or
more), light reddish violet, perianth-segments
unequal; 5–6; Iris Family. b Common
Dragon-plant, *Dracunculus vulgaris:* ♃, up
to 100 cm; spathe purplish red, 25–40 cm
long; 5–6. c Common Arisarum, *Arisarum
vulgare:* ♃, 15–30 cm; spathe brownish red,
hood-like; 10–3. d *Garden Cuckoo-pint,
Arum italicum: ♃, up to 100 cm; outside of
spathe green, inside white; 4–5; b, c and d
belong to the Arum Family. All are Mediterranean plants, growing mainly in cultivated
fields and grassy places.

a Common European White-toothed Shrew, *Crocidura russula:* 9 cm + 4 cm; upper side brownish grey, underside yellowish grey, not sharply contrasting. **b *Lesser European White-toothed Shrew** or **Scilly Shrew**, *Crocidura suaveolens:* 7 cm + 4 cm; back brownish grey, underside white, with long pale hairs standing out from main body of coat. **c Bicolour White-toothed Shrew**, *Crocidura leuocodon:* 8 cm + 3.5 cm; upper side dark greyish brown, underside yellowish white, sharply contrasting. All are widespread in C and S Europe, in gardens and at edges of woods; **b** occurs in the Isles of Scilly, the only part of Britain where this genus occurs, often found foraging on the sea-shore.

All the bats illustrated below belong to the Smooth-faced Bat Family, i.e. their muzzles have no nose-leaves and there is a vertical growth, the tragus, on the front edge of their ears. At rest, the Long-eared Bat wraps its ears back round the body, leaving the tragus standing up. Nathusius' Pipistrelle is not found in Great Britain, and the Mouse-eared Bat and the Particoloured Bat are rare vagrants. Otherwise, all are widespread in Europe, particularly in the south.

	*Serotine Bat	Parti-coloured Bat	Nathusius' Pipistrelle	*Pipistrelle or Common Bat	*Long-eared Bat	Mouse-eared Bat
Scientific Name	*Eptesicus serotinus*	*Vespertilio murinus*	*Pipistrellus nathusii*	*Pipistrellus pipistrellus*	*Plecotus auritus*	*Myotis myotis*
Size	8 cm + 5.7 cm	6.3 cm + 7.5 cm	4.8 cm + 4 cm	4.5 cm + 3.3 cm	5 cm + 5 cm	8 cm + 6 cm
Distinguishing Features	Wingspan 38 cm, body large, coat very dark brown, ears longer than wide	Wingspan 28 cm, upper side musty grey, underside very light-coloured	Body small, thumb long, fifth finger about 4.6 cm long	Body very small, ears short and wide, thumb short	Wingspan 26 cm, ears up to 4 cm long, almost touching above the head	Large, ears wide, tip of tail free, underside much paler than back; shrieks loudly

a Etruscan Shrew or **Savi's Pygmy Shrew**, *Suncus etruscus:* 4 cm + 2.5 cm, weight 1.5–2 grammes; tail long, ears large; Europe's smallest mammal, a southern member of the Shrew Family. **b Kuhl's Pipistrelle**, *Pipistrellus kuhli:* 4.5 cm + 4 cm; membrane between legs partly with a white fringe; Smooth-faced Bat Family. **c European Free-tailed Bat**, *Tadarida teniotis:* 8 cm + 5 cm; largest European species of bat, plump, feet large, long tail beyond membrane; flies strongly, agile climbing about the roosting area, which may be in caves or under iron roofs; its presence may be detected by a strong musky smell; belongs to the large Free-tailed Bat Family.

a *Hedgehog, *Erinaceus europaeus:* 25 cm + 3.5 cm; spiny coat dark brown and grey, ears small; throughout Europe except in the far north. b Algerian Hedgehog, *Erinaceus algirus:* 23 cm + 3.5 cm; spiny coat lighter than that of a, ears large; W Mediterranean coasts. Both feed on insects and other small animals. c *Mole, *Talpa europaea:* 14.3 cm + 3 cm; front feet with a few light-coloured hairs; almost throughout Europe. d Mediterranean Mole, *Talpa caeca:* 12 cm + 2.5 cm; front feet with conspicuous light hairs; S Europe. Moles are found in a wide variety of habitats where burrowing is possible, feeding mainly on worms.

The Striped Field Mouse is found in Germany, E Europe and Asia, the Yellow-necked Mouse, not found in N Europe, usually lives in wooded areas and is a good climber; it occurs in Britain, but has a curiously patchy distribution. The other species live in copses, on cultivated fields and in parks throughout large areas of Europe, in winter being found frequently in buildings. All belong to the Mouse Family and have long, sparsely haired and clearly ringed tails; none hibernates.

	*Harvest Mouse	*Long-tailed Field (Wood) Mouse	*Yellow-necked Mouse	Striped Field Mouse	Eastern House Mouse	*Western House Mouse
Scientific Name	*Micromys minutus*	*Apodemus sylvaticus*	*Apodemus flavicollis*	*Apodemus agrarius*	*Mus musculus musculus*	*Mus musculus domesticus*
Size	5.7 cm + 5.1 cm	8.8 cm + 8.8 cm	10 cm + 11 cm	12 cm + 7.3 cm	8.3 cm + 7.3 cm	10 cm + 10 cm
Distinguishing Features	Back yellowish brown, underside yellowish grey, without back stripe, tail long, prehensile	Back brown, underside white, may have yellow stripe on belly, ears large	Yellow throat-band, back of body rusty brown, underside shining white, sharply contrasted	Black streak on back, tail shorter than body, ears rather small	Back brownish grey, underside white, tail comparatively short, with 140–175 rings	Coat uniformly lead-grey to brownish grey, tail long, with 150–200 rings

a Marbled Polecat, *Vormela peregusna:* 38 cm + 16 cm; back and flanks with distinctive spots; Balkans. b Asiatic Polecat, *Mustela eversmanni:* 37 cm + 17 cm; flanks very light-coloured, face with mask-like markings; probably the wild ancestor of the domestic Ferret. Both belong to the Weasel Family. c Common or Crested Porcupine, *Hystrix cristata:* 60 cm + 10 cm; centre and hind part of back and tail with long spines; S Italy and C Balkans; a rodent with powerful gnawing teeth capable of tackling a wide range of vegetable foodstuffs; belongs to the Porcupine Family. All are dusk and nocturnal animals living in cultivated areas.

a †**Black** or **Ship Rat**, *Rattus rattus:* up to 23 cm + 25 cm; tail longer than head and body, with more than 250 rings, ears large, coat brown with white underside or blackish with grey underside; absent in a large part of N Europe, prefers warm places. b †**Brown** or **Norway Rat**, *Rattus norvegicus:* up to 27 cm + 22 cm; tail shorter than head and body, with at most 220 rings, ears smaller than those of **a**, coat blackish or brown with lighter underside; a common pest almost throughout Europe, in buildings, especially the lower stories and cellars; also occurs in the open. Both species belong to the Mouse Family; introduced into Britain some centuries ago.

The Rock Mouse occurs in the S Balkans, where it builds its nest under rocks. The Lesser Mole Rat inhabits dry cultivated land in the Balkans and Hungary, the Greater Mole Rat similar places in the southern U.S.S.R.; both are blind. The Vole Rat is found in E Europe, and the Migratory or Grey Hamster in parts of the Balkans and S Russia. The Golden Hamster has escaped from captivity and formed small colonies in various parts of Europe. All belong to the Mouse Family. Mole Rats and Hamsters build nests in the ground.

	Rock Mouse	Vole Rat	Golden Hamster	Migratory Hamster	Lesser Mole Rat	Greater Mole Rat
Scientific Name	*Apodemus mystacinus*	*Arvicola terrestris*	*Mesocricetus auratus*	*Cricetulus migratorius*	*Spalax leucodon*	*Spalax microphthalmus*
Size	15 cm + 14 cm	20 cm + 10cm	18 cm + 2 cm	11 cm + 2.5 cm	27 cm + 2.5 cm	31 cm + 3 cm
Distinguishing Features	Ears very large, back brownish grey, underside white	Similar to the Water-vole (page 110) but smaller, tail longer, snout more pointed	Coat brightly coloured, with black spots, belly light-coloured, ears large, tail very short	Upper side grey, coat not very bright, ears large, tail short	Coat brownish grey, ears, eyes and tail not visible, head blunt-ended	Coat grey, forehead white, otherwise similar to Lesser Mole Rat but larger

Common Hamster, *Cricetus cricetus:* up to 28 cm + 6 cm; coat brightly coloured, underside black, tail short; rarely an almost entirely black variety; a dusk and nocturnal animal of the Hamster Family, lives on the plains and in cultivated areas of Europe from France eastwards. It builds underground dwellings in clayey or loamy soil, consisting of several chambers which are used for nesting and living in or for storing food, which consists mainly of grain, roots and insects. The animals are solitary, but sometimes burrows may be fairly closely grouped. In winter the Hamster hibernates at a depth of up to 2 metres.

adult

juvenile

White Stork, *Ciconia ciconia:* 102 cm; plumage snow-white, wings black, legs and bill red, bill of young birds blackish; neck stretched when flying, courtship display includes loud bill clapping, but this is normally a quiet bird; glides well, with legs drooping slightly; migrant, a member of the Stork Family, nests on buildings and occasionally in trees. It is a native of areas with marshy meadows and lakes, but has become very rare in many places, although large flocks may gather on migration, especially where locusts are plentiful. It is found in Europe east of the Rhine, in Spain and Portugal, the Balkans and the U.S.S.R.

All the birds illustrated below belong to the Birds-of-Prey Family; they inhabit open areas where they may nest in trees or on the ground. The Kestrel, which is native throughout Europe, is sometimes found in towns, where it nests on buildings; the Buzzard and the Hobby avoid the north; the Rough-legged Buzzard nests in Norway, the Merlin in Great Britain, Scandinavia and the north of the U.S.S.R.

light form

	*Buzzard	Rough-legged Buzzard	*Kestrel	*Hobby	*Merlin
Scientific Name	*Buteo buteo*	*Buteo lagopus*	*Falco tinnunculus*	*Falco subbuteo*	*Falco columbarius*
Size	51–56 cm	51–61 cm	34 cm	30.5–35.5 cm	26.6–33 cm
Distinguishing Features	Grey or brown to almost white, tail short, darkly barred; soaring flight with mewing call; partial migrant	Legs feathered, tail whitish with dark end-band, head rather light-coloured; migrant	Tail with black end-band, ♂ with reddish brown back, ♀ with barred back; hovering flight; partial migrant	Similar to Peregrine Falcon (page 55), thighs rust-red, under parts streaked; fast, direct flight; migrant	♂ back greyish blue, tail with black band, ♀ tail barred; partial migrant

a

b

a Egyptian Vulture, *Neophron percnopterus:* 58.5–66 cm; tail wedge-shaped, white; partial migrant. **b Griffon Vulture,** *Gyps fulvus:* 97–104 cm; neck-ruff whitish, that of young birds brown; resident. Both are carrion-eaters of the Vulture Family. They nest in holes and on rock-ledges in Mediterranean countries, the Egyptian Vulture also in trees; recently the Griffon Vulture has bred in the Alps. They are likely to be seen soaring on broad, 'fingered' wings with very straight leading edges. Vultures rarely flap their wings, but rise to great altitudes on currents of hot air while scanning the ground for food. Both have been recorded in Britain, well north of their normal range.

a Great Bustard, *Otis tarda:* ♂ 102 cm, ♀ much smaller; head and neck light grey, ♂ with brown breast-band; resident, once common in Britain, now only an irregular visitor. **b Little Bustard**, *Otis tetrax:* 43 cm; ♂ with black and white neck markings during breeding season; partial migrant. **c Macqueen's Bustard**, *Chlamydotis undulata:* 63.5 cm; ♂ and ♀ with short head-crest and long, black and white feathers on neck; resident. All belong to the Bustard Family and nest on the steppes and in large fields, **a** in Brandenburg, SE Europe and Spain, **b** in Spain, France and the Balkans, **c** in N Africa. All are gregarious birds which feed on many plant and animal foods.

The Quail and the Partridge are Game-birds native throughout large areas of Europe, although the Quail, which is trapped in large numbers on migration, is becoming very rare. Both build well-hidden nests on the ground. The Black-bellied Sand-grouse nests in stony countryside in Spain and Portugal and only rarely spreads beyond there. The Larks are native throughout Europe with the exception of the north, though the Crested Lark does not occur in Britain; they nest on the ground in fields. Skylarks fly vertically up and down as they sing.

	*Partridge	*Quail	Black-bellied Sand-grouse	*Skylark	Crested Lark	*Wood Lark
Scientific Name	*Perdix perdix*	*Coturnix coturnix*	*Pterocles orientalis*	*Alauda arvensis*	*Galerida cristata*	*Lullula arborea*
Size	30.5 cm	18 cm	35.5 cm	18 cm	17 cm	15 cm
Distinguishing Features	Head light rust-colour, ♂ with a horse-shoe-shaped spot on belly; resident	Plumage sandy brown with dark streaks; partial migrant	Belly black ♂ throat brown, tail long, without point; resident	Tail long with white outer edges, small head-crest; partial migrant	Tail short with brown outer edges, large head-crest; resident	Tail very short, without white edges, wings with black and white edge-marks; partial migrant

*Cuckoo, *Cuculus canorus:* 33 cm; ♂ plumage chiefly grey, belly with black and white bars, ♀ with grey or reddish brown bars; ♂ calls 'cuckoo', ♀ has a bubbling call; insect-eating; migrant, found throughout Europe. ♀ polyandrous, lays her eggs separately in the nests of other birds, each individual ♀ parasitizing one particular species. In the first few days of life, the young cuckoo pushes the host's eggs and young from the nest, and is then fed by the foster parents; in Britain these are usually Meadow Pipits or Hedge Sparrows, but in all about 50 species have been recorded. Cuckoos prefer bushy countryside, but do also live on open plains.

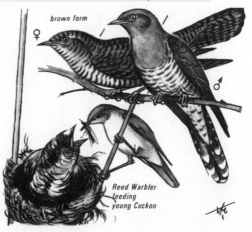

brown form

Reed Warbler feeding young Cuckoo

a *Barn Owl, *Tyto alba:* 34.5 cm; upper parts golden yellow, finely spotted, under parts uniformly silver white or brownish yellow, legs long, disc of feathers round eye moveable, acts as an 'ear-trumpet'; eyesight very good in twilight, but in complete darkness can catch prey by hearing alone; resident. **b †Little Owl,** *Athene noctua:* 21.5 cm; body small, back spotted, head flat; resident. Both prefer to live near human settlements, nesting in buildings and holes in trees. Both are native throughout Europe, except the north; **a** is not found in the S Balkans, and **b** is an introduced species in Britain.

The Swift occurs throughout Europe, Alpine and Pallid Swifts live in the Mediterranean region, the Alpine Swift extending northwards to the Alps. All feed and mate in flight and usually nest in buildings. The Hoopoe, the Roller and the Bee-eater, which all give their names to their families, nest in holes, the Bee-eater in colonies in sandy cliffs. These three birds are mainly southern in distribution, but the Hoopoe occasionally breeds in Britain and the Bee-eater has done so at least once.

	*Swift	**Alpine Swift**	**Pallid Swift**	**Hoopoe**	**Roller**	**Bee-eater**
Scientific Name	*Apus apus*	*Apus melba*	*Apus pallidus*	*Upupa epops*	*Coracias garrulus*	*Merops apiaster*
Size	16.5 cm	21 cm	16.5 cm	28 cm	30.5 cm	28 cm
Distinguishing Features	Plumage soot-black, chin whitish, wings long, sickle-shaped; migrant	Plumage dark brown, belly white, brown breast-band; migrant	Similar to Swift, but lighter, greyish brown, large throat-patch; migrant	Wings and tail with black and white bars, large crest; migrant	Plumage blue, back brown, wings with black margins; migrant	Brightly coloured, throat yellow, two spikes of projecting tail feathers; migrant

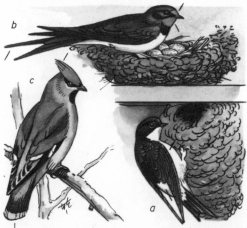

a *House-martin, *Delichon urbica:* 13 cm; rump pure white; builds a mud nest on houses, usually against a vertical wall. **b *Swallow,** *Hirundo rustica:* 19 cm; forehead and throat brownish red, long tail streamers, nests of mud, etc., in buildings, usually on a rafter. Both are insect-eating migrants of the Swallow Family, found throughout Europe with the exception of the very far north. **c *Waxwing,** *Bombycilla garrulus:* 18 cm; long head-crest, tip of tail yellow, vivid waxy tips to secondary wing feathers; nests in northern forests and moves south and west in winter, occasionally coming in large numbers to Britain.

a *Red-backed Shrike or **Butcher Bird,** *Lanius collurio:* 17 cm; back reddish brown, ♂ head and rump grey, dark eye-stripe, ♀ head and rump brown, under parts barred; migrant, in most of Europe, with the exception of the north and most of Spain. **b Great Grey Shrike,** *Lanius excubitor:* 24 cm; plumage black, white and grey, black eye-stripe; partial migrant, not found in Italy, the Balkans or in parts of Scandinavia. Both species nest in thickets, trees and hedges. They store excess food, and their 'larders' of insects and other small animals impaled on thorns may occasionally be found.

The Chiffchaff, the Grasshopper Warbler and the Marsh Warbler are small insectivorous birds belonging to the Warbler Family; the Tawny Pipit belongs to the Pipit Family and the Hedge Sparrow or Dunnock to the Accentor Family. All inhabit large areas of Europe, particularly C Europe. They nest in undergrowth or just above ground level; the Marsh Warbler builds its hanging nest between the stems of waterside plants.

	*Chiffchaff	Tawny Pipit	*Grasshopper Warbler	*Marsh Warbler	*Hedge Sparrow
Scientific Name	*Phylloscopus collybita*	*Anthus campestris*	*Locustella naevia*	*Acrocephalus palustris*	*Prunella modularis*
Size	10.5 cm	16.5 cm	13 cm	13 cm	14.5 cm
Distinguishing Features	Like Willow Warbler (page 60) but legs dark grey; song two repeated notes – 'chiff-chaff'; migrant	Upper parts almost a uniform sandy brown, under parts lighter, cream-coloured eye-stripe; migrant	Back olive-brown with dark stripes, tail faintly barred; ventriloqual song like grass-hopper; migrant	Similar to Reed Warbler (page 117), but legs flesh-coloured, back olive-brown; migrant	Beak slender, back brown with black stripes, breast grey; partial migrant

a Woodchat Shrike, *Lanius senator:* 17 cm; ♂ and ♀ crown reddish brown, head and back of young barred; migrant. **b Lesser Grey Shrike,** *Lanius minor:* 20 cm; forehead black, breast reddish; migrant. Both live in C and S Europe, but are not found in N Germany, or **a** in Spain. **c Masked Shrike,** *Lanius nubicus:* 17 cm; forehead white, crown black; said to be more graceful in its movements than the other Shrikes; migrant, lives in Greece and S Yugoslavia. All make 'larders'. All occur in Britain as rare vagrants. The song of shrikes is mainly a collection of harsh and chattering calls.

a *Blackcap,** *Sylvia atricapilla:* 14 cm; ♂ with black, ♀ with reddish brown cap; partial migrant. **b** *Lesser Whitethroat,** *Sylvia curruca:* 13.5 cm; cap and nape grey, dark cheek-stripe; migrant. **c** *Garden Warbler,** *Sylvia borin:* 14 cm; crown and upper parts uniformly greyish brown, under parts light yellowish brown; migrant. All are insect-eating, migrant song-birds of the Warbler Family, widespread throughout Europe with the exception of the north; **b** and **c** are not found in some parts of the Mediterranean region. All nest in undergrowth, the Lesser Whitethroat often in a patch of stinging nettles.

The Wren, the Firecrest and the Goldcrest are among the smallest European birds; the Robin and the Redstarts are songsters of the Thrush Family. The Firecrest and the Goldcrest build hanging nests on conifers and in undergrowth; the other birds illustrated nest on or near the ground, often near human habitations. All are native throughout almost the whole of Europe. The Robin is the British national bird.

	*Wren	*Firecrest	*Goldcrest	*Robin	*Black Redstart	*Redstart
Scientific Name	*Troglodytes troglodytes*	*Regulus ignicapillus*	*Regulus regulus*	*Erithacus rubecula*	*Phoenicurus ochruros*	*Phoenicurus phoenicurus*
Size	9.5 cm	9 cm	9 cm	14 cm	14 cm	14 cm
Distinguishing Features	Plumage brown, closely barred, tail short, erect; partial migrant	♂ crown reddish, with black border, white eye-stripe ♀ crown yellowish; partial migrant	Similar to Firecrest, but without white eye-stripe; partial migrant	Forehead and breast orange-red, upper parts olive-brown; partial migrant	Tail and rump rust-red, ♂ soot-black, white wing-bar, ♀ slate-grey; partial migrant	Tail rust-red, ♂ breast orange-red, black bib, ♀ brownish; migrant

a *Spotted Flycatcher,** *Muscicapa striata:* 14 cm; plumage greyish brown, breast lightly streaked; has the habit of flying up after insects and returning to the same perch; migrant, nests in holes; found throughout Europe. **b** *Stonechat,** *Saxicola torquata:* 13 cm; ♂ head and throat black with white half-collar, ♀ brownish; partial migrant; C, W and S Europe. **c** *Whinchat,** *Saxicola rubetra:* 13 cm; white eye-stripe, ♂ with more intensive colouring; nests on the ground in vegetation; migrant, not found in S Europe or in the far north. **b** and **c** belong to the Thrush Family; in Britain they are found mainly on moorland slopes.

a *Greenfinch,** *Chloris chloris:* 14.5 cm; ♂ olive-green, with yellow on wings and tail, ♀ duller coloured; has a wide variety of calls and sounds; partial migrant. **b** *Goldfinch,** *Carduelis carduelis:* 12 cm; ♂ and ♀ head black, white and red, black and yellow wingbands; partial migrant. **c** *Linnet,** *Carduelis cannabina:* 13 cm; ♂ forehead and breast red, throat whitish, ♀ head grey, back brown, streaked; partial migrant. All are members of the Finch Family throughout Europe except in the north. They live in gardens and farmland, nesting in available cover. In the autumn they form flocks and large numbers may sometimes be seen.

The Brambling nests at the edge of forests in the far north and is a winter visitor to most of the rest of Europe. The Ortolan Bunting (a rare visitor to Britain), the Corn Bunting and the Hawfinch are not found in the far north, the Yellowhammer not in the extreme south. These are otherwise native throughout almost the whole of Europe. Cirl Buntings are found in W and S Europe. All except the Hawfinch and Cirl Bunting nest on or just above the ground. All belong to the Finch Family.

	*Brambling	Ortolan Bunting	*Corn Bunting	*Cirl Bunting	*Yellow-hammer	*Hawfinch
Scientific Name	*Fringilla montifringilla*	*Emberiza hortulana*	*Emberiza calandra*	*Emberiza cirlus*	*Emberiza citrinella*	*Coccothraustes coccothraustes*
Size	14.5 cm	16.5 cm	18 cm	16.5 cm	16.5 cm	18 cm
Distinguishing Features	Rump white, ♂ head and back black, in winter brownish; migrant	♂ throat yellow, head and breast olive-green, ♀ lighter, young brown, streaked; migrant	Plumage brown, with distinct black stripes, wings and tail without white; partial migrant	♂ face yellow and black, throat black, ♀ striped, rump olive-brown; resident	Much yellow on head and belly, rump reddish brown, ♀ with less yellow; partial migrant	Large conical bill, tail short with white tips, white shoulder-patches, ♀ lighter; partial migrant

a Serin, *Serinus canarius:* 11.5 cm; plumage yellow, with black stripes, rump yellow; the wild ancestor of the canary; partial migrant. **b** *Bullfinch,** *Pyrrhula pyrrhula:* 14.5 cm; black cap, ♂ with carmine, ♀ with pinkish grey breast; a pest in some areas, because it destroys the blossoms of fruit trees in spring in its search for food; resident. **c** Scarlet Grosbeak, *Carpodacus erythrinus:* 14.5 cm; ♂ with red crown, breast and rump, no white wing-bars, ♀ brown, streaked; migrant. All belong to the Finch Family; they nest in bushes, **a** in large areas of Europe but not in Britain, **b** widely, except in the extreme north and south, **c** in NE Germany and further east.

a *Sparrow, *Passer domesticus*: 14.5 cm; ♂ crown grey, throat black, ♀ upper parts matt brown, breast grey; resident, very common in towns and suburbs in much of Europe, but not in Italy. **b *Tree Sparrow**, *Passer montanus*: 14 cm; ♂ and ♀ with black cheek-patch; partial migrant, not found in parts of Scandinavia, Ireland and the Balkans. Both nest in holes, **a** in buildings, **b** in trees. **c Rock Sparrow**, *Petronia petronia*: 14 cm; yellow throat-spot, white spots on tip of tail; resident, nests in clefts in rocks in the Mediterranean region, formerly also in Germany. All belong to the Sparrow Family.

Ravens are native throughout much of Europe. The Rook, which nests socially in rookeries, lives in Britain and C and E Europe. Carrion Crows are found from England, through France to Spain, Hooded Crows in Scotland and in the north, Italy, the Balkans and E Europe. Where their ranges overlap these two species interbreed. With the exception of the Jackdaw, which nests in holes, all nest in trees, the Raven also on cliff-ledges. All belong to the Crow Family.

	*Raven	*Carrion Crow	*Hooded Crow	*Rook	*Jackdaw	*Magpie
Scientific Name	*Corvus corax*	*Corvus corone*	*Corvus cornix*	*Corvus frugilegus*	*Corvus monedula*	*Pica pica*
Size	63.5 cm	47 cm	47 cm	45.5 cm	33 cm	45.5 cm
Distinguishing Features	End of tail wedge-shaped, bill very large, throat feathers shaggy; resident	Body completely black, bill black, large, tail-end straight; resident	Back and under parts grey, remainder of plumage black; partial migrant	Face white, plumage bluish black, bill more slender than in Crow; partial migrant	Plumage black, nape and ear-coverts grey, bill short; partial migrant	Plumage iridescent, black and white, tail very long, stepped; resident

a Italian Sparrow, *Passer italiae*: 14.5 cm; ♂ crown chocolate-brown, ♀ similar to Sparrow in habits, song and flight, but plumage generally brighter; resident, Italy. **b Spanish Sparrow**, *Passer hispaniolensis*: 14.5 cm; sides streaked with black; resident, nests, often colonially, in base of nests of larger birds, for example eagles or storks, otherwise in trees, not usually near houses, Spain, Corsica and Greece. **c Black-headed Bunting**, *Emberiza melanocephala*: 16.5 cm; ♂ under parts yellow, unstriped, ♀ yellow under tail-coverts; migrant, Balkans, E Italy, nests in low vegetation. **a** and **b** belong to the Sparrow Family, **c** to the Finch Family.

a Red-rumped Swallow, *Hirundo daurica:* 19 cm; rump rusty yellow, crown and back dark; migrant, nests on cliffs, buildings and bridges; Swallow Family. **b Rufous Warbler or Rufous Bush Robin,** *Cercotrichas galactotes:* 15 cm; tip of tail with black and white margin; migrant, nests in hedges in S Spain and the Balkans; thought until recently to be a Warbler, now considered to belong to the Thrush Family. **c *Dartford Warbler,** *Sylvia undata:* 13 cm; ♂ back dark grey-brown, under parts purple-brown; resident, in Italy, Spain, W France and S England, where it is near the limit of its range and suffers if there is a hard winter; the nest is built in dense undergrowth.

The Black-winged Kite nests low down in trees in Portugal, the Levant Sparrow-hawk in the Balkans; both are Birds of Prey. The Red-legged or French Partridge (Pheasant Family) and the Andalusian Hemipode nest on the ground in Spain and Portugal, the Red-legged Partridge also in S and W France and in S England. Azure-winged Magpies (Crow Family) build their nests in trees in Spain and Portugal, Blue Rock-thrushes (Thrush Family) in rock-clefts and on buildings in Mediterranean countries.

	Black-winged Kite	Levant Sparrow-hawk	*Red-legged Partridge	Andalusian Hemipode	Azure-winged Magpie	Blue Rock-thrush
Scientific Name	*Elanus caeruleus*	*Accipiter brevipes*	*Alectoris rufa*	*Turnix sylvatica*	*Cyanopica cyanus*	*Monticola solitarius*
Size	33 cm	33–38 cm	34 cm	15 cm	34 cm	20 cm
Distinguishing Features	Shoulders black, tail whitish, eyes dark red; resident	♂ cheeks grey, under parts clearly barred, ♀ throat brown-spotted; migrant	Bill and feet red, flanks with black and white bars; resident	Breast a shining reddish brown, sides with distinct black spots; resident	Black cap, wings and tail blue; resident	♂ plumage greyish blue, ♀ bluish brown, spotted; resident

a Short-toed Lark, *Calandrella brachydactyla:* 14 cm; breast light-coloured, without stripes, sings like Skylark (page 251); migrant, birds recorded in Britain, mainly from lighthouses. **b Lesser Short-toed Lark,** *Calandrella rufescens:* 14 cm; front of breast with delicate streaks; migrant. **c Thekla Lark,** *Galerida theklae:* 16 cm; similar to Crested Lark (page 251), but breast more distinctly marked; resident. Both nest on the ground on fields and waste land in Mediterranean countries. **d Black Lark,** *Melanocorypha yeltoniensis:* 19 cm; ♂ black, winter plumage with brown feather-tips; partial migrant, nests in S Russia near salt-marshes.

summer

a European Whip-snake, *Coluber viridiflavus:* up to 1.8 m, body very slender, large shields on head; bites, but is not poisonous; belongs to the Grass Snake Family. **b Horned Viper,** *Vipera ammodytes:* up to 1 m; horn at end of snout; the longest venomous snake in Europe; belongs to the Viper Family. Both snakes are found in Spain, S France and Italy, the Horned Viper also in the S Tyrol. **c Viperine Snake,** *Natrix maura:* ♂ up to 1 m, ♀ up to 83 cm; upper side of head with nine large shields, pupils round, dark spots with light centres along the sides of the body; non-poisonous; S Europe.

The Glass Snake is a legless lizard of the Slow-worm Family which lives in the Balkans and the south of the U.S.S.R. The Eyed Lizard lives on rocks and walls in the south of France and the Iberian Peninsula, the North Italian Wall Lizard in N Italy. Lilford's Wall Lizard lives only on the Balearic Islands. The Disc-fingered Gecko and the Wall Gecko, of the Gecko Family, live on walls throughout the Mediterranean area.

	Glass Snake	Eyed Lizard	North Italian Wall Lizard	Lilford's Wall Lizard	Wall Gecko	Disc-fingered Gecko
Scientific Name	*Ophiosaurus apodus*	*Lacerta lepida*	*Lacerta sicula campestris*	*Lacerta lilfordi*	*Tarentola mauritanica*	*Hemidactylis turcicus*
Size	Up to 1 m	Up to 50 cm	Up to 20 cm	Up to 20 cm	Up to 18 cm	Up to 10 cm
Distinguishing Features	Body brownish, deep furrow from behind the head to the vent	Tail very long, slender, body green, with black network, spotted with blue 'eyes'	Basic colour green to bluish, with three rows of black spots along back	Predominantly black, belly deep ultramarine, tail thick	Body plump, flattened, tubercled feet with flat toes and broad lamellae underneath	Toes wide, far more than half their length, with adhesive discs, eyes large

a Chameleon, *Chamaeleo chamaelon:* up to 30 cm; body compressed, distinct head, with large protruding eyes which can be moved independently of each other, prehensile tail, tongue can be shot out to a length of up to 25 cm; lives in S Spain. **b Hermann's** or **Greek Tortoise,** *Testudo hermanni:* carapace up to 25 cm; shield over tail divided, horny spur on tail. **c Spur-thighed Tortoise,** *Testudo graeca:* carapace up to 25 cm; conical tubercle on back of thigh, shield over tail undivided. **b** is found in the Balkans, S France and on some Mediterranean islands, **c** from Spain and the N African coast to Persia.

a †Roman Snail, *Helix pomatia:* up to 4 cm wide and 4 cm high; shell a dirty straw colour, at times with indistinct brown bands, aperture thin-lipped, whorls cross-grooved. **b *Common Garden Snail,** *Helix aspersa:* up to 4 cm wide and 3.5 cm high; aperture with distinct white lip, whorls with pitted wrinkles, lengthwise bands wide, sharply defined. Both are lung-breathing land-snails living on chalky soil, **b** only in W Europe; **a,** which is commonly eaten on the Continent, introduced as a food animal into England, where it flourishes on the Downs. When hibernating, snails secrete a plug of mucus, which dries and hardens to provide a protection against cold and moisture-loss (see illustration).

laying eggs

The snails illustrated below are widespread in hedgerows, on walls, stones and meadows. During rain or at nightfall these damp-loving animals leave their hiding-places and feed on leaves and soft fruits. The two Banded Snails and *Arianta arbustorum* belong to the Garden Snail Family. *Eulota fruticum* is a member of the Glass Shell Family, *Zebrina detrita* belongs to the Oleacids and *Clausilia ventricosa*, which has a sinistral (left-spiralling) shell, to the Doorshell Family.

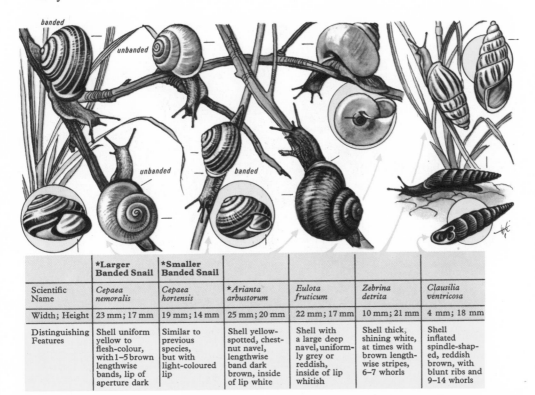

banded
unbanded
unbanded
banded

	*Larger Banded Snail	*Smaller Banded Snail				
Scientific Name	*Cepaea nemoralis*	*Cepaea hortensis*	*Arianta arbustorum*	*Eulota fruticum*	*Zebrina detrita*	*Clausilia ventricosa*
Width; Height	23 mm; 17 mm	19 mm; 14 mm	25 mm; 20 mm	22 mm; 17 mm	10 mm; 21 mm	4 mm; 18 mm
Distinguishing Features	Shell uniform yellow to flesh-colour, with 1–5 brown lengthwise bands, lip of aperture dark	Similar to previous species, but with light-coloured lip	Shell yellow-spotted, chest-nut navel, lengthwise band dark brown, inside of lip white	Shell with a large deep navel, uniformly grey or reddish, inside of lip whitish	Shell thick, shining white, at times with brown lengthwise stripes, 6–7 whorls	Shell inflated spindle-shaped, reddish brown, with blunt ribs and 9–14 whorls

a *Arion ater: 12–15 cm; respiratory pore towards front of right side of shield, body black, brick-red or brown. **b *Great Grey Slug,** *Limax maximus:* 12–15 cm; respiratory pore towards back of right side of shield, hind end of body keeled. **c *Tender Slug,** *Limax tenellus:* 4–6.5 cm; body transparent. **d *Field Slug,** *Limax reticulatus:* 3–6 cm; body with small dark lines. Slugs are closely related to snails and live in a very similar way; their lack of shell leaves them more vulnerable to dessication, but, not requiring the large amount of minerals used to build one, they are very common in gardens and fields.

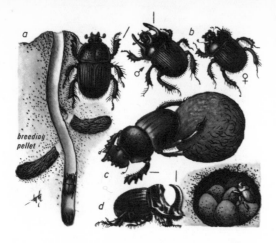

a *Lousy Watchman, *Geotrupes stercorarius:* 20–24 mm; body bluish black, forelegs with digging 'shovels'; fills tunnels with pellets of dung on which it lays its eggs. b *Minotaur Beetle, *Typhoeus typhoeus:* up to 20 mm; ♂ pronotum with three horns. Both are widespread, dung-eating members of the Dor Beetle Family. c *Scarabaeus sacer:* up to 3 cm; digging legs with five powerful teeth; makes spherical balls out of dung and lays its eggs in them. d Spanish Copris, *Copris hispanus:* up to 20 mm; body bluish black, with a horn; makes pear-shaped breeding pellets. c and d are Mediterranean members of the Scarab Family.

With the exception of *Zabrus tenebrioides*, all the Ground Beetles illustrated below are fast-moving predators which hunt insects and their larvae as well as worms and snails; all are widespread in gardens and cultivated fields. *Calosoma sycophanta* is protected in some areas because of its usefulness in controlling pests. The beetle consumes up to 400 caterpillars a year and its larva up to 40; it hunts not only on the ground but also on trees and shrubs. *Zabrus* and its larva are plant-eaters.

| | | | | | | *Tiger Beetle |
Scientific Name	*Carabus auratus	Carabus hortensis	Carabus coriaceus	Calosoma sycophanta	*Zabrus tenebrioides	Cicindela campestris
Size	Up to 24 mm	Up to 28 mm	Up to 40 mm	24–30 mm	14–16 mm	Up to 15 mm
Distinguishing Features	Elytra green, each with three lengthwise ribs	Elytra with bronze sheen and three rows of greenish golden, shining depressions	Elytra leathery, brown-black, intricately wrinkled, upper side clearly convex	Body wide blackish blue, elytra golden green, pronotum violet	Body plump, clearly convex, upper side brown or black, underside lighter, antennae short	Elytra dull grass-green, with usually five light spots

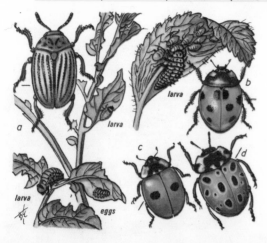

a Colorado Beetle, *Leptinotarsa decemlineata:* 10 mm; elytra yellow, with 10 black lengthwise stripes; introduced from N America, belongs to the Leaf Beetle Family. b *Seven-spotted Ladybird, *Coccinella septempunctata:* 7–8 mm; 4–9; elytra red, with a total of seven black spots. c *Two-spotted Ladybird, *Adalia bipunctata:* 4 to 5 mm; 4–9; body mostly with only two black spots. d *Eyed Ladybird, *Anatis ocellata:* 8–9 mm; 4–9; elytra with up to 10 black, light-edged spots. b, c and d are common members of the Ladybird Family, which feed on plant lice; they may sometimes be found hibernating in the shelter of houses.

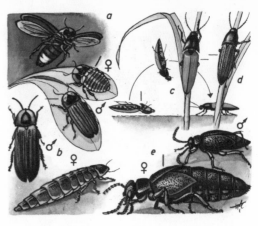

a *Phausis splendidula:* 9–11 mm; thorax with window spots where it overhangs the eyes, to permit vision, ♂ with luminous patch at end of abdomen, ♀ wings scale-like. b *Glow-worm, Lampyris noctiluca:* 11–18 mm; ♂ winged, ♀ wingless, grub-like, end of abdomen shines green in the dark; feeds on snails. Both belong to the Glow-worm Family. c *Elater sanguineus:* 11–13 mm; elytra blood-red. d *Lined Click Beetle, Agriotes lineatus:* up to 10 mm; each elytron with eight rows of spots. c and d belong to the Click Beetle Family. e *Oil Beetle, Meloë proscarabaeus:* ♀ 36 mm, ♂ 10 mm; body plump, elytra short; belongs to the Oil or Blister Beetle Family; can raise blisters on the skin if handled.

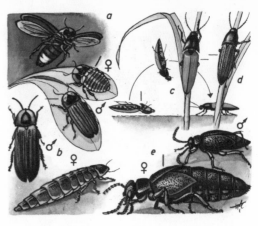

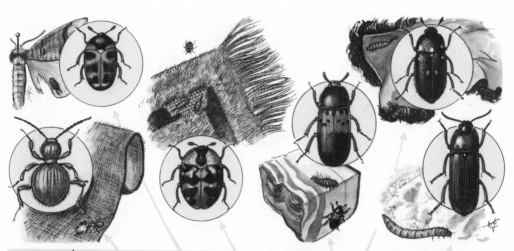

The Golden Spider Beetle or Shining Niptus, a member of the Spider Beetle Family, is a general scavenger. Flour Beetles and their larvae eat cereal crops and flour. The other beetles illustrated belong to the Hide or Carpet Beetle Family. *Anthrenus scrophulariae* and other members of the genus feed on pollen, their larvae on wool. Bacon Beetles live on smoked produce, Two-spotted Carpet Beetles and their larvae on animal hairs.

	*Golden Spider Beetle	*Museum Beetle	*Carpet Beetle	*Bacon Beetle	*Two-spotted Carpet Beetle	*Flour Beetle
Scientific Name	*Niptus hololeucus*	*Anthrenus museorum*	*Anthrenus scrophulariae*	*Dermestes lardarius*	*Attagenus pellia*	*Tenebrio molitor*
Size	Up to 4 mm	2.5–3.5 mm	Up to 4 mm	7–8 mm	4.5–5.5 mm	Up to 17 mm
Distinguishing Features	Head and thorax narrow, abdomen very wide, body covered with dense, brass-coloured hairs	Body wide, with three light-coloured transverse zigzag lines	Similar to Museum Beetle, but body black, transverse bands indistinct	Grey band with dark spots on elytra	Body bluish black, hairy, legs and antennae brown, each elytron with a light spot	Body black, antennae and legs brown, elytra with deep length-wise grooves

a *Black Burying Beetle, Necrophorus humator:* 18–24 mm; body bluish black, last three body segments not covered by elytra. b *Common Burying Beetle, Necrophorus vespillo:* 11–20 cm; elytra with two orange-red bands. c *Silpha obscura:* 13–17 mm; body black, elytra each with three lengthwise ribs. All belong to the Burying Beetle Family; they are strong fliers which may be attracted a long distance by the smell of carrion; using legs and head as shovels, they bury the corpses of small animals to provide food in moist condition for the larvae. d *Hister fimetarius:* 7–7.5 mm; each elytron with one red spot; a carrion-eating member of the Histerid Beetle Family.

a ***Death's-head Hawk Moth,** *Acherontia atropos:* 12 cm; 6–9; thorax with skull-like marking; caterpillars up to 12 cm long, mainly on plants of the Potato Family; throughout Europe, except the north; makes a squeaking noise if handled. b ***Eyed Hawk Moth,** *Smerintha ocellata:* 7.5 cm; 6–8, each hind wing with one large blue eye-spot; well camouflaged on tree-bark, but if surprised by a bird will display the eye-spots to startle it and allow escape; caterpillars on willows, poplars and fruit trees. c ***Spurge Hawk Moth,** *Celerio euphorbiae:* 8 cm; 6–9; hind wings with red and black stripes; caterpillars on species of spurge. All belong to the Hawk Moth Family.

More Hawk Moths are illustrated below. All are widespread through much of Europe. The Elephant Hawk Moths lay their eggs on willow-herb and bedstraw, occasionally also on vines. These moths have a tuft of hairs on the end of the abdomen that looks like a sting, but, like the other moths, they are harmless. The other species are named after the plants on which they usually lay their eggs and on the foliage of which the larvae feed. Many are migratory in their habits.

	*Bedstraw Hawk Moth	*Small Elephant Hawk Moth	*Elephant Hawk Moth	*Lime Hawk Moth	*Privet Hawk Moth	*Convolvulus Hawk Moth
Scientific Name	*Celerio galii*	*Deilephila porcellus*	*Deilephila elpenor*	*Mimas tiliae*	*Sphinx ligustri*	*Herse convolvuli*
Size; Flying	7 cm; 5–6	4.5 cm; 5–8	6 cm; 5–6	6.5 cm; 4–7	10.5 cm; 5–7	11.5 cm; 5–9
Distinguishing Features	Fore and hind wings with wide, yellowish white band	Fore wings somewhat curved, front and outer margins rose-coloured	Wings rose-coloured, hind wings with black base	Fore wings ochre to grey, clouded with brown, hind wings very small	Hind wings and abdomen rose-coloured with black transverse bands	Hind wings with black transverse stripes, abdomen rose, with black stripes

a ***Poplar Hawk Moth,** *Laothoe populi:* 8.5 cm; 5–7; wings ash-grey, margins indented, fore wings with dark band. b ***Narrow-bordered Bee Hawk Moth,** *Hemaris tityus:* 4 cm; 5–6 and 8; wings with large transparent, brown-edged area. c ***Broad-bordered Bee Hawk Moth,** *Hemaris fuciformis:* 4 cm; 5–6 and 7–8; similar to **b,** but wings with wide brown edges. **b** and **c** are bee-mimics. d ***Humming-bird Hawk Moth,** *Macroglossum stellatarum:* 4.5 cm; 6 and 10; hind wings rust-red; flies by day, looks like a humming-bird hovering in front of plants; migratory; eggs on bedstraw. All are widespread in much of temperate Europe.

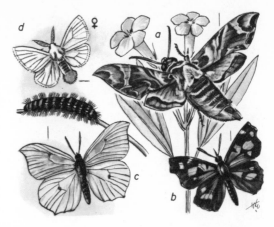

a *Oleander Hawk Moth,** *Daphnis nerii:* up to 8.5 cm; body broad, wings colourful, green, whitish, rose and violet; caterpillars on Oleander; very rare in Britain. **b Short Butterfly.** *Libythea celtis:* up to 4 cm; 5 and 6–7; wings with zigzag edge, brown with orange-red spots; Tortoiseshell Family. **c** *Gonepteryx cleopatra:* 5–6 cm; 7–8 and 3–4; wings lemon, ♀ somewhat lighter; Whites Family. **b** and **c** live in the Mediterranean region. **d** *Browntail,** *Euproctis chrysorrhoea:* ♂ 3.2 cm, ♀ 4 cm; 7–8; tail with dark yellow woolly hairs, a thick tuft on ♀; winter spent in early larval stage in communal silk cocoon (larval hairs can cause skin rash); widespread; Browntail Family.

The insects illustrated below are all Bees. After mating the females of these species lead a solitary life and build simple or branched nests in the ground or in hollows. The Poppy Mason-bee lines its underground nest with the petals of poppies or cornflowers. The Leaf-cutter Bee lines its nest-cells with rose leaves. The Two-coloured Mason-bee often makes its breeding cells in empty snail shells.

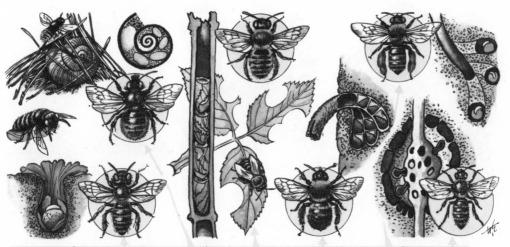

	Poppy Mason-bee	*Two-coloured Mason-bee	*Leaf-cutter Bee			
Scientific Name	*Osmia papaveris*	*Osmia bicolor*	*Megachile centuncularis*	*Anthrophora parietina*	*Dasypoda hirtipes*	*Halictus quadricinctus*
Size	10–15 mm	9–10 mm	Up to 12 mm	13–15 mm	15–17 mm	Up to 14 mm
Distinguishing Features	Body black and yellow, belly with dense hairs, collects pollen on its belly	Head and thorax black, abdomen with dense red hairs	Thorax rusty red, abdomen black, with rust-red pollen brushes on the underside	Body compressed, with dense hairs, thorax yellowish brown; builds in clay walls	Tibia and tarsus of ♀ strongly hairy, forming pollen baskets; nest with branched passages	Body dark, long and narrow, segments of abdomen clearly marked

a *Mottled Umber,** *Erannis defoliaria:* ♂ 25 mm, ♀ smaller, wingless; 10–12; ♂ wings whitish, with darker transverse bands. **b** *Magpie Moth,** *Abraxas grossulariata:* up to 40 mm; 5–6; wings white with black spots and orange-red lines. Both belong to the Geometer Moth Family; the caterpillars live on fruit trees or gooseberries, respectively, and are known as loopers or measuring worms, as they move by humping their body into a loop, then throwing themselves forward. **c** *Clothes Moth,** *Tineola biselliella:* 12 mm; 5–9; body and wings ochre. **d** *Carpet Moth,** *Trichophaga tapetzella:* 12 mm; 6–7; wings white with grey marbling. **c** and **d** belong to the Clothes Moth Family.

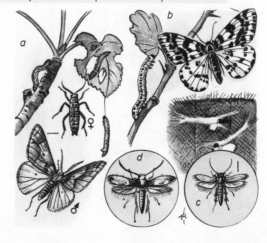

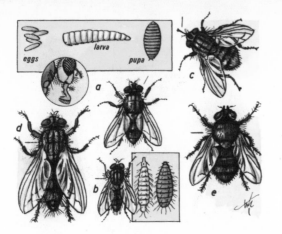

a *House Fly, *Musca domestica:* 10 mm; body black, eyes hairless; a scavenger, breeds mainly in rubbish-dumps; cannot chew, needs moist or liquid food. Inset shows proboscis extended for sucking. **b *Lesser House Fly,** *Fannia canicularis:* up to 6 mm; ♂ thorax with three dark lengthwise stripes; maggots spiny. **c *Stable Fly** or **Biting House Fly,** *Stomoxys calcitrans:* up to 9 mm; proboscis projects horizontally. All of House Fly Family. **d Checkered Flesh Fly,** *Sarcophaga carnaria:* 10–15 mm; thorax with three dark lengthwise stripes; lays living larvae on meat. **e Blue Bottle,** *Calliphora erythrocephala:* 9–13 mm; body steely blue; Blue Bottle Family.

The Brown Centipede has one pair of walking legs on each body segment. *Iulus sabulosus* and *Glomeris marginata* are Millipedes with two pairs of walking legs on each body segment. All are widespread in damp places in rotten wood or under stones, *Glomeris marginata* also being found by paths. *Chelifer cancroides* is a widespread False Scorpion, *Opilio parietinus*, which lives on walls or under stones, is a Harvestman. The Sheep Tick is a parasitic Mite which may attach itself to humans.

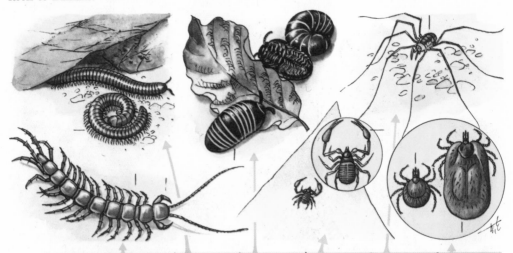

	*Brown Centipede		*Pill Bug			*Sheep Tick
Scientific Name	*Lithobius forficatus*	**Iulus sabulosus*	*Glomeris marginata*	**Chelifer cancroides*	**Opilio parietinus*	*Ixodes ricinus*
Size	2–3 cm	6–17 mm	7–20 mm	Up to 4 mm	8–10 mm	♂ 3.5 mm,
Distinguishing Features	Body flattened, shining chestnut-brown, 15 pairs of legs, mandibles on 1st segment	Body cylindrical, rolls up into spiral, brown to black	Body shining black, ♀ with 17, ♂ with 19 pairs of legs; rolls up	Body wide, flattened, pincers conspicuously large, no poisonous sting	Body light brownish, belly whitish, back with dark marking	♀ 4 mm; blood-sucking, when satiated up to 11 mm long, barbed piercing proboscis

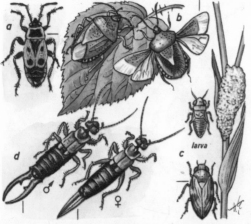

a *Red or **Fire Bug,** *Pyrrhocoris apterus:* 9–11 mm; body vivid black and red, wings short. **b *Sloe Bug,** *Dolycoris baccarum:* up to 12 mm; body brown, elytra horny from base to centre, the remaining half membranous. **a** and **b** are common Plant Bugs, which suck plant juices. **c *Common Frog-hopper,** *Philaenus spumarius:* 5–6 mm; body brown, slender; larvae produce 'cuckoo-spit' and damage young plants in spring. **d *Common Earwig,** *Forficula auricularia:* up to 2 cm; body brown, two forceps at hind end, curved in ♂, straight in ♀; spends day squeezed into small spaces, feeds at night on waste; brood-chambers in soil.

Mountains

In mountains, above foothills rising to about 600 m, several zones or belts may be recognized, according to the height above sea-level. In Central Europe a forest zone of deciduous and mixed trees extends from 600–1400 m, where many well-known woodland plants and animals are found (pages 17–67). This gives way to the subalpine zone which extends from 1400 m to the timber-line, which, depending on the topography, varies between 1800 and 2200 m; this zone is charac-terized by coniferous forests consisting of fir, Swiss pine, larch and spruce, etc. Up to 3000 m and higher, between the timber-line and the snow zone, lies the alpine zone, where dwarf shrubs and 'cushion' plants predominate in alpine meadows, on scree and in crevices of rocks. Many of the plants of the alpine zone are found also in cold regions, for example in Arctic and subarctic Europe, particularly in the mountain tundra. The fauna of the alpine zone is composed of few species, because hardly any animals can survive the winter unless, like the Marmot, they protect themselves by burying in the earth, or, like the Wild Goat or the Chamois, they retreat to lower regions. There is evidence that in ancient times many alpine animals inhabited those lower regions year round, but in the face of growing human persecution they were forced up the higher levels.

a *****Dwarf Juniper,** *Juniperus communis* subsp. *nana:* shrub, up to 100 cm; needles closely set, small, slightly prickly; 5–6; up to 3000 m and higher, also at low altitudes in the north. **b Rock Cedar** or **Savin,** *Juniperus sabina:* shrub, up to 200 cm; leaves small, scale-like, overlapping; poisonous; 4–5; S and C Europe, from 1000–2000 m, also at low altitudes in the east. Both belong to the Cypress Family. **c Rock Buckthorn,** *Rhamnus saxatilis:* shrub, up to 150 cm; tips of branches thorny; 5–6. **d Alpine Buckthorn,** *Rhamnus pumilus:* shrub, 5–20 cm; leaves clustered at ends of branches; 6–7. Both belong to the Buckthorn Family, and occur in the Alps.

The Broad-leaved Spindle-tree is a member of the Spindle-tree Family growing in the Alps and their foothills. The other shrubs shown below are evergreen members of the Heath Family occurring in the dwarf-shrub belt, up to 2400 m. The Rusty-leaved Rhododendron grows on basic rocks, the Alpine Rose and the Ground-cistus on calcareous ground, the latter in the E Alps, the Mountain Azalea and the Black Bearberry on heaths and moors of N and C Europe, the Pyrenees, S Alps and N Balkans.

	Broad-leaved Spindle-tree	Rusty-leaved Rhodo-dendron	Alpine Rose	Ground-cistus	*Mountain Azalea	*Black Bearberry
Scientific Name	*Euonymus latifolius*	*Rhododendron ferrugineum*	*Rhododendron hirsutum*	*Rhodothamnus chamaecistus*	*Loiseleuria procumbens*	*Arctous alpina*
Size	Up to 5 m	Up to 90 cm	Up to 90 cm	10–15 cm	Up to 30 cm	Up to 30 cm
Distinguishing Features; Flowering Time	Shrub or tree, leaves up to 15 cm long, fruit winged; 5–6	Leaves rusty brown beneath, flowers dark red; poisonous; 6–7	Leaves fringed, with rusty brown glandular dots on both sides, flowers red; 6–7	Flowers mainly in twos, 5-lobed almost to their base, style long; 5–7	Branches decumbent, ascending up to 2–6 cm, flowers in few-flowered clusters; 6–8	Decumbent, leaves soft, flowers white and greenish, drupes globose, bluish black; 5–6

a Flesh-coloured Heath, *Erica herbacea:* shrub, 15–35 cm; filaments longer than the corolla-tube; 3–4; mountains of S and C Europe. **b White Arctic Bell-heather,** *Cassiope tetragona:* shrub, 10–30 cm; flowers white, with long stalks, nodding; 7–8; mountains and tundra of N Europe. Both belong to the Heath Family. **c Drooping Rose,** *Rosa pendulina:* shrub, 50–150 cm; plants almost without prickles; 6–7; mountains of S and C Europe. **d *Mountain Avens,** *Dryas octo-petala:* a creeping under-shrub, 2–15 cm; leaves downy beneath, flowers long-stalked; 5–8; mountains and tundra of N and C Europe. Both belong to the Rose Family.

a Brown Willow, *Salix waldsteiniana:* shrub, up to 50 cm; leaves glabrous, catkins short-stalked; 6–7; E Alps and NW Balkans. **b Blunt-leaved Willow,** *Salix retusa:* shrub, 2–30 cm; leaves small; 6–8; Alps, Pyrenees, Apennines, Carpathians and Balkans. **c *Least Willow,** *Salix herbacea:* shrub, 1–10 cm; leaves small, catkins few-flowered; 6–8; mountains and tundra of N Europe, south to the Pyrenees, C Apennines and Bulgaria. **d *Dwarf Willow,** *Salix reticulata:* shrub, 5–30 cm; leaves net-veined, bluish green; 7–8; mountains and tundra of N Europe, south to the S Alps and Macedonia. All belong to the Willow Family and grow on damp grassland and scree at 1600–3000 m.

The Alpine and Black Honeysuckle (shrubs of the Honeysuckle Family) grow in forests and on slopes, sometimes near the timber-line on S and C European and Balkan mountains. The Common Service-berry grows in open woods in S and C Europe. The Common Cotoneaster is widespread but local, the Downy Cotoneaster occurs in mountains of S, C and W Europe and the Balkans, both growing on rocky slopes and open woods. The last three shrubs belong to the Rose Family. The Common Barberry (Barberry Family) is widespread but often local.

	Alpine Honeysuckle	Black Honeysuckle	Common Service-berry	*Common Cotoneaster	Downy Cotoneaster	*Common Barberry
Scientific Name	*Lonicera alpigena*	*Lonicera nigra*	*Amelanchier ovalis*	*Cotoneaster integerrimus*	*Cotoneaster nebrodensis*	*Berberis vulgaris*
Size	50–150 cm	60–150 cm	Up to 300 cm	50–300 cm	50–200 cm	Up to 300 cm
Distinguishing Features; Flowering Time	Leaves sharply pointed, flowers reddish, fruits cherry-red; 5–6	Flowers reddish or white, their stalks 3–4 times as long as the flowers, fruits black; 5–6	Sepals narrow, wedge-shaped, fruits globose, black, sweet, edible; 4–6	Leaves up to 4 cm long, sepals hairy at base, fruits red; 5–6	Leaves up to 4 cm long, calyx and flower-stalks white-downy, fruits red; 4–5	Flowers in drooping racemes; berries scarlet; 5–6

a *Mezereon, *Daphne mezereum:* shrub, 20–120 cm; leaves wedge-shaped, flowers purple, rarely white, in threes on each branch; 2–4; widespread and local. **b *Common Spurge-laurel,** *Daphne laureola:* shrub, 50–150 cm; flowers yellowish green; 2–4; widespread and uncommon. **c Striated Spurge-laurel,** *Daphne striata:* shrub, 7 to 20 cm; leaves linear, flowers red, in terminal umbels; 6–8. **d Garland-flower,** *Daphne cneorum:* shrub, 7–30 cm; leaves spathulate. All are members of the Daphne Family growing in wooded areas, mainly in mountain forests.

a Austrian Clematis, *Clematis alpina*: a woody climber, 1–2 m; flowers large, solitary, violet, long-stalked; 5–7; N, S and C Europe; Buttercup Family. **b Box-leaved Milkwort,** *Polygala chamaebuxus*: shrub, 10–20 cm; flowers yellow or reddish, leaves with sharp point; 4–6; C Europe; Milkwort Family. **c †Barrenwort,** *Epimedium alpinum*: ⨉, 20–30 cm; stems numerous, each with one 2–3-ternate leaf; 3–4; NE Italy, S Austria and NW Balkans, naturalized elsewhere; Barberry Family. **d Common Peony,** *Paeonia officinalis*: ⨉, 30–90 cm; leaves 2-ternate, flowers red, rarely white; 5–6; S and SC Europe; Buttercup Family, sometimes regarded as a separate family—the Peony Family.

The Christmas Rose (E Alps and Apennines), the Green Hellebore (W and C Europe), the Blackish Columbine (Alps and Apennines), the Common Bee-larkspur (NE and C Europe, Yugoslavia and mountains of C Europe) and the Panicled Monkshood (mountains of C Italy and Rumania) grow mainly in mountain forests and alpine grasslands, up to 2150 m. The Small-flowered Columbine is a plant of rocky places and grassy slopes in the Alps, ascending to 2000 m. All belong to the Buttercup Family.

	Christmas Rose	*Green Hellebore	Small-flowered Columbine	Blackish Columbine	Common Bee-larkspur	Panicled Monkshood
Scientific Name	*Helleborus niger*	*Helleborus viridis*	*Aquilegia einseleana*	*Aquilegia atrata*	*Delphinium elatum*	*Aconitum paniculatum*
Longevity, Size	⨉, 10–30 cm	⨉, 10–40 cm	⨉, 15–40 cm	⨉, 20–70 cm	⨉, 60–150 cm	⨉, to 150 cm
Distinguishing Features; Flowering Time	Basal leaves pedate, with 7–9 segments, perianth-segments 5, white or pinkish, poisonous; 11–4	Stem leaves (bracts) digitate, with narrow segments, follicles 20–28 mm; 3–4	Stems few-flowered, flowers small, bluish violet, spur almost straight; 5–6	Flowers brownish violet, nodding, spur straight, with a hooked tip; 5–7	Leaves palmate, with broad lobes, ovaries usually 3, rarely 5; 6–7	Leaves palmately 5–7-partite, flowers violet, long-stalked, spur head-like; 7–9

a *Common Monkshood, *Aconitum napellus*: ⨉, 50–150 cm; upper perianth-segment hood-shaped, broader than high; poisonous; 6–8; W and WC Europe. **b Wolf's Bane,** *Aconitum lasiostomum*: ⨉, 50–250 cm; hood narrow, elongate; 6–7; C and S U.S.S.R. and Rumania. **c Lesser Monkshood,** *Aconitum variegatum*: ⨉, 50–150 cm; hood violet, up to twice as high as wide, hemispherical to conical; 7–9; C Europe, extending to C Italy and W Ukraine. **d *Alpine Meadow-rue,** *Thalictrum alpinum*: ⨉, 5–12 cm; stem usually leafless; 7–8; N Europe, extending to the Pyrenees, Alps and E Carpathians. All belong to the Buttercup Family and grow in meadows, grasslands, on rocky slopes and ledges.

a **Alpine Anemone**, *Pulsatilla alpina*: 4, 15–30 cm; flowers large, white or yellow, much overtopping the bracts; 6–8; S and C Europe. b **Daffodil Anemone**, *Anemone narcissiflora*: 4, 10–50 cm; flowers 3–8, in an umbel; 5–7; S and C Europe. c **Mountain Anemone**, *Pulsatilla montana*: 4, 8–30 cm; bracts multifid, hairy; 3–4; from Switzerland to E Rumania and Bulgaria. d **Tyrolean Anemone**, *Anemone baldensis*: 4, 5–12 cm; stem downy, with solitary flower; 6–8; Alps and mountains of Yugoslavia, up to 3000 m. All are poisonous members of the Buttercup Family, growing in alpine meadows, on rocky slopes and among shrubs in the Alps up to 2200–2800 m.

The members of the Buttercup Family shown below are frequent or local in alpine grasslands, up to at least 2000 m; the Fair Maids of France in C, S, W Europe and the Balkans, the Parnassus-grass Crowfoot in the Alps, Pyrenees and N Spain, the Mountain Crowfoot on most mountains of C Europe, the Ice Crowfoot in N, W and C Europe (on the Finsteraarhorn, in Switzerland, at 4275 m), the Alpine Crowfoot in C and W Europe, and the rare Pyrenean Crowfoot in the Alps, Pyrenees and mountains of Spain and Corsica.

	Fair Maids of France	Parnassus-grass Crowfoot	Mountain Crowfoot	Ice Crowfoot	Alpine Crowfoot	Pyrenean Crowfoot
Scientific Name	*Ranunculus aconitifolius*	*Ranunculus parnassifolius*	*Ranunculus montanus*	*Ranunculus glacialis*	*Ranunculus alpestris*	*Ranunculus pyrenaeus*
Longevity, Size	4, 20–80 cm	4, 4–10 cm	4, 9–15 cm	4, 11–15 cm	4, 5–10 cm	4, 5–15 cm
Distinguishing Features; Flowering Time	Stem many-flowered, basal leaves long-stalked, palmately 3–7-lobed; 5–8	Leaves ovate, heart-shaped at base, woolly on the upper surface, flowers reddish white; 6–8	Stem solid, 1–3-flowered, stem leaves 1–3, deeply divided; 4–8	Flowers white to deep red, calyx dark rusty brown, hairy; 7–8	Stem 1 or 2, upright, usually with a solitary flower, basal leaves long-stalked; 5–9	Stem 1–2-flowered, leaves narrowly lanceolate, petals pure white; 5–9

a **Kidney-leaved Crowfoot**, *Ranunculus thora*: 4, 5–30 cm; lowest stem leaf large, kidney-shaped; poisonous; 5–7; on mountains of C and W Europe and the Balkans. b **Hybrid Crowfoot**, *Ranunculus hybridus*: 4, 10–15 cm; similar to a, but always with a basal leaf; poisonous; 6–8; in the E Alps and N Balkans. c **Dwarf Crowfoot**, *Ranunculus pygmaeus*: 4, 1–4 cm; stem leaves usually 2, deeply trifid; 6–8; on mountains of N and C Europe. d **Callianthemum**, *Callianthemum kerneranum*: 4, 5–20 cm; leaves 2- to 3-pinnate; 6–8; S Alps. All are members of the Buttercup Family, growing in alpine grasslands up to 2400 m and more.

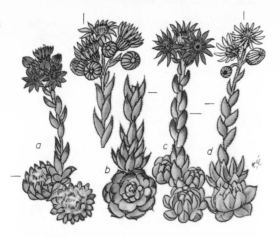

a Cobweb Houseleek, *Sempervivum arachnoideum:* ♃, 5–12 cm; rosette-leaves covered with a dense cobwebby mass of fine glandular hairs; 7–8; Alps and Pyrenees, 280–2900 m. **b Houseleek,** *Sempervivum tectorum:* ♃, 10–35 cm; petals pale red, 3 to 4 times as long as sepals; 7–8; S, C and W Europe, 600–2700 m. **c Mountain Houseleek,** *Sempervivum montanum:* ♃, 5–25 cm; plant with glandular, woolly hairs; 7–9; S, C and W Europe, 1700–3400 m. **d Wulfen's Houseleek,** *Sempervivum wulfenii:* ♃, 10–30 cm; leaves glandular-hairy on margins; 7–8; Alps, 1700–2700 m. All are members of the Stonecrop Family found in alpine grasslands, on rocks and scree.

The Roseroot occurs on mountains in N and C Europe, southwards to the Pyrenees, C Italy and Bulgaria, the Blackish Stonecrop in S and C Europe, and the Annual Stonecrop in N, C and S Europe. These are typical high mountain plants, growing at up to 3000 m and more. The other species are not found above 1500 m; the Mountain Orpine mainly in W and C Europe, the Thick-leaved Stonecrop mainly in S and C Europe, and the White Stonecrop widespread but uncommon in most parts. All belong to the Stonecrop Family.

fruit

	*Roseroot	*Mountain Orpine	Blackish Stonecrop	Annual Stonecrop	†Thick-leaved Stonecrop	†White Stonecrop
Scientific Name	Rhodiola rosea	Sedum telephium subsp. fabaria	Sedum atratum	Sedum annuum	Sedum dasyphyllum	Sedum album
Longevity, Size	♃, 10–35 cm	♃, 20–70 cm	⊙, 3–8 cm	⊙, 5–15 cm	♃, 5–15 cm	♃, 10–30 cm
Distinguishing Features; Flowering Time	Leaves serrate, flowers dioecious, tetramerous, yellowish, tinged with red; 7–8	Leaves wedge-shaped, narrowing into a stalk, petals purplish red; 6–7	Leaves almost terete, flowers white, greenish or reddish, pentamerous; 7–8	Leaves linear, almost flat above, flowers yellow, in loose cyme-like inflorescence; 6–8	Leaves flat above, convex beneath, 3–7 mm long, flowers white or pink; 7–8	Plant grass-green, leaves cylindrical, 5–15 mm long, flowers white or violet; 6–7

a Alpine Stonecrop, *Sedum alpestre:* ♃, 3–15 cm; leaves linear; 6–8; S and C Europe; Stonecrop Family. **b Burser's Saxifrage,** *Saxifraga burseriana:* ♃, 3–8 cm; leaves with pointed tips; 3–6; rocks and scree in the Alps, up to 2500 m. **c Seguier's Saxifrage,** *Saxifraga seguieri:* ♃, 1–4 cm; leaves in a rosette; 6–7; snow patches and screes in the Alps, 3700 m. **d Stonecrop Saxifrage,** *Saxifraga sedoides:* ♃, 2–5 cm; stems 1–3-flowered; 6–9; snow patches and scree in the Alps, Apennines and Balkan mountains. **e Leafless Saxifrage,** *Saxifraga aphylla:* ♃, 2–5 cm; leaves 3–5-fid; 7–9; snow patches and stony places in the Alps. All belong to the Saxifrage Family.

a Two-flowered Saxifrage, *Saxifraga biflora:* ♃, up to 20 cm; leaves opposite, flowers red, usually 2; 7–8; screes and stony and gravelly places, Alps. **b *Yellow Mountain Saxifrage,** *Saxifraga aizoides:* ♃, 10–30 cm; leaves fleshy, petals yellow with orange-red spots; 6–8; damp places, N and C Europe, Pyrenees, to C Italy and the Balkans. **c Round-leaved Saxifrage,** *Saxifraga rotundifolia:* ♃, 10–70 cm; basal leaves long-stalked, hairy; 6–9; damp and shady places, S and C Europe, 800–2200 m. **d Silver Saxifrage,** *Saxifraga paniculata:* ♃, 10–45 cm; margins of leaves with white lime-secreting glands; 5–8; N, S and C Europe, Balkans, up to 3415 m. All belong to the Saxifrage Family.

The members of the Saxifrage Family shown below grow at altitudes over 3000 m on mountain moraines, rocks and scree, and in crevices and snow patches. The Starry and the Purple Saxifrages are widespread and common. The Musk Saxifrage grows in the Alps up to 4000 m; the Bluish in S and C Europe and the Balkans; the Stiff-haired Saxifrage in the Alps, up to 4000 m, the Apennines and the Pyrenees; the Rock-jasmine Saxifrage in C Europe and the Balkans.

	Musk Saxifrage	*Starry Saxifrage	Stiff-haired Saxifrage	*Purple Saxifrage	Bluish Saxifrage	Rock-jasmine Saxifrage
Scientific Name	*Saxifraga moschata*	*Saxifraga stellaris*	*Saxifraga aspera*	*Saxifraga oppositifolia*	*Saxifraga caesia*	*Saxifraga androsacea*
Longevity, Size	♃, 1–12 cm	♃, 2–15 cm	♃, 3–6 cm	♃, up to 25 cm	♃, 4–12 cm	♃, 1–10 cm
Distinguishing Features; Flowering Time	Stems upright, leaves usually 3–5-fid, flowers yellow, rarely purple; 7–8	Leaves in a rosette, often coarsely toothed, fleshy, flowering stem glandular-hairy; 6–8	Plant forming a 'cushion', leaves prickly toothed, petals cream-coloured; 7–8	Stem densely leafy, flowers solitary, terminal, lilac to wine-coloured; 5–7	Plant forming a 'cushion', leaves curved, bluish green; 6–9	Plant forming a 'cushion', leaves usually with 3 teeth at tip, gland-ular-fringed on margins; 5–7

a Wood Goatsbeard, *Aruncus sylvestris:* ♃, 90 to 120 cm; panicles dense, terminal; 5–7; woods, thickets, banks of streams in W, C and E Europe. **b *Alpine Lady's Mantle,** *Alchemilla alpina:* ♃, 10–30 cm; lower leaves palmately 5–7-lobed, densely silky hairy beneath; 6–8; widespread and common, mountain grassland, crevices and scree, up to 2600 m. **c *Least Cinquefoil,** *Sibbaldia procumbens:* ♃, 2–20 cm; leaves ternate, with 3 teeth at tip; 6–8; mountain-tops and grassland in most of Europe, 1350-3330 m. **d Frigid Cinquefoil,** *Potentilla frigida:* ♃, 5–15 cm; leaves ternate, inflorescence downy; 6–7; rock-crevices and screes, Alps and Pyrenees. All belong to the Rose Family.

a Dwarf Cinquefoil, *Potentilla brauniana:*
♃, 5–15 cm; leaves ternate, flowers yellow,
solitary; 6–8; Alps and Pyrenees. **b Golden
Cinquefoil,** *Potentilla aurea:* ♃, 4–35 cm;
leaves with shining silky hairs on margins;
6–9. **c *Alpine Cinquefoil,** *Potentilla crant-
zii:* ♃, 5–20 cm; stems hairy, basal leaves
palmate, with 5 leaflets; 6–9; in mountains
of C Europe and the Balkans. **d Stem Cinquefoil,** *Potentilla caulescens:* ♃, 10–30 cm;
leaves with 3–7 unequal teeth at tip, petals
notched; 7–9; S and C Europe and the Balkans. All belong to the Rose Family and grow
in stony mountain grassland and on scree,
up to 3300 m.

The first three species shown belong to the Rose Family. They grow in alpine meadows and on
rocky slopes; Clusius's Cinquefoil in the Alps (up to 3300 m) and Balkans, the Creeping Avens
in the Alps (above 2000 m), Carpathians and Balkans, the Mountain Avens in S and C Europe,
usually at about 1500 m. The trefoils (Pea Family) occur in similar habitats; the Alpine Trefoil
in S, W and C Europe (up to 3100 m) and the Balkans, the Brown Trefoil in C Europe (up to
3000 m), the Tufted in the W Alps (up to 2500 m), Jura, Apennines, Pyrenees and Spain.

	Clusius's Cinquefoil	Creeping Avens	Yellow Mountain Avens	Alpine Trefoil	Brown Trefoil	Tufted Trefoil
Scientific Name	*Potentilla clusiana*	*Geum reptans*	*Geum montanum*	*Trifolium alpinum*	*Trifolium badium*	*Trifolium thalii*
Longevity, Size	♃, 4–6 cm	♃, 5–15 cm	♃, 5–25 cm	♃, 5–15 cm	☉-☉, 8–25 cm	♃, 5–15 cm
Distinguishing Features; Flowering Time	Leaves usually pinnately 5–lobed, leaflets with 5 teeth at tip, flowers whitish; 6–8	Stoloniferous, basal leaves lyrate, term-inal leaflet slightly lar-ger than the others; 7–8	Basal leaves lyrate, term-inal leaflet very large; 5–8	Leaves ternate, long-stalked, flowers purple, in umbel-like heads; 6–8	Leaflets finely serrate, stip-ules ovate, sharp-tipped, flowers becom-ing chestnut brown; 6–8	Stipules membranous, whitish, flowers white, becoming pink; 7–8

a Western Pea, *Lathyrus laevigatus* subsp.
occidentalis: ♃, 20–60 cm; raceme one-sided,
3–12-flowered; 6–8; S Alps. **b Common
Mountain Milk-vetch,** *Oxytropis montana:*
♃, 5–15 cm; flowers violet, 5–15 in each
raceme; 7–8; N, W and C Europe, 1700 to
3000 m. **c *Yellow Mountain Milk-vetch,**
Oxytropis campestris: ♃, 5–15 cm; flowers
yellowish white, in head-like racemes; 7–8;
N Europe, Alps (1800–2000 m), Pyrenees and
Carpathians. **d Stemless Milk-vetch,** *Astragalus exscapus:* ♃, up to 15 cm; flowers yellow,
3–9; 5–7; S and SC Europe. All belong to the
Pea Family and occur in dry mountain meadows, on stony slopes and rocky ledges.

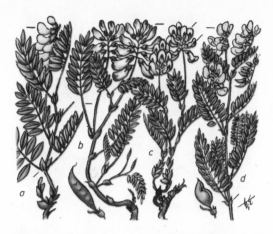

a Frigid Milk-vetch, *Astragalus frigidus:* ♃ 20–40 cm; stipules 1–2 cm long, pale green, flowers yellowish white; 7–8; N Europe, Alps, Carpathians, Balkans. **b *Alpine Milk-vetch,*** *Astragalus alpinus:* ♃, 10–30 cm; leaflets 17 to 25, wings white, standard violet; 7–8; N and C Europe, Pyrenees. **c Swiss Milk-vetch,** *Astragalus helveticus:* ♃, 10–30 cm; leaflets 11–13, flowers whitish, keel violet at tip; 5–6; Alps, Pyrenees, Apennines, Balkans. **d Drooping Milk-vetch,** *Astragalus penduliflorus:* ♃, up to 50 cm; stipules up to 1 cm long, leaflets 5–23, flowers yellow; 7–8; Alps and Carpathians. All belong to the Pea Family; stony mountain meadows up to 2200 m.

The Sheath Vetch is widespread in dry mountain grassland and scrub at 2230–2880 m, in C Europe, Italy and Yugoslavia, the Alpine Hedysarum in S and C Europe; both of Pea Family. The Gravel Willow-herb (Willow-herb Family) grows by streams in the Alps, up to 2500 m, the Alpine Milkwort (Milkwort Family), in meadows of the Alps (up to 2300 m), Jura and Pyrenees, the Alpine Rock-rose (Rock-rose Family) in the Alps (up to 2950 m) and Pyrenees, the Slender St John's Wort (St John's Wort Family), widespread, in open situations.

	Sheath Vetch	Alpine Hedysarum	Gravel Willow-herb	Alpine Milkwort	Alpine Rock-rose	*Slender St John's Wort
Scientific Name	*Coronilla vaginalis*	*Hedysarum hedysaroides*	*Chamaenerion fleischeri*	*Polygala alpestris*	*Helianthemum alpestre*	*Hypericum pulchrum*
Longevity, Size	♃, 10–25 cm	♃, 1–25 cm	♃, 10–40 cm	♃, 5–15 cm	Up to 12 cm	♃, 15–80 cm
Distinguishing Features; Flowering Time	Leaves bluish green, short-stalked, with 2–9 pairs of leaflets, pods jointed; 5–7	Leaves with 5–9 pairs of leaflets, raceme dense, pods jointed; 7–8	Leaves linear, stalkless, flowers long-stalked, petals pale purple; 7–9	Flowers 4–5 mm long, blue or white, fruit-stalks curved backwards; 6–7	Under-shrub, flowers shining-yellow, sepals downy; 6–8	Stem terete, leaves half-clasping, bluish green beneath; 7–9

a White Poppy, *Papaver sendtneri:* ♃, 5–20 cm; leaves simply pinnate, flowers very large, pure white, fruits up to 1 cm long; 7–8; grows in the Alps. **b Rhaetean Poppy,** *Papaver rhaeticum:* ♃, 5–15 cm; leaves 1–2-pinnate, usually very hairy, flowers large, yellow; or sometimes orange; 7–8; Alps (up to 3040 m) and Pyrenees. **c Burser's Poppy,** *Papaver burseri:* ♃, 5–15 cm; leaf-segments narrowly linear, flowers white; 7–8; grows high in the Alps and Carpathians. All are high-alpine members of the Poppy Family, which occur on gravelly scree of rivers and streams.

a Fladnitz's Whitlow-grass, *Draba fladnizensis:* ♃, 1–8 cm; leaves obovate, hairy; 6–8; 1600–3400 m. **b Frigid Whitlow-grass,** *Draba dubia:* ♃, 3–14 cm; stem usually hairy to the top; 4–7; 1700–3800 m. **c *Yellow Whitlow-grass,** *Draba aizoides:* ♃, 5–10 cm; stem leafless, flowers yellow, in terminal corymbose racemes; 4–8; 1600–3800 m. **d Downy Whitlow-grass,** *Draba tomentosa:* ♃, 3–12 cm; stem, leaves and fruit downy; 6–7; 1600–3800 m. All belong to the Crucifer Family and form 'cushions', growing on scree and in rock-crevices on mountains of S and C Europe; **a** also in arctic and subarctic Scandinavia, **d** also in the Balkans.

The members of the Crucifer Family shown below grow on basic limestone rocks and screes, all preferring high mountain situations, up to 3400 m; only the Candy Mustard (up to 1850 m) and the Dwarf Rock-cress (3000 m) are found at lower altitudes. The Pyrenean Rock-beauty occurs in the Pyrenees, Alps and Carpathians; the Alpine Rock-cress in mountain areas in most of Europe; the Dwarf Rock-cress in the Alps and Apennines; the Alpine Hutchinsia, the Candy Mustard and the Round-leaved Penny-cress mainly in S and C Europe.

	Pyrenean Rock-beauty	*Alpine Rock-cress	Dwarf Rock-cress	Alpine Hutchinsia	Candy Mustard	Round-leaved Pennycress
Scientific Name	*Petrocallis pyrenaica*	*Arabis alpina*	*Arabis pumila*	*Hutchinsia alpina*	*Aethionema saxatile*	*Thlaspi rotundifolium*
Longevity, Size	♃, 2–8 cm	♃, 6–40 cm	♃, 5–20 cm	♃, 5–12 cm	♃, 5–20 cm	♃, 5–15 cm
Distinguishing Features; Flowering Time	Leaves in a rosette, 3-lobed, 4–6 mm long, flowers pale lilac, in racemes; 6–7	Rosette-leaves ovate, coarsely toothed, rough, flowers in dense racemes; 5–9	Basal leaves entire, rough, stem leaves 1–3, flowers few, in corymbose racemes; 6–8	Leaves pinnate, stalked, fruit-stalks hairy; 6–8	Leaves oblong-linear, flowers white or reddish, fruits broadly winged; 4–6	Basal leaves thickish, infructescence short, fruits spreading horizontally; 7–8

a Rock Scurvy-grass, *Kernera saxatilis:* ♃, 10–30 cm; basal leaves in a rosette, hairy; 6–8; 1600–3800 m. **b Mignonette-leaved Bitter-cress,** *Cardamine resedifolia:* ♃, 5 to 15 cm; stem leaves pinnate, with larger terminal lobe; 6–8; 1500–2380 m. **c Pinnate Coral-wort,** *Cardamine heptaphylla:* ♃, 30–60 cm; leaves pinnate, with 3–9 leaflets; 4–5; up to 1800 m. **d Finger-leaved Coral-wort,** *Cardamine pentaphyllos:* ♃, 25–50 cm; leaves digitate, with 5 leaflets; 4–6; up to 1700 m. All belong to the Crucifer Family; **a** and **b** grow on rocks, stony slopes and gravel, in S and C Europe, **c** and **d** in woods of W and C Europe.

a ***Mountain Pansy**, *Viola lutea:* ♃, 8 to 12 cm; flowers yellow, stipules palmatifid; 5–8; W and C Europe. b **Spurred Violet**, *Viola calcarata:* ♃, 4–10 cm; leaves with 1–3 notches on each side, flowers large, blue or yellow; 6–8; Alps and Jura. c **Twin-flowered Violet**, *Viola biflora:* ♃, 7–20 cm; leaves kidney-shaped, stipules entire; 5–6; in damp and shady places on mountains in most of Europe. All belong to the Violet Family and are found on rock ledges, scree, and in mountain meadows and pasturelands up to 3000 m. c **Perennial Flax**, *Linum alpinum:* ♃, 10–30 cm; petals overlap only at base; 6–8; N and S Alps; Flax Family.

The rare Bavarian Masterwort occurs in dry meadows and open woodlands of the E Alps, up to 2700 m, the Small Masterwort is common in the Pyrenees, Alps and Apennines. The Alpine Eryngo is a rare plant of alpine meadows in C Europe. The Crowfoot Hare's-ear is found on mountains of S and C Europe, the Dwarf Lovage and the Alpine Lovage in the Alps and Carpathians, the latter also in the Balkans; these species grow in stony grasslands, on screes, rocks and stony slopes, up to 2800 m. All belong to the Carrot Family.

	Bavarian Masterwort	Small Masterwort	Alpine Eryngo	Crowfoot Hare's-ear	Alpine Lovage	Dwarf Lovage
Scientific Name	*Astrantia bavarica*	*Astrantia minor*	*Eryngium alpinum*	*Bupleurum ranunculoides*	*Ligusticum mutellina*	*Ligusticum mutellinoides*
Longevity, Size	♃, 20–50 cm	♃, 15–40 cm	♃, 30–80 cm	♃, 6–50 cm	♃, 10–50 cm	♃, 3–15 cm
Distinguishing Features; Flowering Time	Leaves palmately 5-lobed, umbels 10–15 mm wide, overtopped by bracts; 6–7	Leaves digitately 5–9-lobed, umbels not overtopped by bracts; 7–8	Basal leaves orbicular, coarsely serrate, bracts amethyst-blue; 7–9	Leaves grasslike, stem leaves stalkless, bracteoles yellowish green, in fives; 7–8	Stem leaves only 1–2, bracts 0–2, petals purple; 6–8	Leaves all basal, bracts 5–10, mostly pinnatifid; 7–8

a **Austrian Rib-seed**, *Pleurospermum austriacum:* ☉-♃, up to 150 cm; stem thick, furrowed, hollow, 6–8; woods, thickets, mountain grassland, in S and C Europe, extending to Sweden. b **Narrow-leaved Laserwort**, *Laserpitium siler:* ♃, 30–100 cm; basal leaves very long, up to 1 m; 6–8; dry mountain meadows, open woodland, S and C Europe. c **†Common Laser**, *Laser trilobum:* ♃, 60–120 cm; smelling of caraway, leaflets roundish; 5–6; S, E, EC and C Europe. d ***Sweet Cicely**, *Myrrhis odorata:* ♃, 50–100 cm; with strong aromatic smell, leaves bristly-woolly beneath, fruits up to 2.5 cm long; 5–7; widespread, in woody meadows and grassland. All belong to the Carrot Family.

a Alpine False-flax, *Thesium alpinum:* ♃, 10–30 cm; flowers one-sided, perianth much longer than fruit; 6–7; stony grassy places, S and C Europe and S Sweden. **b Intermediate False-flax,** *Thesium linophyllon:* ♃, 15–30 cm; flowers in loose inflorescence, perianth much shorter than fruit; 5–6; dry grasslands, S, C and E Europe, Balkans. Both belong to the Sandalwood Family; up to 2800 m. **c †Monk's Rhubarb,** *Rumex alpinus:* ♃, up to 200 cm; basal leaves up to 50 cm long; 6–8; S and C Europe. **d Snow Dock,** *Rumex nivalis:* ♃, 7–20 cm; flowers dioecious, leaves thickish; 7–8; Alps, Balkans. Both belong to the Dock Family; alpine meadows, scree.

The Great Sorrel, the Mountain Sorrel and the Alpine Bistort, all members of the Dock Family, are widespread in mountain pastures, on scree, rocky and grassy slopes, up to 3000 m and more. The other species shown belong to the Pink Family. The Lesser Rayseed occurs in S and C Europe, the Alpine Rayseed in the E Alps and N Balkans, both growing in damp stony places, on scree and on gravel by stream beds. The Common Rock-pink or Tunic Flower is found in most of Europe, on dry turf and stony slopes up to 2500 m.

	Great Sorrel	*Mountain Sorrel	*Alpine Bistort	Lesser Rayseed	Alpine Rayseed	†Common Rock-pink
Scientific Name	*Rumex arifolius*	*Oxyria digyna*	*Polygonum viviparum*	*Heliosperma pusilla*	*Heliosperma alpestris*	*Petrorhagia saxifraga*
Longevity, Size	♃, 30–100 cm	♃, 5–15 cm	♃, 5–25 cm	♃, 5–20 cm	♃, 5–25 cm	♃, up to 45 cm
Distinguishing Features; Flowering Time	Stem leafy, leaves thin, lower stem leaves stalkless, with sharp basal obes; 7–8	Stem leafy only at base, leaves kidney-shaped, long-stalked; 6–7	Stem simple, with terminal spike bearing purple bulbils in the lower part; 5–8	Leaves narrowly linear, petals white, usually 4-toothed; 6–9	Leaves linear-lanceolate, up to 9 mm wide, petals 4–6-toothed; 6–8	Stem much-branched, flowers solitary, epicalyx-scales short-awned; 6–9

a *Alpine Catchfly, *Lychnis alpina:* ♃, 5–15 cm; plant not sticky, inflorescence dense, head-like; 7–8; widespread. **b Alpine Pink,** *Dianthus alpinus:* ♃, 2–20 cm; petals with red and white spots in the throat; 6–8; E Alps. **c Mountain Wood Pink,** *Dianthus sylvestris:* ♃, 5–30 cm; petals not bearded in the throat; 6–8; mountains of W Europe, Alps and Balkans. **d Bearded Alpine Pink,** *Dianthus monspessulanus:* ♃, 10–20 cm; petals with blackish hairs in the throat; 7–8; mountains of S, W and C Europe. All belong to the Pink Family and grow in stony mountain pastureland, on rocks and scree and in bushy places.

Mountains

a *Maoss Campion, *Silene acaulis:* ♃, 1 to 4 cm; forming flat 'cushions', flowers solitary, short-stalked; 6–9; 1500–3600 m. **b Rock Catchfly,** *Silene rupestris:* ☉–♃, 10–25 cm; petals deeply notched at tip; 7–8; 1600 to 2900 m. **c *Alpine Pearlwort,** *Sagina saginoides:* ♃, 3–6 cm; leaves with short point at tip; 6–7; up to 2400 m. **d Rock Sandwort,** *Minuartia rupestris:* ♃, 4–15 cm; flowers pentamerous, stamens 10; 7–8; 1900–2800 m. **e Cushion Sandwort,** *Minuartia cherlerioides:* ♃, 2–5 cm; forming 'cushion', flowers tetramerous; 7–8; 2000–4300 m. All belong to the Pink Family; widespread in high mountainous areas, in rock-crevices, stony ground and scree, snow patches.

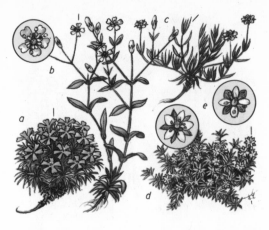

The members of the Pink Family shown below grow in stony pastureland, on scree, rocky slopes and in rock-crevices. With the exception of the Irish and the Two-flowered Sandwort (up to 2300 m), all are found up to and above 3000 m. The Spring Sandwort and Irish Sandwort are widespread, the Cyphal occurs in the Pyrenees, Alps, Carpathians and in Scotland, the Twin-flowered Sandwort in N Europe and the Alps, the Moss Sandwort and the Two-flowered Sandwort on mountains of S and C Europe.

	*Cyphal	Twin-flower-ed Sandwort	*Spring Sandwort	Moss Sandwort	*Irish Sandwort	Two-flower-ed Sandwort
Scientific Name	*Minuartia sedoides*	*Minuartia biflora*	*Minuartia verna*	*Moehringia muscosa*	*Arenaria ciliata*	*Arenaria biflora*
Longevity, Size	♃, 1–5 cm	♃, 3–10 cm	♃, 3–15 cm	♃, 5–20 cm	♃, up to 5 cm	♃, up to 8 cm
Distinguishing Features; Flowering Time	Flowers usually solitary, petals absent or inconspicuous; 7–8	Plant densely tufted, flowers usually in pairs, flower-stalks up to 5 mm long; 6–8	Inflorescence usually forked, petals white, as long as the calyx; 5–9	Leaves thread-like, flowers usually tetramerous, petals white; 5–9	Leaves lance-olate, fringed, petals twice as long as the calyx; 6–9	Plant decumbent, flowers usually in pairs, petals somewhat longer than the calyx; 7–9

a **Rock Soapwort,** *Saponaria ocymoides:* ♃, 10–35 cm; inflorescence panicle-like; 5–10; S and C Europe. **b Lesser Soapwort,** *Saponaria pumila:* ♃, up to 8 cm; stem short, with a solitary flower; 7–9; Alps and Carpathians. **c Creeping Gypsophila,** *Gypsophila repens:* ♃, 8–25 cm; leaves linear, fleshy; 5–8; S and C Europe. **d Broad-leaved Mouse-ear Chickweed,** *Cerastium latifolium:* ♃, 4 to 15 cm; flowers up to 3 cm wide; 7–8; Alps and Apennines. **e *Alpine Mouse-ear,** *Cerastium alpinum:* ♃, 6–20 cm; flowers 1–5; 7–9; widespread. All belong to the Pink Family and grow in mountain pastureland and on rocks and scree, **a** also in open woodlands.

a Entire-leaved Primrose, *Primula integrifolia:* ♃, 2–6 cm; leaves soft, somewhat hairy; 6–7; Alps and Pyrenees, 1530–3050 m. **b Long-leaved Primrose,** *Primula halleri:* ♃, 10–30 cm; leaves glabrous, mealy beneath, flowers reddish lilac; 6–7; Alps, Carpathians and Balkans. **c Hairy-leaved Primrose,** *Primula hirsuta:* ♃, 1–7 cm; plant with glandular sticky hairs; 4–6; Alps and Pyrenees, 1500–3600 m. **d Gold Primrose,** *Vitaliana primuliflora:* ♃, 1–5 cm; leaves narrowly linear, soft-hairy beneath; 5–7; Alps, 1700 to 3100 m. All belong to the Primrose Family and grow on mountains in rock-crevices, on scree, turf and in snow patches.

The Purple Sowbread grows in damp mountain forests in S and C Europe, up to 2000 m, and in the Balkans. The other species shown grow in rock-crevices, mountain pastureland, scree and in some cases in snow patches above 2000 m; the widespread Bird's-eye Primrose also in flat moorland and near streams; the Bear's-ear Primrose in the Alps, Apennines and Carpathians; the Dwarf Primrose in the Alps and the Balkans; Clusius's Primrose in the Alps; the Sticky Primrose in the Pyrenees and Alps. All belong to the Primrose Family.

	Bear's-ear Primrose	Dwarf Primrose	Clusius's Primrose	*Bird's-eye Primrose	Sticky Primrose	Purple Sowbread
Scientific Name	*Primula auricula*	*Primula minima*	*Primula clusiana*	*Primula farinosa*	*Primula glutinosa*	*Cyclamen purpurascens*
Longevity, Size	♃, 5–25 cm	♃, 1–4 cm	♃, 2–10 cm	♃, 5–30 cm	♃, 2–7 cm	♃, 6–15 cm
Distinguishing Features; Flowering Time	Flowers fragrant, calyx very short; 4–7	Leaves with large, cartilaginous saw-like teeth, densely glandular-hairy; 6–7	Leaves oval, with whitish cartilaginous margins, flowers mostly solitary, bright red; 5–7	Leaves mealy beneath, corolla-tube with yellow throat; 5–7	Leaves finely toothed, very sticky, flowers dull violet finally, sticky; 7–8	Leaves kidney-shaped, white-spotted, petals reflexed; 8–10

a Lesser Soldanella, *Soldanella pusilla:* ♃, 2–10 cm; corolla cut into narrow slender lobes in upper $\frac{1}{8}$; 5–8. **b Alpine Soldanella,** *Soldanella alpina:* ♃, 5–15 cm; corolla cut to the middle into narrow slender lobes; 4–6. **c Mountain Soldanella,** *Soldanella montana:* ♃, 20–30 cm; flowers bluish violet, leaves crenate; 5–6. **d Dwarf Soldanella,** *Soldanella minima:* ♃, 4–9 cm; flowers pale lilac to white; 5–7. All belong to the Primrose Family and are found on damp mountain pasturelands, up to 3000 m; **a, b** and **c** in S and C Europe and the Balkans, **d** mainly in the S Alps and C Apennines.

a Dwarf Rock-jasmine, *Androsace chamae-jasme*: ♃, 2–10 cm; scape, flower-stalks and calyx hairy, leaves lanceolate, bearded at margins; 6–8; Pyrenees, Alps and Carpathians, 1600–3000 m. **b Milk Rock-jasmine,** *Androsace lactea*: ♃, 5–16 cm; scape glabrous, leaves narrowly linear; 6–8; Alps and Carpathians, 1600–2200 m. **c Flesh-red Rock-jasmine,** *Androsace carnea*: ♃, 2–8 cm; scape downy, corolla flesh-red with a yellow throat; 6–7; Alps and Pyrenees, 2000–3000 m. **d Swiss Rock-jasmine,** *Androsace helvetica*: ♃, 2 to 5 cm; forming silver-grey cushions; 5–7; Alps, up to 3500 m. All belong to the Primrose Family and occur in rock-crevices, on scree and in mountain pastureland.

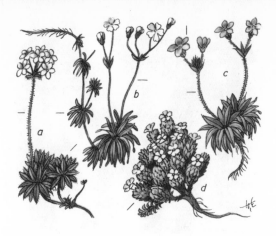

The Woolly Rock-jasmine occurs on rocks, from 1600–2300 m, the Alpine up to 4200 m, both in the Alps. The Blunt-leaved Rock-jasmine grows in pastureland in the Alps (up to about 3000 m), Apennines, Carpathians and other C European mountains, the Alpine-sanicle in meadows and woods in the Alps (1100–1900 m), Carpathians and NC Russia. All belong to the Primrose Family. The Alpine Thrift (Sea-lavender Family) and the Lomatogonium (Gentian Family) grow on pastureland in the Alps, the latter also in the Carpathians.

	Woolly Rock-jasmine	Alpine Rock-jasmine	Blunt-leaved Rock-jasmine	Alpine-sanicle	Alpine Thrift	Lomato-gonium
Scientific Name	*Androsace villosa*	*Androsace alpina*	*Androsace obtusifolia*	*Cortusa matthioli*	*Armeria alpina*	*Lomatogonium carinthiacum*
Longevity, Size	♃, 3–6 cm	♃, 2–5 cm	♃, 5–10 cm	♃, 15–40 cm	♃, 10–30 cm	☉, 1–13 cm
Distinguishing Features; Flowering Time	Leaves in a dense rosette, with long, silky hairs, flowers white or reddish; 6–7	Plant forming loose tufts, stem densely leafy, flowers pinkish red to white; 7–8	Leaves entire, in a rosette, petals white to reddish; 6–8	Leaves large, roundish, flowers purple, 3–12 in each umbel; 6–8	Leaves linear, flowers dark purple, involucral bracts brown; 5–10	Flowers pale blue or white, solitary, terminal, long-stalked; 8–10

a Purple Gentian, *Gentiana purpurea*: ♃, 20–60 cm; calyx sheath-like, two-lobed; corolla purple; 7–9; in the Alps, Apennines and in Norway. **b Yellow Gentian,** *Gentiana lutea*: ♃, 45–140 cm; corolla deeply 5–6-lobed; 7–8; on mountains of S and C Europe. **c Dotted Gentian,** *Gentiana punctata*: ♃, 20–60 cm; flowers light yellow with dark violet spots; 7–9; in the Pyrenees, Alps, and Carpathians and in the Balkans. All belong to the Gentian Family and are found in alpine pastures and meadows and among dwarf shrubs.

a Bavarian Gentian, *Gentiana bavarica:* ♃, 4–20 cm; stem long, with a solitary flower, without a leaf-rosette; 7–9; S and C Europe. **b Broad-leaved Gentian,** *Gentiana kochiana:* ♃, 5–10 cm; leaves broad, calyx with wide sinuses between the lobes; 6–8; S and C Europe. **c Round-leaved Gentian,** *Gentiana orbicularis:* ♃, 7–8 cm; leaves roundish, flowers comparatively large; 7–8; Alps, Pyrenees and Balkans. **d Hungarian Gentian,** *Gentiana pannonica:* ♃, 15–90 cm; flowers purple, with dark dots; 8–9; Alps, Balkans and Carpathians. All belong to the Gentian Family and grow in alpine pastureland, and on gravel and scree up to 3000 m and more.

The species shown below are all members of the Gentian Family, and occur mainly in poor alpine pastures, rock-crevices and ledges and on scree, at at least 2500 m. The Snow Gentian, the Spring Gentian and the Delicate Gentian are widespread in most of Europe; the Fringed Gentian, a plant of dry alpine meadows, scrubland and open woodlands, the Rough Gentian and the Short-leaved Gentian all grow in S and C Europe.

	Fringed Gentian	*Snow Gentian	*Spring Gentian	Rough Gentian	Short-leaved Gentian	Delicate Gentian
Scientific Name	*Gentianella ciliata*	*Gentiana nivalis*	*Gentiana verna*	*Gentianella aspera*	*Gentiana brachyphylla*	*Gentianella tenella*
Longevity, Size	♃, 7–30 cm	☉, 1–15 cm	♃, 3–12 cm	☉, 4–20 cm	♃, 3–6 cm	☉, 3–6 cm
Distinguishing Features; Flowering Time	Stem often with solitary flower, corolla 4-lobed, fringed with long hairs; 8–10	Stem very slender, corolla 8–12 mm wide, corolla-tube whitish; 7–8	Stem with a solitary flower, calyx winged at edges; 4–8	Leaf-margins with short hairs, corolla violet, lilac or whitish, calyx rough-hairy; 5–9	Rosette-leaves with papillose cartilaginous margins, flowers short-stalked or stalkless; 7–8	Stem branched only at the base, flowers solitary, tetramerous, calyx bell-shaped; 3–6

a *Diapensia, *Diapensia lapponica:* ♃, 3 to 5 cm; matted stems form 'cushion', flowers solitary, yellowish white; 6–7; Arctic Europe and hill-tops in Scotland; Diapensia Family. **b Dwarf Gentian,** *Gentianella nana:* ☉, 2–5 cm; corolla tubular-bell-shaped; 7–9; in the Alps, from 2200–2800 m. **c Stemless Gentian,** *Gentiana clusii:* ♃, 4–10 cm; stem very short; in mountains of S and C Europe, up to 2860 m. **d Overlapping Gentian,** *Gentiana terglouensis:* ♃, 3–6 cm; stem with overlapping leaves; 7–8; Alps. All are members of the Gentian Family, growing in alpine pastures and meadows and on scree.

a Mountain Lungwort, *Pulmonaria montana*: ♃, up to 25 cm; basal leaves about 4 cm wide, gradually tapering into stalks, anthers dark violet; 4–5; C Europe. **b Narrow-leaved Lungwort,** *Pulmonaria longifolia*: ♃, 12–35 cm; basal leaves up to 3 cm wide, inflorescence with stalked glandular hairs; 4–5; N, E and C Europe. **c Alpine Waxflower,** *Cerinthe glabra*: ♃, 30–45 cm; corolla with 5 recurved teeth; 6–8; C Europe, up to 2660 m. **d *Alpine Forgetmenot,** *Myosotis alpestris*: ♃, 2–10 cm; stems densely hairy, flowers blue; 6–7; 1600–3000 m. All belong to the Borage Family; **a, b** and **c** grow in alpine meadows, scrub and open woodlands, **d** in alpine grassland and on rocks.

The members of the Figwort Family described below grow in stony mountain pastures, on gravelly slopes, on scree and in crevices; the Fairy Foxglove in S, W and C Europe, at 1500 to 2350 m, the Shrubby Speedwell locally in S and E Europe, from 550–2700 m, the Alpine Toadflax in the Alps, up to 4200 m, the Alpine Speedwell and the Rock Speedwell in most of Europe. The Straw Foxglove is a rare mountain forest plant of W and CW Europe.

	Alpine Toadflax	†Fairy Foxglove	†Straw Foxglove	Shrubby Speedwell	*Alpine Speedwell	*Rock Speedwell
Scientific Name	*Linaria alpina*	*Erinus alpinus*	*Digitalis lutea*	*Veronica fruticulosa*	*Veronica alpina*	*Veronica fruticans*
Longevity, Size	♃, 4–15 cm	♃, 10–20 cm	♃, 50–100 cm	♃, 10–30 cm	♃, 4–15 cm	♃, 5–15 cm
Distinguishing Features; Flowering Time	Leaves bluish green, flowers bluish violet, with yellowish red palate, spur 2 cm long; 6–9	Basal leaves in a rosette, flowers violet, in corymb-like racemes; 4–6	Leaves pale green, with distant teeth, flowers almost horizontal, pale yellow; 6–8	Flower-stalks glandular-hairy, flowers pink, with darker veins, fruits oblong; 7	Stem and leaves herbaceous, flowers bluish violet, corolla 5 mm wide; 7–8	Stem woody at base, leaves leathery, glossy, flowers deep blue, corolla 10 mm wide; 6–7

a Dwarf Fairy-borage, *Eritrichium nanum*: ♃, 2–5 cm; plant cushion-like, with glossy silky hairs; 7–8; Alps and Carpathians, rock-crevices, scree and alpine grassland, 2500 to 3390 m; Borage Family. **b Pyrenean Dead-nettle,** *Horminium pyrenaicum*: ♃, 10–25 cm; basal leaves large, crenate; 6–8; dry alpine grassland, Pyrenees and Alps, 300–2450 m. **c Alpine Calamint,** *Calamintha alpina*: ♃, 10–30 cm; leaves serrate at tip; 6–8; dry alpine meadows and scrubland in S, W and C Europe, 2500–3390 m. **d Alpine Skullcap,** *Scutellaria alpina*: ♃, 20–40 cm; leaves stalked; 7–8; on scree, mainly in S and C Europe and the Balkans. The last three species belong to the Thyme Family.

a Leafless Speedwell, *Veronica aphylla*: 4, 3–8 cm; leaves crowded at base, racemes 2–4-flowered; 6–8; open woodlands and heaths in mountains of S and C Europe (1200–2800 m), and the Balkans. **b Daisy-like Speedwell**, *Veronica bellidioides*: 4, 5–20 cm; densely hairy, basal leaves larger than stem leaves; 6–8; dry alpine grassland in S and C Europe, 1400–3100 m. **c Blue Speedwell**, *Paederota bonarota:* 4, 8–15 cm; leaves deeply toothed, hairy on margins, flowers bluish lilac; 6–8; rock-crevices in the Alps, up to 2500 m. **d Lapp Lousewort**, *Pedicularis lapponica:* 4, 10–20 cm; racemes few-flowered; 7–8; in tundra of Arctic Europe. All belong to the Figwort Family.

Louseworts belong to the Figwort Family. The Yellow and the Flesh-red Louseworts occur in meadows and pastureland rich in humus, the former in the Alps, Carpathians and Arctic Europe, the latter on mountains of C Europe and the Pyrenees. The Beaked and the Whorled Louseworts occur in stony mountain pastures, the first in the Alps, the second in S, W and C Europe and the Balkans, the Alpine Lousewort in damp meadows and scrubland in the Alps, and the rare Sudeten Lousewort in the Sudeten.

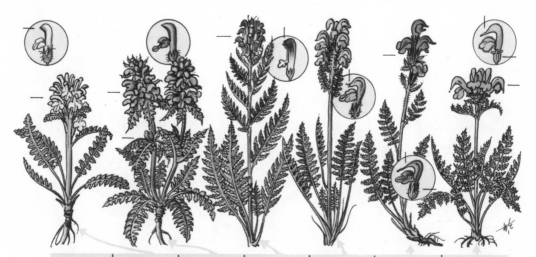

	Yellow Lousewort	Whorled Lousewort	Alpine Lousewort	Sudeten Lousewort	Flesh-red Lousewort	Beaked Lousewort
Scientific Name	*Pedicularis oederi*	*Pedicularis verticillata*	*Pedicularis recutita*	*Pedicularis sudetica*	*Pedicularis rostratospicata*	*Pedicularis rostratocapitata*
Longevity, Size	4, 5–15 cm	4, 5–30 cm	4, 15–40 cm	4, 10–20 cm	4, 15–45 cm	4, 5–20 cm
Distinguishing Features; Flowering Time	Leaves pinnatisect, flowers yellow, upper lip glabrous, purple at tip; 6–7	Leaves in whorls of 3–4, raceme dense, flowers purple; 6–8	Stem solitary, flowers brownish red, upper lip without a beak; 7–8	Calyx 5-lobed, with serrate teeth, flowers purplish, upper lip with short beak and two teeth; 6–8	Flowers flesh-red, in a loose raceme, upper lip with a long beak, calyx hairy; 7–8	Flowers in a short head-like raceme, upper lip with a long beak, calyx usually glabrous; 7–8

a Dwarf Eyebright, *Euphrasia minima:* ⊙, 1–10 cm; leaves with short bristles and 2–3 teeth on each side; 7–8. **b Spotted Eyebright**, *Euphrasia picta:* ⊙, 3–15 cm; flowers white or lilac, with a violet upper lip; 6–9. **c Alpine Rattle**, *Rhinanthus alpinus:* ⊙, 10–30 cm; corolla-tube strongly curved upwards; 7–8; **d *Alpine Bartsia**, *Bartsia alpina:* 4, 5–10 cm; upper leaves tinged with violet, flowers dark violet; 5–8. All belong to the Figwort Family and grow in alpine grasslands in S and C Europe, up to 3000 m, **d** also on the mountains of N and Arctic Europe.

a Alpine Tozzia, *Tozzia alpina:* ♃, 10 to 70 cm; lower corolla lip spotted; 7–8; damp alpine grassland, S and C Europe and the Balkans; Figwort Family. **b Heart-leaved Globe-daisy,** *Globularia cordifolia:* ♃, 3 to 10 cm; flowering stem leafless, leaves notched at tip; 5–8; rocks, stony places, alpine grassland, S and C Europe. **c Naked-stalked Globe-daisy,** *Globularia nudicaulis:* ♃, 10 to 30 cm; leaves rounded at tip; 5–8; S and C Europe, on scree, in alpine pastures, and open woodland. **d Common Globe-daisy,** *Globularia elongata:* ♃, 3 to 40 cm; stem leafy; 5–6; grassland and stony slopes, S, W and C Europe, Balkans. All belong to the Globe-daisy Family, and occur up to 2700 m.

The Wulfenia is a rare relic of the Rhododendron zone in the Gaital (Carinthia), found also in Montenegro; it belongs to the Figwort Family. The other species shown below grow mainly on gravelly slopes, scree and in mountain pastureland, up to 2800 m; the Dwarf Valerian and the Alpine Valerian in the Alps; the Rock Valerian in mountain areas of S and C Europe, the Mountain Valerian and the Three-winged Valerian in S, W and C Europe (also in stony mountain forests). All belong to the Valerian Family.

	Wulfenia	Dwarf Valerian	Rock Valerian	Mountain Valerian	Three-winged Valerian	Alpine Valerian
Scientific Name	*Wulfenia carinthiaca*	*Valeriana supina*	*Valeriana saxatilis*	*Valeriana montana*	*Valeriana tripteris*	*Valeriana celtica*
Longevity, Size	♃, 20–40 cm	♃, 3–15 cm	♃, 5–30 cm	♃, 20–60 cm	♃, 10–60 cm	♃, 2–15 cm
Distinguishing Features; Flowering Time	Leaves in a rosette, crenate, raceme one-sided, corolla blue, throat bearded; 7–8	Leaves spathulate to roundish, with fringed margins, inflorescence almost head-like; 7–8	Leaves entire or slightly toothed, fringed, cymes few-flowered; 6–8	Basal leaves stalked, flowers in terminal cymes, white to light lilac; 4–7	Basal leaves heart-shaped at base, stem leaves pinnatisect, ovate, flowers white or reddish; 4–7	Stem with 1–2 pairs of leaves, leaves obovate, corolla long; 7–8

a Swiss Bedstraw, *Galium helveticum:* ♃, 2–10 cm; fruit-stalks recurved; 7–8; on rocks and scree in the Alps; Bedstraw Family. **b Alpine Plantain,** *Plantago alpina:* ♃, 2–10 cm; leaves linear-lanceolate; 5–7. **c Mountain Plantain,** *Plantago atrata:* ♃, 10–30 cm; bracts bearded at tip; 5–8. Both belong to the Plantain Family and occur in alpine pastureland in the mountains of S and C Europe. **d Ovate Rampion,** *Phyteuma ovatum:* ♃, 20–100 cm; leaves usually heart-shaped at base; 7–8; in damp meadows, scrubland and open woodlands on mountains of S and C Europe; Bellflower Family.

a Dwarf Rampion, *Phyteuma nanum:* ⟁, 1–15 cm; leaves linear-spathulate; 7–9; Alps, Carpathians and the Balkans. **b Betony-leaved Rampion,** *Phyteuma betonicifolium:* ⟁, 20–70 cm; stem nearly leafless above, stigmas 3; 6–9; Alps. **c Grass-leaved Rampion,** *Phyteuma hemisphaericum:* ⟁, 4–10 (30) cm; inflorescence head-like, almost globose, 10–12-flowered; 7–8; mainly in SC Europe. **d Clustered Rampion,** *Phyteuma comosum:* ⟁, 5–15 cm; flowers pale lilac, in a head-like umbel, stigmas 2; 6–7; Alps. All belong to the Bellflower Family and grow in stony alpine pastureland, on scree and in rock-crevices, **b** also among shrubs and in open woodlands.

The members of the Bellflower Family shown below occur mainly in poor alpine meadows and pastureland, in rock-crevices, on gravel and scree slopes, sometimes among shrubs, up to 2200 m. The Bearded Bellflower grows in SC Europe and Norway, occurring also in open woodlands, the Lesser Bellflower (up to 3000 m), the Scheuchzer's Bellflower (up to 3100 m) and the Alpine Bellflower are common in mountains of SC Europe, the Dark Bellflower and the rare Dwarf Bellflower in the E and S Alps.

	Lesser Bellflower	Scheuchzer's Bellflower	Alpine Bellflower	Bearded Bellflower	Dark Bellflower	Dwarf Bellflower
Scientific Name	*Campanula cochleariifolia*	*Campanula scheuchzeri*	*Campanula alpina*	*Campanula barbata*	*Campanula pulla*	*Campanula zoysii*
Longevity, Size	⟁, 8–15 cm	⟁, 5–40 cm	⟁, 3–15 cm	⟁, 4–40 cm	⟁, 5–15 cm	⟁, 2–10 cm
Distinguishing Features; Flowering Time	Flowers blue, light blue or white, broadly bell-shaped, 1–6, in racemes; 6–8	Stem usually with a solitary flower, calyx-teeth more than half length of corolla; 7–9	Flower-stalks with 2 linear bracteoles, corolla light blue, fringed inside; 7–8	Flowers stalked, somewhat spreading, corolla bearded; 6–8	Flowers solitary, terminal, drooping, 17–22 mm long, dark violet; 7–8	Flowers pale bluish violet, 1–4, in racemes, calyx-teeth bristle-fringed; 7–8

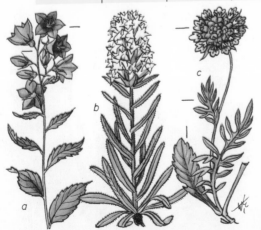

a Rhomboidal Bellflower, *Campanula rhomboidalis:* ⟁, 20–50 cm; flowers long-stalked; 6–8; Alps, Jura and Pyrenees. **b Dense-flowered Bellflower,** *Campanula thyrsoidea:* ☉, 10–50 cm; leaves stiff-hairy, flowers yellowish white, in a dense cylindrical spike; 6–8; SC European and Balkan mountains. Both belong to the Bellflower Family and occur in dry alpine grassland, on scree and stony slopes. **c Shining Scabious,** *Scabiosa lucida:* ⟁, 10–30 cm; heads 2–3 cm wide, with receptacle-bracts, each flower surrounded by a scarious epicalyx; 7–9; scree slopes on mountains in SC Europe (up to 2700 m) and the Balkans; Teasel Family.

a Glandular Fleabane, *Erigeron atticus:* ♃, 25–60 cm; upper leaves glandular, heads 1–40, purple; 7–9; rare, Alps. **b Single-headed Fleabane,** *Erigeron uniflorus:* ♃, 3–8 cm; heads solitary, white or pale lilac; 7–9; widespread. **c Glabrous Fleabane,** *Erigeron polymorphus:* ♃, 5–30 cm; heads 1–6, upper leaves upright, involucral bracts usually glabrous; 7–9; SC Europe, Pyrenees, Balkans. **d Alpine Fleabane,** *Erigeron alpinus:* ♃, 2–20 cm; outer disc-florets slender, ♀; 7–9; SW and SC Europe. **e Swiss Fleabane,** *Erigeron gaudinii:* ♃, 10–30 cm; stem branched, branches with solitary heads; 7–8; Alps. All belong to the Daisy Family and occur in stony alpine pastures, on scree and rocks.

The White Butterbur grows on stream-banks and in damp woodlands in C and N Europe and the Pyrenees; the Alpine Butterbur on gravelly or sandy stream-banks and damp scree in SC Europe and the Pyrenees; the Alpine Aster and the Daisy-star Aster on stony ground in SC European mountains, the latter also in the Pyrenees; the Lion's-foot on scree and rock-crevices in SC Europe, up to 3400 m, the Pyrenees and Balkans; the Carpathian Cat's-foot in high meadows in SC and Arctic Europe and the Pyrenees. All belong to the Daisy Family.

	†White Butterbur	Alpine Butterbur	Alpine Aster	Daisy-star Aster	Lion's-foot	Carpathian Cat's-foot
Scientific Name	*Petasites albus*	*Petasites paradoxus*	*Aster alpinus*	*Aster bellidiastrum*	*Leontopodium alpinum*	*Antennaria carpatica*
Longevity, Size	♃, 15–30 cm	♃, 30–60 cm	♃, 5–20 cm	♃, 10–35 cm	♃, 5–15 cm	♃, 5–12 cm
Distinguishing Features; Flowering Time	Flowering stem with pale scales, leaves white-woolly beneath, flowers whitish; 3	Flowering stem with reddish scales, leaves white-downy beneath, flowers reddish; 3–4	Flowering stem with one or few heads, head 3–5 cm wide; 7–8	Flowering stem with solitary head, ray-florets white or violet, pappus present; 5–7	Flowering stem with 5–6 heads in a terminal cyme, bracts large, white-woolly; 7–9	Leaves white-woolly on both sides, bracts brownish; 6–8

a Alpine Cat's-foot, *Antennaria alpina:* ♃, 4–15 cm; ♂ and ♀ heads of similar colour; 6–9; SC and Arctic Europe. **b *Dwarf Cudweed,** *Gnaphalium supinum:* ♃, 2–12 cm; heads 5–6 mm long; 6–9; widespread, in most of mountainous Europe. **c Alpine Cudweed,** *Gnaphalium hoppeanum:* ♃, 2–10 cm; heads in a loose raceme; 7–8; SC Europe and the Balkans. **d *Highland Cudweed,** *Gnaphalium norvegicum:* ♃, 5–30 cm; leaves usually 3-veined; 7–9; widespread. **e Glabrous Adenostyles,** *Adenostyles glabra:* ♃, 30 to 80 cm; leaf-veins hairy; 7–8; mountain forests in SC Europe. All belong to the Daisy Family and occur, except **e**, in alpine grassland, damp scree and rock-crevices.

a Grey Adenostyles, *Adenostyles alliariae:* ♃, 60–120 cm; leaves unequally toothed, grey-downy beneath; 7–8; SC Europe and the Pyrenees, 1900–2000 m. **b Black Milfoil,** *Achillea atrata:* ♃, 10–25 cm; bracts with black margins, ray-florets 7–12; 7–8; Alps, up to 4200 m. **c White Milfoil,** *Achillea clavenae:* ♃, 15–30 cm; plant with white, silky-downy hairs, stem angled; 7–9; Alps, up to 2500 m. **d Broad-leaved Milfoil,** *Achillea macrophylla:* ♃, 50–150 cm; leaves pinnatisect, segments up to 10 mm wide; 7–9; SC Europe, up to 2000 m. All belong to the Daisy Family; **a** and **d** grow in alpine meadows and open woodlands; **b** and **c** on stony pastures, scree and in snow patches.

The Large-headed Leopardsbane occurs in the Alps and Pyrenees, the Heart-leaved Leopardsbane in the Alps, Apennines and Balkans, both only on calcareous soils, particularly on rocky scree, Clusius's Leopardsbane on non-calcareous ground in the Alps, Spain and the Carpathians; the Glacier Leopardsbane on scree and stony pastures in the Alps; the Austrian Leopardsbane in alpine meadows, scrub and woodlands of the Alps and S Europe; the Common Leopardsbane mainly in mountain forests of SW and SC Europe. All belong to the Daisy Family.

	Large-headed Leopards-bane	Glacier Leopards-bane	Clusius's Leopards-bane	Austrian Leopards-bane	Common Leopards-bane	Heart-leaved Leopards-bane
Scientific Name	*Doronicum grandiflorum*	*Doronicum glaciale*	*Doronicum clusii*	*Doronicum austriacum*	*Doronicum pardalianches*	*Doronicum columnae*
Longevity, Size	♃, 10–60 cm	♃, 3–25 cm	♃, 3–30 cm	♃, 30–150 cm	♃, 30–90 cm	♃, 15–45 cm
Distinguishing Features; Flowering Time	Stem usually with a solitary head, leaves with coarse teeth, upper ones clasping stem; 7–8	Upper leaves slightly clasping the stem, head 3–4.5 cm wide; 7–8	Leaves with shaggy hairs on margins, head 3.5–6 cm wide; 7–9	Basal leaves absent at flowering time, stem leaves narrowed towards the base; 7–8	Plant with stolons, basal leaves present at flowering time, deeply heart-shaped; 5–9	Plant without stolons, basal leaves toothed, heart-shaped; 5–8

a Grey Ragwort, *Senecio incanus:* ♃, 5 to 15 cm; leaves grey-downy, bracts 8; 7–9; Alps and Apennines. **b Leopardsbane Ragwort,** *Senecio doronicum:* ♃, 20–40 cm; stem leaves leathery, heads 1–3, flowers orange-yellow; 7–8; SC Europe. **c Alpine Ragwort,** *Senecio alpinus:* ♃, 30–120 cm; stem strongly angled, heads with 13–16 ray-florets; 7–8, SC Europe and the Balkans. **d Rock Ragwort,** *Senecio rupestris:* ☉-♃, 15–40 cm; heads with ray-florets, fruits hairy, pappus falling off. All are members of the Daisy Family found up to 3000 m; **a** in stony mountain grassland and on scree; **b, c** and **d** in alpine meadows and scrubland, **d** sometimes also in damp open woodlands.

a Mountain Ragwort, *Senecio subalpinus:* ♃, 30–70 cm; upper leaves pinnatisect with toothed auricles, heads with 21 ray-florets; 7–9; Alps, Carpathians, N Balkans. **b Golden Ragwort,** *Senecio helenitis:* ♃, 20-120 cm; stalks of lower leaves winged; 4–6; SC and SW Europe, Balkans. **c Glandular Ragwort,** *Senecio ovirensis:* ♃, 20–80 cm; stem branched at top, basal leaves narrowly lanceolate-ovate, coarsely toothed; 5–7; E Alps, Balkans. **d Willow-leaved Oxeye,** *Buphthalmum salicifolium:* ♃, 25–80 cm; stem leafy, with few branches, heads solitary; 6–9; SC and C Europe. All are members of the Daisy Family found in alpine meadows and woodlands, up to and above 2000 m.

The saussureas are high-alpine plants which grow in rock-crevices and on stony pastureland above 1800 m; the Dwarf Saussurea in the E Alps, the Downy Saussurea in SC Europe, the Alpine Saussurea in SC, N and Arctic Europe. The Alpine Thistle and the Mountain Thistle grow in the stunted-wood and dwarf-shrub belt; the Willemetia in damp meadows and on flat moorland in the Alps, up to 2200 m, the E Pyrenees and the Balkans. All belong to the Daisy Family.

	Dwarf Saussurea	Downy Saussurea	*Alpine Saussurea	Alpine Thistle	Mountain Thistle	Willemetia
Scientific Name	*Saussurea pygmaea*	*Saussurea discolor*	*Saussurea alpina*	*Carduus defloratus*	*Carduus personata*	*Willemetia stipitata*
Longevity, Size	♃, 5–26 cm	♃, 15–40 cm	♃, 7–25 cm	♃, 25–120 cm	♃, 60–120 cm	♃, 15–45 cm
Distinguishing Features; Flowering Time	Stem with a solitary head, head about 2.5 cm wide, leaves linear; 7–8	Leaves white-downy beneath, stalks not winged, heads 3–8; 7–9	Leaves grey-downy beneath, stalks winged, heads in corymbs; 7–9	Heads usually solitary, nodding, long-stalked, 1.5–3 cm wide, red, rarely white; 7–9	Lower leaves often deeply pinnatisect, heads usually 3–5 in each cluster, rarely white; 7–8	Leaves sinuate-toothed, florets golden yellow, in a long stalked head; 6–8

a Alpine Chrysanthemum, *Chrysanthemum alpinum:* ♃, 3–20 cm; upper leaves entire; 7–9; S and SC Europe, up to 1600 m. **b Blackish Chrysanthemum,** *Chrysanthemum atratum:* ♃, 10–40 cm; leaves coarsely serrate; 7–9; Alps, above 1500 m. **c Purple Coltsfoot,** *Homogyne alpina:* ♃, 10–40 cm; plant with stolons, leaves green beneath; 6–8; S and SC Europe, up to 2300 m, and the N Balkans. **d Downy Coltsfoot,** *Homogyne discolor:* ♃, 10–25 cm; leaves white-downy beneath; 6–8; Alps, above 1400 m. All belong to the Daisy Family; **a, b** and **d** grow in alpine pastures, on scree and in snow patches, sometimes among shrubs; **c** in damp alpine meadows, scrubland and open woodlands.

a Sticky Thistle, *Cirsium erisithales:* ♃, 20–50 cm; outer involucral bracts with black resinous markings, florets yellowish white; 7–9; S, C, EC and W Europe. **b *Melancholy Thistle,** *Cirsium heterophyllum:* ♃, 50 to 150 cm; leaves white-downy beneath, florets purple; 6–8; in most of Europe. **c Prickly Thistle,** *Cirsium spinosissimum:* ♃, 20–50 cm; heads clustered, surrounded by yellowish prickly involucral bracts, florets yellowish white; 7–9; Alps. **d †Mountain Bluet,** *Centaurea montana:* ♃, 15–75 cm; leaves decurrent, head usually solitary; 5–7; S, C and W Europe. All belong to the Daisy Family and grow up to 2000 m; **a, b** and **d** in meadows, open woodlands, **c** in damp turf.

The members of the Daisy Family shown below grow on grassy slopes and in dry turf and shrubby heaths, up to and above 2000 m. The Swiss Knapweed occurs in the Alps, the Variegated Knapweed in the Pyrenees, S and SC Europe and the Balkans, the Grey Hawkbit and the Swiss Hawkbit in SC and C Europe (in the Alps up to 2100 m) and the Balkans, the former on calcareous, the latter on non-calcareous ground. The Alpine Hawkbit is restricted to the Alps, the Greater Hawkbit is widespread throughout most of Europe.

	Swiss Knapweed	Variegated Knapweed	Grey Hawkbit	Alpine Hawkbit	Swiss Hawkbit	*Greater Hawkbit
Scientific Name	*Rhaponticum lyratum*	*Centaurea triumfettii*	*Leontodon incanus*	*Leontodon montanus*	*Leontodon helveticus*	*Leontodon hispidus*
Longevity, Size	♃, 30–100 cm	♃, 5–60 cm	♃, 10–60 cm	♃, 3–10 cm	♃, 10–30 cm	♃, 8–50 cm
Distinguishing Features; Flowering Time	Leaves white-downy beneath, basal leaves up to 60 cm long, heads solitary, florets purple; 7–9	Leaves white-downy, decurrent, more than 1 cm wide; 5–7	Plant grey-downy, with 3–4-forked hairs, heads nodding at first; 5–6	Leaves with simple hairs, scape and bracts black-woolly; 7–8	Leaves with simple hairs, scape with 2–6 scale-like bracts; 7–9	Plant with an upright or oblique, usually branched stock, scape with 0–2 scale-like bracts; 6–10

a Blackish Dandelion, *Taraxacum nigricans:* ♃, up to 20 cm; involucral bracts blackish; 7–9; C Europe and the Balkans. **b Alpine Dandelion,** *Taraxacum alpinum:* ♃, 5–20 cm; involucral bracts dark-green to blackish; 6–9; S, SC, C and W Europe, Balkans. **c French Sow-thistle,** *Cicerbita plumieri:* ♃, 80 to 150 cm; leaves glabrous, bluish green; 7–8; Pyrenees, SC, C and W Europe. **d *Blue Sow-thistle,** *Cicerbita alpina:* ♃, 50–200 cm; plant with stiff reddish glandular hairs; 7–9; most of Europe. All are members of the Daisy Family, found up to 2000 m; **a** and **b** in alpine turf, pastureland and snow patches; **c** and **d** in damp woodlands, sometimes on moist alpine rocks.

a Alpine Wormwood, *Artemisia mutellina:*
♃, 10–25 cm; leaves silvery-shining; 7–9;
Pyrenees, Alps and Apennines. **b Black
Wormwood,** *Artemisia genipi:* ♃, 5–15 cm;
stem leaves 1–2-pinnate, with linear-lanceolate segments; 7–9; Alps. **c Shining
Wormwood,** *Artemisia nitida:* ♃, 5–20 cm;
heads globose, nodding; 8–9; Alps and mountains of N Italy. **d Glacier Wormwood,**
Artemisia glacialis: ♃, 5–15 cm; leaves ternately palmate, heads in dense, almost globose
clusters, florets golden yellow; 7–8; Alps. All
belong to the Daisy Family and are found on
rock-ledges, scree and in rock-crevices, up to
3000 m.

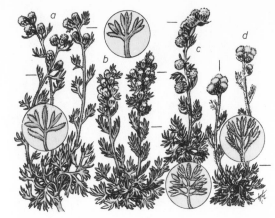

The hawksbeards are widespread in alpine meadows and turfs and on scree slopes, also in tall
herb meadows, from 1200–2700 m; the Golden Hawksbeard in S and SC Europe, the Moth
Hawksbeard in the Pyrenees and SC Europe, the Swiss Hawksbeard in the Alps, and the
Jacquin's Hawksbeard in SC Europe. The Cat's-ear is frequent in alpine meadows and dwarf-
shrub heaths up to 2600 m in SC Europe, the Gum-succory on gravel and sand of streams
in the Alps, up to 1500 m, the Apennines and Corsica. All belong to the Daisy Family.

	Golden Hawksbeard	Moth Hawksbeard	Swiss Hawksbeard	Jacquin's Hawksbeard	Single-headed Cat's-ear	Alpine Gum-succory
Scientific Name	*Crepis aurea*	*Crepis blattaroides*	*Crepis terglouensis*	*Crepis jacquinii*	*Hypochoeris uniflora*	*Chondrilla chondrilloides*
Longevity, Size	♃, 5–30 cm	♃, 25–70 cm	♃, 2–5 cm	♃, 5–30 cm	♃, 20–60 cm	♃, 15–30 cm
Distinguishing Features; Flowering Time	Head solitary, rarely up to 3, involucre densely shaggy, fruits with 20 ribs; 5–9	Upper leaves stalkless, with arrow-shaped base, heads large, up to 4 cm wide; 6–8	Leaves with crosssaw-like teeth, heads up to 5 cm wide, with dense, black, shaggy hair; 7–8	Stem with up to 5 or more solitary-head-ed branches, upper leaves pinnatisect; 6–8	Scape stiff, hairy, usually with a solitary head, outer involucral bracts fringed; 7–9	Rosette-leaves with cartilag-inous teeth, scapes glab-rous, heads in an umbellate panicle; 7–8

a †Brownish-orange Hawkweed, *Hieracium
brunneocroceum:* ♃, 20–50 cm; leaves yellowish green, oblong to oblanceolate, ligules
brownish orange; 6–8; C Europe, naturalized
elsewhere. **b Woolly Hawkweed,** *Hieracium
villosum:* ♃, 10–35 cm; plant with long white
hairs; S and SC Europe and the Balkans.
c Sea-lavender Hawkweed, *Hieracium stati-
cifolium:* ♃, 15–40 cm; florets light sulphur-
yellow; 6–8; Alps, French Jura and Balkans.
d Glacier Hawkweed, *Hieracium glaciale:*
♃, 5–20 cm; heads 2–7, leaves thickish; 7–8;
rare, Alps. All belong to the Daisy Family,
growing up to 2700 m; **a, b** and **d** in alpine
meadows, turf, on scree and rocks, **c** on gravelly stream-sides.

a *Three-leaved Rush**, *Juncus trifidus:* ♃, 8–30 cm; flowers 1–3 between axils of 2–3 long and narrow bracts; 7–8; high mountains in most of Europe. **b** †**Snow-white Woodrush**, *Luzula nivea:* ♃, 30–90 cm; leaf-margins with long hairs, flowers snow-white; 6–8; Pyrenees, Alps, Apennines. **c Brown Woodrush**, *Luzula alpinopilosa:* ♃, 10 to 30 cm; leaves almost glabrous, flowers brown; 7–8; Pyrenees, Alps, Carpathians, Apennines. All belong to the Rush Family; **a** and **c** grow on scree, rocks, turf, 3000 m and above, **b** in scrub and open woodlands. **d Dark White-hellebore**, *Veratrum nigrum:* ♃, 60–100 cm; panicle downy, flowers purple; 7–8; scrub, open woods, SC Europe, Balkans; Lily Family.

The Common White-hellebore (Pyrenees, S, C and N Europe), the Snowdon Lily (SC and NW Europe and the Balkans), and the Bulb-bearing Lily (S and C Europe) grow in alpine meadows, pastures, on ridges and in crevices of rocks, above 2200 m; all belong to the Lily Family. The Long-rooted Garlic (SC Europe, Pyrenees and Balkans), the Narrow-leaved Daffodil (mainly in the Alps), and the Pheasant's-eye Daffodil (S, SW and C Europe) occur in alpine grasslands; they belong to the Daffodil Family.

	Common White-hellebore	Snowdon Lily	Long-rooted Garlic	Bulb-bearing Lily	Narrow-leaved Daffodil	†Pheasant's-eye Daffodil
Scientific Name	*Veratrum album*	*Lloydia serotina*	*Allium victoriale*	*Lilium bulbiferum*	*Narcissus stellaris*	*Narcissus poeticus*
Longevity, Size	♃, 60–150 cm	♃, 7–10 cm	♃, 30–70 cm	♃, 45–100 cm	♃, 20–30 cm	♃, 30–60 cm
Distinguishing Features; Flowering Time	Leaves broadly elliptical, flowers white, greenish outside; poisonous; 7–8	Basal leaves 2, very narrow, flowers solitary, 1.5 cm wide; 7–8	Leaves 2–3, 2–5 cm wide, flowers yellowish, in globose inflorescence; 7–8	With bulbils in leaf-axils, flowers red, funnel-shaped, solitary or several; 6–7	Leaves 2–5 mm wide, perianth-segments not overlapping; 3–5	Leaves 5–15 mm wide, perianth-segments overlapping; 4–5

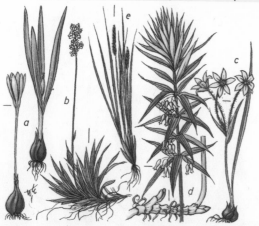

a Alpine Saffron, *Colchicum alpinum:* ♃, 10–20 cm; smaller than Meadow Saffron (page 191); 7–9; Alps. **b** *Scottish Asphodel**, *Tofieldia pusilla:* ♃, 5–15 cm; bracts 3-lobed; 6–8; Alps, N and Arctic Europe. **c Alpine Yellow-star-of-Bethlehem**, *Gagea fistulosa:* ♃, up to 15 cm; radical leaf tubular; 6–7; Alps, Pyrenees, Apennines and in Corsica. **d** *Whorled Solomon's Seal**, *Polygonatum verticillatum:* ♃, 30–60 cm; leaves in whorls; 5–6; widespread, in mountain forests. All belong to the Lily Family. **e Mouse-tail Kobresia**: *Kobresia myosuroides:* ♃, 10–20 cm; spike up to 2.5 cm long; 6–8; scree and dry turf in most of Europe, up to and above 3000 m; Sedge Family.

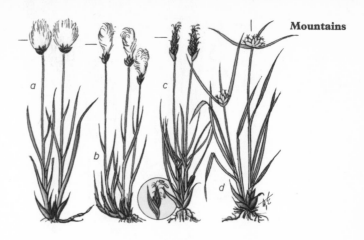

a Scheuchzer's Cotton-grass, *Eriophorum scheuchzeri:* 24, 15–30 cm; stem terete, inflorescence solitary, globose; 7–8; flat moorland, boggy meadows and stream-banks, 1500–2600 m. **b *Alpine Club-rush,** *Scirpus hudsonianus:* 5–35 cm; stem 3-angled, perigone bristles 4–6, at fruiting time 2 cm long; 4–5; on moors, up to 2000 m. **c *Common False-sedge,** *Kobresia simpliciuscula:* 24, 5–30 cm; leaf blades grooved; 7–8; damp calcareous ground, 1600–2800 m. **d Mount Baldo Sedge,** *Carex baldensis:* 24, 8-30 cm; bracts whitish, stigmas 3; 4–8; by streamsides, on rocks and scree. All belong to the Sedge Family; **a** and **c** in the Pyrenees, S, C, N and Arctic Europe, **b** C and N Europe, **d** Alps.

The members of the Sedge Family shown below are common on rock-ledges, scree slopes, in alpine meadows and pastureland or on marshy ground, between 1000 m (1900 m) and 2600 m (3100 m). The Cushion Sedge occurs in the Pyrenees and SC Europe, the Evergreen Sedge and the Rusty Sedge in the Pyrenees, S, SC Europe and the Balkans; the Sooty Sedge, the Black Sedge and the Hair Sedge are widespread on most European mountains, also in N and Arctic Europe.

	Cushion Sedge	Evergreen Sedge	Rusty Sedge	Sooty Sedge	*Black Sedge	*Hair Sedge
Scientific Name	*Carex firma*	*Carex sempervirens*	*Carex ferruginea*	*Carex misandra*	*Carex atrata*	*Carex capillaris*
Longevity, Size	24, 5–20 cm	24, 15–45 cm	24, 30–60 cm	24, 10–30 cm	24, 20–40 cm	24, 3–15 cm
Distinguishing Features; Flowering Time	Leaves 2 mm wide, short, stiff, rough, 3-angled at tip, ♀ spikes 3–6-flowered; 6–8	Leaf-sheaths long, lower leaves short, ♀ spikes long-stalked; 5–6	♀ spikes 2–3, loose, long-stalked; 6–9	Leaf-sheaths pale, terminal spike ♀ at top, ♂ below, fruit narrow, with gradually tapering beak; 6–8	Leaf-sheaths dark brown, terminal spike hermaphrodite, glumes usually black, fruit broad; 6–8	Forming small dense tufts, leaves 1–2 mm wide, grooved, ♂ spike pale, erect, ♀ spikes nodding; 5–7

a Curved Sedge, *Carex curvula:* 24, 5–10 cm; leaves curved, stigmas 3; 7–8; Pyrenees, SC and SW Europe, Balkans. **b Fetid Sedge,** *Carex foetida:* 24, 5–30 cm; spikelets 8–15; 7–8; Pyrenees, Alps. Both belong to the Sedge Family. **c Creeping Meadow-grass,** *Poa cenisia:* 24, 20–40 cm; with creeping rhizomes, lower branches of panicle 1–2; 7–8; Pyrenees, S and SC Europe, Balkans. **d *Alpine Meadow-grass,** *Poa alpina:* 24, 3–50 cm; densely tufted, culm coated with remains of old leaf-sheaths at base; 5–6; widespread. **e Alpine Fescue,** *Fescuta alpina:* 24, 6–10 cm; leaves hair-like; 7–8; S and SC Europe, Balkans. **c, d** and **e** belong to the Grass Family and grow in alpine grasslands, on scree and rock-ridges.

a Variable Fescue, *Festuca varia*: ♃, 15 to 35 cm; leaf-blades bristle-like, spikelets 5–8-flowered; 7–8; Pyrenees, SC Europe, Balkans. **b Violet Fescue**, *Festuca violacea*: ♃, 15–40 cm; spikelets mostly blackish violet; 6–7; S Europe, Alps, Balkans. **c Mountain Meadow-oat**, *Helictotrichon versicolor*: ♃, 15–30 cm; leaves glabrous, with white, translucent margins, spikelets mostly 5-flowered; 7–8; Pyrenees, S and SC Europe, Balkans. **d Small Fescue**, *Festuca pumila*: ♃, 10–20 cm; leaves inrolled, spikelets 3-flowered, often violet, palea fringed with long hairs; 7–9; distribution similar to **c**. All belong to the Grass Family and grow in poor grassland up to 3000 m.

The members of the Grass Family shown below are common in alpine meadows and pastures, on rocky slopes and on scree. The Alpine Cat's-tail is widespread; the Rock Bent grows in the Pyrenees, S and C Europe and the Balkans; the Alpine Bent in the Pyrenees, S and C Europe and Spain; the Variable Small-reed in S and SC Europe and in Sweden, also in scrubland and open woodlands; the Spiked Oat-grass in the Alps, Pyrenees and N and Arctic Europe; the Two-rowed Oat-grass in the Alps, Pyrenees and Carpathians.

	*Alpine Cat's-tail	Rock Bent	Alpine Bent	Variable Small-reed	Spiked Oat-grass	Two-rowed Oat-grass
Scientific Name	*Phleum alpinum*	*Agrostis rupestris*	*Agrostis alpina*	*Calamagrostis varia*	*Trisetum spicatum*	*Trisetum distichophyllum*
Longevity, Size	♃, 10–15 cm	♃, 5–20 cm	♃, 10–20 cm	♃, 30–100 cm	♃, 10–35 cm	♃, 10–20 cm
Distinguishing Features; Flowering Time	Uppermost leaf-sheath inflated, panicle up to 7 cm long violet; 6–7	Leaves bristle-like, lemma 2-toothed, with a geniculate awn; 7–8	Culm leaves 1–2, stiff, panicle-branches rough, 1–3 at each node, contracted after flowering; 7–8	Leaves up to 7 mm wide, rough, glumes pale violet, twice as long as hairs at base of lemma; 7–8	Panicle dense, short-branched, dark or yellow, spikelets 2-flowered, awn 3 mm long; 7–9	Leaves glabrous, in 2 distinct rows on sterile shoots, panicle up to 6 cm long, loose; 7–8

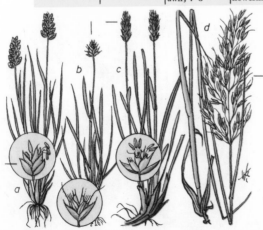

a Two-rowed Moor-grass, *Oreochloa disticha*: ♃, 10–20 cm; leaves bristle-like, spikelets in two rows; 7–9; Pyrenees, C Alps, S Carpathians. **b Small-headed Moor-grass**, *Sesleria ovata*: ♃, 1–10 cm; leaves up to 1 mm wide; 7–8; Alps. **c *Blue Moor-grass**, *Sesleria caerulea*: ♃, 10–50 cm; leaves 1–4 mm wide, lemma with broad 3–5-toothed tip; 4–5; subsp. *calcarea* in Britain, SC and C Europe, Iceland; subsp. *caerulea* Scandinavia, E and C Europe. **d Silver Rough-grass**, *Achnatherum calamagrostis*: ♃, 30–120 cm; panicle up to 30 cm long, lemma long-hairy on back; 6–9; S and SC Europe. All belong to the Grass Family; stony mountain pastures, dry turf, scree, rocks.

a *Small White Orchid, *Leucorchis albida:*
♃, 10–25 cm; flowers whitish, 5 mm long,
central lobe of lip longer than lateral ones;
5–9; widespread. **b Short-spurred Scented
Orchid,** *Gymnadenia odoratissima:* ♃, 15 to
50 cm; flowers strongly scented, central lobe
of lip pointed; 6–8. **c Common Black-
orchid,** *Nigritella nigra:* ♃, 5–25 cm; flowers
brownish black, vanilla-scented; 6–9. **d Red
Black-orchid,** *Nigritella miniata:* ♃, 5 to
30 cm; flowers reddish pink; 5–7. All are
members of the Orchid Family found in dry
turf and damp alpine meadows up to 2300 m;
a, b and **c** are widespread; **d** occurs in the
Alps and S Carpathians.

The two members of the Orchid Family shown below grow in mountain meadows and stony
pastureland, the Globose Orchid in S, SE and C Europe and the Pyrenees, the Alpine False-
orchid in SC and C Europe and in Scandinavia. All the ferns illustrated (Polypody Family) are
widespread, mainly in mountain areas. The Parsley-fern is locally abundant, on acid-rock
scree. The Green Spleenwort and the Mountain Bladder-fern are local and rare, occurring in
crevices and ridges, usually of basic rocks. The Hard Shield-fern grows locally in woodlands.

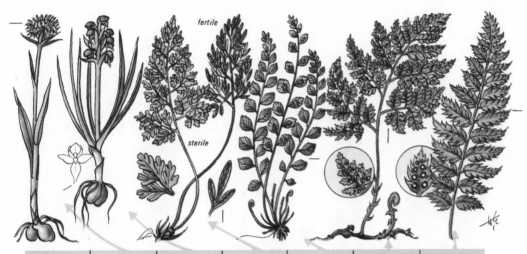

	Globose Orchid	Alpine False-orchid	*Parsley-fern	*Green Spleenwort	*Mountain Bladder-fern	*Hard Shield-fern
Scientific Name	*Traunsteinera globosa*	*Chamaeorchis alpina*	*Cryptogamma crispa*	*Asplenium viride*	*Cystopteris montana*	*Polystichum aculeatum*
Longevity, Size	♃, 20–60 cm	♃, 5–12 cm	♃, 15–30 cm	♃, up to 20 cm	♃, up to 40 cm	♃, 30–100 cm
Distinguishing Features; Flowering or Sporing Time	Spikes globose, flowers light red, central lobe of the lip as long as wide; 5–8	Leaves basal, about 8, flowers small, lip ovate to rhombic; 6–7	Sterile frond yellowish green, fertile frond with cylindrical in-rolled terminal segments; 7–9	Frond simply pinnate, its stalk not winged, much shorter than the blade; 7–9	Rhizome creeping, blade much shorter than stalk, in-dusium sub-orbicular, fal-ling off; 7–8	Frond firm, leathery, segments up to 1.5 cm long, with spine-pointed teeth, sori large; 6–9

a *Maidenhair Fern, *Adiantum capillus-
veneris:* ♃, up to 50 cm; frond-segments unequally lobed; 7–9; crevices of basic rocks,
S and W Europe. **b *Oblong Woodsia,**
Woodsia ilvensis: ♃, 10–12 cm; rachis and
underside of frond-segments scaly, indusium with long hair points; 7–8; crevices of
siliceous rocks, N and Arctic Europe,
south to S Alps and SW Russia. **c Seelos's
Spleenwort,** *Asplenium seelosii:* ♃, 10–15 cm;
frond white-downy; 7–9; calcareous rocks,
C and E Alps. All belong to the Polypody
Family. **d *Tunbridge Filmy-fern,** *Hyme-
nophyllum tunbrigense:* ♃, 2–8 cm; fronds
moss-like, indusium valves toothed; 7–8;
rocks, tree-trunks, local; Filmy-fern Family.

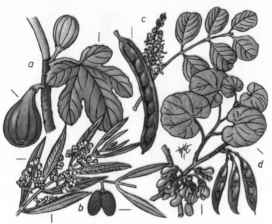

a †**Fig,** *Ficus carica:* small tree or shrub, 2–8 m; leaves palmately 3–5-lobed, soft-hairy beneath; 6–8; Mulberry Family. **b Olive Tree,** *Olea europaea:* up to 20 m; leaves leathery, silvery-hairy beneath, flowers white, scented; 4–6; Olive Family. **c Carob Tree** or **Locust Bean,** *Ceratonia siliqua:* tree up to 6 m; leaves leathery, reddish brown beneath, pods long, brownish violet; 5–9. **d Judas-tree,** *Cercis siliquastrum:* tree up to 8 m; flowers rose-red, leaves roundish-heart-shaped; 4–5. **c** and **d** belong to the Pea Family. All are woody plants which grow wild on mountains in the Mediterranean region and are widely cultivated.

Of the commonly cultivated trees described below, the Caucasus Fir (Pine Family) is a native of the W Caucasus and N Anatolia and has been planted for timber in S and C Europe and elsewhere; the Cut-leaved Whitebeam (Rose Family) is an uncommon native of N Europe and NE Germany; the Tartarian Maple (Maple Family) grows wild in SE Europe; the Common Walnut (Walnut Family) and the Common Horse-chestnut (Horse-chestnut Family) in the Balkans; the Sweet or Spanish Chestnut (Beech Family) in the Mediterranean region.

	Caucasus Fir	Cut-leaved Whitebeam	Tartarian Maple	Common Horse-chestnut	Sweet Chestnut	Common Walnut
Scientific Name	*Abies nordmanniana*	*Sorbus intermedia*	*Acer tataricum*	*Aesculus hippocastanum*	*Castanea sativa*	*Juglans regia*
Size	Up to 50 m	Up to 10 m	Up to 20 m	Up to 30 m	Up to 20 m	Up to 25 m
Distinguishing Features; Flowering Time	Bark grey, needles widened at base, cones 20 cm long, upright; 5	Leaves hairy beneath, with 6–8 veins on each side, fruits red, oblong; 5–6	Leaves entire, serrate, flowers white, in panicles, fruits often scarlet; 5	Winter buds sticky, leaves palmate, petals 5, white; 4–5	Bark smooth, olive-brown, leaves with short-awned teeth, flowers monoecious; 6	Leaves pinnate, leaflets 7–9, hairy, in axils of veins beneath, flowers in catkins; 4–5

a **Bay Laurel,** *Laurus nobilis:* tree up to 8 m; leaves evergreen, flowers dioecious, scented; 3–4; Laurel Family. **b Olive-leaved Daphne,** *Daphne oleoides:* shrub up to 50 cm; leaves leathery, flowers white, scented; 5–7; Daphne Family. **c Sicilian Milk-vetch,** *Astragalus siculus:* shrub, 15–20 cm; forming dense, spiny cushions; 5–7; Pea Family. **d Scarlet Pompone Lily,** *Lilium pomponium:* ♃, 50–90 cm; leaves narrowly linear; 6–7; Lily Family. All these plants occur in mountain areas of the Mediterranean region.

a Alpine Marmot, *Marmota marmota:* up to 5.7 cm + 16 cm; body compressed, ears, legs and tail short; a burrowing member of the Squirrel Family, lives in colonies, building deep, branched passages with large nesting chambers on sunny slopes from 1000–2700 m, in which it hibernates throughout the winter. **b *Mountain Hare,** Lepus timidus:* up to 61 cm + 6.5 cm; coat brown, white in winter, ears of medium length, tail uniformly white; occurs in Ireland, Scotland and mountainous areas of Europe. **c Cape Hare,** *Lepus capensis:* 50 cm + 9 cm; coat gives the appearance of being black-spotted on the back; upland areas of Spain, Portugal and Sardinia. **b** and **c** belong to the Rabbit Family.

The Mediterranean Water Shrew and the Alpine Shrew are members of the Shrew Family, the former found in the mountains of W and S Europe up to 3000 m, the latter up to 2000 m. The bats illustrated all belong to the Smooth-faced Bat Family and occur in mountains up to 2000 m, Savi's Pipistrelle up to 2600 m; the Northern Bat also occurs in N and NE Europe. The insect-eating Spiny Mouse is found in semi-deserts on the limestone rocks of Crete and Cyprus.

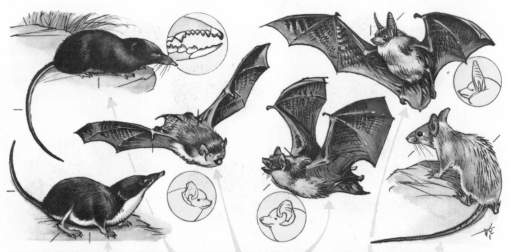

	Mediterranean Water Shrew	Alpine Shrew	Savi's Pipistrelle	Northern Bat	Lesser Mouse-eared Bat	Spiny Mouse
Scientific Name	*Neomys anomalus*	*Sorex alpinus*	*Pipistrellus savii*	*Eptesicus nilssonii*	*Myotis blythi*	*Acomys caharinus*
Size	Up to 8.8 cm	Up to 7.7 cm	Up to 4.8 cm	Up to 5.4 cm	7 cm	Up to 12.8 cm
Distinguishing Features	Upper side slate, underside white, hind feet with short swimming bristles, tail 6 cm	Coat almost uniformly dark slate colour, underside somewhat lighter, tail 7.5 cm	Body small, hairs on back with light tips, thumbs short, tail 3.9 cm	Upper side tinged with gold, underside yellowish, tail 4.7 cm	Similar to the Mouse-eared Bat (p.247),but smaller, ears and muzzle more pointed, tail 5.6 cm	Bristly, pointed hairs down centre of back, coat light, whiskers long, tail brittle, 12 cm

a Brown Bear, *Ursus arctos:* length up to 2.5 m + 14 cm, height at shoulder up to 1.1 m; coat light to dark brown, hump on withers; walks on soles of feet (not on toes); once widespread over much of Europe including Britain, where it became extinct in the 12th century, now restricted to remote areas in the Pyrenees, Balkans and Scandinavia. **b Egyptian Mongoose** or **Ichneumon,** *Herpestes ichneumon:* 55 cm + 45 cm; root of tail very thick; coat a uniform brownish grey. **c European Genet,** *Genetta genetta:* up to 58 cm + 48 cm; coat with rows of dark spots. All live in hilly areas, **b** in S Spain, **c** throughout Spain and W France; **b** and **c** belong to the Civet Family.

a Ibex, *Capra ibex:* up to 1.45 m + 15 cm; coat pale brown to pale grey, ♂ horns curved, with uniformly strong cross-ridges on the upper side, ♀ with short, only slightly curved horns, ♂ bearded. **b Chamois,** *Rupicapra rupicapra:* up to 1.3 m + 4 cm; ♂ and ♀ with horns which are hooked at the tip, coat in summer reddish brown with black stripe down middle of back, in winter brownish black. Both are Horned Ruminants of the Goat Subfamily. They live in hill forests and above the tree-line, where they graze during the day-time. **a** is almost extinct and is strictly protected; it will interbreed with domestic goats and most are probably now of mixed stock.

The species illustrated below all live in high mountainous areas, the Norwegian Lemming down as far as the birch forests of Scandinavia; Martino's Snow Vole in the dwarf-tree zone of the mountains of Yugoslavia. Savi's Vole is found on cultivated land up to 2000 m in Italy and the W Mediterranean region, the Mediterranean Pine Vole and Guenther's Vole in the Balkan mountains, the Snow Vole as far as the snow-line in the mountains of C and S Europe. All belong to the Mouse Family.

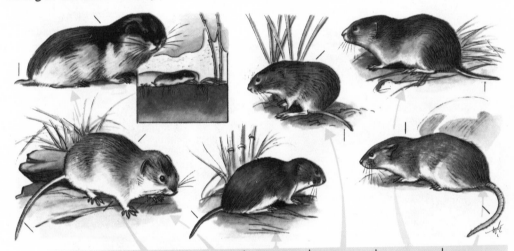

	Norwegian Lemming	Martino's Snow Vole	Savi's Vole	Mediterranean Pine Vole	Guenther's Vole	Snow Vole
Scientific Name	*Lemmus lemmus*	*Dolomys bogdanovi*	*Pitymys savii*	*Pitymys duo-decimcostatus*	*Microtus guentheri*	*Microtus nivalis*
Size	15 cm + 1.9 cm	14 cm + 12 cm	10 cm + 3.4 cm	10.7 cm + 3 cm	12 cm + 4 cm	14 cm + 7.5 cm
Distinguishing Features	Upper side brightly coloured, yellow and black, paws wide, tail very short	Coat light grey, under-side whitish, tail long, hairs silky, very dense	Ears small, tail short, coat lighter than on the European Pine Vole (p. 200), feet larger	Ears and tail very short, coat reddish, belly grey	Larger, strong-er than Com-mon Vole (p. 200), only differ-entiated by shape of skull	Coat light grey, thick and long, tail light, rather long

a Spanish Ibex, *Capra pyrenaica:* up to 1.48 m + 13 cm; end of horns turned up-wards; Iberian Peninsula. **b Wild Goat,** *Capra hircus:* 1.48 m + 13 cm; horns scimi-tar-shaped, ♂ with long beard; Mediterranean islands. **c Caucasian Tur,** *Capra caucasica:* 1.35 m + 17 cm; cross-section through horns triangular-round; Caucasus. All are Horned Ruminants. **d Barbary Ape,** *Macaca sylvana:* up to 71 cm + 0 cm; ears short, muzzle bare; the only native European monkey, though probably introduced by man, lives on Gibraltar; belongs to the Old World Monkey Group.

a *Capercaillie*, *Tetrao urogallus*: ♂ 86 cm, ♀ 61 cm; ♂ plumage blackish green with a metallic sheen, chin with 'beard', tail fan-shaped, ♀ brown, with dark bars and rust-coloured patch on breast; in spring, the cocks gather to posture and make display flights before the watching hens. **b Caucasian Snowcock**, *Tetraogallus caucasicus*: 58 cm; throat white, breast grey, finely striped. Both belong to the Grouse Family and live in high mountainous areas. **a** is found also in coniferous forests in hilly countryside, and has been re-introduced into Scotland; **b** in the high alpine zone of the Caucasus. Both are resident and nest on the ground.

These birds live in the Alps and in other mountainous areas of S Europe. They nest in rock-crevices and holes, the Wall Creeper from about 1800 m to the snow-line, the Rock-thrush between 900 m and 2400 m, the Alpine Accentor, a relative of the Hedge Sparrow, up to the snow-line, and the Crag Martin (Swallow Family) in the lower areas and also along the rocky coasts of Mediterranean countries. The Corsican Nuthatch is found only on Corsica, the Rock Nuthatch only in the Balkans.

	Corsican Nuthatch	Rock Nuthatch	Crag Martin	Wall Creeper	Rock-thrush	Alpine Accentor
Scientific Name	*Sitta whiteheadi*	*Sitta neumayer*	*Ptyonoprogne rupestris*	*Tichodroma muraria*	*Monticola saxatilis*	*Prunella collaris*
Size	12 cm	14 cm	15 cm	16.5 cm	19 cm	18 cm
Distinguishing Features	Crown black, with white stripe above eye, ♀ colouring more matt; resident	Lighter than the Nuthatch (p. 59), tail without white spots; resident	Similar to the Sand-martin (p. 116), but without breast-band; partial migrant	Wings round, black, with red and white spots, bill slender; partial migrant	♂ head blue, rump white, ♀ brownish, tail orange-red; migrant	Throat with dark spots, flanks with reddish brown stripes; partial migrant

a *Ptarmigan*, *Lagopus mutus*: 37 cm; wings and belly white; ♂ upper parts blackish brown, ♀ yellowish brown, winter plumage white; ♀ moults to summer plumage before ♂, which acts as decoy for enemies while ♀ is incubating the eggs; remains on high ground throughout the winter. **b Rock Partridge**, *Alectoris graeca*: 36 cm; black bib on throat, upper parts greyish brown. Both are Game-birds. **c Pygmy Owl**, *Glaucidium passerinum*: 17 cm; smallest European owl; eyes yellow. **d Tengmalm's Owl**, *Aegolius funereus*: 25.4 cm; eye-discs light-coloured, sharply defined. **c** and **d** are mountain members of the Owl Family; both are resident.

summer   winter

*Golden Eagle, *Aquila chrysaëtos:* 80–93 cm; body uniformly dark brown, crown and nape golden yellow, tail of young white, with broad, dark end-band, root of the hand-like pinions a striking white; resident. The Golden Eagle is a very large member of the Birds-of-Prey Family which is able to soar and glide magnificently in search of its prey; it usually eats grouse, hares and other small animals, but will take carrion. It is widespread throughout Europe, inhabiting mountainous areas and coastal cliffs, where it builds large nests on rock-ledges or in trees; it is the only eagle native to Britain, where it is now restricted to the Scottish Highlands.

Citril and Snow Finches are purely birds of high mountainous areas. The Rock Bunting, the Siskin and the Redpoll are also found in lower areas. Snow Finches build their nests in rock-crevices on and above the tree-line; the Siskin and the Citril Finch in conifers; the Rock Bunting on or just above ground level; the Redpoll, in groups, in trees and bushes. A coastal variety of the Water Pipit, the Rock Pipit, occurs in Britain. This belongs to the Pipit Family, the others to the Finch Family.

	Water Pipit	Snow Finch	Rock Bunting	*Redpoll	*Siskin	Citril Finch
Scientific Name	*Anthus spinoletta*	*Montifringilla nivalis*	*Emberiza cia*	*Carduelis flammea*	*Carduelis spinus*	*Carduelis citrinella*
Size	17 cm	18.5 cm	16.5 cm	13 cm	12 cm	12 cm
Distinguishing Features	Legs dark, breast reddish, edges of tail white; partial migrant	Head grey, throat black, back brown, belly cream-coloured, white on wings; resident	Head grey with black stripes, belly cinnamon-brown, ♀ with duller colours; migrant	Forehead red, chin black, ♂ with reddish breast; partial migrant	Plumage yellowish green, ♂ crown and chin black, ♀ breast striped; partial migrant	Greenish, nape grey, wing-band green, rump yellowish green; resident

a Nutcracker, *Nucifraga caryocatactes:* 31.8 cm; plumage brown, heavily spotted with white, square tail, with prominent white under tail-coverts; predominantly resident. **b *Chough,** *Coracia pyrrhocorax:* 39.5 cm; bill and feet red, plumage bluish black; resident. **c Yellow-billed** or **Alpine Chough,** *Coracia graculus:* 38 cm; similar to **b,** but bill yellow, straighter, shorter; resident. All belong to the Crow Family and occur in mountains forests, **b** also along coasts; **a** nests in conifers, **b** and **c** in rock-crevices and ruins. **b** is found along the west coast of Great Britain and inland in Wales, where the spectacular mating display flights may sometimes be seen in spring.

a *****Vendace,** *Coregonus vandesius:* 30 cm; 10–1; mouth superior, 1st gill arch with 36–52 gill-rakers; lakes in N Europe, east to Russia. **b** *****Powan,** *Coregonus lavaretus:* 50 cm; 10–12; mouth inferior, eyes small, 20–34 gill-rakers. **c** *****Coregonus pidschian:* 40 cm; 6–10; eyes large, 16–27 gill-rakers; Alpine, and marine and fresh Arctic waters. **d** *Coregonus macrophthalmus:* 32 cm; 7–10; eyes large, 36–44 gill-rakers; sub-alpine region. All belong to the Salmon Family. Various fishes of the genus *Coregonus* are widespread in N and C European lakes, some also occurring in the Baltic and North Sea. Many British lakes contain whitefish (their collective name) similar to the Continental forms.

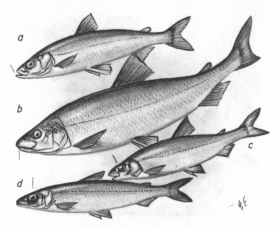

All members of the Salmon Family are distinguished by a small, rayless fin, the adipose fin, set behind the dorsal fin. The species shown prefer clear, fast-flowing water, especially near springs or oxygen-rich lakes of the Alps and upland areas, the Salbling being found up to more than 2000 m. Huchen are confined to the Danube basin, Grayling are found in rivers thoughout most of Europe except Ireland and the Mediterranean region. The Brook Trout was introduced from America in 1882.

	Surface Whitefish	†Brook Trout	Salbling	Huchen	*Lake Trout	*Grayling
Scientific Name	*Coregonus wartmanni*	*Salvelinus fontinalis*	*Salvelinus salvelinus*	*Salmo hucho*	*Salmo trutta lacustris*	*Thymallus thymallus*
Size; Spawning	50 cm; 11–1	45 cm; 10–3	80 cm; 9–1	150 cm; 3–5	140 cm; 10–12	50 cm; 3–5
Distinguishing Features	Body slender, torpedo-shaped mouth opening small, not extending to eyes, long gill-rakers	Mouth cleft extending to behind eyes, ♂ with red belly during spawning time	Light dots along sides, white margin on front edge of pectoral, pelvic and anal fins	Body spindle-shaped, snout pointed, mouth cleft large, extending to behind eyes, fins small	Body compressed, cylindrical, mouth extends to behind eyes, colouring very variable	Head small, pointed, dorsal fin very long, purplish red, mouth narrow, with hooked teeth

a *****Salmon,** *Salmo salar:* up to 150 cm; 10–2; back bluish grey, sides with black spots, ♂ with hooked jaw, deep black back during mating season; first few years of life spent in the upper reaches of rivers, then migrates to the sea, probably off the coast of Greenland, returning when fully adult to breed. **b** *****Brown Trout,** *Salmo trutta fario:* up to 60 cm; 10–2; snout short, mouth cleft extending to behind the eyes, colouring very variable. **c** †**Rainbow Trout,** *Salmo gaiedneri:* up to 60 cm; 12–5; reddish band along side, skin spotted with black; introduced from America. All are members of the Salmon Family which live in clear waters.

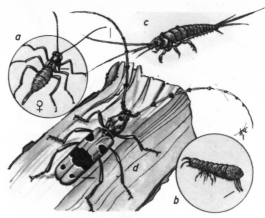

a *Boreus hyemalis*: 4–5 mm; 10–3; head extended like a beak; a wingless Scorpion Fly which occurs as a winter species on lower ground in the western and northern part of its range; found at other times of the year in the higher areas of S Europe. **b** *Isotoma saltans*: 2.5 mm; body covered with dense black hairs; a Springtail. **c** *Machilis tirolensis*: 12–14 mm; antennae as long as body. **b** and **c** are primitive insects found up to a height of almost 4000 m. **d** *Rosalia alpina*: 22–36 mm; body covered with fine pale blue hairs, with black spots; Longhorn or Timber Beetle Family; found in the higher areas of S Europe and W Asia.

Of the many species of Alpine butterflies, the illustration shows members of the Swallowtail Family, the largest of which is the Apollo. The Lesser Apollo is found at greater heights than the others; its caterpillar is often found under water, feeding on a river-growing stonecrop. The Whites Family is represented by *Synchloë* and the Green Mountain Butterfly, which is a very rapid flyer. The Browns Family contains many Alpine species, some of them very rare; *Erebia pluto* is illustrated.

	Apollo	Lesser Apollo	Muse		Green Mountain Butterfly	
Scientific Name	*Parnassius apollo*	*Parnassius phoebus*	*Parnassius mnemosyne*	*Synchloë callidice*	*Colias phicomone*	*Erebia pluto*
Size; Flying	7.5 cm; 5–9	6.2 cm; 7–8	6.2 cm; 5–8	4.6 cm; 6–8	4.2 cm; 6–9	4.4 cm; 6–8
Distinguishing Features	Fore wings with black spots, hind wings with red eye-spots	♂ with one, ♀ with three red eye-spots on each fore wing	Wings white, with black spots only, almost transparent	Wings white, those of ♂ with rows of black spots, those of ♀ with brownish spots	Wings of ♂ greenish yellow, of ♀ whitish, marginal band blackish with rose-coloured edge	Body almost uniformly dark brown, wings with or without eye-spots

a Glacier Butterfly. *Oeneis aëllo:* 4.8 cm; 6–8; fore wings usually with two eye-spots, hind wings with one; abundant in alternate years on edges of snow-fields; Browns Family. **b** *Albulina orbitulus:* 2.6 cm; 5–7; ♂ upper side silvery grey, ♀ brown; eggs on milk-vetches; Blues Family. **c *Mountain Burnet,** *Zygaena exulans:* 3–3.2 cm; 7–8; fore wings with five carmine spots; a diurnal Burnet Moth; caterpillars, in Britain (Aberdeenshire only), feed on Crowberry (page 70), on Continent on various alpine plants, take probably 4 years to mature; cocoon usually on underside of Crowberry stems. **d** *Endrosa aurita:* 3–3.4 cm; veins wide; eggs on rock-lichens. All found mainly in the Alps.

Glossary / Bibliography / Index

Glossary

The meanings given apply to the words only as they are used in this book; for example, Tibia, defined as one of the segments of an arthropod leg, is also a bone in the vertebrate leg, but is not used in this sense in the text. Words printed in the definition in **bold type** are explained either in the Glossary or in the text, where they may be found by using the Index.

Abdomen, (*zool.*) in arthropods, the last group of body segments; diagram on page 311.

Achene, (*bot.*) a small dry **indehiscent** one-seeded **fruit.**

Acuminate, (*bot.*) gradually narrowed to a point.

Adipose fin, (*zool.*) see page 299, centre.

Adventitious, (*bot.*) of roots, buds, etc., which arise from an abnormal position.

Alternate, (*bot.*) arranged spirally, or in two rows on opposite sides of a stem, etc., on different levels; cf. **opposite.**

Anal fin, see diagram on page 305.

Annual, (*bot.*) plant which completes its life-cycle within one year; cf. **biennial, perennial.**

Antenna, (*zool.*) one of a pair of often prolonged feelers on the head of arthropods and certain other invertebrates; in insects, they usually carry scent organs.

Anther, (*bot.*) the part of the **stamen** which contains the **pollen;** diagram on page 305.

Antheridium, (*bot.*) organ containing the male reproductive cells in cryptogams.

Apothecium, (*bot.*) fruiting organ of lichens.

Aquatic, living in water; cf. **terrestrial.**

Archegonium, (*bot.*) organ containing the female reproductive cell in cryptogams and most gymnosperms.

Aril, (*bot.*) a fleshy structure enveloping the seed in some plants, developed from stalk or base of ovule.

Auricle, (*bot.*) small ear-like or claw-like structure at base of a leaf-blade.

Awn, (*bot.*) slender bristle-like projection, in grasses, etc. **Awned,** having an awn or awns.

Axial skeleton, (*zool.*) the bones of the limbs, in vertebrates.

Axil, (*bot.*) angle between stem and leaf or stem and bract.

Axis, (*bot.*) the main stem of a plant, leaf, inflorescence or, in grasses, of a spikelet.

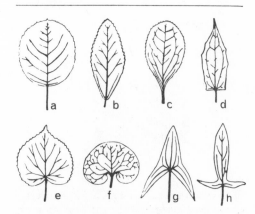

Leaf bases: a rounded; **b** blunt or obtuse; **c** wedge-shaped or cuneate; **d** truncate (acuminate at tip); **e** heart-shaped (apiculate at tip); **f** kidney-shaped or reniform; **g** arrow-shaped; **h** halberd-shaped or hastate.

Barbel, (*zool.*) beard-like, usually sensory appendage on the jaws of some fishes; diagram on page 305.

Beak, (*bot.*) pointed projection at the tip of a fruit.

Berry, (*bot.*) a rounded, fleshy **fruit** with many seeds.

Biennial, (*bot.*) plant which completes its life-cycle within two years, producing a food-storage rosette in the first and flowering in the second; cf. **annual, perennial.**

Bifid, deeply split into two segments.

Bipartite, (*bot.*) divided nearly to the base into two parts.

Bisexual, hermaphrodite.

Blade, (*bot.*) the often flattened part of a leaf above the stalk.

Blowhole, (*zool.*) the nostrils of whales, situated on top of the head; single in toothed whales, double in baleen whales.

Body whorl, (*zool.*) the coil of a mollusc shell which contains the body of the animal; diagram on page 311.

Bract, (*bot.*) a modified leaf, small and leaf-like or scale-like, below the inflorescence or at the base of a flower-stalk. **Bracteole,** a small bract.

Bud, (*bot.*) undeveloped shoot, consisting of a short stem and miniature leaves.

Bulb, (*bot.*) underground bud-like structure consisting of a short stem and swollen fleshy leaves or scale-leaves, often clothed in thin membranous outer scales.

Bulbil, (*bot.*) a small **bud,** formed in an axil, which can grow into a new plant.

Byssus, (*zool.*) tuft of horny threads by which some bivalve molluscs anchor themselves to objects.

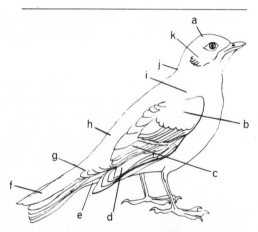

Bird plumage: **a** crown; **b** wing-coverts; **c** secondary wing feathers; **d** primary wing feathers; **e** under tail-coverts; **f** tail feathers; **g** upper tail-coverts; **h** rump; **i** shoulder-coverts; **j** nape; **k** ear-coverts.

Calcareous, chalky or limey.

Calyptra, (*bot.*) hood or cap covering the capsule of a moss.

Calyx, (*bot.*) the whole **sepal-system** of a flower, sometimes fused at the base, often forming a tube.

Cap, (*bot.*) the umbrella-like part of a fungus **fruit-body,** with **gills** or **tubes** on the underside.

Capsule, (*bot.*) a dry dehiscent **fruit** of two or more **carpels;** in mosses, organ bearing **spores.**

Carapace, (*zool.*) the shell of a crab, tortoise, etc.

Carnivorous, (*zool.*) flesh-eating.

Carpel, (*bot.*) one segment of an **ovary.**

Cartilaginous, (*zool.*) made of cartilage, a gristly substance which forms certain parts of the skeleton of most vertebrates and the whole of that of the cartilaginous fishes (sharks, rays, etc.); (*bot.*) tough and flexible like cartilage.

Casual, (*bot.*) an introduced plant which in wild conditions appears periodically but cannot completely establish itself.

Caterpillar, (*zool.*) the **larva** of a butterfly or moth.

Catkin, (*bot.*) an elongate, pendent **inflorescence** of tiny flowers of one sex.

Caudal fin, see diagram on page 305.

Chitin, (*zool.*) horny substance covering the body of arthropods.

Chrysalis, pupa.

Cladode, (*bot.*) modified stem with appearance and function of a leaf.

Climber, (*bot.*) a plant which climbs, usually by twining, sometimes supported by **tendrils, thorns,** etc.

Clitellum, (*zool.*) centrally situated belt-like segment by which worms unite during mating.

Colony, (*zool.*) a number of organisms, usually of the same species, living together as a community.

Column, (*bot.*) combined **stamens** and **stigma** in orchids; (*zool.*) the body of a sea anemone or similar animal.

Commensal, (*zool.*) describes two animals of different species living together in a mutually beneficial association; cf. **parasite, symbiosis.**

Compound, (*bot.*) of **inflorescence,** with branched axis (diagram on page 306); of leaf, divided into distinct and separate leaflets (diagram on page 307).

Compressed, (*bot.*) flattened.

Conceptacle, (*bot.*) a hollow case covering the reproductive organs in algae.

Cone, (*bot.*) conical, rounded or elongate structure in whose axils lie organs bearing pollen, seeds or spores.

Contiguous, close together and touching.

Corolla, (*bot.*) the whole **petal-system** of a flower, sometimes fused at the base, often forming a tube.

Corona, (*bot.*) structures longer than the petals and forming a ring round the centre of the flower inside the corolla; also **crown.**

Corymb, (*bot.*) a **raceme** in which the flower-stalks become shorter towards the top.

Cosmopolitan, with world-wide distribution.

Cotyledon, (*bot.*) leaf forming part of the **embryo;** in monocotyledons usually one, in dicotyledons usually two, in gymnosperms a whorl. See also pages 3, 5.

Covert, (*zool.*) a group of feathers covering the quill-bases of a bird's wing or tail feathers, etc.

Crenate, (*bot.*) scalloped (edge); see diagram on page 308.

Crown, (*bot.*) the branching system of a tree; the remains of the **calyx** on a fruit.

Culm, (*bot.*) stem of grasses.

Cushion plant, (*bot.*) a plant with a much-branched densely packed system of shoots which form a hemispherical cushion.

Cuspidate, (*bot.*) having a rigid point.

Cyme, (*bot.*) an **inflorescence,** usually **obconical** in outline, formed by successive lateral branches arising below terminal flowers. **Cymose,** bearing cymes.

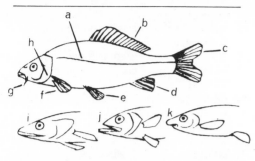

Fish parts: a lateral line; **b** dorsal fin; **c** caudal or tail fin; **d** anal fin; **e** pelvic fin; **f** pectoral fin; **g** barbel; **h** gill-cover. **Fish mouths: i** terminal; **j** superior; **k** inferior.

Deciduous, (*bot.*) shedding leaves, stipules, catkins, sepals, petals, fruits, etc., at maturity or once a year; cf. **evergreen.**

Decumbent, (*bot.*) **prostrate,** but with tip growing upwards.

Decurrent, (*bot.*) of a leaf, with base prolonged down stem.

Deflexed, bent backwards or downwards.

Dehiscent, (*bot.*) opening at maturity to shed seeds, pollen or spores.

Dentate, (*bot.*) toothed.

Denticulate, (*bot.*) minutely toothed.

Dichotomous, dividing into two equal branches.

Digitate, palmate.

Dioecious, (*bot.*) having male and female flowers on separate plants.

Disc, (*zool.*) the central part of the body of a starfish, from which the arms grow.

Disc-floret, (*bot.*) tube-like flower in centre of **head,** in some daisies.

Display flight, (*zool.*) a preliminary to mating in some birds and insects; a particular colour pattern may be displayed, or a noise made which is used only at this time.

Dissected, (*bot.*) deeply cut out into narrow segments.

Distant, (*bot.*) describes similar organs which are not growing close together.

Diurnal, (*zool.*) active in day-time.

Dorsal fin, see diagram above.

Downy, (*bot.*) with short soft hairs.

Drift-line, the line along a shore where water-borne material is left by tides.

Drupe, (*bot.*) a fleshy **fruit** containing seeds enclosed by a hard stone. **Druplet,** a small drupe which is part of a compound fruit, e.g. bramble, page 20, centre.

Ear-covert, (*zool.*) group of feathers covering the ear area of birds; diagram on page 304.

Ear-tuft, (*zool.*) in owls, a tuft of feathers which can be erected on top of the head; plays no part in hearing.

Elytron (plural **elytra**), (*zool.*) fore wing of a beetle modified to form a protective case for the hind wing.

Embryo, rudiment of the plant in seed, or of animal in egg, womb, etc.

Entire, (*bot.*) with an even margin, not toothed or divided; diagram on page 308.

Epicalyx, (*bot.*) calyx-like structure outside the true calyx.

Epidermis, outermost tissue of a plant or animal.

Evergreen, (*bot.*) in leaf throughout the year; cf. **deciduous.**

Exserted, (*bot.*) projecting or protruding.

External skeleton, (*zool.*) the outer covering of many invertebrate animals, especially arthropods, which supports and protects the body.

Eye-disc, (*zool.*) in owls, the collection of small feathers which lie outwards from the eye, giving a flattened appearance to the face.

Eye-ring, (*zool.*) in birds, a ring round the eye, sometimes without feathers, usually of distinct colour.

Eye-spot, (*zool.*) a marking with an eye-like appearance, as on a butterfly's wing.

Eyrie, (*zool.*) the nest of a bird of prey.

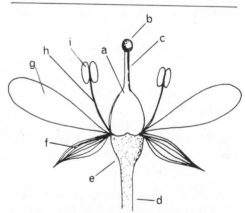

Flower parts: a ovary, **b** stigma, **c** style—together called the pistil; **d** stalk; **e** receptacle; **f** sepal; **g** petal; **h** filament, **i** anther—together called the stamen.

Family, see pages, 2, 7.

Feathery, (*bot.*) cut into fine segments which themselves are further cut.

Female flower, (*bot.*) one with an ovary but lacking stamens; cf. **male flower.**

Femur, (*zool.*) in insects, the third segment of a leg; diagram on page 311.

Feral, (*zool.*) wild, usually used to describe animals, once domesticated, which have returned to the wild state.

Fertile, (*bot.*) capable of producing **seed;** also, having normally developed viable pollen grains; cf. **sterile.**

Fetid, (*bot.*) with a strong, disagreeable smell.

305

Filament, (*bot.*) thread-like stalk of the **anther** (diagram on previous page); thread-like segment of thallus of lichens.

Flexuous, (*bot.*) wavy.

Floret, (*bot.*) a single flower in a close-packed **inflorescence.**

Foetus, (*zool.*) unborn mammal sufficiently developed for the basic characteristics of its species to be recognizable.

Follicle, (*bot.*) a dry, dehiscent **fruit** formed of one **carpel.**

Foot, (*zool.*) in molluscs, a muscular extension on the underside of the body, used for anchoring and locomotion.

Frond, (*bot.*) the leaf of a fern, including the stalk; leaf-shaped structure in the brown and red algae.

Fruit, (*bot.*) structure containing the **seeds** produced by a single flower.

Fruit-body, (*bot.*) in fungi, a body with reproductive organs arising from the vegetative part.

Fruit-receptacle, (*bot.*) **receptacle,** spiny above, which becomes hard when ripe.

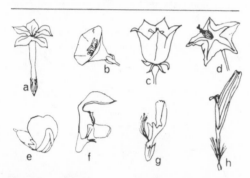

Flower shapes: a tubular; **b** funnel-shaped; **c** bell-shaped; **d** rotate; **e** papilionate; **f** two-lipped; **g** one-lipped; **h** ligulate.

Gall, an abnormal development of plant tissue induced by a wound or by parasites, e.g. some wasps.

Geniculate, bent abruptly like a knee.

Genus, see pages 2, 7.

Gill-cover, (*zool.*) a skin-fold which protects the gills.

Gill-raker, (*zool.*) horny, comb-like structure, associated with the gills, in some fishes, which filters food from the water.

Gills, (*bot.*) in fungi, thin flat structures radiating on the underside of the cap, bearing a spore-producing surface; (*zool.*) the respiratory organ of fishes and other water-living animals.

Glabrous, (*bot.*) without hairs.

Gland, a secreting organ.

Glaucous, (*bot.*) with a bloom, often waxy, which gives a bluish-green surface colour.

Globose, nearly spherical.

Glume, (*bot.*) in grasses, an empty **bract** at the base of a spikelet; usually two: upper and lower.

Gregarious, (*zool.*) living in flocks or herds.

Grub, (*zool.*) an insect larva.

Habitat, the normal living-place of a plant or animal.

Hastate, (*bot.*) halberd-shaped; leaf, diagram on page 303.

Head, (*bot.*) a crowded **inflorescence** or **infructescence** at the top of a common stalk.

Helmet, (*bot.*) a hood formed by **perianth-segments** in some flowers.

Herb, (*bot.*) any **vascular,** non-woody plant.

Herbivorous, (*zool.*) plant-eating.

Hexamerous, (*bot.*) having parts in sixes.

Hermaphrodite, bearing the reproductive organs of both sexes; (*bot.*) having **stamens** and **pistils** in the same flower, spikelet, etc.

Hibernation, (*zool.*) the state of rest, accompanied by reduced metabolic activity, in which many insects, reptiles and mammals pass the winter.

Hinge, (*zool.*) in bivalves, the area at which the two valves of the shell are joined by a ligament; may be of several different types, sometimes with interlocking teeth of various shapes.

Hybrid, offspring of a cross between different **species,** having some characters of each parental species.

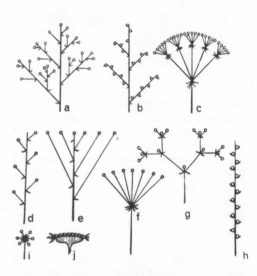

Inflorescences: a panicle; **b** compound spike; **c** compound umbel; **d** raceme; **e** corymb; **f** umbel; **g** cyme; **h** spike; **i, j** heads.

Imbricate, (*bot.*) overlapping, like slates on a roof.

Incised, (*bot.*) cut sharply into margin.

Indehiscent, (*bot.*) not opening; cf. **dehiscent.**

Indusium, (*bot.*) structure covering or enclosing a **sporangium** or group of sporangia.

Inferior, below; of fish mouth, see diagram on page 305.

Inflorescence, (*bot.*) the flower-bearing part of a stem or culm; diagrams opposite.

Infructescence, (*bot.*) **inflorescence** when it is in fruit.

Insectivorous, insect-eating.

Internode, (*bot.*) the part of a stem, etc., between two **nodes.**

Intertidal zone, the part of the shore left dry at low tide.

Introduced, not originally native, brought in accidentally or intentionally.

Invertebrate, (*zool.*) an animal without an internal skeleton of bone and/or cartilage.

Involucre, (*bot.*) bracts surrounding an **inflorescence** or a single flower; adjective, **involucral.**

Involute, (*bot.*) rolled inwards.

Iris, (*zool.*) in vertebrates, a pigmented diaphragm in front of the lens which controls the amount of light admitted to the eye through a variable aperture in its centre, the **pupil.**

Irregular, (*bot.*) **zygomorphic.**

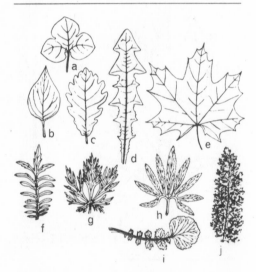

Simple leaves: a palmately lobed; **b** entire; **c** pinnately lobed; **d** pinnately parted or pinnatipartite; **e** palmately parted or palmatipartite; **f** pinnately divided or pinnatisect; **g** palmately divided or palmatisect; **h** pedate; **i** lyrate; **j** bipinnately divided or bipinnatisect.

Juvenile, (*zool.*) young.

Keel, (*bot.*) a sharp ridge on an organ resembling the keel of a boat.

Laciniate, (*bot.*) deeply and irregularly divided into narrow segments.

Lamella, (*zool.*) a ridge or flap of skin or horny material.

Lamina, (*bot.*) **blade.**

Lanceolate, (*bot.*) lance-shaped; leaf, diagram on page 309.

Larva, (*zool.*) in some animals, a juvenile stage markedly different from the adult form, to which it develops by metamorphosis; e.g., in insects, the stage between egg and **pupa.**

Lateral line, (*zool.*) a line along the side of a fish corresponding to the position of a series of sensory organs; diagram on page 305.

Leaflet, (*bot.*) a leaf-like segment of a compound leaf.

Leaf-sheath, (*bot.*) the lower part of some leaves forming a sheath round the stem.

Lemma, (*bot.*) in grasses, the lower of two scales enclosing the flower; cf. **palea.**

Ligulate, (*bot.*) strap-shaped.

Ligule, (*bot.*) in grasses, a membranous outgrowth at the inner junction of leaf-sheath and blade.

Linear, (*bot.*) long and narrow with parallel sides; leaf, diagram on page 309.

Lip, (*bot.*) in the Thyme and Figwort Families, modified lip-like **petals;** in the Orchid Family, the lowest **perianth-segment** of the inner whorl, differing in shape from the others.

Lobe, part or segment of a deeply divided structure.

Lung, (*zool.*) internal respiratory organ of many air-breathing animals.

Lung book, (*zool.*) respiratory organ of some air-breathing spiders and scorpions, arranged like the leaves of a book.

Lyrate, (*bot.*) lyre-shaped, describes pinnatifid leaves in which the lobes become larger from the stalk and which end in one very large lobe; diagram on this page.

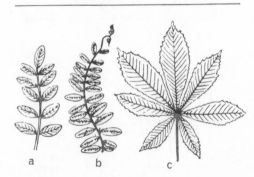

Compound leaves: a, b pinnate; **c** palmate or digitate.

Maggot, (*zool.*) insect **larva,** especially of a fly.

Male flower, (*bot.*) one with **stamens** but lacking an **ovary;** cf. **female flower.**

Mandible, (*zool.*) either part of a bird's bill (in other vertebrates, the lower jaw); in arthropods, one of the first pair of mouthparts.

Mantle, (*zool.*) in molluscs, a flap of skin, surrounding the mantle cavity, which enfolds the whole creature and which secretes the shell; attachment to the shell is along the pallial line, which is indented by the **pallial sinus.**

Maquis, a **xerophytic** type of Mediterranean vegetation, usually comprising dense thorny thickets of small evergreen trees and shrubs, with aromatic herbs and grasses.

Marine, living in the sea.

Mature, developed to the stage of being able to reproduce; of fruits, ripe.

Medusa, (*zool.*) the free-swimming generation of jellyfishes and similar animals; they reproduce sexually to produce **polyps,** which in turn reproduce asexually, budding off another generation of medusae.

Megaspore, (*bot.*) larger of the two kinds of **spore** produced by certain ferns.

Metabolic rate, speed of the chemical process in the cells of a plant or animal which breaks down foodstuffs and produces energy.

Metamorphosis, (*zool.*) a change from one distinct form to another, more mature form, e.g. in insects, amphibia.

Metatarsal tubercle, (*zool.*) a protuberance on the metatarsus, the part of the foot between the ankle and the toes.

Microspecies, a variety of a **species.**

Migrant, (*zool.*) a bird or other animal which periodically moves from one habitat to another; cf. **resident.**

Monoecious, (*bot.*) with male and female flowers on the same plant; cf. **dioecious.**

Mother-of-pearl, (*zool*). iridescent layer lining the shells of some molluscs.

Mouthparts, (*zool.*) structures surrounding the mouth of an insect, etc., associated with feeding; may be simple or specialized, as for piercing or sucking.

Mucronate, (*bot.*) abruptly tipped with a short point of the same texture.

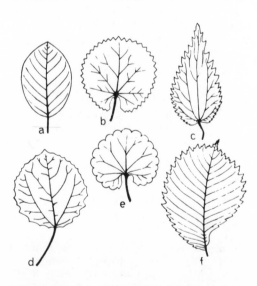

Leaf margins: a entire; **b** toothed; **c** serrate; **d** sinuate; **e** crenate; **f** doubly serrate or biserrate.

Naked, (*bot.*) hairless; also, without a **perianth.**

Native, occurring naturally in an area, not known to have been introduced.

Naturalized, introduced, but established and breeding.

Nectary, (*bot.*) a **gland** in many flowers which produces a sweet fluid (**nectar**) attractive to insects.

Needle, (*bot.*) a stiff **linear leaf.**

Nocturnal, (*zool.*) active by night.

Node, (*bot.*) point on stem or culm at which leaves, bracts and sometimes roots arise.

Nose-leaf, (*zool.*) a membranous appendage on the muzzle of some species of bats.

Nut, (*bot.*) a hard and **indehiscent** one-seeded **fruit.**

Nymph, (*zool.*) immature stage of some insects which do not undergo complete metamorphosis (e.g. grasshoppers), resembling adult but with undeveloped wings and reproductive organs.

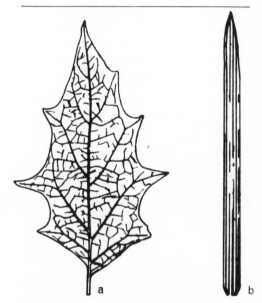

Leaf veins: a net-veined; **b** parallel-veined.

Ob-, prefix denoting inversion; e.g. **obconical,** conical but attached to stalk by the point instead of the base.

Oblong, (*bot.*) with nearly parallel sides and blunt ends, longer than wide; leaf, see diagram on page 309.

Obscure, (*bot.*) uncertain; hidden.

Ochrea, (*bot.*) tubular structure surrounding a stem, formed of one or both **stipules.**

Opposable, (*zool.*) describes the thumbs and great toes of various climbing animals, which can be bent across the palm of the hand or sole of the foot (as can the thumb in man), enabling them to be used for grasping.

Opposite, (*bot.*) situated on opposite sides of a stem, etc., and on the same level; cf. **alternate.**

Orbicular, (*bot.*) circular in outline.

Organ, structural unit of a plant or animal; e.g. a leaf, eye.

Ovary, (*bot.*) the organ in the flower containing the **ovules** and consisting of one or more **carpels;** diagram on page 305.

Ovipositor, (*zool.*) the egg-laying organ of insects, some fishes, etc.

Ovule, (*bot.*) structure in the **ovary** developing into a **seed** after fertilization.

Palea, (*bot.*) in grasses, the upper of two bracts enclosing a floret; cf. **lemma.**

Pallial sinus, (*zool.*) see under **mantle.**

Palmate, hand-shaped; leaf, diagram on page 307.

Panicle, (*bot.*) a branched **racemose inflorescence;** diagram on page 306.

Papilionate, butterfly-shaped; (*bot.*) describes a **corolla** with a large upper petal (standard), two lateral petals (wings) and two lower petals usually fused by their lower edges (keel).

Pappus, (*bot.*) hairs, bristles or scales on the top of a fruit, in the Daisy Family.

Parapodium, (*zool.*) one of the paddle-like appendages of some marine worms.

Parasite, a plant or animal which lives at the expense of another without rendering it any service in return; cf. **commensal, symbiosis.**

Partial, (*bot.*) describes secondary divisions of a structure.

Partial migrant, (*zool.*) a bird species only some members of which migrate.

Passage migrant, (*zool.*) a bird which passes through certain areas in migration.

Pectoral fin, (*zool.*) the anterior paired fins of a fish; diagram on page 305.

Pedicle, (*zool.*) in deer, the base of an antler.

Pelvic fin, (*zool.*) posterior paired fins of a fish; diagram on page 305.

Pentamerous, (*bot.*) having parts in fives.

Perennial, (*bot.*) living more than two years; cf. **annual, biennial.**

Perfoliate, (*bot.*) of leaves, with stem appearing to pass through the middle; diagram on this page.

Perianth, (*bot.*) the outer, sterile parts of a flower (floral leaves), often differentiated into **calyx** and **corolla.**

Perianth-segment, (*bot.*) a separate floral leaf; commonly used when the sepals and petals are similar in shape and colour.

Perigone, (*bot.*) undifferentiated **perianth.**

Persistent, (*bot.*) remaining attached to the axis, not shed.

Petal, (*bot.*) a segment of the inner whorl of the **perianth (petal-system)** surrounding the reproductive parts of a flower, usually conspicuously coloured.

Phyllode, (*bot.*) flattened, leaf-like leaf-stalk.

Pinion, (*zool.*) **primary.**

Pinnate, (*bot.*) describes a leaf with leaflets (**pinna,** plural **pinnae**) arranged in two rows

as in diagram on page 307; the leaflets themselves may be pinnate, when the leaf is called **bipinnate;** similarly, **tripinnate,** etc., if further divided. **Pinnatifid,** of a leaf, divided into lobes about half-way to the midrib.

Pistil, (*bot.*) the female part of a flower, usually consisting of **ovary, style** and **stigma;** diagram on page 305.

Plankton, floating plants and animals, mostly small and many in a larval state, found in the sea, especially in polar regions.

Plumose, (*bot.*) feathery.

Pod, (*bot.*) a dry many-seeded **fruit** formed by one capsule.

Podetium (plural **podetia**), (*bot.*) in some lichens, a stalked structure bearing the **apothecia.**

Pollen, (*bot.*) small grains produced in the **anthers,** containing male reproductive cells.

Pollen basket, (*zool.*) **tibia** of the hind leg of some bees, flattened and with stiff hairs curved over it, forming a basket in which pollen is carried from flowers.

Polyandrous, (*zool.*) of a female, having several mates at one time; cf. **polygamous.**

Polygamous, (*zool.*) of a male, having several mates at one time; (*bot.*) with hermaphrodite and unisexual flowers on the same or different individuals of the same species.

Polyp, (*zool.*) a sedentary coelenterate.

Prehensile, (*zool.*) capable of grasping.

Primary, one of the large flight feathers of a bird, attached to the 'hand bones' of the wing; diagram on page 304.

Proboscis, (*zool.*) in insects, mouthparts adapted for sucking; also, a prolonged snout.

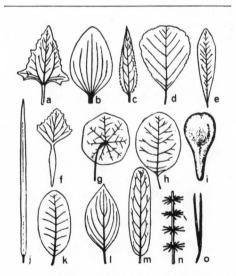

Leaf outlines: a triangular or deltoid; **b** ovate (blunt at tip); **c** lanceolate (acute at tip); **d** obovate; **e** oblanceolate (blunt at tip); **f** rhombic; **g** orbicular (perfoliate); **h** roundish (rounded at tip); **i** spathulate (notched at tip); **j** linear; **k** oblong (rounded at tip); **l** elliptic (acute at tip); **m** narrowly oblong; **n** bristle-like; **o** needle-like.

Procumbent, (*bot.*) trailing over the ground.

Pronotum, (*zool.*) the dorsal part of the front segment of an insect's **thorax.**

Prostrate, (*bot.*) lying flat on the ground.

Pupa, (*zool.*) an intermediate, usually passive form in the metamorphosis of an insect, between **larva** and adult. **Pupation,** the process of becoming a pupa.

Pupil, (*zool.*) variable opening in the **iris** through which light enters the eye; appears as a dark circle or slit.

Race, a group of individuals within a **species,** usually existing in a certain geographical area, distinguished from remainder of the species only by superficial features such as colouring.

Raceme, (*bot.*) a simple, elongate **inflorescence** with flowers or spikelets stalked directly on to the axis; diagram on page 306. **Racemose,** like or having racemes.

Rachis, (*bot.*) main axis.

Radical, (*bot.*) arising from the root.

Ray, (*bot.*) the branch of a **partial umbel;** (*zool.*) one of the supporting bones of a fish fin; also, one of several species of cartilaginous fishes.

Ray-floret, (*bot.*) strap-shaped **floret** in the head of some members of the Daisy Family.

Receptacle, (*bot.*) the enlarged uppermost part of stem bearing crowded flowers, or the uppermost part of flower-stalk bearing the floral parts.

Recurved, curved backwards.

Reflexed, (*bot.*) growing backwards or downwards.

Regular, (*bot.*) of a flower, radially symmetrical, with more than one plane of symmetry; cf. **zygomorphic.**

Resident, (*zool.*) animal that does not migrate.

Respiratory pore, (*zool.*) external opening of breathing organs in some invertebrates, e.g. starfishes.

Rhizome, (*bot.*) an underground stem with scale-like leaves, persisting for more than one growing season; also, a fern stem, thick at ground-level, bearing roots and fronds.

Root, (*bot.*) part of vascular plants which grows into soil, anchoring plant and absorbing water and salts.

Rosette, (*bot.*) an arrangement of leaves crowded at the base of a stem, often lying in a circle on the ground.

Rostrum, (*zool.*) snout.

Rotate, wheel-shaped; (*bot.*) with united petals in a plane with very short tube.

Ruminant, (*zool.*) a member of group of mammals which chew the cud (food brought back from the rumen or first stomach to be chewed again).

Salting, a marshy area near the sea, flooded by the tide or with standing brackish water.

Saprophyte, (*bot.*) plant living on decaying organic matter.

Scale, (*bot.*) a small, usually dry and colourless leaf or bract; also, a translucent structure of epidermal origin; (*zool.*) a thin plate on the skin of many fishes and reptiles; in some ants, a small protuberance on the thorax.

Scape, (*bot.*) the leafless axis of an inflorescence arising directly from ground-level.

Scarious, (*bot.*) dry and papery, sometimes transparent.

Scavenger, (*zool.*) animal living on dead flesh or plants.

Scorpioid, (*bot.*) of a **cyme,** with **alternate** branches at right angles to the axis, which is itself coiled up (like a scorpion's tail).

Scree, a mass of rocks and stones on a slope.

Scute, (*zool.*) a shield-like plate of bone on the skin of some reptiles and fishes, e.g. sturgeon.

Secondary, (*zool.*) one of the group of feathers attached to the forearm part of a bird's wing, mainly responsible for the lift required for flight; diagram on page 304.

Seed, (*bot.*) reproductive structure formed from a fertilized **ovule.**

Seed-leaf, (*bot.*) cotyledon.

Sepal, (*bot.*) a segment of the outer perianth whorl (**sepal-system**), usually green.

Serrate, (*bot.*) toothed like a saw, with teeth pointing forwards.

Shoot, (*bot.*) new young growth in flowering plants.

Shrub, (*bot.*) a woody **perennial** with several stems arising from the base.

Simple, (*bot.*) not divided or branched.

Sinistral, (*zool.*) of shells, with a left-handed spiral.

Siphon, (*zool.*) water-pumping organ in various aquatic animals which extract food, etc., from the water.

Solitary, (*bot.*) arising singly.

Somite, (*zool.*) body segment.

Sorus (plural **sori**), (*bot.*) a cluster of fern **sporangia,** often covered with an **indusium.**

Spadix, (*bot.*) a dense **spike** with a thick fleshy axis.

Spathe, (*bot.*) a large sheath-like **bract** enclosing the **spadix.**

Spathulate, spoon-shaped or paddle-shaped.

Spawn, (*zool.*) a mass of eggs, as laid by fishes, amphibians, etc.; also used as a verb.

Species, see pages 2, 7.

Speculum, (*zool.*) a bright patch or band on a duck's wing.

Spike, (*bot.*) an elongate **inflorescence** with stalkless flowers or spikelets on the main axis; diagram on page 306.

Spikelet, (*bot.*) a unit of the grass **inflorescence,** usually consisting of two glumes and one or more florets.

Sporangium, (*bot.*) organ in which **spores** are produced.

Spore, (*bot.*) a small, usually single-celled, asexual reproductive body.

Spur, (*bot.*) a hollow projection from a **petal** or **sepal,** often containing **nectar.**

Stamen, (*bot.*) the male part of a flower, consisting of **filament** and **anther;** diagram on page 305.

Standard, (*bot.*) the upper, largest **petal** in a **papilionate** flower.

Stem, (*bot.*) the main axis of a plant; a supporting stalk of a fungus fruit-body.

Steppe, an extensive treeless plain of grassland, as in SE Europe and parts of Russia.

Sterile, (*bot.*) not capable of producing **seed;** also, not producing viable seeds or pollen; cf. **fertile.**

Stigma, (*bot.*) tip of the female part of a flower, which receives the **pollen.**

Stipules, (*bot.*) small, usually leaf-like structures at the base of a leaf or leaf-stalk.

Stolon, (*bot.*) a creeping stem, rooting at the nodes and producing new vegetative shoots and stems or culms. **Stoloniferous,** having stolons.

Striate, with parallel furrows or stripes.

Style, (*bot.*) prolongation of **carpel** supporting the **stigma.**

Sub-, prefix signifying either below, as in subterranean, or nearly, as in subglobose.

Subspecies, see pages 2,7.

Subtend, (*bot.*) of leaves, bracts, etc., to have arising from the axil, branches, flowers, etc., i.e. a leaf subtends a flower.

Subulate, (*bot.*) awl-shaped; with a sharp point.

Succulent, (*bot.*) fleshy, juicy.

Superior, (*bot.*) of an ovary, one with a perianth round its base; (*zool.*) of fish mouth, see diagram on page 305.

Symbiosis, an association of two plants or animals of different species, or of an animal and a plant, in which both benefit to such an extent that neither can survive without the other; cf. **commensal, parasite.**

Tail-covert, see **covert** and diagram on page 304.

Tarsus, (*zool.*) foot; in arthropods, the fifth segment of a leg.

Tendril, (*bot.*) a thread-like twining structure, modified from a leaf or stem.

Tentacle, (*zool.*) arm-like grasping organ of octopus, sea anemone, etc.

Terete, cylindrical.

Terminal, at the top or end; of fish mouth, see diagram on page 305.

Ternate, (*bot.*) of a leaf, divided into three approximately equal parts.

Terrestrial, growing or living on land; cf. **aquatic.**

Tetramerous, (*bot.*) having parts in fours.

Thallus, (*bot.*) a vegetative body not differentiated into stem and leaves.

Thorax, (*zool.*) in insects, the second body segment, behind the head, which carries the legs and wings; diagram on this page.

Thorn, (*bot.*) in some plants, a branch modified into a sharp woody projection.

Tibia, (*zool.*) in arthropods, the fourth segment of a leg; diagram on this page.

Tree-line, the limit within the Arctic Belt and on mountains beyond which trees do not grow because of the severe climate.

Tine, (*zool.*) one of the spikes of an antler.

Trachea, (*zool.*) a main tube, leading from pores on the outside of the body, of the respiratory system of insects, centipedes and millipedes.

Tracheal spiracle, (*zool.*) external opening of **trachea.**

Tragus, (*zool.*) a cartilaginous prominence in front of the entrance to the external ear.

Trailing, (*bot.*) lying on the ground but not rooting at the nodes; cf. **stolon.**

Trifid, (*bot.*) split deeply into three segments.

Tube, (*bot.*) the fused part of a **calyx** or **corolla;** in fungi, tubular structures in a compact layer on the underside of the cap, each opening by a pore and lined with a spore-producing surface.

Tuber, (*bot.*) swollen, underground part of stem or root, a food store for the plant.

Tundra, see page 68.

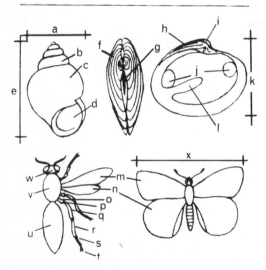

Shells: (univalve) a width; **b** spire; **c** body whorl; **d** aperture; **e** height; **(bivalve) f** valve or shell; **g** hinge ligament; **h** hinge teeth; **i** umbo; **j** shell-closing muscles; **k** width; **l** pallial sinus. **Insects: m** fore wings; **n** hind wings; **o** coxa; **p** trochanter; **q** femur; **r** tibia; **s** tarsus or foot; **t** claw; **u** abdomen; **v** thorax; **w** head; **x** wingspan.

Umbel, (*bot.*) umbrella-shaped **inflorescence** in which flower-stalks arise from a single point at the top of the stem; in a

compound umbel, rays arise from the top and themselves bear umbels; diagram on page 306; **Umbellate,** forming or having an umbel.

Umbo, (*zool.*) the protuberant, oldest part of a bivalve shell; diagram on previous page.

Umbrella, (*zool.*) the disc of a jellyfish or medusa.

Unarmed, (*bot.*) without prickles, spines or thorns.

Undulate, (*bot.*) wavy along margin in a plane perpendicular to the surface; cf. **wavy.**

Unisexual, of one sex only; cf. **hermaphrodite.**

Uropod, (*zool.*) an appendage on the last abdominal segment of some crustaceans; forms the fan-like tail of, e.g., lobsters.

Vagrant, (*zool.*) an individual found well beyond the normal range of its species.

Valve, (*bot.*) one of the parts into which a capsule separates at maturity; (*zool.*) a shell, but usually one of the halves of a bivalve shell.

Vascular bundle, (*bot.*) a strand of specialized conducting and strengthening tissues, in vascular plants.

Vascular system, system of hollow conducting vessels, e.g. the blood system, plant vascular bundles.

Vein, (*bot.*) **vascular bundle** of a leaf, etc.; (*zool.*) in insects, one of the minute horny tubes forming the framework of a wing.

Ventral fin (*zool.*) an unpaired fin on the belly of a fish.

Vertebrate, (*zool.*) an animal with an internal skeleton of bone and/or cartilage.

Vesicle, (*bot.*) a small bladder or cavity.

Vibrissa, (*zool.*) a touch-sensitive bristle, whisker.

Viviparous, (*bot.*) producing new plants on the parent plant by **adventitious buds, bulbils,** etc.; (*zool.*) producing live offspring, not eggs.

Vocal sac, (*zool.*) in frogs and toads, an inflatable pouch in the throat used in the production of sounds.

Water meadow, meadow periodically flooded by neighbouring streams, etc.

Wavy, (*bot.*) with regular curved notches on the margin in same plane as the surface; cf. **undulate.**

Wedge-shaped, (*bot.*) of the base of an organ, narrowed towards the point of attachment; diagram on page 303.

Whorl, (*bot.*) the circular arrangement of more than two organs at a node on an axis; (*zool.*) one of the coils of a shell; diagram on page 311.

Wing, (*bot.*) any dry thin expansion of an organ; also, a lateral petal of a papilionate flower.

Wing-covert, see **covert** and diagram on page 304.

Woolly, (*bot.*) with long soft, more or less tangled hairs.

Xerophytic, (*bot.*) describes plants adapted to subsist in drought and dry conditions.

Zygomorphic, (*bot.*) describes flowers which are symmetrical only in one plane, cf. **regular.**

Bibliography - Further Reading

The following list includes only books in English and thus tends to concentrate on the flora and fauna of the British Isles. Many of these books, however, contain further bibliographies listing books dealing with the natural history of other countries and areas of Europe in the languages of the region.

General:

Curry-Lindahl, K., *Europe: A Natural History*, Hamish Hamilton, London

Useful series:

Little Guides in Colour, Paul Hamlyn
New Naturalist series, Collins, London
Observer's Pocket Series, Warne, London
Pocket Guides, Collins
Wayside and Woodland series, Warne

Non-flowering Plants:

Dickinson, C.I., *British Seaweeds*, Kew Series, Eyre & Spottiswoode, London
Hyde H.A. & Wade, A.E., *Welsh Ferns*, Nat. Mus. Wales
Lange, M. & Hora, F.B., *Guide to Mushrooms and Toadstools*, Collins
Taylor, P.G., *British Ferns and Mosses*, Kew Series, Eyre & Spottiswoode
Watson, E.V. & Richards, P., *British Mosses and Liverworts*, Cambridge

Flowering Plants:

Barton, J.G., *Wild Flowers*, Spring Books
Butcher, R. W., *A New Illustrated British Flora*, · L. Hill
Clapham, A.R., Tutin, T. G., & Warburg, E. F., *Flora of the British Isles*, 4 vols., Cambridge
Davis, P.H., & Cullen, J., *The Identification of Flowering Plant Families*, Oliver & Boyd, Edinburgh
Duperrex, A., *Orchids of Europe*, Blandford, London
Hubbard, C.E., *Grasses*, Penguin, London
Hulten, E., *Atlas of the Distribution of Vascular Plants in North-west Europe*, Stockholm
Hutchinson, J., *Wild Flowers in Colour*, Penguin
Makins, F.K., *The Identification of Trees and Shrubs*, Dent, London

Martin, W. K., *The Concise British Flora in Colour*, Michael Joseph, London
Melderis, A. & Bangerter, E.B., *A Handbook of British Flowering Plants*, Ward, Lock, London
Nicholson, B.E., Ary, S. & Gregory, M., *The Oxford Book of Wild Flowers*, Oxford
Perring, F.H. & Walters, S.M., *Atlas of the British Flora*, Nelson, London
Tutin, T.G., *et. al.*, *Flora Europaea*, Vol. 1, Cambridge
Vedel, H. & Lange, J., *Trees and Bushes in Wood and Hedgerow*, Methuen, London
Webb, D.A., *An Irish Flora*, Dundalgan, Dundalk
Atchley, S.C., *Wild Flowers of Attica*, Oxford
Gjaerevoll, O. & Jørgensen, R., *Mountain Flowers of Scandinavia*, F. Bruns, Trondheim
Polunin, O. & Huxley, A., *Flowers of the Mediterranean*, Chatto and Windus, London
Schroter, C., *Coloured Vade-mecum to the Alpine Flora*, Zurich

Invertebrates:

Buchsbaum, R. & Milne, L.J., *Living Invertebrates of the World*, Hamish Hamilton
Clark, A.M., *Starfishes and Their Relations*, British Museum (Natural History)
Green, J., *A Biology of the Crustacea*, Witherby, London
Mellanby, H., *Animal Life in Fresh Water*, Methuen
Wigglesworth, V.B., *The Life of Insects*, Weidenfeld & Nicholson, London

Vertebrates:

Corbet, G.B., *The Terrestrial Mammals of Western Europe*, Foulis, London
Hellmich, W., *Reptiles and Amphibians of Europe*, Blandford
Peterson, R., Mountfort, G., & Hollom, P.A.D., *A Field Guide to the Birds of Britain and Europe*, Collins
Schindler, O., *Guide to Freshwater Fishes*, Thames & Hudson, London
Southern, H.N. (ed.), *The Handbook of British Mammals*, Blackwell Scientific, Oxford
Vaurie, C., *The Birds of the Palearctic Fauna*, 2 vols., Witherby
Voous, K. H., *Atlas of European Birds*, Nelson

Index